BIOORGANIC MECHANISMS

VOLUME II

FRONTIERS IN CHEMISTRY

Ronald Breslow and Martin Karplus, Editors
Columbia University

BIOORGANIC MECHANISMS

VOLUME II

THOMAS C. BRUICE
University of California, Santa Barbara

STEPHEN J. BENKOVIC
The Pennsylvania State University

W. A. BENJAMIN, Inc.   1966
New York   Amsterdam

CHEMISTRY

BIOORGANIC MECHANISMS: VOLUME II

Library of Congress Catalog Card Number 66-13993
Manufactured in the United States of America

*The manuscript was put into production on June 23, 1965;
this volume was published on May 25, 1966*

W. A. BENJAMIN, INC.
New York, New York 10016

Preface

In the borderline areas of science the creation of hybrid terms—molecular biology, molecular biochemistry, and biophysics—appears to be a sign of our times. With some trepidation we offer the term "bioorganic mechanism." In this text, studies of bioorganic mechanisms are defined as those mechanistic studies likely to be of importance in the understanding of enzymic reactions or chemical transformations of biochemically important compounds such as the cofactors. The area of bioorganic mechanisms is of mutual interest to enzymologists and physical organic chemists.

The objectives of the authors have been twofold. The text is intended to meet a need for a reference work and to assist the entry of interested researchers and advanced graduate students into the study of bioorganic mechanisms. In this regard the coverage of the subjects considered has been made reasonably complete. Second, the subject material has been so arranged that the text may serve in the facile development of a graduate-level course. Chapter 1 includes a modern treatment of acid-base catalytic concepts. It is essential that the reader grasp an understanding of the fundamentals of this topic in order to understand not only the remainder of the text but also to be able to evaluate proposed mechanisms for enzyme catalysis.

The topics included in Volumes I and II have been selected on the basis of the intense and continuing interest in these areas. Material presented in the chapters concerned with hydrolysis and hydration reactions has been chosen on the basis of easy extrapolation to physiological conditions. Thus, reactions in strong acid and base have generally been omitted. Some of the compounds considered are not analogs of naturally occurring substances but their study has furnished important evidence as to the possible mechanisms of biologically important reactions. The chapter on phosphorohalides, for example, contains the best models of nucleophilicity toward pentacovalent phosphorus. It has not been our intention to provide a comprehensive source of enzyme studies. Some introductory material has been included in order to help the reader understand the biological importance of the subject material and to

v

provide a contrast between the "model" and enzymic reactions.   Chymotrypsin is the only enzyme discussed at length because of extensive current
experimentation and because of our belief that many of the concepts
derived from "model-studies" are directly reflected in the present state of
understanding the mechanisms of chymotrypsin action.

In the development of most chapters we have attempted to provide
perspective by discussing the topics from a historical viewpoint. A
knowledge of the historical development of a mechanism or concept
provides a tempered appreciation of the present state and lessens the
tendency of students to take this as gospel.   When the current concepts
of a mechanism are highly speculative we have attempted, as far as
possible, to present the pertinent literature associated with a given topic
along with the respective author's viewpoint.   We have, therefore, tried
to refrain from undue bias except if the experimental facts warrant
criticism.   Thus, in these instances the ultimate judgment is left to the
reader and it is hoped that this approach may stimulate research on his
part.

Undoubtedly certain subjects have been omitted that demand attention, for example, cofactors such as B_{12} and riboflavin and the enzyme
ribonuclease.   It is our intention that such topics may form the nucleus
of Volume III.   We acknowledge with appreciation the assistance of
Mrs. Dorothy Campbell who checked the references for several chapters,
typed the manuscript, and contributed greatly to the drawing of the
structural formulas and equations.   We also wish to thank Mr. Donald
Tanner who checked the correctness of the formulas and equations, read
the entire text, and shared with Mrs. Campbell the responsibility for the
art work.   In addition we are grateful to Mrs. Stephen Benkovic for
checking the references for the majority of the text.

THOMAS C. BRUICE
STEPHEN J. BENKOVIC

Santa Barbara, California
January 1966

Contents

viii   Contents

Phosphate Esters

I. INTRODUCTION

The considerable importance of phosphate derivatives in biological systems can be visualized most readily through a representative listing of the variety present. In Table 5-1[1] both general types and specific

[1] E. M. Kosower, "Molecular Biochemistry," McGraw-Hill, New York, 1962, pp. 228–229.

Table 5-1 * *Biologically important phosphate derivatives*

General formula	General types	Specific examples
PO_4H_3	Orthophosphoric acid	
$ROPO_3H_2$	Hydroxyalkyl phosphates	α-D-Glucose-1-phosphate
		D-Glucose-6-phosphate
		D-Fructose-1,6-diphosphate
		D-Glyceraldehyde-3-phosphate
		Adenosine monophosphate (AMP)
	Alkyl phosphate	Pyridoxal-5-phosphate
	Enol phosphate	Phosphoenolpyruvic acid
	Acyl phosphate	Acetyl phosphate
		3-Phospho-D-glyceryl-phosphate
$RNHPO_3H_2$	Phosphoramidate	Creatine phosphate
		Arginine phosphate
$(RO)_2PO_2H$	Dialkyl phosphate	α-Lecithin
		Adenosine-2′,3′-cyclic phosphate
		RNA, DNA
$(RO)_3PO$	Trialkyl or triaryl phosphate	Tri-o-cresyl phosphate [a]
$ROPO_2HX$	Acyl adenylate	Acetyl adenylate
		Adenyl sulfate

$$RO\text{—}\overset{\overset{\displaystyle O}{\|}}{\underset{\underset{\displaystyle OH}{\|}}{P}}OPO_3H_2$$

	Alkyl pyrophosphate	Adenosine diphosphate (ADP)

$$RO\text{—}\overset{\overset{\displaystyle O}{\|}}{\underset{\underset{\displaystyle OH}{\|}}{P}}\text{—}O\text{—}\overset{\overset{\displaystyle O}{\|}}{\underset{\underset{\displaystyle OH}{\|}}{P}}\text{—}OR' \quad {}^{b}$$

	P_1P_2-Dialkyl pyrophosphate	NAD, coenzyme A

$$HO\text{—}\overset{\overset{\displaystyle O}{\|}}{\underset{\underset{\displaystyle OH}{\|}}{P}}\text{—}O\text{—}\overset{\overset{\displaystyle O}{\|}}{\underset{\underset{\displaystyle OH}{\|}}{P}}\text{—}OH \quad {}^{b}$$

	Pyrophosphoric acid	

$$RO\text{—}\overset{\overset{\displaystyle O}{\|}}{\underset{\underset{\displaystyle OH}{\|}}{P}}\text{—}O\text{—}\overset{\overset{\displaystyle O}{\|}}{\underset{\underset{\displaystyle OH}{\|}}{P}}\text{—}O\text{—}\overset{\overset{\displaystyle O}{\|}}{\underset{\underset{\displaystyle OH}{\|}}{P}}\text{—}OH \quad {}^{b}$$

	Alkyl triphosphate	Adenosine triphosphate (ATP)

$$(RO)_2\overset{\overset{\displaystyle O}{\|}}{P}\text{—}O\text{—}\overset{\overset{\displaystyle O}{\|}}{P}(OR)_2 \quad {}^{b}$$

	Tetralkyl pyrophosphate	Tetrabenzyl pyrophosphate [a]

---

* Ref. 1.   [a] Function as inhibitors.   [b] Discussed in Chapter 7.

examples of these compounds are given; however, the phosphoro- and phosphonofluoridates are omitted and will be discussed in a following chapter.   The reader may have noted that the unsubstituted P—O bond in the phosphates has been written as a double bond, a convention which will be utilized for all phosphate compounds.   In reality some uncertainty exists as to whether the P—O bond has predominant double bond or single dipolar [2] bond character, although the former is generally favored.[3–4a]

It will be the aim of this chapter to make an inquiry into the mechanisms by which phosphates, such as those listed above, react, in order to gain an insight into their biochemical behavior.   For that reason the experimental complexities of the supposedly simpler "model" systems will be examined in some detail.   For the present it should be realized that the hydrolysis of organic phosphates is complicated by several factors.[5] First, there is the problem of determining which of the possible forms of the substrate is the reactive species under specified conditions.   This identificat:on can usually be made from the pH-rate profile and the dissociation constants of the substrate.   However, the enigma of kinetic indistinguishability always remains, and more definite identification of the reacting species is made through recourse to other experimental information.   Second, there is the possibility that reaction may occur with either or both C—O and P—O bond fission.   This distinction is usually made through use of O^{18} as a tracer, although complications may arise owing to concomitant exchange in reactants and products.   Third, the involvement of the solvent as a nucleophilic species does not allow determination of the molecularity of the reaction through consideration of the kinetic order.[5]   Unfortunately the last problem is in many ways insurmountable even for the acid catalyzed reactions because of the invalidity of many of the existing criteria, such as the Zucker-Hammett hypothesis, etc.

II. HYDROLYSIS

A. Monoesters

The hydrolysis of methyl phosphate at varying pH values (Fig. 5-1) yields a pH-rate profile typical of an alkyl phosphate monoester.[5]   The

[2] R. G. Gillis, J. F. Horwood, and G. L. White, *J. Am. Chem. Soc.* **80,** 2999 (1958).
[3] L. Larsson, *Svensk Kem. Tidskr.* **71,** 336 (1959).
[4] D. W. Cruickshank, *J. Chem. Soc.* 5486 (1961).
[4a] P. Haake, W. B. Miller, and D. A. Tyssee, *J. Am. Chem. Soc.* **86,** 3577 (1964).
[5] C. A. Bunton, D. R. Llewellyn, K. G. Oldham, and C. A. Vernon, *J. Chem. Soc.* 3574 (1958).

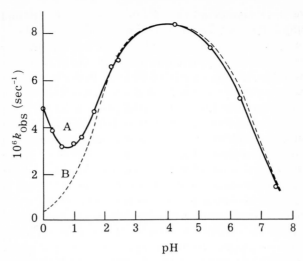

Fig. 5-1   *Hydrolysis of monomethyl phosphate at 100.1°.   A: Experimental.   B: Calculated.   (Ref. 5.)*

essential features of the pH-rate profile of monoalkyl phosphates, such as glycerol phosphates and ethyl phosphate, have been known for some time, the rate of hydrolysis being at a maximum at about pH 4 and then falling to smaller values at more acidic [6-8] or alkaline [9, 10] pH.   In strong acid solution the rate of hydrolysis again rises.   Bailly and Desjobert, who pioneered kinetic research in this area suggested that this phenomenon was due to a facile reaction of the monoanion, which is the predominant ionic species in solutions of most phosphate esters between pH 2 and 6.   This view has since then received considerable support.[5, 11, 12]

The overall rate of hydrolysis of methyl phosphate can be obtained at any acidity within the range pH 7.5 to 7 M perchloric acid at 100° by solving equation (5-1)[5]:

$$10^6 v = 8.23[M] + 0.50[N]e^{0.423\mu} + 3.08[N][H^{\oplus}] \qquad (5-1)$$

The terms [M] and [N] represent the concentration of ester in the mono-anionic and neutral forms, respectively, as calculated from the dissociation constants for methyl phosphate ($pK'_{a1} = 1.61$ and $pK'_{a2} = 6.85$ at 100°).

[6] M. C. Bailly, *Bull. Soc. Chim. France* **9**, 340, 405 (1942).
[7] P. Fleury, *Compt. Rend.* **221**, 416 (1945).
[8] A. Desjobert, *Bull. Soc. Chim. France* **14**, 809 (1947).
[9] M. J. Cavalier, *Compt. Rend.* **127**, 60 (1898).
[10] R. H. A. Plimmer and F. H. Scott, *J. Chem. Soc.* **93**, 1699 (1908).
[11] W. W. Butcher and F. H. Westheimer, *J. Am. Chem. Soc.* **77**, 2420 (1955).
[12] J. Kumamoto and F. H. Westheimer, *J. Am. Chem. Soc.* **77**, 2515 (1955).

The remaining $[H^{\oplus}]$ term represents the hydrogen ion concentration, and the exponential describes the salt effect on the hydrolysis of the neutral species. The good agreement between the experimental and calculated results can be seen through inspection of Fig. 5-1, the deviation in the strong acid region arising from the fact that the second and third terms of equation (5-1) were not employed in the calculation. Thus the monoanion appears to be the principally reacting species in the pH range 1–7. However, this analysis does not exclude the possibility that the reactive species are indeed the neutral species and hydroxide ion,[12] rather than the monoanion and a water molecule, because the expressions for both pathways are kinetically indistinguishable. Yet calculation[5] of the specific rate coefficient for a hydrolysis based on reaction of the neutral species with hydroxide ion results in a value of ca. 10^7 liter mole^{-1} sec^{-1}. This is chemically inexplicable when compared to the value 3.3×10^{-2} liter mole^{-1} sec^{-1} for the known second-order reaction between trimethyl phosphate and hydroxide ion at 100°.[13] Thus, the interpretation that the monoanion is the reactive species is preferred. Bunton *et al.* also observed that the monoanion of dimethyl phosphate undergoes hydrolysis some 10,000 times slower than the monoanion of methyl phosphate[14] (based on P—O bond cleavage).

The isotope experiments on the hydrolysis of methyl phosphate revealed that hydrolysis of the monoanion proceeds with P—O bond fission.[5] This has also been found, among many, in the hydrolysis of the mono-anion species of glycerol-1- and glycerol-2-phosphate,[15] 2-methoxy-1-methylethyl phosphate[11] (through stereochemical considerations), and benzyl phosphate monoesters.[12] It will become even more apparent in subsequent discussions that the facile hydrolysis of a monoanion species proceeding via P—O bond scission is general for most monosubstituted phosphate compounds. Instances of monoalkylated phosphate esters where a pH-rate profile does not exhibit a maximum near pH 4 appear to be due to some facile reaction of the neutral species, as is the case in the acid catalyzed hydrolysis of benzyl phosphate.[12] A second cause may be attributed to large differences in the activation energies of the various pathways available to either species, an example of which is the hydrolysis of *p*-nitrophenyl phosphate which shows a distinct rate maximum at pH 4 at 76.9°,[16] but none at 37°.[17] 2,4-Dinitrophenyl dihydrogen

[13] P. W. C. Barnard, C. A. Bunton, D. R. Llewellyn, C. A. Vernon, and V. A. Welch, *J. Chem. Soc.* 1636 (1961). 2670

[14] C. A. Bunton, M. M. Mhala, K. G. Oldham, and C. A. Vernon, *J. Chem. Soc.* 3293 (1960).

[15] P. A. T. Swoboda and E. M. Crook, *Biochem. J.* **59**, 24 (1959).

[16] K. A. Holbrook and L. Ouellet, *Can. J. Chem.* **36**, 686 (1958).

[17] A. Desjobert, *Bull. Soc. Chim. France* 683 (1963).

orthophosphate is considerably more reactive than the mononitrophenyl phosphate, and does not show a rate maximum at pH 3–4.[17a] Instead the rate increases from a minimum at pH 2, and there is a well defined plateau from pH 6–12. At higher pH the rate increases again because of attack of hydroxide ion upon the phosphate dianion. In the region pH 6–12 the reacting species is the dianion, showing that it can fragment with P—O bond scission provided that the leaving anion is sufficiently stable.

The specific requirements for the rapid hydrolysis of the monoanion, which dictates the presence of a proton, not an alkyl group, on one of the phosphate oxygen atoms and proceeds via rupture of the P—O bond, led Westheimer and Vernon and their collaborators to suggest a special mechanistic scheme.[5, 11, 12, 18] The reaction is assumed to proceed through formation of an unstable monomeric metaphosphate ion intermediate (5-2 IV), which reacts very rapidly with water to give inorganic phosphate.[19]

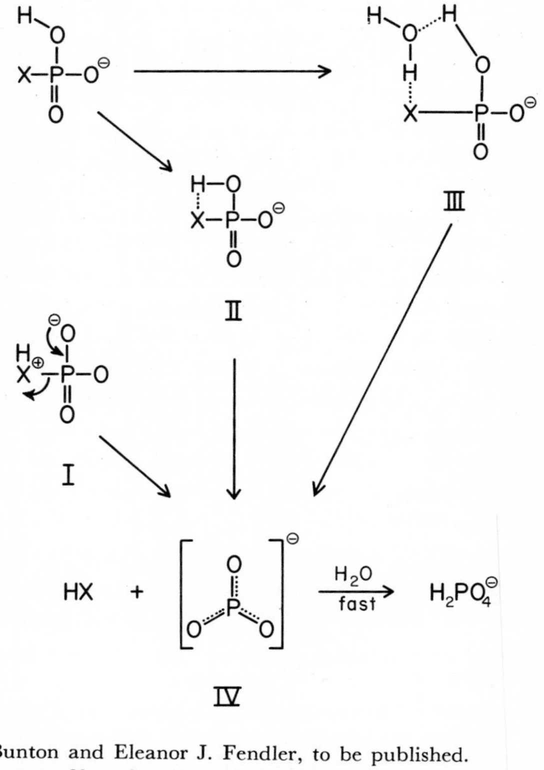

$$(5\text{-}2)^{19}$$

[17a] C. A. Bunton and Eleanor J. Fendler, to be published.
[18] C. A. Vernon, *Chem. Soc. (London) Spec. Publ.* No. 8, 17 (1957).
[19] W. P. Jencks, *Brookhaven Symp. Biol.* **15**, 143 (1962).

In mechanism (5-2) the function of the proton is to convert the alkoxide group, X, to an energetically more favorable leaving group. At the same time, transfer of the proton to the leaving group leaves the phosphate moiety of the molecule with two negative charges, which provide a driving force for expulsion of the leaving group.[5, 19] With either a monoester dianion or diester, such a transfer is impossible. This proton transfer could occur in three ways (5-2): (1) a pre-equilibrium transfer to give the zwitterion (I), (2) a concerted proton transfer through a four-membered ring, which accompanies the P—O bond breaking (II), and (3) avoidance of the energetically unfavorable four-membered ring by carrying out the proton transfer through a six-membered ring formed by incorporating a molecule of water (III).[5, 11, 12, 14, 18] The probability that protonation of the leaving group does occur is strengthened by the marked insensitivity of the rates of hydrolysis of the monoester monoanions to the nature of the leaving group (Table 5-2).[19] This behavior is readily rationalized on the basis of the metaphosphate mechanism, since an electron-withdrawing substituent, which would aid the expulsion of the leaving group, will hinder proton transfer to the leaving group, and vice versa.[19] This equality of monoanion rates is reflected in the approximately constant E_a and $\Delta S^{\ddagger}$ values for this particular hydrolytic pathway. Irrespective of the substrate, E_a is ca. 30 kcal mole^{-1} and $\Delta S^{\ddagger}$ is ca. 0 (Table 5-3).[19a]

Table 5-2 *   *Hydrolysis of substituted benzoyl phosphates* [a]

Substituent	Monoanion (pH 2.7–3.1) $k \times 10^3$ (min^{-1})
p-CH$_3$O	4.8
p-CH$_3$	5.7
H	6.1
p-Cl	5.6
m-NO$_2$	8.2
p-NO$_2$	8.1
3,5-di-NO$_2$	17.0 [b]

* Refs. 19, 20.
[a] $T = 39°$, H$_2$O.
[b] In 0.1 M HCl.

[19a] Arguments opposed to the metaphosphate hypothesis have been advanced; see for example, J. A. Maynard and J. M. Swan, *Australian J. Chem.* **16,** 596 (1963). However, their rationale does not irrevocably exclude the intermediacy of metaphosphate in their experiments.

[20] G. DiSabato and W. P. Jencks, *J. Am. Chem. Soc.* **83,** 4400 (1961).

Table 5-3 *

Compound	Relative rate (monoanion)	E_a (kcal mole^{-1})
Methyl phosphate	1.00	30.6
Phenyl phosphate	32.0	28.3
p-Nitrophenyl phosphate	66.8	29.7
α-D-Glucose-1-phosphate	1.85	30.0
Glycerol-1-phosphate	1.66	29.9
Glycerol-2-phosphate	3.34	30.3
Ethanolamine phosphate	3.72	29.6

* Ref. 18.

As indicated in equation (5-1), the hydrolysis of methyl phosphate also proceeds through a neutral species. Advantage is taken of the large positive salt effect exhibited by the hydrolysis of the neutral species to increase its percentage of the total rate in order to obtain meaningful tracer studies. The hydrolysis of this species proceeds mainly with C—O bond fission with the following S_N2 mechanism favored [5]:

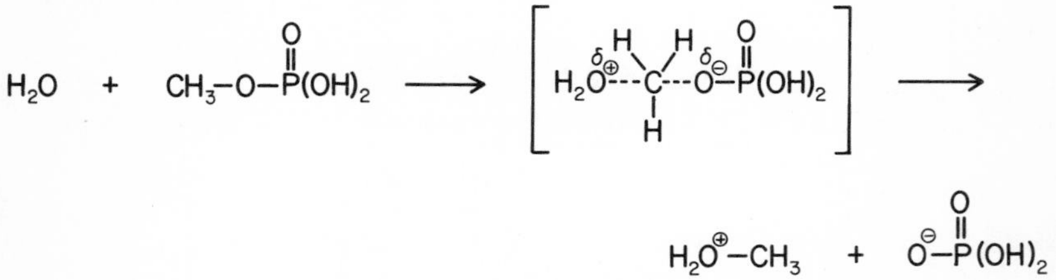

$$H_2O \; + \; CH_3\text{—}O\text{—}\overset{\overset{O}{\|}}{P}(OH)_2 \longrightarrow \left[H_2\overset{\delta\oplus}{O}\text{---}\overset{\overset{H}{\diagup}\overset{H}{\diagdown}}{\underset{H}{C}}\text{---}\overset{\delta\ominus}{O}\text{=}\overset{\overset{O}{\|}}{P}(OH)_2 \right] \longrightarrow$$

$$H_2\overset{\oplus}{O}\text{—}CH_3 \; + \; \overset{\ominus}{O}\text{—}\overset{\overset{O}{\|}}{P}(OH)_2$$

$$(5\text{-}3)$$

Formation of a methyl carbonium ion which is the alternative S_N1 pathway appears energetically unfeasible.

Hydrolysis of methyl phosphate via the acid catalyzed pathway is thought to involve the conjugate acid of the phosphate. Isotope experiments here revealed that both C—O and P—O bond fission occur. In addition the reaction is little affected by change of solvent from H_2O to D_2O, which was interpreted as signifying that the formation of the conjugate acid is not part of the rate-determining step. The proposed mechanism for hydrolysis of the conjugate acid involves an S_N2 nucleophilic attack by water on either the phosphorus or carbon atom of the appropriate conjugate acid form (5-4):

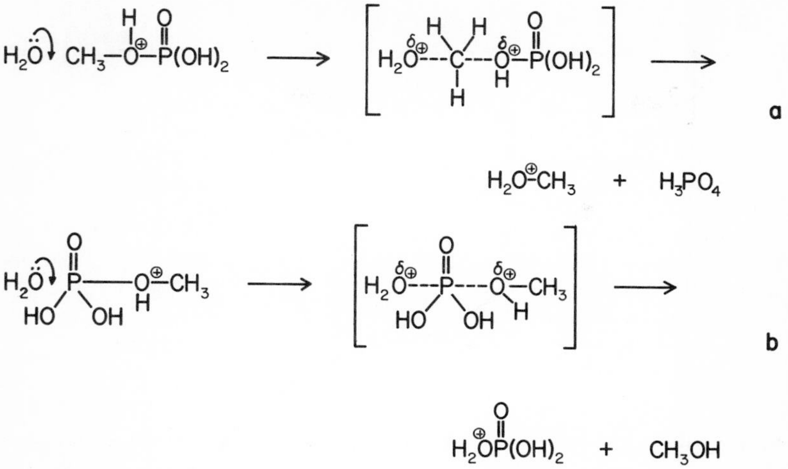

a

$$H_2O^{\oplus}CH_3 \quad + \quad H_3PO_4$$

b

$$H_2\overset{\oplus}{O}\overset{O}{\underset{\parallel}{P}}(OH)_2 \quad + \quad CH_3OH$$

(5-4)

It may be added that the rate is proportional to the stoichiometric acidity, which, from the point of view of the Zucker-Hammett hypothesis, implies that the reaction is bimolecular and involves a water molecule in the rate-determining step. Although it is quite possible that a meta-stable addition intermediate (5-5 I), analogous to the tetrahedral inter-mediate (discussed in Chapter 1), does form along reaction pathway (5-4b), there is no kinetic evidence for its existence. On the other hand,

(5-5)

I   II

Ramirez has reported the synthesis of pentacovalent phosphorus struc-tures, the cyclic unsaturated [21] and saturated oxyphosphoranes [22] (5-5 II). The former is synthesized from the reaction of trialkyl or triaryl phosphites with o-quinones or α-diketones.

The biologically important α-D-glucose-1-phosphate undergoes a very rapid hydrolysis in acid solution which results in the masking of the rate maximum (Fig. 5-2). The main features of the pH-rate profile had been

[21] F. Ramirez and N. B. Desai, *J. Am. Chem. Soc.* **82**, 2652 (1960).
[22] F. Ramirez, N. Ramanathan, and N. B. Desai, *J. Am. Chem. Soc.* **84**, 1317 (1962).

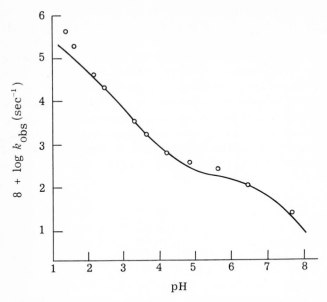

Fig. 5-2   *Hydrolysis of α-D-glucose-1-phosphate at 82.0°.*   ○, *Experimental values.*
(*Ref. 24.*)

established by Desjobert [23] and were later confirmed through a kinetic
and isotopic investigation by Vernon, Bunton, and co-workers. [24]

The rates of hydrolysis for this substrate in the pH range 1–8 can be
interpreted in terms of two reactions [24]: (1) involving the monoanion and
proceeding with P—O bond fission, and (2) involving the neutral species
and proceeding with C—O bond fission.   In strongly acidic media there
is a rapid increase in rate, proceeding with C—O bond scission.

As expected, the magnitude of the specific rate coefficient for the
monoanion form of α-D-glucose-1-phosphate and methyl phosphate is
similar, therefore mechanistically the previous arguments apply.   More
unusual is the fact that the neutral species of the sugar phosphate is
ca. 10^5 times more reactive at the same temperature than that of methyl
phosphate.   *A priori* this is suggestive of a change in mechanism, which
is strengthened by the analogy to other known reactions of sugar compounds. [24]   For example, the acid catalyzed reaction of methyl-β-D-
glucopyranoside probably proceeds by way of a cyclic carbonium ion, a

[23] A. Desjobert, *Bull. Soc. Chim. Biol.* **33,** 42 (1951).
[24] C. A. Bunton, D. R. Llewellyn, K. G. Oldham, and C. A. Vernon *J. Chem. Soc.*
3588 (1958).

postulate which has been supported through measurement of the oxygen isotope effect.[25]   A second case is the reaction of 2,3,4,6-tetra-O-methyl-α-D-glucopyranosyl chloride with methanol, which is first-order in the halide.   The kinetic order remains unaffected by addition of methoxide ion or chloride ion.   The product is 94% the inverted β-glucoside.   This percentage can be altered by the addition of chloride ion.   Collectively these observations seem to indicate the presence of a reactive intermediate which is the ion pair generated by ionization of the substrate to a gluco-pyranosyl carbonium ion.[26]   Consequently the hydrolysis of α-D-glucose-1-phosphate is best interpreted as an S_N1 process (5-6) [24] with slow heter-olysis of the C—O bond.   To gain an insight as to the relative stability

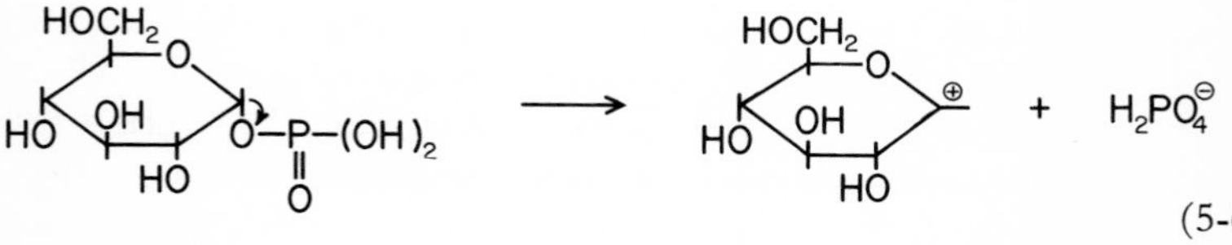

$$(5\text{-}6)$$

of the glucopyranosyl carbonium ion, it is of interest to note that the acid hydrolysis of t-butyl-β-D-glucopyranoside gives rise to a t-butyl carbonium ion and glucose.[27]

The acid catalyzed hydrolysis of α-D-glucose-1-phosphate shows a considerable increase in rate on change of solvent to D_2O.   A log plot of the specific rate constant for this process versus Hammett's acidity function, H_0, for both sulfuric and perchloric acids yields a straight line of slope -0.94.   This has been interpreted as suggestive of a rate-determining step involving formation of the glucopyranosyl carbonium ion from the conjugate acid.[24]   For reasons stated above, it is not believed that formation of the carbonium ion proceeds with ring opening (5-7). Osborn and Whalley have arrived at a similar conclusion, namely, that

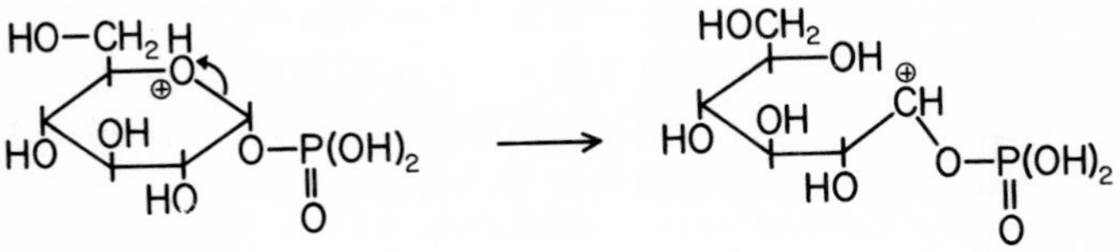

$$(5\text{-}7)$$

[25] B. E. C. Banks, Y. Meinwald, A. J. Rhind-Tutt, I. Sheft, and C. A. Vernon, *J. Chem. Soc.* 3240 (1961).

[26] A. J. Rhind-Tutt and C. A. Vernon, *J. Chem. Soc.* 4637 (1960).

[27] C. Armour, C. A. Bunton, S. Patai, L. H. Selman, and C. A. Vernon, *J. Chem. Soc.* 412 (1961).

the acid catalyzed reaction is unimolecular, through measurements of the pressure effect on this reaction.[28]

The hydrolysis of α-D-glucose-1-phosphate catalyzed by prostatic acid phosphatase has many features in common with the nonenzymic hydrolysis of the monoanion species.[29] It occurs with P—O bond cleavage and has a pH of optimum catalytic activity where the monoanion is the predominant species.[30] The appearance of not more than one atom of O^{18} per inorganic phosphate produced disfavors the possibility of a pentacovalent phosphorus intermediate.[30] Moreover, prostatic phosphatase catalyzes the transfer of phosphoryl groups from substrates, not only to water, but also to organic hydroxyl compounds.[31-37] However, the extrapolation between the enzymic and nonenzymic systems breaks down if one considers the enzyme catalyzed rates of monoanion hydrolysis for various substrates. In general, the V_m values differ, although a group of substrates (i.e., p-nitrophenyl phosphate, glycerol and adenylic phosphates) is known for which the V_m values are similar.[38-41] In a series of terminal alkyl monophosphates, a strikingly large increase in the rates of the enzymic hydrolysis has been noted upon increasing the alkyl chain length from one carbon to nine.[42]

Since, in biological systems, glucose-1-phosphate may also function as a glucosyl donor in the presence of a class of enzymes termed phosphorylases, it is of interest to review briefly some mechanistic aspects of this enzymic process. In general all phosphorylase reactions involve transfer of some group other than phosphate, such as a glucosyl group, from an organic linkage to inorganic phosphate or, in the reverse direction, from the phosphorylated form of the group, such as glucose-1-phosphate,

[28] A. R. Osborn and E. Whalley, *Can. J. Chem.* **39**, 597 (1961).
[29] M. Cohn, *J. Cellular Comp. Physiol.* **54**, Suppl. 1, 17 (1959).
[30] M. Cohn, *J. Biol. Chem.* **180**, 771 (1949).
[31] J. Appleyard, *Biochem. J.* **42**, 596 (1948).
[32] H. Green and O. Meyerhof, *J. Biol. Chem.* **197**, 347 (1952).
[33] G. Brawerman and E. Chargaff, *J. Am. Chem. Soc.* **75**, 4113 (1953).
[34] K. K. Tsuboi and P. B. Hudson, *Arch. Biochem. Biophys.* **43**, 339 (1953).
[35] B. Axelrod, *Advan. Enzymol.* **17**, 159 (1956).
[36] V. N. Nigam and W. H. Fishman, *J. Biol. Chem.* **234**, 2394 (1959).
[37] R. K. Morton, in S. P. Colowick and N. O. Kaplan (eds.) "Methods in Enzymology," Academic Press, New York, 1955, Vol. II, p. 556.
[38] G. S. Kilsheimer and B. Axelrod, *J. Biol. Chem.* **227**, 879 (1957).
[39] K. K. Tsuboi and P. B. Hudson, *Arch. Biochem. Biophys.* **55**, 191 (1955).
[40] V. N. Nigam, H. M. Davidson, and W. H. Fishman, *J. Biol. Chem.* **234**, 1550 (1959).
[41] G. Schmidt, in P. D. Boyer, H. Lardy, and K. Myrbäck (eds.) "The Enzymes," Academic Press, New York, 1961, Vol. V, pp. 40–41.
[42] G. Bartsch, S. J. Thannhauser, and G. Schmidt, *Federation Proc.* **19**, 332 (1960).

to an organic acceptor.[43]   They are readily reversible (5-8).   Consistent

$$X-Y + P \overset{\text{Enz}}{\rightleftharpoons} X-O-P + Y \tag{5-8}$$

with the above, specific reactions [43] may be written, such as (5-9) occurring in the presence of the polysaccharide phosphorylases, (5-10) in the

$$[\text{Glucose}]_n + H_3PO_4 \rightleftharpoons \text{glucose-1-phosphate} + [\text{glucose}]_{n-1} \tag{5-9}$$

$$\text{Sucrose} + H_3PO_4 \rightleftharpoons \text{glucose-1-phosphate} + \text{fructose} \tag{5-10}$$

$$\text{Maltose} + H_3PO_4 \rightleftharpoons \text{glucose-1-phosphate} + \text{glucose} \tag{5-11}$$

presence of sucrose phosphorylase, and (5-11) in the presence of maltose
phosphorylase.

A unifying feature of phosphorylase reactions appears to be the probability that they proceed with X—O bond fission or, as in glucose-1-phos-
phate, C—O bond cleavage. This has been demonstrated through
employment of O^{18} for reactions catalyzed by polysaccharide and sucrose
phosphorylase,[30] to mention only two. This point of common cleavage
appears to imply a simple nucleophilic displacement by phosphate anion
on C-1 of the glycoside. However, stereochemical studies utilizing the
presence of an asymmetric carbon at the point of cleavage have revealed,
for example, that polysaccharide and sucrose phosphorylase reactions
occur with retention of configuration in contrast to a number of phosphorylases, of which maltose phosphorylase is a member, involving inversion.[43]   Second, H_3PO_4 does not exchange with glucose-1-phosphate in
the presence of polysaccharide and maltose phosphorylase, in contrast to
sucrose phosphorylase.[43]   Thus, just on the basis of these mechanistic
criteria, it is obvious that a simple mechanistic concept of a bimolecular
S_N2 nucleophilic displacement is an inadequate explanation for the above
experimental findings. There is the possibility of a stable intermediate
glucosyl enzyme [44] with sucrose phosphorylase, which undergoes a second
displacement reaction leading to net retention of configuration.[45]   In the
case of polysaccharide phosphorylase,[43] an $S_N i$ mechanism as found in the
reaction of thionyl chloride with 1-phenylethanols might be invoked.[46]
Consequently, although the unusual reactivity of the neutral species of

[43] M. Cohn, in P. D. Boyer, H. Lardy, and K. Myrbäck (eds.) "The Enzymes,"
Academic Press, New York, 1961, Vol. V, pp. 179–204.
[44] M. Doudoroff, H. A. Barker, and W. Z. Hassid, *J. Biol. Chem.* **168,** 725 (1947).
[45] D. E. Koshland, Jr., in W. D. McElroy and B. Glass (eds.) "The Mechanism of
Enzyme Action," Johns Hopkins Press, Baltimore, 1954, p. 608.
[46] E. M. Kosower and S. Winstein, *J. Am. Chem. Soc.* **78,** 4347 (1956).

α-D-glucose-1-phosphate most likely is important in the enzymic process, the extrapolation based on present knowledge between the enzymic and nonenzymic systems leaves much to be desired.

At pH values up to 4, glucose-6-phosphate behaves like other simple alkyl phosphates.[46a]   Its hydrolysis is acid catalyzed, and its rate decreases to a minimum at pH 1 and then increases again to a plateau at pH 4, where the monoanion is the major component.   However, with increasing pH the rate then increases, showing that, quite unexpectedly, the dianion is more reactive than the monoanion.   The 1-hydroxyl group of glucose is relatively acidic, because of the hemiacetal grouping, and it is probable that the high reactivity of the dianion is caused by an intramolecular proton transfer to the 6-oxygen atom of the glucose phosphate which allows ready phosphorus oxygen fission of the dianion.   Although the mechanism of the dianion hydrolysis is not fully understood, these results suggest that it should be easy to induce reactivity in alkyl phosphate dianions by having a good hydrogen bonding donor in proximity to the reaction center.

In connection with the hydrolysis of the monoesters, it is of interest to take note of the oxygen exchange between water and orthophosphoric acid.   This study [47] was carried out in dilute aqueous solutions and revealed that oxygen exchange between solvent and orthophosphoric acid, and its anions, proceeds by mechanisms analogous to those responsible for P—O bond fission during the hydrolysis of monoalkyl phosphates. The pH dependence for the rate of exchange is very similar to that observed for the hydrolysis of methyl phosphate.   In fact, the rate of phosphate exchange for the monoanion of orthophosphoric acid and the rate of hydrolysis for the monoanion of methyl phosphate are of the same order of magnitude.   Rates of exchange for the neutral and conjugate acid species of orthophosphoric acid exceed those for the corresponding hydrolytic process in methyl phosphate.   The exchange reaction may proceed either through a pentacovalent intermediate or through a simple displacement reaction.   There is no reason to prefer the former.

The comparable magnitudes for the rate of exchange versus the rate of hydrolysis may be the cause of certain experimental discrepancies that have arisen concerning the relative amounts of C—O and P—O cleavage (see Ref. 64).   In addition it may give rise to experimental complications that might erroneously indicate a pentacovalent intermediate in the study of enzyme catalyzed O^{18} exchange with inorganic phosphate.

Exchange\ has been observed between phosphate and H_2O^{18} in the

---

[46a] C. A. Bunton and H. Chaimovich, to be published.

[47] C. A. Bunton, D. R. Llewellyn, C. A. Vernon, and V. A. Welch, *J. Chem. Soc.* 1636 (1961).

presence of alkaline phosphatase [48] but not prostatic acid phosphatase [49]; it has also been observed nonenzymically in the hydrolysis of methyl and dimethyl phosphate.[5, 14, 64]

B. Diesters

Hydrolysis of a phosphate diester such as dimethyl phosphate differs markedly from that of its monoalkylated homolog. As mentioned previously, dialkylation greatly reduces the reactivity of the monoanion. Six hydrolytic mechanisms have been identified in all for the hydrolysis of dimethyl phosphate.[14] In addition to those previously discussed, mechanisms involving P—O bond cleavage of the neutral species and hydroxide ion attack on the monoanion species were discovered. The former was not found in the hydrolysis of the neutral species of methyl phosphate probably because of experimental difficulties arising from the small contribution to hydrolysis via this pathway. As with methyl phosphate, hydrolysis of the neutral species exhibits a positive salt effect. Moreover, the acid catalyzed hydrolysis of dimethyl phosphate also exhibits a positive salt effect, whereas that of the monoester does not. The reasons for this difference are not clear.[14]

The mechanism for P—O fission of the neutral species of dimethyl phosphate is formulated simply as a bimolecular displacement of methoxide ion (5-12a).[14] The expulsion of MeO$^\ominus$ by water, however, is improbable and it is quite possible that an alternate unimolecular pathway involving a monomeric ester of metaphosphate is operative (5-12b).

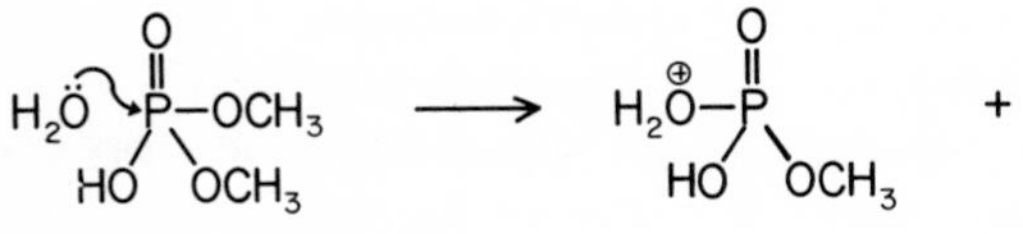

(5-12a)

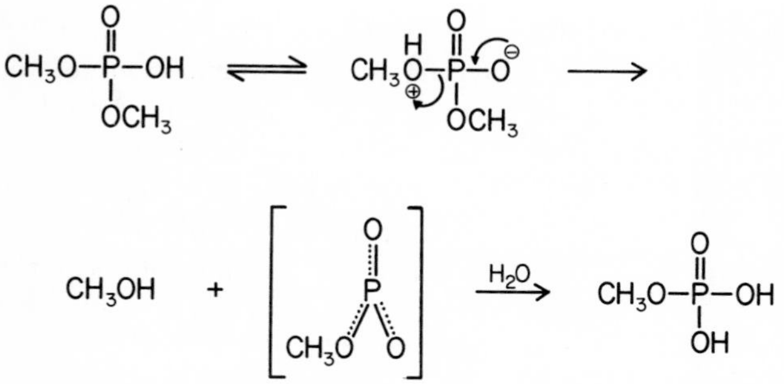

(5-12b)

[48] D. E. Koshland, Jr., Z. Budenstein, and A. Kowalsky, *J. Biol. Chem.* **211**, 279 (1954).

[49] C. A. Bunton, B. L. Silver, and C. A. Vernon, *Proc. Chem. Soc.* 348 (1957).

Precedents for such an intermediate may be furnished in the acid catalyzed hydrolysis of enol phosphates (see p. 159). The occurrence of P—O bond fission in the hydrolysis of the neutral species also has been observed for aryl phosphates where the hydrolysis of phenyl phosphate,[18] for example, is some 32 times faster than that of the corresponding reaction with dimethyl phosphate.[14]

The slight incursion of a hydroxide-ion catalyzed hydrolysis of the monoanion species (C—O fission) probably reflects the diminishing electrostatic repulsion directed against the attacking negative ion. Qualitatively one would expect the same behavior for other simple dialkylated esters, with the variation in the rates of the individual reactions involving C—O bond fission being similar to that found for other bimolecular substitutions on carbon. Tertiary alkyl groups in the esters may lead to carbonium ion mechanisms.

The biologically important polymeric phosphates, DNA and RNA, which exist as diesters, will be treated in the section dealing with intramolecular hydroxyl group participation due to their mode of hydrolysis.

C. Triesters

Hydrolytic reactions of phosphate triesters are unique because of the rapid hydrolysis observed in alkaline media.[10, 50—52] Bunton, Vernon, and co-workers have shown that the alkaline hydrolysis of trimethyl and triphenyl phosphate proceeds with P—O bond scission.[13] The reaction is depicted as a simple nucleophilic displacement, identical to those already mentioned:

$$\text{(5-13)}$$

The observed activation energy ($E_a = 10.2$ kcal mole^{-1}) is considerably lower than that observed for the monoanions of monoesters listed in Table 5-3. Due to this, it was originally thought that the hydroxide-ion catalyzed hydrolysis might proceed via a metastable intermediate such as I of (5-5). Exchange experiments designed to test this hypothesis proved fruitless.[13] Other workers, notably Halmann, also have reported that the hydrolysis of phosphorofluoridates is not accompanied by isotope exchange (see Chapter 6). Consequently the pentacovalent adduct has not been favored.

[50] R. H. A. Plimmer and W. J. N. Burch, *J. Chem. Soc.* 279 (1929).
[51] O. Bailly and J. Gaumé, *Bull. Soc. Chim. France* **3**, 1396 (1936).
[52] R. F. Hudson and D. C. Harper, *J. Chem. Soc.* 1356 (1958).

The results obtained with triphenyl phosphate in mixed solvents allow a comparison between the nucleophilicity of water and hydroxide ion toward phosphorus.[13] It may safely be assumed that for structural reasons the attack by water also proceeds via P—O bond fission. Against phosphorus, hydroxide ion is a better nucleophile than water by a factor of ca. 10^8. For attack on a saturated carbon atom the corresponding factor is much smaller, ca. 10^4. Thus, in a trisubstituted phosphate ester in which both carbon and phosphorus are vulnerable to nucleophilic attack, hydroxide ion and water will tend to be selective for phosphorus and carbon, respectively.[13] Consistently, trimethyl phosphate in neutral solution hydrolyzes with C—O bond fission.

D. Cyclic Phosphates

The hydrolysis of five-membered cyclic phosphates is greatly accelerated in comparison with the corresponding open-chain analogs.[53–57] A gross comparison of the rate constants without regard to the mode of bond fission reveals that ethylene phosphate hydrolyzes in both alkali,[12, 58] and acid,[59, 60] ca. 10^7 times faster than dimethyl phosphate. The rate of saponification of the cyclic triester, methyl ethylene phosphate, is similarly enhanced relative to trimethyl phosphate.[65] Yet the six-membered cyclic phosphate, trimethylene phosphate, hydrolyzes in alkali only slightly faster than dimethyl phosphate.[61, 62] This is in contrast to the hydrolysis of lactones where the six-membered ring hydrolyzes most rapidly with about a 6000-fold boost in the rate over that of the open-chain ester.[63] The stability of the seven-membered cyclic phosphate to alkaline hydrolysis appears to be slightly greater than that of the six-membered compound.[61, 63a]

Haake and Westheimer[64] have studied the hydrolysis of ethylene phosphate in acidic and basic solutions, using O^{18} as a tracer to determine

[53] O. Bailly, *Bull. Soc. Chim. France* **31**, 848 (1922).
[54] A. Fono, *Arkiv Kemi* **24A**, 14–15 (1947).
[55] R. Markham and J. D. Smith, *Biochem. J.* **52**, 552 (1952).
[56] D. M. Brown and A. R. Todd, *J. Chem. Soc.* 2708 (1952).
[57] T. Ukita, N. A. Bates, and H. E. Carter, *J. Biol. Chem.* **216**, 867 (1955).
[58] J. Lecocq, *Compt. rend.* **242**, 1902 (1956).
[59] F. H. Westheimer, *Chem. Soc. (London) Spec. Publ.* **8**, 1 (1957).
[60] J. R. Cox, Jr., Ph.D. Thesis, Harvard University (1959).
[61] H. G. Khorana, G. M. Tener, R. S. Wright, and J. G. Moffatt, *J. Am. Chem. Soc.* **79**, 430 (1957).
[62] E. Cherbuliez, H. Probst, and J. Rabinowitz, *Helv. Chim. Acta* **42**, 1377 (1959).
[63] R. Huisgen and H. Ott, *Tetrahedron* **6**, 253 (1959).
[63a] R. E. Wall, Jr., Ph.D. Thesis, Harvard University (1960).
[64] P. C. Haake and F. H. Westheimer, *J. Am. Chem. Soc.* **83**, 1102 (1961).

the position of hydrolytic cleavage. The cyclic ester was found to hydrolyze *exclusively* with P—O bond fission at any pH. In addition it was discovered that oxygen exchange accompanies the hydrolysis of ethylene phosphate in acid solution, but not in base (5-14). Knowledge of the point of bond cleavage allows a recalculation of the earlier factor

$$
\begin{array}{ccc}
 & \xrightarrow{k_h} & HOCH_2-CH_2-OPO_2O^{18}H_2 \\
\underset{H_2C-O}{\overset{H_2C-O}{\big|}}PO_2H & & \\
+ & & \underset{H_2C-O}{\overset{H_2C-O}{\big|}}POO^{18}H + H_2O \\
H_2O^{18} & \xrightarrow{k_e} &
\end{array} \tag{5-14}
$$

of 10^7 obtained as the difference between both the acidic and basic hydrolysis of dimethyl phosphate versus that of ethylene phosphate. Specifically Westheimer and Haake [64] compared the hydrolysis of the neutral species of dimethyl phosphate, proceeding via P—O bond cleavage (their value for the % of P—O bond cleavage differs somewhat from that of Bunton et al.[14]), to that of the acid catalyzed hydrolysis of ethylene phosphate. Similarly compared were the hydroxide-ion catalyzed hydrolysis of the monoanion species of either compound. Correction for the fact that the hydrolysis of the two compounds was not studied at the same temperature nevertheless led to a factor of ca. 10^8 for both hydrolytic pathways.

The cause of this enormous kinetic acceleration appears to originate from relief of strain in the cyclic ester upon hydrolysis. Thermochemical studies had revealed, for example, that the heat of hydrolysis of methyl ethylene phosphate exceeds that for dimethyl hydroxyethyl phosphate by about 7–9 kcal mole^{-1},[65] later corrected to ca. 5–6 kcal mole^{-1}.[67] The discovery of the rapid exchange of oxygen atoms between the solvent and ethylene phosphate during the acid catalyzed hydrolysis requires that this strain be relieved in the transition states for *both* hydrolysis and exchange. Implicit of course is the assumption that hydrolysis and exchange occur by a similar pathway.[64]

The geometries of three possible activated complexes for hydrolysis and exchange are illustrated in pairs in (5-15).[64] Each formula represents a nucleophilic attack by a water molecule on the conjugate acid of

[65] J. R. Cox, Jr., R. E. Wall, Jr., and F. H. Westheimer, *Chem. Ind. (London)* 929 (1959).

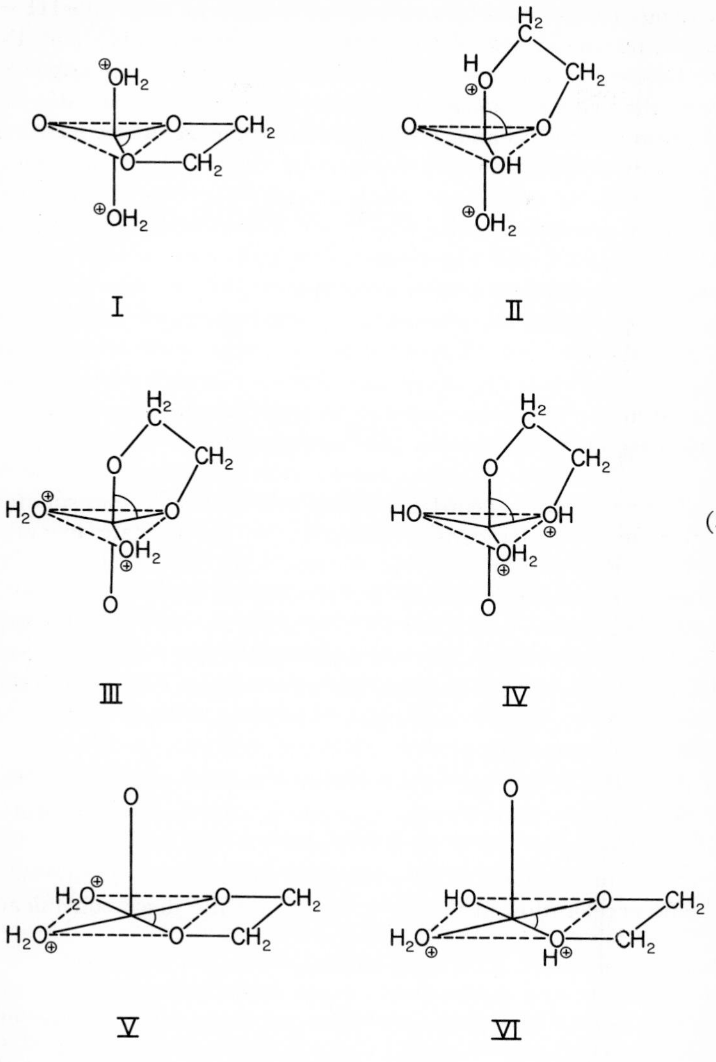

I

II

III

IV   (5-15)

V

VI

ethylene phosphate. The transition states I and II are those expected for an ordinary S_N2 displacement reaction identical to those found in bimolecular nucleophilic displacements on an sp^3 carbon atom. In I and II the ring has been respectively expanded for hydrolysis and contracted for exchange from its normal 98°, and it is improbable that both alterations could lead to comparable energies relative to the ground state. Transition states III and IV represent trigonal bipyramids in which the entering and leaving groups are at basal positions, and stereochemically III would probably lead to inversion of configuration. In both III and IV the O—P—O angle in the ring is 90°, and therefore both are comparable in energy to the ground state of the ester. The same ring angle is seen in the transition states V and VI, which have the geometry of a square pyramid with entering and leaving groups again in basal positions, but stereochemically V would most likely lead to retention of configuration.

For those transition states which are energetically similar, namely [III and IV] and [V and VI], both hydrolysis and exchange would occur at comparable velocities, which is consistent with the experimental evidence ($k_e/k_h \approx 4.9$). Insofar as the methanolysis of optically active esters is applicable (see Chapter 6, p. 128), the nucleophilic attack of methoxide on an optically active phosphinate proceeds with inversion of configuration.[66] The reader should note that the transition states pictured in (5-15) can serve to represent pentacovalent intermediates.[66a]

In connection with the kinetic acceleration found in cyclic phosphates, it is of interest to also regard the hydrolytic rates of cyclic sulfates and sulfites. The first-order rates of solvolysis of ethylene sulfate, trimethylene sulfate, and dimethyl sulfate are in the ratio 12:1:6 at 30°.[67] The second-order rates with hydroxide ion are in the ratio 103:1:5.5 at 30°.[67] Thus the acceleration is not nearly as great as in the cyclic phosphates, but the five-membered cyclic ester hydrolyzes most rapidly at any pH. The heats of reaction indicate that the five-membered cyclic sulfate, like the five-membered cyclic phosphate, is less stable than the open-chain analog by ca. 5–6 kcal mole^{-1}.[67]

In the sulfite series, the cyclic ethylene sulfite reacts in acidic solution[68] less rapidly than the corresponding dimethyl sulfite, but upon alkaline hydrolysis is 360 times as fast at 25° as the dimethyl ester.[69] Of great importance, in view of the concept of strain as being responsible for the kinetic acceleration in the cyclic esters, are the thermochemical data

[66] For a recent review of the stereochemistry of displacement reactions at phosphorus see R. F. Hudson and M. Green, *Angew. Chem. Intern. Ed. Engl.* **2**, 11 (1963).

[66a] The structure of a pentaoxyphosphorane (the adduct of phenanthrenequinone-triisopropyl phosphite) has been shown by X-ray analysis to be a nearly perfect trigonal bipyramid with the phosphorus atom at its center, the phenanthrene ring attached to one basal and one apical oxygen atom, and the isopropyl groups attached to the remaining two basal and one apical oxygens. This evidence may be interpreted to favor structure pairs III and IV of (5-15). W. C. Hamilton, S. J. LaPlaca, and F. Ramirez, *J. Am. Chem. Soc.* **87**, 127 (1965).

[67] E. T. Kaiser, M. Panar, and F. H. Westheimer, *J. Am. Chem. Soc.* **85**, 602 (1963).

[68] C. A. Bunton, P. D. B. de la Mare, A. Lennard, D. R. Llewellyn, R. B. Pearson, J. G. Pritchard, and J. G. Tillett, *J. Chem. Soc.* 4761 (1958).

[69] R. E. Davis, *J. Am. Chem. Soc.* **84**, 599 (1962).

which show that the heats of hydrolysis of cyclic and noncyclic sulfites are nearly equal.[69] Finally, it should be noted that the ratios of the rates of hydrolysis of a five-membered cyclic ester of phosphonic acid, lithium propylphosphonate, and a six-membered analog, lithium butylphosphonate, relative to sodium ethyl ethylphosphonate are in acid $5 \times 10^4 : 3 : 1$ and in alkali $6 \times 10^5 : 24 : 1$ [67, 70, 70a] (tracer studies increase the ratios slightly in favor of the cyclic esters).

On the basis of these data, Westheimer[67] and co-workers have concluded that neither of the following rationales alone adequately explains the source of the observed thermochemical strain: (1) that the phosphorus atom imposes a sharp torsional angle upon the ring atoms, because this demands the presence of two C—O—P bonds,[12] (2) that the eclipsing of the hydrogen atoms or unpaired electrons on the ester oxygen atoms is responsible for all of the strain,[12] in view of the thermochemical data available on the cyclic sulfites and their lack of kinetic acceleration in acid solution. Westheimer *et al.*[67] presently propose that partial double-bonding between the heteroatom and the ester oxygen atoms is essential to the kinetic acceleration.[60, 64] Formation of the double bond is required by this hypothesis to be partially repressed by the presence of an unshared pair of electrons on phosphorus or sulfur in the sulfites or phosphites. Evidence for the existence of partial double-bond character in phosphates stems from X-ray crystallographic studies[71] and n.m.r. spectra[72] (see also Chapter 6, p. 117). At present there is little information pertaining to p_π—d_π bonding in the phosphites.

If indeed p_π—d_π overlap is important in the ester bonds of phosphates[4] and sulfates, then inclusion of the ester into a ring may diminish the extent of the double bonding. To the degree that double bonding is lessened, the cyclic compounds are less stabilized than their open-chain analogs.[72a] Consequently this explanation places less emphasis on ring strain than on stabilization of the noncyclic esters.[67] In any event ring strain alone cannot account for the data in the cyclic systems.

E. Acyl Phosphates

An extensive study of the mechanism for hydrolysis of acyl phosphates has been carried out by DiSabato and Jencks.[20] They have compiled a

[70] J. R. Van Wazer, "Phosphorus and Its Compounds," Interscience, New York, 1958, Vol. I, p. 36.

[70a] A. Eberhard and F. H. Westheimer, *J. Am. Chem. Soc.*, **87**, 253 (1965).

[71] J. D. Dunitz and J. S. Rollett, *Acta Cryst.* **9**, 327 (1956).

[72] H. S. Gutowsky and D. W. McCall, *J. Chem. Phys.* **22**, 162 (1954).

[72a] An n.m.r. study of P^{31} chemical shifts of five-membered cyclic phosphate esters is consistent with the deduction that d_π—p_π bonding is diminished in these systems. G. M. Blackburn, J. S. Cohen, and A. R. Todd, *Tetrahedron Letters* **39**, 2873 (1964).

considerable volume of evidence supporting the hypothesis that the hydrolysis of simple acyl phosphates proceeds in neutral solutions through the monomeric metaphosphate ion.

Acetyl phosphate ($pK'_{a_2} = 4.95$ at 39°, $\mu = 0.6$) [73] exists near neutrality in both the monoanion ($AcP^\ominus$) and dianion forms ($AcP^\ominus$) (5-16). The hydrolysis of $AcP^\ominus$ [74-76] occurs readily at 39°, whereas other phos-

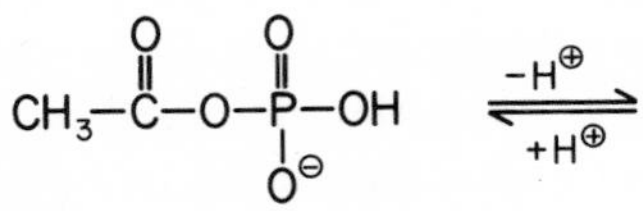

$$\text{CH}_3-\overset{\overset{\text{O}}{\|}}{\text{C}}-\text{O}-\overset{\overset{\text{O}}{\|}}{\underset{\underset{\text{O}^\ominus}{|}}{\text{P}}}-\text{OH} \quad \underset{+\text{H}^\oplus}{\overset{-\text{H}^\oplus}{\rightleftharpoons}} \quad \text{CH}_3-\overset{\overset{\text{O}}{\|}}{\text{C}}-\text{O}-\overset{\overset{\text{O}}{\|}}{\underset{\underset{\text{O}^\ominus}{|}}{\text{P}}}-\text{O}^\ominus \qquad (5\text{-}16)$$

phate monoanion hydrolyses are conveniently studied at higher temperatures; the calculated rate of $AcP^\ominus$ hydrolysis at 100° is 10^4 times faster than that for the monoanion species of methyl phosphate. In contrast, the rate of hydrolysis of the monoanion species of acetyl phenyl phosphate ($AcPhP^\ominus$) at 39° is some 70 times slower than $AcP^\ominus$.

Jencks and DiSabato have proposed that the rapid hydrolysis of the monoanion species of acetyl phosphate may be due to an internal proton transfer through a cyclic six-membered ring, not requiring solvent participation (5-17). In addition it is anticipated that, as the leaving

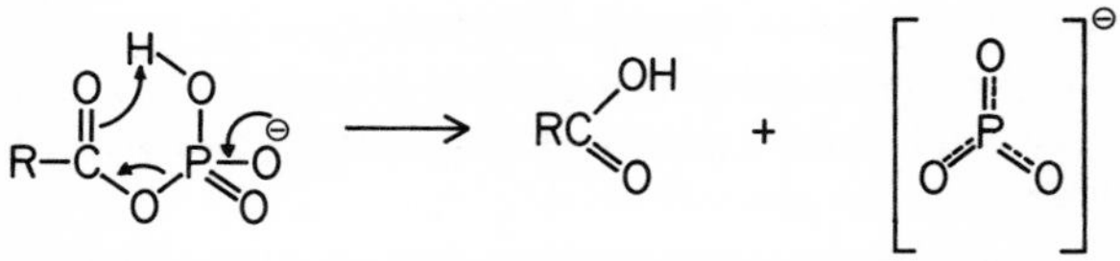

$$(5\text{-}17)$$

group ($RCOO^\ominus$) becomes more electron-withdrawing, a pathway analogous to (5-17) but not involving a proton transfer will become operational. This has been proposed for the hydrolytic mechanism of the acyl phosphate dianions and 2,4-dinitrophenyl phosphate.[19]

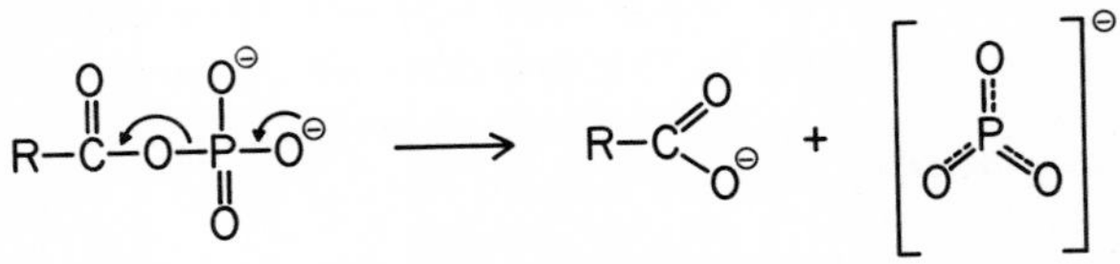

$$(5\text{-}18)$$

In contrast, the solvolysis of $AcPhP^\ominus$ is thought to proceed through a bimolecular nucleophilic displacement reaction. Unlike the rates of hydrolysis of $AcP^\ominus$ and $AcP^\ominus$, the rate of hydrolysis of $AcPhP^\ominus$ increases

[73] F. Lipmann and L. C. Tuttle, Arch. Biochem. Biophys. 13, 373 (1947).
[74] F. Lynen, Ber. 73, 367 (1940).
[75] D. E. Koshland, Jr., J. Am. Chem. Soc. 73, 4103 (1951).
[76] D. E. Koshland, Jr., J. Am. Chem. Soc. 74, 2286 (1952).

with increasing buffer concentration, a point to be discussed in some detail in a later section.   Thus this solvolysis can be formulated as [20]:

$$(5\text{-}19)$$

Consistent with the above, it has been established through tracer studies that the hydrolysis of AcP$^\ominus$ and AcP$^\ominus$ proceeds via P—O bond cleavage.[77, 78]   Moreover, fluoroacetyl phosphate dianion, possessing a considerably better leaving group than acetyl phosphate, undergoes hydrolysis 63 times faster than the dianion of acetyl phosphate.[79]   As has been previously noted (see p. 7), the rates of hydrolysis of the mono-anion forms for a series of substituted benzoyl phosphates show little variance with change in the substituent.   Yet the rates of hydrolysis of the dianions of this same series of benzoyl phosphates illustrate the greater favorability for hydrolysis in the presence of an electron-withdrawing substituent.   A Hammett plot for the hydrolysis of the dianion species gives a ρ of $+1.2$.

Jencks and DiSabato cite other experimental evidence in support of the metaphosphate mechanism for the hydrolysis of monosubstituted acyl phosphates, which is also applicable to phosphate monoesters.   Data for the hydrolysis of AcPhP$^\ominus$ will be included as a basis of comparison.

First, the entropies of activation for the neutral hydrolysis of AcP$^\ominus$, AcP$^\ominus$, and AcPhP$^\ominus$ are 3.7, -3.6, and -28.8 entropy units, respectively. In general it may be expected for reactions which carry similar charges in ground and transition states, but which involve attack by solvent, that $\Delta S^{\ddagger}$ will be negative.[80]   This is largely attributed to a requirement for orientation of the attacking solvent molecules.   In contrast a unimolecu-lar reaction, again with similar charge distribution in ground and tran-sition states, will exhibit a $\Delta S^{\ddagger}$ value near zero.[80]

Second, the rates of hydrolysis of AcP$^\ominus$ and AcP$^\ominus$ are not significantly

[77] R. Bentley, *J. Am. Chem. Soc.* **71**, 2765 (1949).

[78] J. H. Park and D. E. Koshland, Jr., *J. Biol. Chem.* **233**, 986 (1958).

[79] A. Marcus and W. B. Elliott, *J. Am. Chem. Soc.* **80**, 4287 (1958).

[80] F. A. Long, J. G. Pritchard, and F. E. Stafford, *J. Am. Chem. Soc.* **79**, 2362 (1957).

altered upon change of solvent to D_2O. Yet the rate of hydrolysis of $AcPhP^\ominus$ is decreased 2.5-fold in D_2O. The pH-independent solvolysis or spontaneous hydrolysis of activated acyl groups through attack by water is usually decreased 2–3-fold in D_2O solution.[81-84] The effects of D_2O on the solvolysis of $AcP^\ominus$ and $AcPhP^\ominus$ are those expected for a unimolecular and bimolecular reaction, respectively. Interpretation of the deuterium isotope effect in the case of the $AcP^\ominus$ is complicated by the possibility of pre-equilibrium or concerted proton transfers.

Third, the volumes of activation for the neutral hydrolysis of $AcP^\ominus$, $AcP^\ominus$, and $AcPhP^\ominus$ are -1.0 ± 1.0, -0.6 ± 1.0, and -19 ± 2 cm^3 mole^{-1}, respectively.[85] Values of $\Delta V^\ddagger$ may be interpreted in a manner similar to $\Delta S^\ddagger$ values, again providing that charge distribution in ground and transition states is similar.[86-90] Thus, the values for $\Delta V^\ddagger$ are in accord with a unimolecular reaction for both species of acetyl phosphate and suggest a bimolecular reaction for $AcPhP^\ominus$.

Fourth, addition of 30–50% acetonitrile to the solvent markedly decreases the rate of hydrolysis of $AcPhP^\ominus$. The rates of hydrolysis of $AcP^\ominus$ and $AcP^\ominus$ remain practically unchanged by this addition of acetonitrile. The spontaneous hydrolysis of activated acyl groups is generally decreased considerably by the addition of nonpolar solvents to water, presumably because of the decrease in the amount of water available for nucleophilic attack or changes in activities.[81, 91]

Finally the formation of pyrophosphate is observed during the solvolysis of acetyl phosphate in nonaqueous solvents and in the presence of concentrated $NaClO_4$. Formation of polyphosphates has been observed in other phosphate solvolyses.[92-94] Since a direct attack by $HPO_4^\ominus$ on acetyl phosphate cannot be demonstrated, pyrophosphate formation most

[81] W. P. Jencks and J. Carriuolo, *J. Am. Chem. Soc.* **83,** 1743 (1961).

[82] W. P. Jencks and J. Carriuolo, *J. Biol. Chem.* **234,** 1272, 1280 (1959).

[83] A. R. Butler and V. Gold, *Proc. Chem. Soc.* 15 (1960).

[84] C. A. Bunton, N. Fuller, S. G. Perry, and V. J. Shiner, Jr., *Chem. Ind. (London)* 1130 (1960).

[85] G. DiSabato, W. P. Jencks, and E. Whalley, *Can. J. Chem.* **40,** 1220 (1962).

[86] J. Koskikallio, D. Pouli, and E. Whalley, *Can. J. Chem.* **37,** 1360 (1959).

[87] E. Whalley, *Trans. Faraday Soc.*, **55,** 798 (1959).

[88] J. Koskikallio and E. Whalley, *Trans. Faraday Soc.* **55,** 809, 815 (1959).

[89] S. D. Hamann, "Physico-Chemical Effects of Pressure," Butterworths, London, 1957, Chap. 9.

[90] J. Koskikallio and E. Whalley, *Can. J. Chem.* **37,** 788 (1959).

[91] E. R. Garrett, *J. Am. Chem. Soc.* **82,** 711 (1960).

[92] D. M. Brown and N. K. Hamer, *J. Chem. Soc.* 1155 (1960).

[93] V. M. Clark, D. W. Hutchinson, G. W. Kirby, and A. R. Todd, *J. Chem. Soc.* 715 (1961).

[94] V. M. Clark, D. W. Hutchinson, and A. R. Todd, *J. Chem. Soc.* 722 (1961).

likely represents the trapping of a metaphosphate intermediate. Collectively, these arguments constitute strong evidence that hydrolysis of acetyl and acetyl phenyl phosphate do proceed by the mechanisms indicated.

The enzymic hydrolysis of acetyl phosphate in the presence of acyl phosphatase occurs with P—O bond scission.[77] In this respect the non-enzymic hydrolysis is analogous to the enzymic counterpart; however, the possible involvement of Mg(II) in the activity of acetyl phosphatase [95] dictates that further discussion be deferred until metal-ion catalysis has been considered. An apparent exception to the P—O bond cleavage, which appears to be general for the phosphatases,[29] is the C—O bond cleavage of acetyl phosphate by glyceraldehyde-3-phosphate dehydrogenase. Koshland and Park [77] suggest, however, that the acyl enzyme bond rather than the C—O bond of acetyl phosphate is the one being hydrolytically cleaved.

F. Hydrolysis through Elimination

Although the phosphate esters to be discussed in this section, for the most part, fall under the heading of phosphomonoesters, they are characterized by a rapid hydrolysis in alkaline media. Presence of an electron-withdrawing substituent β to the phosphate linkage leads, in several well-documented cases, to base catalyzed β-eliminations.

The unique lability in alkali of the serine phosphate ester bonds [96] in proteins, such as casein and vitellin, led to the hypothesis that the reaction was one of elimination rather than hydrolysis,[97] which was tested [98] by dephosphorylating bovine casein with alkali in water enriched with O^{18}. No incorporation of the isotope into inorganic phosphate was found, thereby supporting a probable β-elimination. Serine phosphate also serves as (1) a substrate for a specific phosphatase,[99-102] which appears to act as a hydrolytic enzyme but probably via P—O bond cleavage, (2) an immediate precursor in serine biosynthesis.[103] The importance of β-elimination in biosynthesis is implied through tracer studies on the formation of threonine from O-phosphohomoserine with the enzyme threonine synthetase.[104]

[95] A. L. Lehninger, *J. Biol. Chem.* **162**, 333 (1946).
[96] G. E. Perlmann, *Advan. Protein Chem.* **10**, 1 (1955).
[97] D. K. Mecham and H. S. Olcott, *J. Am. Chem. Scc.* **71**, 3670 (1949).
[98] L. Anderson and J. J. Kelley, *J. Am. Chem. Snc.* **81**, 2275 (1959).
[99] L. F. Borkenhagen and E. P. Kennedy, *Biochim. Biophys. Acta* **28**, 222 (1958).
[100] L. F. Borkenhagen and E. P. Kennedy, *J. Biol. Chem.* **234**, 849 (1959).
[101] F. C. Neuhaus and W. L. Byrne, *Biochim. Biophys. Acta* **28**, 223 (1958).
[102] F. C. Neuhaus and W. L. Byrne, *J. Biol. Chem.* **234**, 113 (1959).
[103] A. Ichihara and D. M. Greenberg, *J. Biol. Chem.* **224**, 331 (1959).
[104] M. Flavin and T. Kono, *J. Biol. Chem.* **235**, 1109 (1960).

Samuel and Silver have investigated the elimination and hydrolytic reactions of serine phosphate in a detailed nonenzymic study.[105] In the strongly alkaline range pH > 14, the rate of formation of inorganic phosphate increases with higher $OH^\ominus$ concentration. The products of the reaction are ammonia and pyruvic acid, which tracer studies confirm as being formed through C—O bond fission. Substitution of deuterium at the α-hydrogen atom led to an observed kinetic isotope effect of 1.85, revealing that the proton abstraction is rate-determining. A mechanism compatible with these findings is depicted in (5-20).

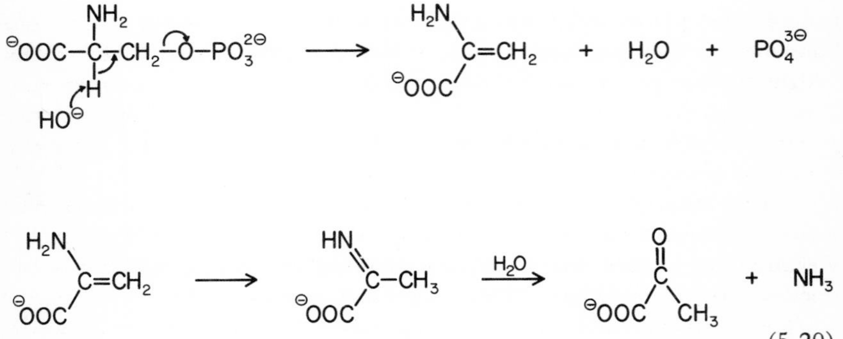

$$(5\text{-}20)$$

This mechanism is similar to that proposed for the pyridoxal catalyzed breakdown of serine phosphate in the presence of Cu(II). In the latter, complexation of the metal ion with the imine formed from pyridoxal and serine phosphate results in polarization of the α C—H bond, leading to ready elimination of the orthophosphate group.[106] The intermediate imine undergoes rapid hydrolysis under the experimental conditions [107] (see Chapter 8).

Over the weakly alkaline range, pH 7.0–13.5, the observed rate is independent of pH. Product isolation, tracer studies, and deuterium substitution indicate that the reaction again is solely one of β-elimination. However, the lack of dependence of the reaction on hydroxide ion invalidates mechanism (5-20) as being operative in this pH range. A conceivable mechanism involves intramolecular attack by the phosphate group on the α-hydrogen atom (5-21).

[105] D. Samuel and B. L. Silver, J. Chem. Soc. 289 (1963).
[106] D. E. Metzler and E. E. Snell, J. Biol. Chem. 198, 353, 363 (1952).
[107] R. Roger and D. G. Neilson, Chem. Rev. 61, 179 (1961).

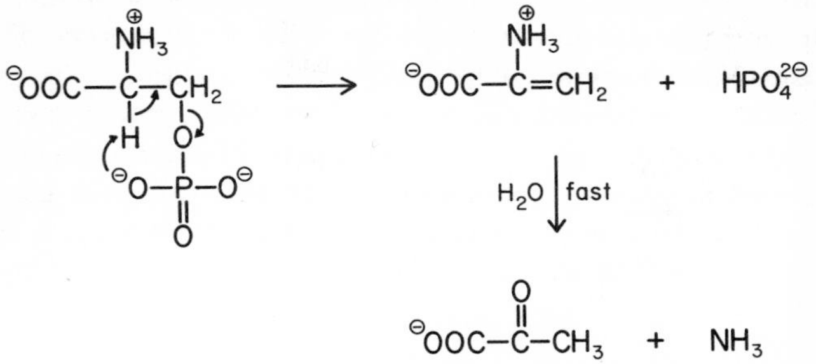

$$(5\text{-}21)$$

In the pH range 2–7 both elimination and hydrolysis occur simultaneously. Approximately 20% of the total rate is due to elimination. The pH-rate profile for the hydrolysis of serine phosphate without elimination qualitatively and quantitatively approaches that of ethanolamine phosphate,[108] and is typical of the pH-rate profiles of the monoesters already discussed.

Activation of the C—H bond β to the phosphorylated hydroxyl group by groups such as —CN, —CONH$_2$, —SO$_3$H, and —COOH leads to elimination rather than hydrolysis of the phosphoryl group as has been shown by Cherbuliez, Rabinowitz, and co-workers.[109-114] Phosphate esters containing such groups as 2-cyanoethyl phosphate and 2-sulfoxyethyl phosphate exhibit a large increase in the rate of appearance of inorganic phosphate in the pH region 12–14 and hydrolyze through C—O bond fission. The hydrolytic products, although not isolated, decolorize bromine and permanganate solutions. Replacement of both C—H bonds, as in 2-methyl-2-cyanopropyl phosphate, destroys all alkaline lability. Thus, the evidence is clearly in agreement with a β-elimination mechanism.

The alkaline lability of phosphate esters of certain carbohydrates also appears to arise from β-elimination. Among several well-documented cases are the following examples: (1) alkaline catalyzed hydrolysis of

[108] A. Desjobert, Ph.D. Thesis, Lons-le-Saunier (1951).

[109] E. Cherbuliez and J. Rabinowitz, *Helv. Chim. Acta* **40,** 526 (1957).

[110] E. Cherbuliez, H. Probst, J. Rabinowitz, and S. Sandrin, *Helv. Chim. Acta* **41,** 1163 (1958).

[111] E. Cherbuliez, C. Gandillon, A. de Picciotto, and J. Rabinowitz, *Helv. Chim. Acta* **42,** 2277 (1959).

[112] E. Cherbuliez, G. Cordahi, and J. Rabinowitz, *Helv. Chim. Acta* **43,** 863 (1960).

[113] E. Cherbuliez, H. Probst, and J. Rabinowitz, *Helv. Chim. Acta* **45,** 1071 (1962).

[114] E. Cherbuliez, H. Dahn, H. Moll, H. Probst, and J. Rabinowitz, *Helv. Chim. Acta* **45,** 1075 (1962).

glyceraldehyde-3-phosphate to yield lactic acid [115, 116] (5-22), and (2) the alkaline hydrolysis of adenosine-5′-phosphate and adenosine-5′-benzyl phosphate derivatives, which serves as a model for a process of stepwise degradation of polynucleotides [117] (5-23).

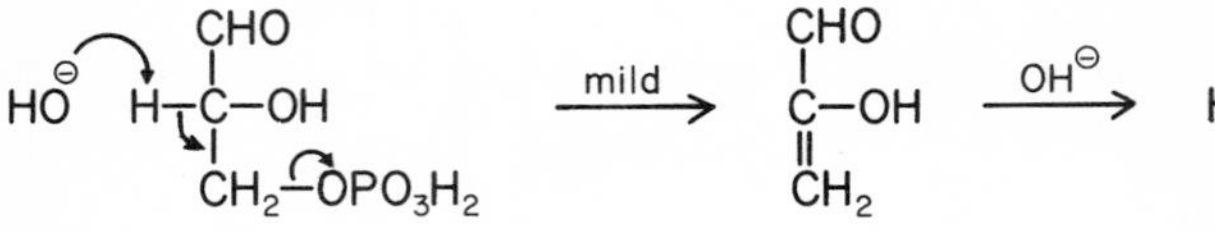

$$
\begin{array}{ccc}
\text{CHO} & \text{CHO} & \text{COOH} \\
\text{H--C--OH} & \xrightarrow{\text{mild}} \quad \text{C--OH} & \xrightarrow{\text{OH}^\ominus} \quad \text{HCOH} \quad (5\text{-}22) \\
\text{CH}_2\text{--OPO}_3\text{H}_2 & \text{CH}_2 & \text{CH}_3
\end{array}
$$

85% elimination of inorganic phosphate and benzyl phos— phate, pH 10.5, 3 hours.

where R=H,
R=CH₂—   (5-23)

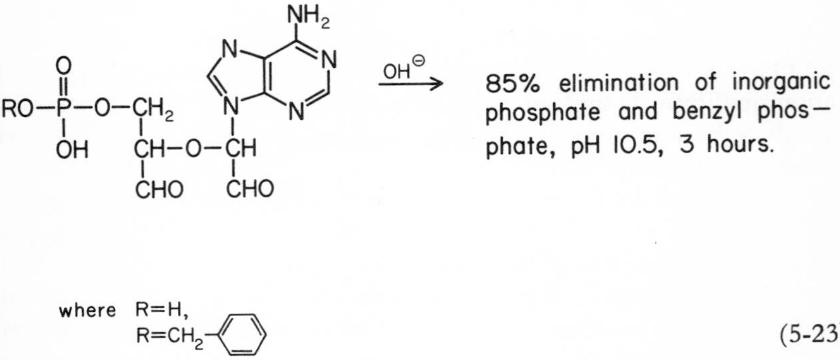

Lee [118] has also shown that treatment of fructose-1,6-diphosphate with aqueous sodium or potassium hydroxide, 0.1–0.5 N, results in the release of 1.3–1.5 moles of inorganic phosphate, with the remaining phosphate being very stable toward hot alkali. Examination of the mixture of products by paper chromatography showed that no less than ten to fifteen components were present. The very rapid initial release of inorganic phosphate is thought to arise from a β-elimination mechanism, but it is obvious that other reaction pathways exist. Attempts to isolate (5-24 I), 1-deoxy-D-erythro-2,3-hexodiulose-6-phosphate, were unsuccessful. However, enolization of the fructose diphosphate to the 2,3-enediol followed by β-elimination is in harmony with the known behavior of glucose-3-phosphate and other related compounds.[119, 120]

[115] Ö. Meyerhof and K. Lohmann, Biochem. Z. **271**, 89 (1934).
[116] E. Baer and H. O. L. Fischer, J. Biol. Chem. **150**, 223 (1943).
[117] D. M. Brown, M. Fried, and A. R. Todd, J. Chem. Soc. 2206 (1955).
[118] J. B. Lee, J. Org. Chem. **28**, 2473 (1963).
[119] D. M. Brown, F. Hayes, and A. R. Todd, Ber. **90**, 936 (1957).
[120] G. Machell and G. N. Richards, J. Chem. Soc. 1938, 1924, 1932 (1960).

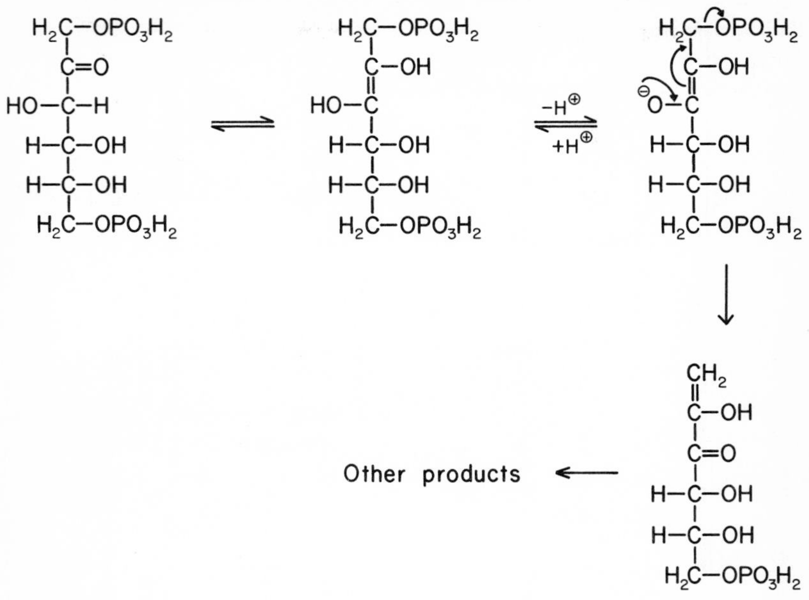

$$
\begin{array}{ccc}
\begin{array}{l}
H_2C\!-\!OPO_3H_2 \\
\quad | \\
\quad C\!=\!O \\
\quad | \\
HO\!-\!C\!-\!H \\
\quad | \\
H\!-\!C\!-\!OH \\
\quad | \\
H\!-\!C\!-\!OH \\
\quad | \\
H_2C\!-\!OPO_3H_2
\end{array}
\;\rightleftharpoons\;
&
\begin{array}{l}
H_2C\!-\!OPO_3H_2 \\
\quad | \\
\quad C\!-\!OH \\
\quad \| \\
HO\!-\!C \\
\quad | \\
H\!-\!C\!-\!OH \\
\quad | \\
H\!-\!C\!-\!OH \\
\quad | \\
H_2C\!-\!OPO_3H_2
\end{array}
&
\overset{-H^{\oplus}}{\underset{+H^{\oplus}}{\rightleftharpoons}}
\begin{array}{l}
H_2C\!-\!OPO_3H_2 \\
\quad | \\
\quad C\!-\!OH \\
\quad \| \\
O^{\ominus}\!\!-\!C \\
\quad | \\
H\!-\!C\!-\!OH \\
\quad | \\
H\!-\!C\!-\!OH \\
\quad | \\
H_2C\!-\!OPO_3H_2
\end{array}
\end{array}
$$

$$
\downarrow
$$

$$
\text{Other products} \;\longleftarrow\;
\begin{array}{l}
CH_2 \\
\| \\
C\!-\!OH \\
| \\
C\!=\!O \\
| \\
H\!-\!C\!-\!OH \\
| \\
H\!-\!C\!-\!OH \\
| \\
H_2C\!-\!OPO_3H_2
\end{array}
$$

$$(5\text{-}24)$$

Rate data for various phosphate esters are presented in Table 5-4.

III. NUCLEOPHILIC CATALYSIS

A. Bimolecular Nucleophilic Catalysis

The most extensive research on nucleophilic reactivity toward phosphate compounds has been conducted with the phosphorofluoridates and phosphonofluoridates to be discussed in the following chapter. However, Jencks and DiSabato [121] in an investigation of the reactions of acetyl phosphate have discovered reactions which represent nucleophilic catalysis of phosphoryl transfer. For this discussion those reactions which give P—O bond cleavage will be stressed.

Park and Koshland [78] had demonstrated earlier that the reaction of pyridine with acetyl phosphate proceeded with P—O bond cleavage. Jencks and DiSabato [121] found that reactions of acetyl phosphate with several tertiary amines, including triethylenediamine, pyridine, 4-methyl-

[121] G. DiSabato and W. P. Jencks, *J. Am. Chem. Soc.* **83,** 4393 (1961).

Table 5-4   Rate constants for selected phosphate esters

Compound	Species	Cleavage	T (°C)	k	Conditions	Ref.
H_3PO_4	$H_2PO_4^{\ominus}$	P—O	100	4.03×10^{-6} sec^{-1}		47
	H_3PO_4	P—O	100	1.28×10^{-6} sec^{-1}		47
	$H_4PO_4^{\oplus}$	P—O	100	5.45×10^{-6} liter mole^{-1} sec^{-1}		47
$CH_3OPO_3H_2$	$CH_3OPO_3H^{\ominus}$	P—O	100	8.23×10^{-6} sec^{-1}	$\mu = 0$	5
	$CH_3OPO_3H_2$	C—O	100	0.50×10^{-6} sec^{-1}	$\mu = 0$	5
	*$CH_3OPO_3H_3^{\oplus}$	C—O	100	2.00×10^{-6} liter mole^{-1} sec^{-1}	$\mu = 0$	5
	*$CH_3OPO_3H_3^{\oplus}$	P—O	100	1.08×10^{-6} liter mole^{-1} sec^{-1}	$\mu = 0$	5
$(CH_3O)_2PO_2H$	$[OH^{\ominus}][(CH_3O)_2PO_2^{\ominus}]$	P—O	125	ca. 0.6×10^{-6} liter mole^{-1} sec^{-1}	$\mu = 1.16$	*
	$[OH^{\ominus}][(CH_3O)_2PO_2^{\ominus}]$	C—O	125	ca. 5.4×10^{-6} liter mole^{-1} sec^{-1}	$\mu = 1.16$	*
	$(CH_3O)_2PO_2H$	C—O	100	3.3×10^{-6} sec^{-1}	$\mu = 0$	14
	$(CH_3O)_2PO_2H$	P—O	100	0.9×10^{-6} sec^{-1}	$\mu = 0$	14
	*$(CH_3O)_2PO_2H_2^{\oplus}$	C—O	100	0.91×10^{-6} liter mole^{-1} sec^{-1}	$\mu = 0$	14
	*$(CH_3O)_2PO_2H_2^{\oplus}$	P—O	100	0.11×10^{-6} liter mole^{-1} sec^{-1}	$\mu = 0$	14
$(CH_3O)_3PO$	$[OH^{\ominus}][(CH_3O)_3PO]$	P—O	35	3.3×10^{-4} liter mole^{-1} sec^{-1}	$\mu = 0$	13

Neutral					
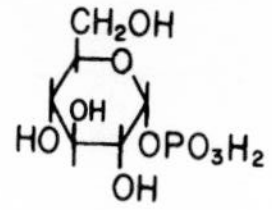 CH₂OH / HO / OH / OPO₃H₂ (glucose phosphate ring)	C—O	82	4.00×10^{-3} sec⁻¹		24
cyclic ethylene phosphate: O=P–OH with –O–CH₂–CH₂–O– ring; (OH)⁻	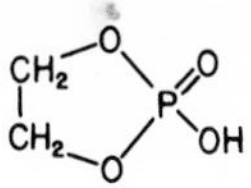 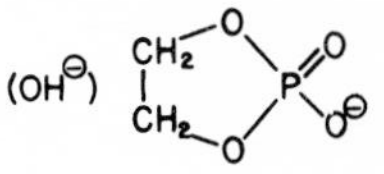 P—O	25	4.7×10^{-4} liter mole⁻¹ sec⁻¹	KOH ($\mu = 0.66$)	64
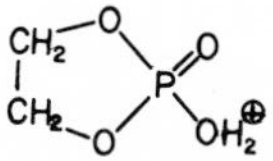 cyclic ethylene phosphate: O=P⊕–OH₂ with –O–CH₂–CH₂–O– ring	P—O	30	6.18×10^{-2} liter mole⁻¹ sec⁻¹	—	64
CH₃–C(=O)–O–P(=O)(O⁻)–OH	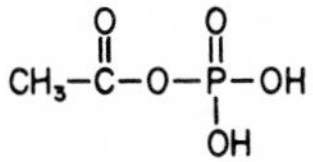 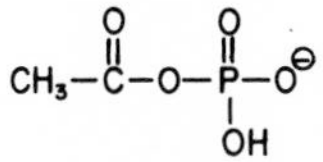 P—O	25	3.25×10^{-5} sec⁻¹	0.1 M KHCO₃	20
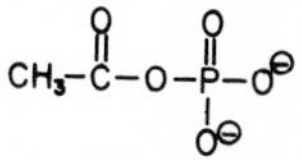 CH₃–C(=O)–O–P(=O)(O⁻)–O⁻	P—O	25	9.34×10^{-6} sec⁻¹	0.1 M K₃PO₄	20
⊖O–P(=O)(O⊖)–OCH₂–CH–COO⊖ / NH₂	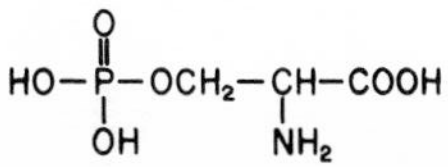 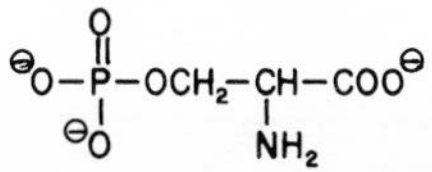 C—O	100	3.34×10^{-6} sec⁻¹	0.025 M borate (pH 9.65)	105
HO–P(=O)(OH)–OCH₂–CH–COOH / NH₂					

* J. R. Cox, Jr., Ph.D. Thesis, Harvard University. Some uncertainty is present over the division of the rate into C—O and P—O modes of cleavage, as is mentioned in the text, for the starred species.[64]

pyridine, and probably triethylamine, also give P—O bond fission. In contrast, the heterocyclic tertiary amines, imidazole and N-methyl-imidazole, attack the acyl group leading to C—O bond fission. The effect of pK_a' seems immaterial; aniline has a basicity similar to pyridine yet attacks the acyl group. Also, seemingly unrelated are simple structural considerations, since a heterocyclic tertiary amine, such as pyridine, gives P—O bond cleavage whereas a second, such as imidazole, gives C—O bond cleavage. Thus, no ready explanation is apparent.

The reactions of acetyl phosphate characterized by attack at the acyl group are subject to general catalysis by acid and base. Jencks and DiSabato prefer to describe the reaction of acetyl phosphate near neutral pH with nucleophiles such as glycine, ammonia, morpholine, and aniline as attack of the free base on the monoanion of acetyl phosphate, rather than attack by the conjugate acid of the base on the ester dianion.[123] General-base catalysis at the acyl group of AcP$^\ominus$ was found with only one nucleophile, hydroxylamine. More numerous are the general-base catalyzed reactions found at the acetyl group of AcP$^\ominus$ in the presence of ammonia, n-butylamine, and glycine. It was also shown that Ca(II) catalyzes the attack of glycine and mercaptoacetate on the carbonyl group, probably through neutralization of negative charge and general-acid catalyzed expulsion of the leaving group. Cations such as Mg(II),[75] Ca(II),[122] and Li(I) [123] have long been known to catalyze the hydrolytic reactions of acetyl phosphate.

The reactions found at phosphorus leading to P—O bond scission could occur through: (1) direct attack by amine on phosphorus (5-25)

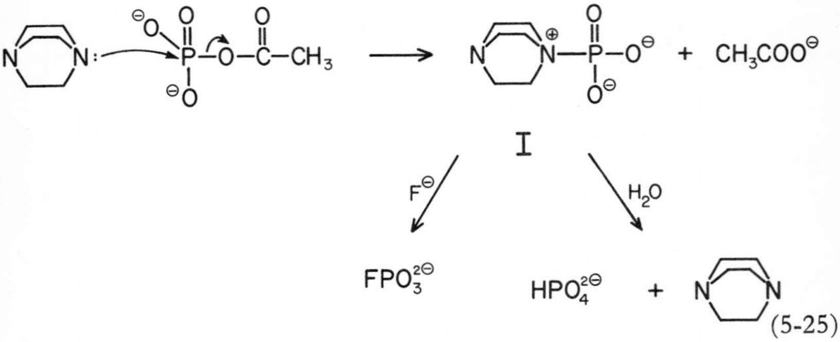

(5-25)

to give an unstable phosphoramidate intermediate (I), (2) general-base catalysis involving attack by solvent, (3) attack by the amine on the

[122] F. Lipmann and L. C. Tuttle, *J. Biol. Chem.* **153,** 571 (1944).
[123] J. L. Kurz and C. D. Gutsche, *J. Am. Chem. Soc.* **82,** 2175 (1960).

carbonyl group to form a tetrahedral intermediate which readily eliminates metaphosphate, acetate, and amine.

Mechanism (1) is strongly supported by the finding that if fluoride is added as a trapping reagent, under conditions where there is no direct reaction between acetyl phosphate and fluoride, fluorophosphate can be isolated. The yield of fluorophosphate increases with increasing fluoride concentration. Fluorophosphate is formed over that expected from fluoride attack alone, when fluoride is added to solutions of AcP$^\ominus$ and AcP$^\ominus$ undergoing pyridine, 4-methylpyridine, and trimethylamine catalyzed hydrolysis. Mechanism (2), on the other hand, is made less likely by the absence of a deuterium solvent isotope effect in the pyridine catalyzed hydrolysis. There is no experimental support for the final mechanism, thus (5-25) is preferred.

Fluoride, usually considered deficient in properties necessary for nucleophilicity, is found to react with the phosphorus atom of the mono-anion species AcP$^\ominus$ but not AcP$^\ominus$. Although the monoanion AcP$^\ominus$ appears to react through a unimolecular pathway forming the reactive metaphosphate intermediate, fluoride does not appear to act as a trapping agent, since the rate of disappearance of AcP$^\ominus$ is increased by fluoride.

Substitution of acetyl phenyl phosphate for acetyl phosphate in reactions with the same series of nucleophilic reagents produced some surprising results. With no amine, including the tertiary amines already cited, was there evidence for P—O bond fission. Nucleophilic attack by all reagents is directed at the carbonyl group of acetyl phenyl phosphate. For example, the reaction of pyridine with acetyl phenyl phosphate monoanion in the presence of mercaptoacetic acid results in acetylation of the thiol group, presumably via an intermediate acetylpyridinium ion. This sequence is possible since thiol anions alone are very poor nucleophiles toward acetyl phosphates. A summary of the data found for

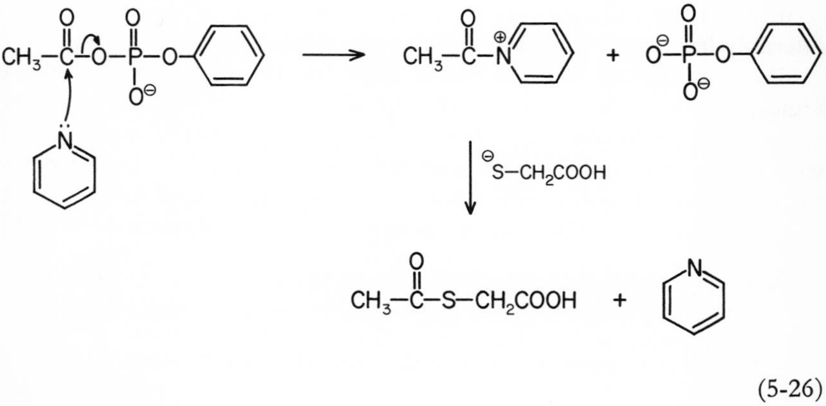

$$(5\text{-}26)$$

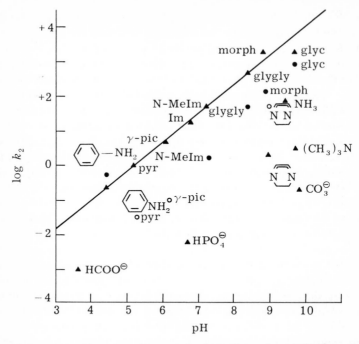

Fig. 5-3   *Rates of reactions with acetyl phenyl phosphate and acetyl phosphate monoanions at 39° plotted against the basicity of the attacking reagent:* ▲, *acetyl phenyl phosphate;* ●, *acetyl phosphate, C—O bond cleavage;* ○, *acetyl phosphate, P—O bond cleavage.*   (*Ref. 121.*)

these reactions is plotted in Fig. 5-3. The slope of this plot is similar to that obtained for the amine reactions with phenyl acetates.[124-126] The reagents acetate, arsenate, phosphate, and tris(hydroxymethyl)amino-methane do not appear to act as catalysts toward acetyl phosphate. This further indicates that negatively charged oxy- and thioanions are considerably less reactive toward acyl phosphate than phenyl acetates.

For a phosphate ester in which there is no second alternate site of attack, i.e., phenyl and *p*-nitrophenyl phosphate, tertiary heterocyclic bases seem ineffective. Pyridine, 3-methyl and 4-methyl pyridine, as well as the anions of nicotinic and isonicotinic acids, do not effectively catalyze the hydrolysis of either ester.[127] The rates of nucleophilic attack by various amines on the phosphorus of *p*-nitrophenyl phosphate are of the

[124] W. P. Jencks and J. Carriuolo, *J. Am. Chem. Soc.* **82,** 675 (1960).
[125] T. C. Bruice and R. Lapinski, *J. Am. Chem. Soc.* **80,** 2265 (1958).
[126] W. P. Jencks and J. Carriuolo, *J. Am. Chem. Soc.* **82,** 1778 (1960).
[127] J. D. Chanley and E. Feageson, *J. Am. Chem. Soc.* **85,** 1181 (1963).

order of 10^{-5} to 10^{-6} liter mole^{-1} min^{-1} (H_2O, $\mu = 1.0$, 39°).[127a] There is some preliminary evidence that a cyclic amine may attack the phosphorus atom of a cyclic acyl phosphate.[179]

Oxygen anions such as methoxide, ethoxide, and phenoxide appear to function as nucleophilic reagents toward a "shielded" phosphate triester.[183] Against dimethyl phenyl phosphate, both methoxide and phenoxide [128] are effective nucleophiles, the former attacking at the phosphorus atom, the latter at the methyl carbon. Methoxide ion will also attack trimethyl phosphate, but at the methyl carbon.[129] With the cyclic phosphate, adenosine-2′,3′-phosphate,[130, 131] the monoanions methoxide, ethoxide, n-propoxide, and n-butoxide yield the corresponding open diester through nucleophilic attack on the phosphorus atom. No reaction occurs with the sterically restricted i-propoxide and t-butoxide. The reaction of ethanolamine with ethylene phosphate monoanion also gives the corresponding open phosphate diester.[132]

B. Intramolecular Nucleophilic Catalysis

1. AMINO GROUP In general, phosphate esters appear to be resistant to attack by an amino group, even if the latter be suitably situated for intramolecular attack through formation of a five- or six-membered cyclic intermediate. But in the presence of sodium or potassium hydroxide, alkyl diphenyl phosphates possessing an amino function, β to the phosphorylated hydroxyl group as in O-diphenylphosphoryl serine ethyl ester, appear to lose two moles of phenol rapidly.[133, 134] Normal alkaline hydrolysis of alkyl diphenyl phosphates yields one mole of phenol, the anion of the diester being resistant to further hydrolysis.[135]

Wilson [136] and co-workers have found identical behavior during the hydrolysis of 2-aminoethyl diphenyl phosphate in strongly alkaline solution. For this ester there is observed an initial rapid release of one mole

[127a] A. J. Kirby and W. P. Jencks, J. Am. Chem. Soc. **87,** 3209 (1965).

[128] H. D. Orloff, J. Worrel, and F. X. Markley, J. Am. Chem. Soc. **80,** 734 (1958).

[129] There are many examples of attack by widely varying nucleophiles including amines, phenols, thiourea, and mercaptide on carbon in triesters which will not be discussed. A key reference is D. W. Osborne, J. Org. Chem. **29,** 3570 (1964).

[130] D. Lipkin and J. S. Dixon, Science **116,** 525 (1952).

[131] G. R. Barker, M. D. Montague, R. J. Moss, and M. A. Parsons, J. Chem. Soc. 3786 (1957).

[132] C. Dekker and J. Lecocq, Experientia **15,** 27 (1959).

[133] H. A. C. Montgomery, J. H. Turnbull, and W. Wilson, J. Chem. Soc. 4603 (1956).

[134] G. Riley, J. H. Turnbull, and W. Wilson, J. Chem. Soc. 1373 (1957).

[135] P. W. C. Barnard, C. A. Bunton, D. R. Llewellyn, K. G. Oldham, B. L. Silver, and C. A. Vernon, Chem. Ind. (London) 760 (1955).

[136] G. J. Durant, J. H. Turnbull, and W. Wilson, Chem. Ind. (London) 157 (1958).

of phenol followed by the slow production of a second mole. Paper chromatography revealed the presence of 2-aminoethyl phosphate and a trace of 2-aminoethyl phenyl phosphate. The latter ester yields no phenol under identical experimental conditions, therefore it cannot be an intermediate. Wilson and co-workers postulate the formation of a cyclic intermediate involving amino group participation as being responsible for facilitation of the hydrolysis (5-27).

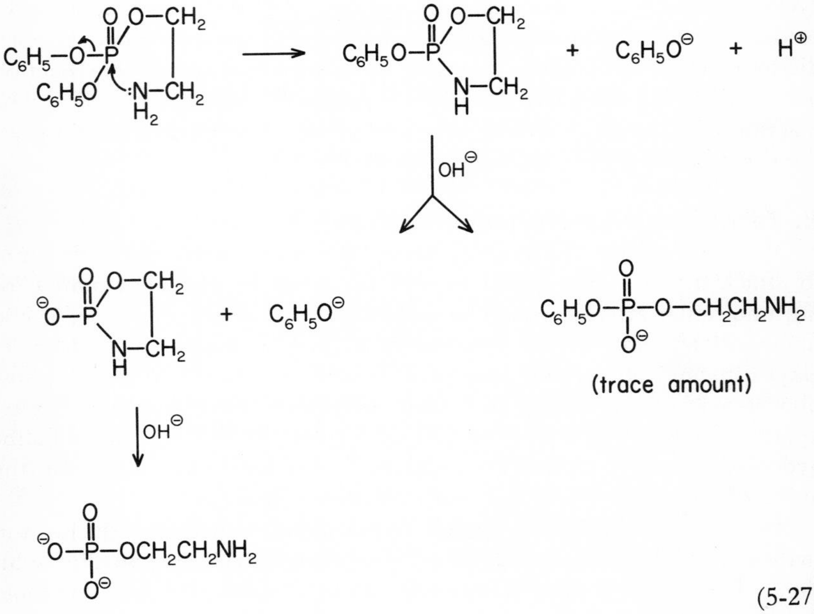

(5-27)

It should be noted that the above mechanism utilizes a free amino group. Under the strong basic conditions employed, the possibility exists that the attacking nucleophile is indeed the amino anion, $-NH^{\ominus}$.

In solutions of lower hydroxide ion concentration, 2-aminoethyl diphenyl phosphate tends to undergo C—O bond scission with liberation of diphenyl phosphate anions. This leads to formation of polymeric ethyleneimines, whose presence was also detected by Brown and Osborne [137] in the hydrolysis of 2-aminoethyl diphenyl phosphate in aqueous sodium carbonate.

[137] D. M. Brown and G. O. Osborne, *J. Chem. Soc.* 2590 (1957).

$$C_6H_5O-\overset{\overset{O}{\|}}{\underset{C_6H_5O}{P}}-O-\overset{CH_2}{\underset{CH_2-NH_2}{|}} \quad + \quad \left[\underset{H_2}{\overset{CH_2-CH_2}{N^{\oplus}}}\right] \quad + \quad (C_6H_5O)_2-\overset{\overset{O}{\|}}{P}-O^{\ominus}$$

$$(5\text{-}28)$$

Polymeric ethyleneimines

2. HYDROXYL GROUP   The effect of a neighboring hydroxyl group on the phosphoryl moiety is quite dramatic and complex, since it leads to the highly reactive five-membered cyclic phosphate.[19]   Nevertheless, the basic elements of the reaction may be represented as in (5-29).

The generalized scheme (5-29) illustrates the requirement of a vicinal free hydroxyl group which may act to produce an acid catalyzed phosphoryl migration with a mono- or diester [138] ($I \rightleftharpoons II$) or an acid catalyzed hydrolysis of a diester ($I \rightarrow VI$).   It may act in alkali to facilitate the base catalyzed expulsion of R_3OH ($III \rightarrow V$; $IV \rightarrow V$).   In the scheme, the base catalyzed pathway is represented as involving the ionized hydroxyl group attacking a neutral phosphate moiety and expelling R_3OH only for reasons of simplicity; actually very little is known about the nature of either pathway.   The cyclic compounds V and VI have been isolated from the acid or base catalyzed hydrolysis products of the diester.[138]   Esterification of VI has been mentioned (see p. 35).

It is possible to write a pentacovalent intermediate along each pathway.   If invoked as an intermediate along the base catalyzed route, it might be expected that a direct pathway ($III \rightleftharpoons IV$) in some instances would become operable (5-30).   However, it is quite possible that expulsion of the alkoxide ion, $R_3O^{\ominus}$ is energetically more favorable for the cyclic pentacovalent intermediate than opening of the ring.   Insofar as the analogy is applicable, Ramirez and co-workers [139, 140] have observed in the hydrolysis of cyclic oxyphosphoranes and cyclic phosphotriesters that the cyclic structure is always preserved.   They postulate that these

[138] D. M. Brown, D. I. Magrath, A. H. Neilson, and A. R. Todd, *Nature* **177,** 1124 (1956).

[139] F. Ramirez, N. B. Desai, and N. Ramanathan, *J. Am. Chem. Soc.* **85,** 1874 (1963).

[140] F. Ramirez, O. P. Madan, N. B. Desai, S. Meyerson, and E. M. Banas, *J. Am. Chem. Soc.* **85,** 2681 (1963).

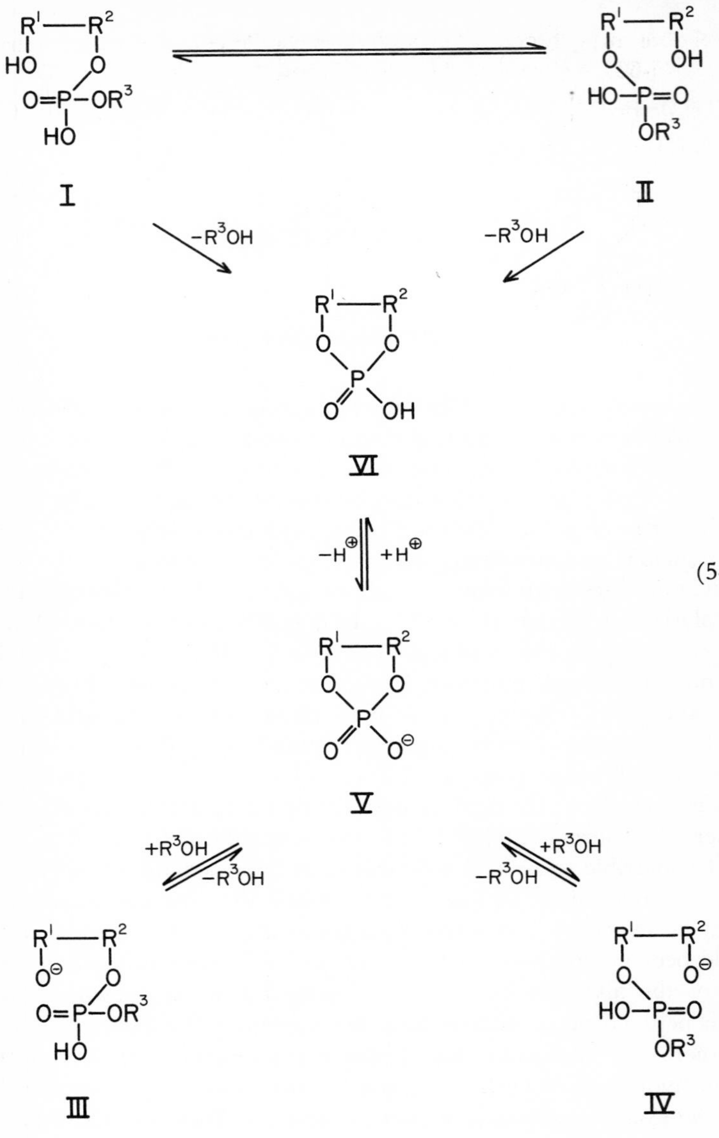

I

II

$-R^3OH$ $-R^3OH$

VI

$-H^{\oplus} \Uparrow +H^{\oplus}$ (5-29)

V

$+R^3OH$ $+R^3OH$
$-R^3OH$ $-R^3OH$

III   IV

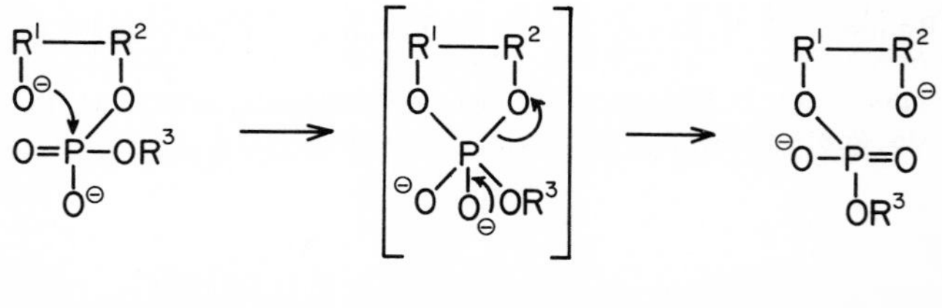

(5-30)

reactions may proceed through a cyclic oxyphosphorane intermediate, as in (5-33), where R = H in (5-32) and R = CH$_3$ in (5-31).

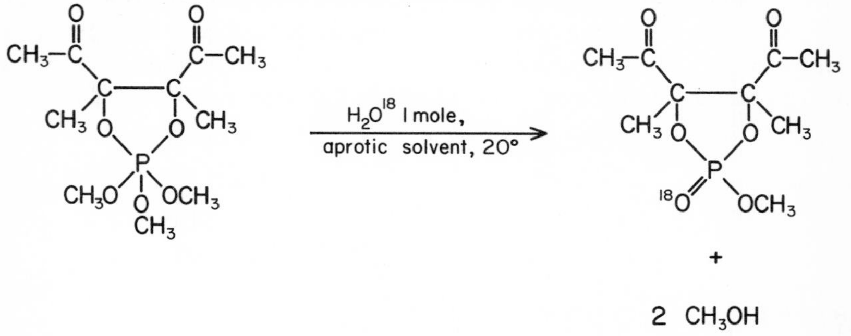

$$\xrightarrow[\text{aprotic solvent, 20°}]{H_2O^{18} \text{ I mole,}}$$

+

2 CH$_3$OH

(5-31)

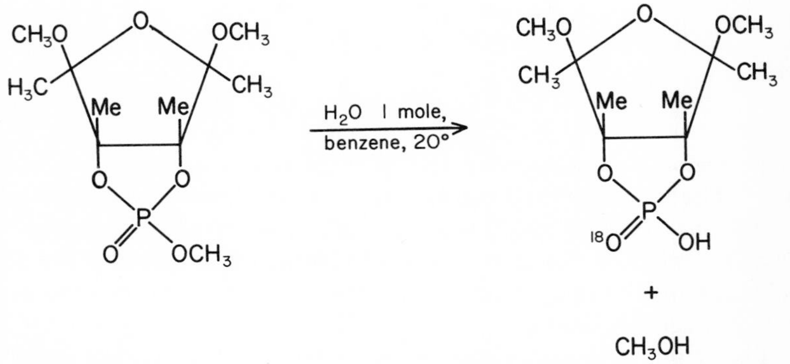

$$\xrightarrow[\text{benzene, 20°}]{H_2O \text{ I mole,}}$$

+

CH$_3$OH

(5-32)

$$\left[\begin{array}{c} \text{CH}_3\text{O} \quad \text{O} \\ \text{RO–P} \\ \text{HO} \quad \text{O} \end{array} \right]$$

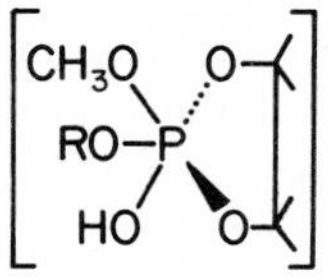

(5-33)

Although cyclic phosphate formation in alkaline solution occurs only with the phosphate diester, it is possible that a neighboring hydroxyl group may act to enhance the rate of alkaline hydrolysis of a monoester (recall glucose-6-phosphate). Bender[176] has shown that 8-hydroxyl-1-naphthyl phosphate dianion hydrolyzes about 10-fold faster than the dianion of the 8-methoxy ester. This may be due to the operation of a proton-transfer mechanism, whose characteristics will be developed in the following section.

For the acid catalyzed reaction, many instances of experimental evidence for the equilibrium (I $\rightleftharpoons$ II) have been recorded. For this pathway a pentacovalent intermediate [141, 142] may be visualized, which in the case of a cyclic phosphate diester may partition so as to give a phosphoryl transfer or a hydrolytic cyclic product. The latter product may then undergo further hydrolysis. Nevertheless, the experimental evidence is

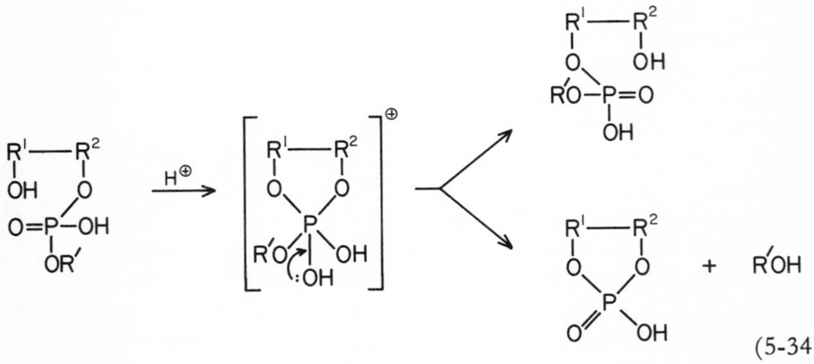

$$(5\text{-}34)$$

not so overwhelming as to rule out an S_N2 type of displacement for either case. The base catalyzed reaction can simply be pictured as a displacement of an alkoxide ion,[143] whereas in the acid catalyzed process either a water or alcohol molecule may be displaced. The following discussion will be focused on some structural variations which affect the final hydrolytic product distribution.

Phosphate monoesters such as glycerol-1- and -2-phosphates,[144–146] and ribonucleoside-2'- and -3'-phosphates [141, 147] undergo a facile acidcatalyzed migration. At equilibrium, the mixture of glycerol phosphate esters is about 87% glycerol-1-phosphate and 13% glycerol-2-phosphate.[57, 148] Interconversion of the isomeric glycerol phosphates under acidic conditions appears to be governed by the relative rates of closure of the isomer to give a cyclic transition state or intermediate (5-34). Acidic hydrolysis of the cyclic glycerol-1,2-phosphate initially gives ap-

[141] D. M. Brown and A. R. Todd, *J. Chem. Soc.* 52 (1952).
[142] E. Baer and M. Kates, *J. Biol. Chem.* **175**, 79 (1948).
[143] D. Lipkin, P. T. Talbert, and M. Cohn, *J. Am. Chem. Soc.* **76**, 2871 (1954).
[144] M. Bailly, *Compt. Rend.* **206**, 1902 (1938); **208**, 443, 1820 (1939).
[145] P. E. Verkade, J. C. Stoppelenburg, and W. D. Cohen, *Rec. Trav. Chim.* **59**, 886 (1940).
[146] E. Chargaff, *J. Biol. Chem.* **145**, 455 (1942).
[147] D. M. Brown and A. R. Todd, *J. Chem. Soc.* 44 (1952).
[148] T. Ukita, K. Nagasawa, and M. Irie, *Chem. Pharm. Bull. (Tokyo)* **5**, 127 (1957).

proximately equal amounts of glycerol-1- and -2-phosphates, which upon subsequent equilibration are present at the above relative concentrations.[148] Thus, the isomer ratio at equilibrium is not determined by any tendency of the related cyclic phosphodiester to open preferentially at the secondary or primary position, the initial hydrolytic products from the cyclic compound being subject to kinetic control. A second example of such behavior is found in the acidic hydrolysis of D-glyceric acid-2,3-cyclic phosphate,[149] which initially gives 55% of the 1-isomer, as against 81% at migration equilibrium.

The migratory ability of the phosphoryl group in acidic medium may be the cause of the high rates of the acidic hydrolysis of certain sugar phosphates.[150] Migration to C-1 by the phosphoryl group forming the very acid labile glycosidic linkage would confer lability upon the phosphoryl group. The higher rate of hydrolysis of D-glucose-2 phosphate [151] relative to D-glucose-6-phosphate may in part be due to this phenomenon. However, acid catalyzed β-elimination [152] reactions are possible in the sugar phosphates, which also may lead to high rates of acidic hydrolysis. Therefore, even apart from structural considerations, phosphoryl migrations, although important, are only one of many contributors to the complexity of sugar phosphate hydrolyses.

At the diester level there are two major classes of naturally occurring phosphate esters which bear suitably located hydroxyl functions for five-membered cyclic phosphate formation. They are (1) the cephalins, lecithins, phosphoinositides, and other complex phospholipids, all of which are derivatives of glycerol phosphates, and (2) the ribonucleic acids.[150]

Early research by Bailly and Gaumé [153] had shown that, although glycerol-1-phosphate is stable to alkali, glycerol-1-methyl phosphate is readily hydrolyzed to a mixture of glycerol-1- and -2-phosphates with no methyl phosphate being produced. A similar phenomenon was later observed by Baer and Kates [142] in the alkaline hydrolysis of α-L-glycerophosphorylcholine, which liberated choline and formed isomeric glycerol phosphates. The relative amounts of the two isomeric glycerol phosphates formed were the same as those found for the alkaline hydrolysis of glycerol-1,2-cyclic phosphate. Other experiments [141] with 2-hydroxyethyl dimethyl phosphate and 2-methoxyethyl dimethyl phosphate demonstrated that only the hydroxy ester lost both methyl groups under alkaline

[149] R. F. Webb and A. J. Duke, *J. Chem. Soc.* 3627 (1959).
[150] H. G. Khorana, "Some Recent Developments in the Chemistry of Phosphate Esters of Biological Interest," Wiley, New York, 1961, pp. 45–66.
[151] K. R. Farrar, *J. Chem. Soc.* 3131 (1949).
[152] J. Baddiley, *Chem. Soc. (London) Spec. Publ.* **8**, 119 (1957).
[153] O. Bailly and J. Gaumé, *Bull. Soc. Chim. France* **2**, 354 (1935).

42   BIOOGRANIC MECHANISMS

conditions. These experiments clearly indicate the requirement of a
free vicinal hydroxyl group for alkaline lability and the involvement of a
cyclic intermediate in the hydrolytic pathway.

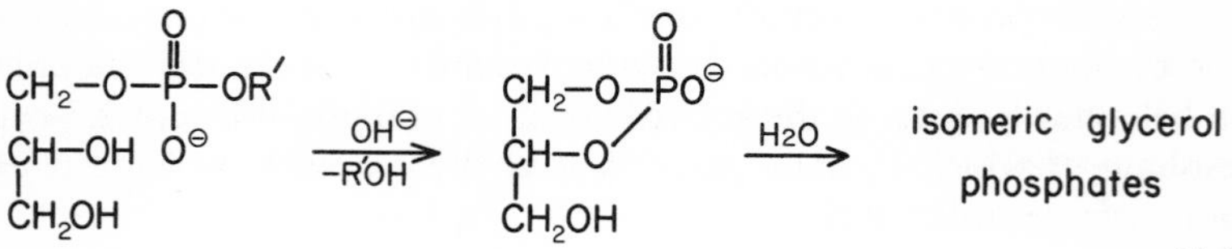

(5-35)

The alkaline lability of the glycerol phosphate diesters has proven to
be in every way analogous to the alkaline behavior of the ribonucleic
acids. The separation of two isomeric adenylic acids from alkaline
hydrolyses of yeast ribonucleic acid by Carter and Cohn,[154] followed by
the separation of the other three nucleotides into isomeric pairs, served
as the starting point for this comparison. Experiments were then designed
by Todd and co-workers [155] to elucidate the effect of acid and base on the
behavior of nucleotides, such as the monoesters adenosine-2′- and -3′-phos-
phate and the corresponding nucleotide benzyl diesters. Their findings
led to an enlightened understanding of the internucleotide linkages in the
ribonucleic acids, illustrated in (5-36). Absence of a hydroxyl group at

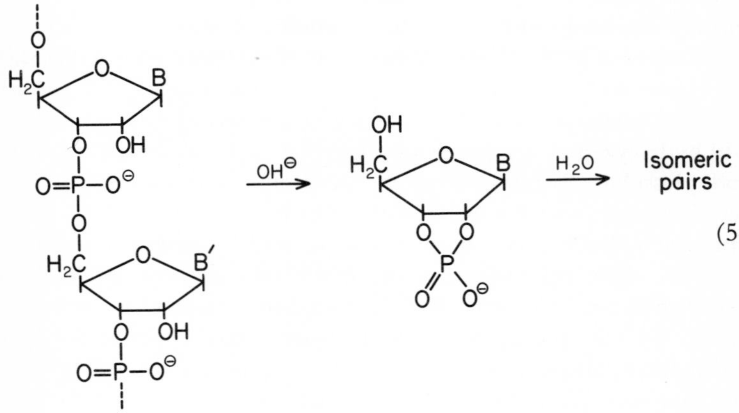

(5-36)

where B = purine or pyrimidine

[154] W. E. Cohn, in E. Chargaff and J. N. Davidson (eds.) "The Nucleic Acids,"
Academic Press, New York, 1955, Vol. I, p. 288.
[155] D. M. Brown and A. R. Todd, in E. Chargaff and J. N. Davidson (eds.) "The
Nucleic Acids," Academic Press, New York, 1955, Vol. I, p. 409.

C-2, a characteristic feature of the deoxyribonucleic acids, serves then to explain their alkaline stability. This proposal was first advanced by Fono [54] and later developed and experimentally verified by Todd [155] and his collaborators.

In order to determine the position of esterification of phosphate in the phosphoinositides, some interesting "model" studies were undertaken which further serve to clarify the phenomenon of neighboring hydroxyl group participation. The possible structure of a simple lipid [156] in this class, without regard for depicting the point of esterification, is given in (5-37).

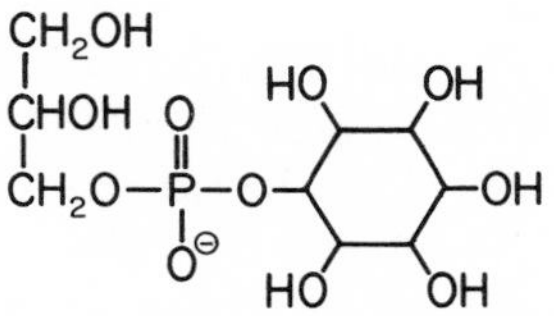

$$
\begin{array}{c}
CH_2OH \\
| \\
CHOH \quad O \\
| \qquad\qquad || \\
CH_2O-P-O- \\
| \\
O^{\ominus}
\end{array}
$$

(5-37)

Previous experiments on the acid and base catalyzed hydrolysis of benzyl-2-hydroxycyclohexyl phosphate [157] had indicated that this ester behaved like other vicinal hydroxyl phosphate diesters with the hydrolysis proceeding via 1,2-cyclohexylidene phosphate. The rates, as expected, were in the order cis > trans isomer. Brown and Higson then examined the hydrolytic behavior of the more complicated, yet more apropos, phosphate ester, glycerol-1-(2-hydroxycyclohexyl) phosphate, which may be degraded by either or both of the pathways (a) and (b) of (5-38).[158] In sodium hydroxide solution, both the cis and trans esters hydrolyzed via

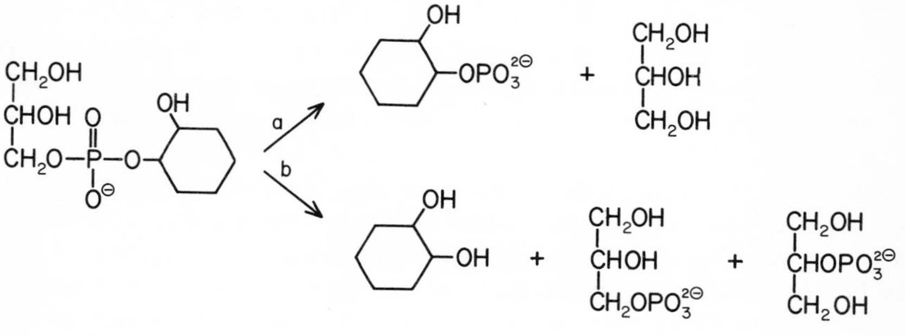

(5-38)

paths (a) and (b). By estimating the amount of total glycerol phosphate produced, it was shown that the cis ester hydrolyzes predominantly by

[156] J. Folch and F. N. LeBaron, *Can. J. Biochem. Physiol.* **34**, 305 (1956).
[157] D. M. Brown and H. M. Higson, *J. Chem. Soc.* 2034 (1957).
[158] D. M. Brown, G. E. Hall, and H. M. Higson, *J. Chem. Soc.* 1360 (1958).

path (a) (85% diol phosphate) while, with the trans ester, path (b) (75% glycerol phosphate) is preferred. The expectation that the cyclic glycerol-1,2-phosphate is an intermediate in the hydrolysis by path (b) was confirmed by measuring the amount of glycerol-1-phosphate (42%) [148] formed upon alkaline hydrolysis of the cyclic phosphate. The amount of glycerol-1-phosphate produced by alkaline hydrolysis of the trans ester is comparable (45%). In the case of acid hydrolysis, the cis ester yields mainly diol phosphate (path a) whereas the trans ester again goes almost completely to glycerol phosphates.

Kinetic studies, for which no great accuracy is claimed, suggested that the alkaline hydrolysis of the glycerol cis ester is first-order in substrate and hydroxide ion, which may be rationalized most simply by assuming that removal of the proton from the vicinal hydroxyl group occurs prior or simultaneously with the rate-determining cyclization step. It by no means establishes whether the process is specific or general-base catalyzed. Interestingly, the cis and trans isomers hydrolyze at similar rates despite their following different pathways. These rates are greater than that for the benzyl cyclohexyl phosphates, and appear to indicate that the presence of two neighboring hydroxyl groups further assists the reaction (see Chapter 6). It may be significant from this aspect that glycerol-2-methyl phosphate is hydrolyzed considerably faster than the 1-isomer.[159]

Before drawing definite conclusions in regard to the original aim of their research, Brown and co-workers also studied the hydrolysis of the glycerol esters of myoinositol-1- and -2-phosphates.[160] When the glycerol ester of myoinositol-2-phosphate (5-39 I) is treated with N sodium hydroxide at 60°, hydrolysis is complete in 30 minutes. Paper chromatography revealed that glycerol-1- and -2-phosphates and inositol-1- and -2-phosphates are present, but no inorganic phosphate. Identical products are formed from (5-39 II) upon alkaline hydrolysis. The relative proportions of the phosphorylated products (glycerol-1-P:glycerol-2-P; inositol-1-P:inositol-2-P) arising from the hydrolysis of both I and II are in accord with the isomeric ratio found for the alkaline hydrolysis of the cyclic phosphate, glycerol-1,2-phosphate and inositol-1,2-phosphate, respectively. This is clear evidence that the cyclic five-membered phosphates are obligatory intermediates in the two competing hydrolytic pathways. Lack of production of a third isomeric inositol phosphate is in agreement with the conclusions of Pizer and Ballou [161] that, in the hydrolysis of the 1-isomer (II), little or no attack by the *trans*-6-hydroxyl group

[159] P. Fleury, J. Lecocq, and L. LeDizet, *Bull. Soc. Chim. France* 1193 (1956).

[160] D. M. Brown, G. E. Hall, and R. Letters, *J. Chem. Soc.* 3547 (1959).

[161] F. L. Pizer and C. E. Ballou, *J. Am. Chem. Soc.* **81**, 915 (1959).

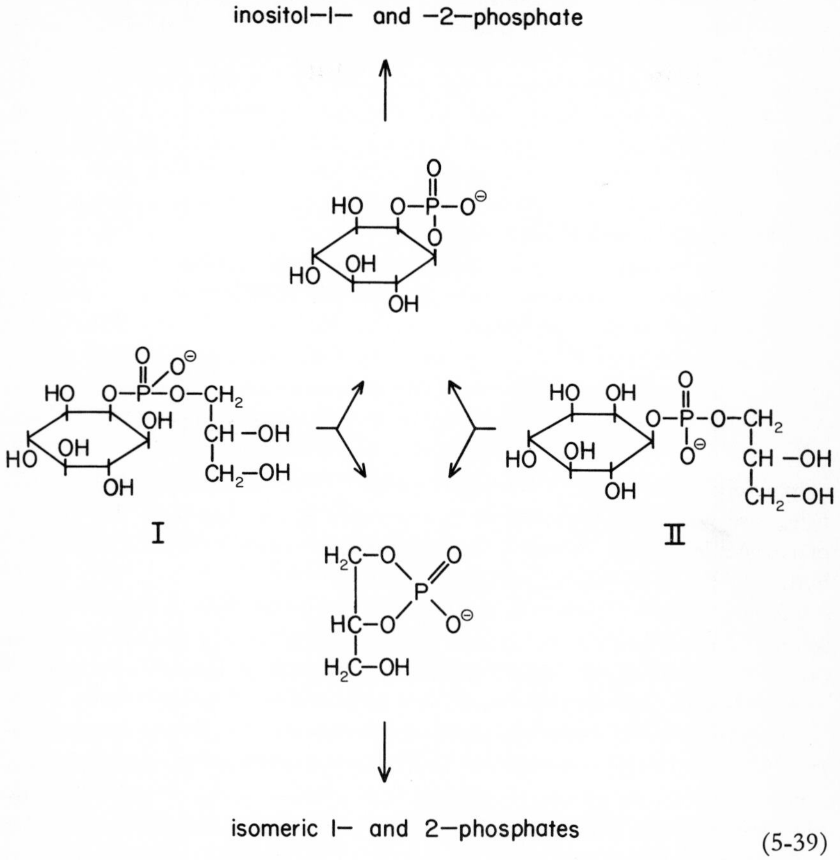

inositol–l– and –2–phosphate

isomeric l– and 2–phosphates

(5-39)

takes place. Thus the evidence suggests a greater conformational rigidity in the inositol compounds relative to the cyclohexane diol phosphates where a *trans*-hydroxyl group will participate. Further, the quantitative measure of the hydrolytic products established that the ratio of total glycerol phosphate to total inositol phosphate is significantly different depending on its source. This is not unexpected since the transition states for the internal displacement cannot be the same for each ester. Therefore, in (5-39), I may be distinguished from II by this criterion. A proviso must be made, since compound I is a ($\pm$) glycerol ester but II is a mixture of the ($\pm$) glycerol esters of ($\pm$) inositol-1-phosphate. It is conceivable that the diastereoisomers in II could give different proportions of products upon hydrolysis.

Six-membered cyclic phosphates have occurred as intermediates in the hydrolysis of diesters of phosphoric acid,[150] even though their formation is much less likely.   An interesting example is the alkaline hydrolysis of thymidine-3'-p-nitrophenyl phosphate,[162] of which more than 50% hydrolyzes via the 3',5'-cyclic phosphate (5-40).[163]   In contrast, the alkaline hydrolysis of uridine-5'-p-nitrophenyl phosphate gives no sign

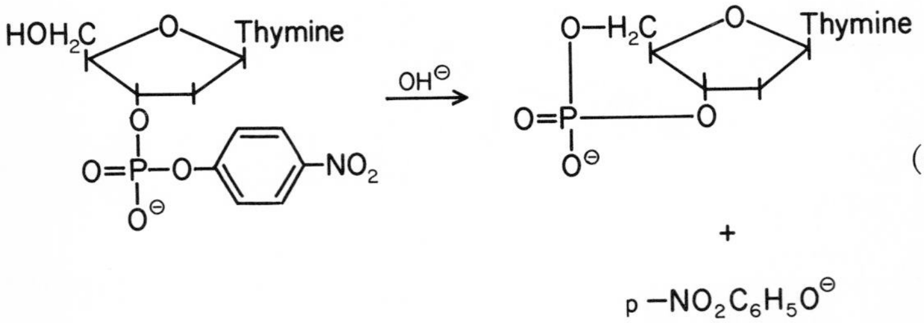

$$(5\text{-}40)$$

of participation by the 3'-hydroxyl group.   The influence of the nucleotide base is also of importance in the rates of hydrolysis of the diesters of ribonucleic acids, where it is thought they affect the pK_a' of the C-2 hydroxyl group through hydrogen bonding.[164–166]

At the triester level, a displacement similar to that recorded in the section on intramolecular participation of the amino group has been observed.[167]   Dibenzyl $trans$-2-hydroxycyclohexyl phosphate in 2 N alkali at 100° hydrolyzes with the formation of cyclohexene oxide (5-41).

It is evident that the normal hydrolytic route of the phosphate ester (5-41 I) is path (d).   By having available the dibenzyl phosphate monoanion as a leaving group, it appears that a base-catalyzed back side displacement by the hydroxyl anion on carbon (path c) becomes observable (0.3 mole of oxide per mole of ester).   The amount of epoxide is, of course, a direct measure of the relative importance of path (c).   Vigorous hydrolysis of benzyl $trans$-2-hydroxycyclohexyl phosphate, possessing a poorer leaving group, gives only 2-hydroxy-cyclohexyl phosphate.   The stereochemical requirements are emphasized by the observation that dibenzyl 2-hydroxyethyl phosphate under identical conditions yields only 0.01–0.02 mole of ethylene oxide per mole of ester.

[162] A. F. Turner and H. G. Khorana, *J. Am. Chem. Soc.* **81,** 4651 (1959).

[163] M. Smith, G. I. Drummond, and H. G. Khorana, *J. Am. Chem. Soc.* **83,** 698 (1961).

[164] J. J. Fox and D. Shugar, *Biochim. Biophys. Acta* **9,** 369 (1952).

[165] J. J. Fox, L. F. Cavalieri, and N. Chang, *J. Am. Chem. Soc.* **75,** 4315 (1953).

[166] H. Witzel, *Ann.* **635,** 182 (1960).

[167] D. M. Brown and N. K. Hamer, *J. Chem. Soc.* 406 (1960).

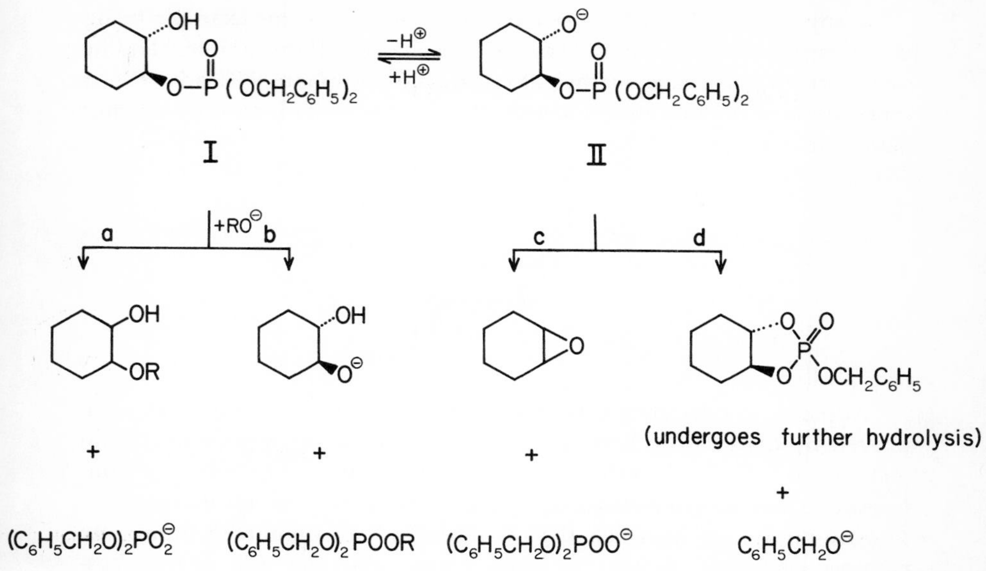

OH
O
O—P(OCH2C6H5)2
I
−H⊕
+H⊕
O⊖
O
O—P(OCH2C6H5)2
II
a
+RO⊖
b
c
d
OH
OR
OH
O⊖
O
O
O
P
O
OCH2C6H5
(undergoes further hydrolysis)
+
+
+
+
(C6H5CH2O)2PO2⊖
(C6H5CH2O)2POOR
(C6H5CH2O)2POO⊖
C6H5CH2O⊖

(5-41)

Treatment of the ester (5-41 I) with potassium *t*-butoxide in *t*-butyl alcohol likewise affords cyclohexene oxide (0.31–0.34 mole per mole of ester). The amount of dibenzyl phosphate produced both with sodium hydroxide and with potassium *t*-butoxide is numerically identical to that of the oxide produced, indicating that paths (a) and (b) appear unimportant. Change of solvent to sodium methoxide in dry methanol results in no cyclohexene oxide from ester (5-41 I). Only trace amounts of dibenzyl hydrogen phosphate were found. However, cyclohexane-1,2-diol is formed (ca. 0.9 mole per mole of ester), with the phosphate present as the mono- and di-transesterified methyl esters. This evidence suggests that path (b) is preferred, and that the importance of neighboring hydroxyl group participation in methanol diminishes. This may result from a large difference between the nucleophilicity of methoxide in methanol versus hydroxide ion in water toward phosphorus. Further studies to clarify this point are necessary.

In contrast, a ribonucleoside-3′-dimethyl phosphate, such as uridine-3′-dimethyl phosphate,[168] bearing a *cis*-hydroxyl function in a furanose ring, is labile at any pH. The hydrolytic products here are 10% ribonucleoside-2′,3′-cyclic phosphate and 90% a mixture of the acyclic methyl ribonucleosides-2′- and -3′-phosphates.[150]

[168] D. M. Brown, D. I. Magrath, and A. R. Todd, *J. Chem. Soc.* 4396 (1955).

Many structural problems remain in this area, a prime example being the hydrolysis of unsymmetrical cyclic phosphates. For example, alkaline hydrolysis of the cyclic methyl glucoside-4,6-phosphate [169] leads to 4–5 times as much methyl α-D-glucoside-4- as -6-phosphate, no other isomer being present.

(5-42)

Absence of interference by the 2- and 3-hydroxyl groups has been proven by benzylating both groups, hydrolysis of this compound again yielding a 4–5-fold prevalence of the 4-phosphate. The effect of conformation has been investigated by hydrolyzing the methyl β-D-galactoside-4,6-phosphate in which the pyranose and six-membered phosphate ring are cis-fused. Again, the same relative amounts of 4- and 6-phosphate are found, proving that the conformation is without marked influence. The underlying reasons for this hydrolysis favoring a secondary phosphate are therefore unknown. That a secondary phosphate is not always the final product is indicated by the cyclic propane-1,2-phosphate, which hydrolyzes in both acid and alkali to give only the 1-phosphate, the primary phosphate ester.[148]

Biologically the ribonucleoside-2',3'-cyclic phosphates, formed as already discussed by the action of alkali on RNA, were first encountered as intermediates in the pancreatic ribonuclease enzymic degradation of RNA.[55] The reader is referred to the footnoted article for a recent review of developments concerning the mode of action of the ribonucleases, which is a rapidly changing area.[169a]

3. CARBOXYL GROUP The facile hydrolyses of o-carboxyaryl phosphates have been extensively studied by Chanley [170-172] and others.[173-175] The hydrolyses of the dianions of these compounds are much faster than the hydrolysis of the monoanion of phenyl or α-naphthyl phosphate.

[169] P. Szabo and L. Szabo, J. Chem. Soc. 3758 (1960).

[169a] J. P. Hummel and G. Kalnitsky, Ann. Rev. Biochem. 33, 15 (1964).

[170] J. D. Chanley, E. M. Gindler, and H. Sobotka, J. Am. Chem. Soc. 74, 4347 (1952).

[171] J. D. Chanley and E. M. Gindler, J. Am. Chem. Soc. 75, 4035 (1953).

[172] J. D. Chanley and E. Feageson, J. Am. Chem. Soc. 77, 4002 (1955).

[173] J. Arai, J. Biochem. (Tokyo) 20, 465 (1934).

[174] F. R. Atherton, Chem. Soc. (London) Spec. Publ. 8, 77 (1957).

[175] C. Manaka, J. Biochem. (Tokyo) 14, 191 (1931); 14, 481 (1932).

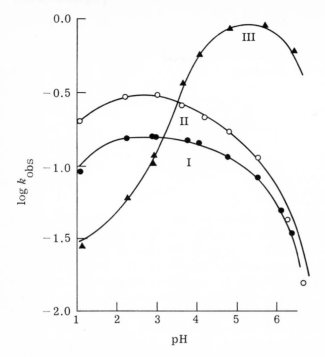

Fig. 5-4   *Logarithms of the observed rates of hydrolysis at 80° for compounds I, II, and III at various pH values are indicated by* ●, ○, *and* ▲, *respectively.   The solid curve is the theoretical one.   The compounds are m-carboxyphenyl (I), p-carboxyphenyl (II), and 8-carboxy-α-naphthyl (III) phosphate.   (Ref. 172.)*

Moreover, the ease of their hydrolysis is not due to electronic effects, for the analogous *m*- and *p*-substituted carboxyaryl phosphates do not exhibit enhanced reactivity.[172]   In Fig. 5-4 is plotted the pH-rate profile for 8-carboxy α-naphthyl phosphate (III), which graphically demonstrates this unique behavior.   The mechanism originally proposed for these reactions envisaged a nucleophilic attack by the *o*-carboxylate anion on the phosphorus atom, as depicted in the scheme for salicyl phosphate (5-43).   Two routes for decomposition of the phosphate appear likely: (1) path *a* involving a direct breakdown of I to products, assuming a water molecule is intimately bound to I, and (2) path *b* proceeding via hydrolysis of the intermediate salicyloyl phosphate (II).

Bender and Lawlor [176] recently reopened the question as to the role of the *o*-carboxyl group in the hydrolysis of salicyl phosphate.   They

---

[176] M. L. Bender and J. M. Lawlor, *J. Am. Chem. Soc.* **85,** 3010 (1963).

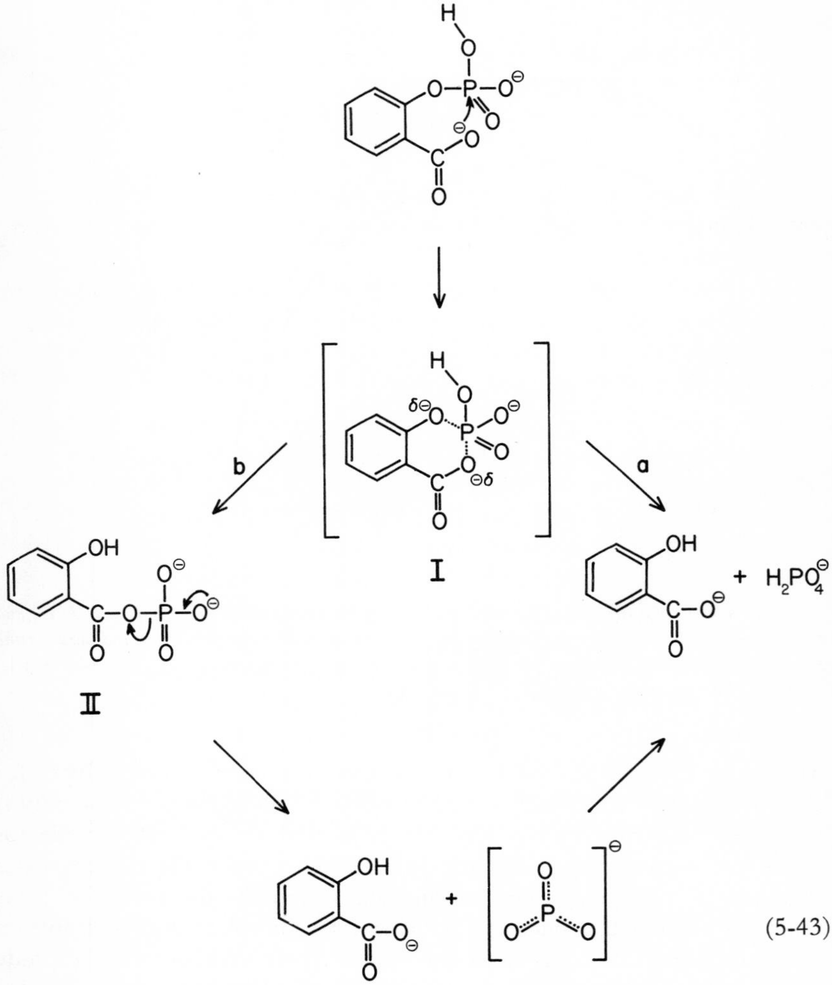

(5-43)

note, as has been discussed, the requirement of a proton as an essential feature in the rapid hydrolysis of monoanions of phosphate esters. As indicated in (5-2), this proton is transferred intramolecularly or via a participating solvent molecule prior to formation of the initial reaction product. On this basis, it was reasoned that a compound containing an ionized phosphate group favorably located to participate in a proton transfer from an acidic group in the same molecule should undergo rapid hydrolysis. Such a molecule is the dianion of salicyl phosphate (5-44), which species is kinetically indistinguishable from the dianion of (5-43).

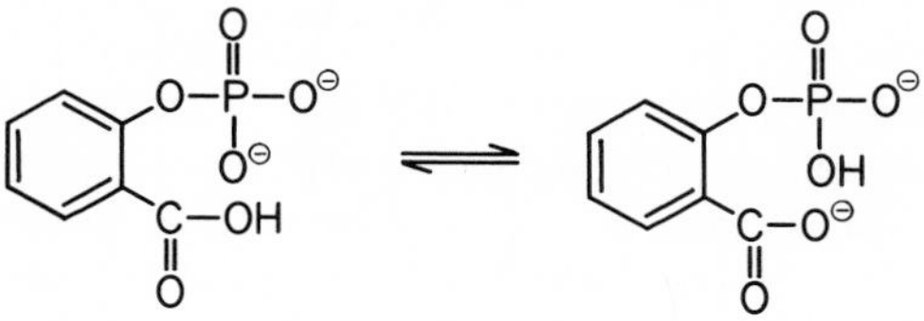

$$(5\text{-}44)$$

To test this hypothesis experimental evidence was sought to eliminate mechanisms involving nucleophilic attack by either the phosphate dianion or carboxylate anion.

The phosphate group in its dianionic form could attack the o-carboxylic acid group to expel hydroxide ion and produce a cyclic acyl phosphate (5-45). The intermediate cyclic acyl phosphate, although not isolated, is implied to exist during the hydrolysis of salol phosphate

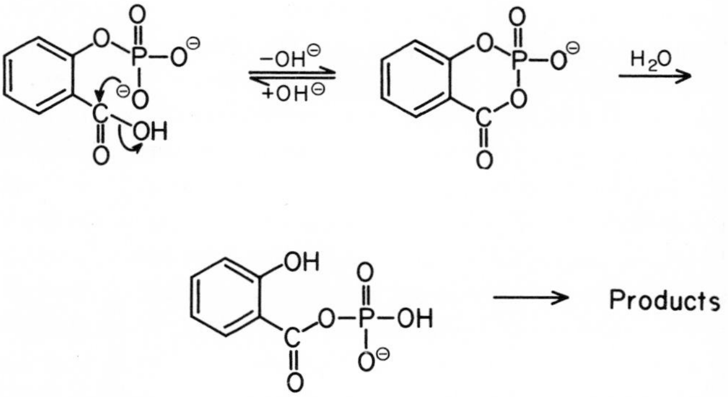

$$(5\text{-}45)$$

(5-46), which rapidly loses phenol at an increasing rate up to neutral pH. At higher pH values where the ester is completely in the dianionic form,

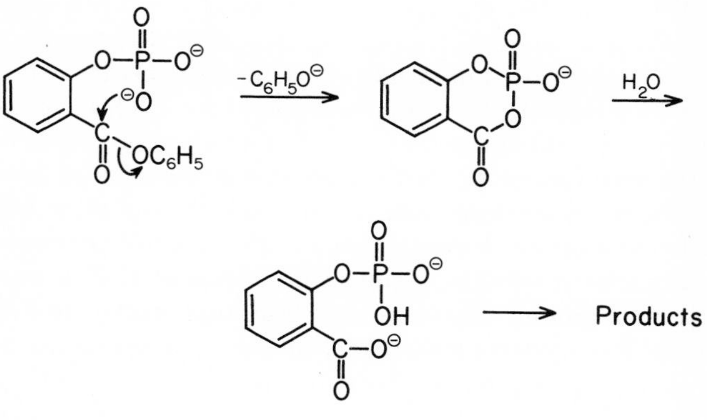

$$(5\text{-}46)$$

the rate of hydrolysis is independent of hydrogen ion concentration.[173]
The pH-rate profile for the hydrolysis of salol phosphate, based on the
formation of salicylate and inorganic phosphate, markedly resembles the
pH-rate profile for the hydrolysis of salicyl phosphate.[173] However, as
had been previously demonstrated, the rate of production of salicylate
and inorganic phosphate from the cyclic acyl phosphate was slower than
that from salicyl phosphate, a finding confirmed by Bender and Lawlor.
Therefore, salicyl phosphate rather than being the precursor of the cyclic
acyl phosphate must be an intermediate in its hydrolytic decomposition.
The intermediacy of salicyl phosphate in the hydrolysis of the cyclic acyl
phosphate was confirmed by spectrophotometric evidence.

The possibility that a tetrahedral addition compound, formed by the
nucleophilic attack of the phosphate dianion on the carboxylic acid group,
decomposes directly to products does not offer a reasonable explanation
for the required weakening of the phosphate ester bond.[174] Furthermore,
nucleophilic addition of the dianion to a more reactive acceptor, such
as is available in salicylaldehyde phosphate, should lead to a more facile
hydrolysis of the phosphate ester group.   However, salicylaldehyde phosphate manifests no unusual hydrolytic behavior.   The experimental
evidence is then against nucleophilic attack by phosphate dianion.

The original proposal of nucleophilic attack by the carboxylate anion,
which may involve formation of salicyloyl phosphate, was investigated
through the utilization of reagents capable of trapping the salicyloyl phosphate.   Separate experiments with salicyloyl phosphate, independently
synthesized, revealed a very rapid reaction with hydroxylamine leading
to the readily detectable hydroxamic acid.   Yet no hydroxamic acid
appeared to be formed during the hydrolysis of salicyl phosphate in
hydroxylamine buffer.   Furthermore, hydrolysis of salicyl phosphate in
H_2O^{18} leads to no incorporation of O^{18} into the salicylic acid isolated
after hydrolysis.   This is in contrast to a small but measurable incorporation of O^{18} into acetate during the hydrolysis of acetyl phosphate [178] (the
unimolecular pathway is, of course, predominant).   These results, in conjunction with other literature evidence, do not support the existence of an
acyl phosphate intermediate, salicyloyl phosphate.   This does not experimentally rule out the direct collapse of (5-43 I) to products.

Bender and Lawlor presently favor a mechanism not involving an
intramolecular nucleophilic attack, but incorporating a complete, rapid
pre-equilibrium proton transfer (5-47).   This is preferred over an alternate mechanistic possibility, identical in scheme to (5-47), but invoking
a slow partial proton transfer in the transition state.   The distinction
between the two mechanisms is based on the expected deuterium kinetic

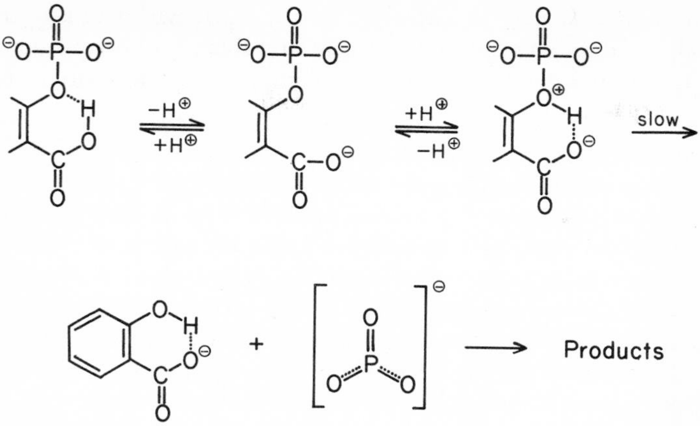

$$(5\text{-}47)$$

solvent isotope effects. As discussed by Westheimer,[177] the magnitude of the deuterium kinetic solvent isotope effect is at a maximum when the system $A \cdots H \cdots B$ is indeed symmetric (when the proton is partially transferred in the transition state), but when the system is not symmetric (when the proton is not transferred or is fully transferred in the transition state) the isotope effect decreases markedly. The deuterium isotope effect found for salicyl phosphate dianion is in accord with the view of pre-equilibrium proton transfer (Table 5-5). It is also consistent with other hydrolytic reactions thought to involve possible internal proton transfer.

It may then be asked why proton transfer from an internal carboxylic acid group leads to a more facile reaction than proton transfer from the phosphoric acid itself. Bender and Lawlor suggest that the stability of zwitterion I is superior to that of zwitterion II on both steric and electro-

Table 5-5 *Deuterium oxide kinetic solvent isotope effects in some hydrolytic reactions of compounds containing an acidic group*

Hydrolysis	k^{H_2O}/k^{D_2O}	Ref.
Methyl phosphate monoanion	0.87	5
Acetyl phosphate monoanion	1.1	20
Salicyl phosphate dianion	0.96	177
2-Hydroxyphenyl-1,3–dioxanes	1.26, 1.33, 1.29	178

[177] F. H. Westheimer, *Chem. Rev.* **61**, 265 (1961).
[178] M. L. Bender and M. S. Silver, *J. Am. Chem. Soc.* **85**, 3006 (1963).

static grounds. It may be argued that the carboxylic acid is a stronger
acid than the dianion of phosphoric acid and therefore the transfer of the
proton to produce zwitterion I is more complete than to zwitterion II.

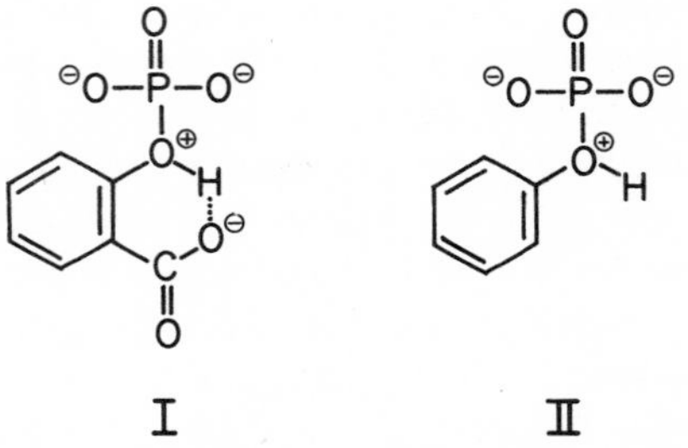

(5-48)

I   II

Direct nucleophilic attack by the carboxyl group on the phosphorus
atom may occur when the phosphate is a di- or triester and suitably
located for formation of a five-membered ring.   Rapid hydrolysis of the
diphenyl, methylphenyl, and dimethyl esters of phosphoenol pyruvic acid
to free phosphoenol pyruvic acid takes place under mildly acid conditions
(pH = 2.5–6) at room temperature.[179]   However, at pH 8 and higher
temperature only one of the alkoxy groups is slowly liberated.   A probable

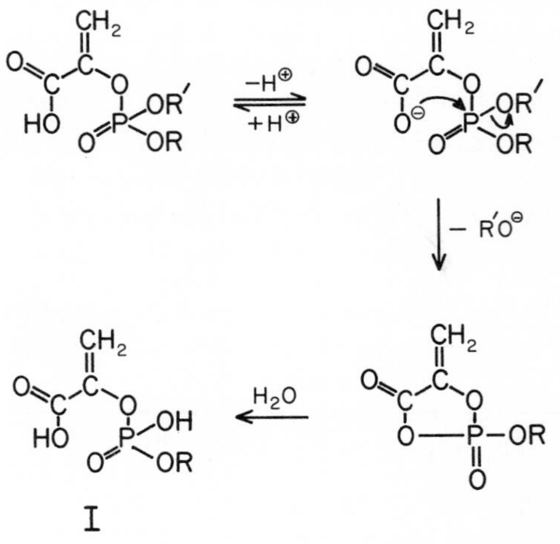

(5-49)

I

where   R = R′ = CH_3
        R = R′ = C_6H_5
        R = CH_3; R′ = C_6H_5

[179] V. M. Clark and A. J. Kirby, *J. Am. Chem. Soc.* **85,** 3705 (1963).

kinetic scheme for the latter situation may involve carboxylate anion participation which is interrupted after the loss of only one ester group, perhaps because of electrostatic repulsion arising from the ionization of both carboxyl and phosphoryl groups in (5-49 I) or an increased electron density on phosphorus. On the other hand, the acidic de-esterification may be rationalized in terms of (5-47). Preliminary experiments with a compound, thought to be the cyclic anhydride, indicate that it may act as a phosphorylating agent in contrast to the open-chain acyl phosphates, which are normally acylating agents. Carboxylate anion participation may be responsible for the rapid loss of a mole of phenol from O-diphenylphosphorylserine in alkaline solution although amino group participation cannot be excluded.[180] In contrast, the hydrolysis of *cis*-methyl-3-(O,O'-dimethylphosphoryloxy)but-2-enoate in alkaline solution is not abnormal,[181] which may be associated with the difficulty in expelling $CH_3O^{\ominus}$ relative to $C_6H_5O^{\ominus}$ or the need to form a six-membered ring. Nor is the behavior of (5-50) at pH 5–7 unusual since there is no maximum

$$CH_3O-\underset{\underset{CH_3O}{|}}{\overset{\overset{O}{||}}{P}}-O-\overset{CH_3}{\underset{}{C}}=\overset{H}{\underset{COOH}{C}} \tag{5-50}$$

in the rate of hydrolysis as with salicyl and α-carboxynaphthyl phosphate. This behavior parallels that of the steroid esters of salicyl phosphate, which do not undergo the facile hydrolysis characteristic of the monoester.[134] Thus it appears that the carboxyl group in salicyl phosphate is indeed promoting the expulsion of the monomeric metaphosphate ion, most likely through a proton transfer.

4. AMIDE GROUP Zioudrou and Schmir have demonstrated amide group participation in the solvolysis of phosphoric acid triesters in both alkaline and neutral media.[182, 183] The solvolysis in alkaline media is depicted in (5-51).

Kinetic experiments revealed that the cyclization reaction at 28° occurs with exceptional facility in the presence of dilute *t*-butoxide (e.g., $t_{1/2}$ in 0.003 M *t*-butoxide varies from 2.9 min for $n = 2$, R $= C_6H_5$, to 2 sec for $n = 1$, R $= C_6H_5$), and that the pseudo-first-order rate constant for cyclization increases with, but is not proportional to, base concentration. Experiments on a preparative scale with the phosphotriester under

[180] A. Cosmatos, I. Photaki, and L. Zervas, *Ber.* **94**, 2644 (1961).
[181] E. Y. Spencer, A. R. Todd, and R. F. Webb, *J. Chem. Soc.* 2968 (1958).
[182] G. L. Schmir and C. Zioudrou, *Biochemistry* **2**, 1305 (1963).
[183] C. Zioudrou and G. L. Schmir, *J. Am. Chem. Soc.* **85**, 3258 (1963).

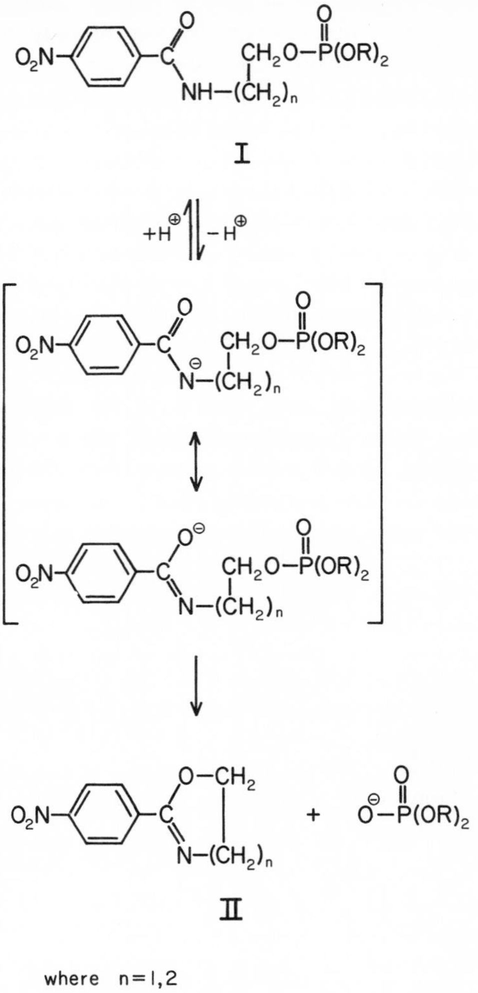

$$(5\text{-}51)$$

where n = 1, 2

similar conditions resulted in the isolation in high yield and identification of the cyclic products as Δ^2-oxazolines ($n = 1$) and dihydrooxazine ($n = 2$). These observations suggest that the transformation (5-51) consists of a two-step process: (1) ionization of the amide group, and (2) intramolecular, rate-determining, nucleophilic displacement on carbon by the oxygen anion. Support for the existence of the amide anion stems from kinetic and spectrophotometric evidence. Mechanisms analogous to (5-51) have been proposed for base catalyzed displacements by amide groups of halide and arylsulfonate ions in compounds similar to I of (5-51) [184, 185] (see Chapter 1).

The unusual facility of the intramolecular process ($k_1 \approx 1.0$ min^{-1} for all the phosphotriesters) directs the solvolysis in ethoxide solution predominantly toward cyclization (intramolecular attack on carbon) rather than toward transesterification (intermolecular attack on phosphorus). The ratio of these two paths, based on the rates of solvolysis in ethoxide solution of the triester, ethyl diphenyl phosphate, and the diphenyl ester of N-(2-hydroxyethyl)-p-nitrobenzamide, is of the order of 10–25 in favor of cyclization. Variation in the nature of the alkoxide ion may considerably alter this ratio: in the presence of t-butoxide, cyclization alone takes place, whereas methoxide leads to transesterification followed by cyclization.

It is of interest to note that, although the amide anion may be considered to possess two nucleophilic centers (see Chapter 1), there is no evidence for the alternate intramolecular reaction involving nucleophilic attack by the nitrogen on the phosphorus atom. At present this is consistent with the seeming unreactivity of nitrogeneous bases toward phosphorus esters.

Treatment of the same phosphotriester with ethanolic potassium acetate at 78° results in the formation of the identical cyclic products in high yield. It is proposed that the cyclization reaction is a consequence of intramolecular nucleophilic displacement by the *un-ionized* amide group upon the alkyl carbon of the triesters. This postulate is supported by the following experimental evidence: (1) the rate of cyclization of the phosphotriester ($n = 1$, $R = C_6H_5$) is independent of the concentration of added potassium acetate over a 10-fold change in salt concentration and proceeds almost equally fast in the complete absence of potassium acetate; (2) the rate constant for cyclization is independent of pH in the range 5.0–7.4. In aqueous solution, hydrolysis of the Δ^2-oxazoline ensues, but its intermediacy can be detected spectrophotometrically with the rate of disappearance of this intermediate being identical to that of an authentic sample at four different pH values. Thus, the mechanism (5-51) need be only slightly modified for the transformation of the phosphotriester in neutral aqueous solution. Unlike the solvolysis in alkaline media, the rate of cyclization appears to be more sensitive to the nature of the leaving group, since diphenyl phosphate ion is expelled some 13 times faster than dibenzyl phosphate ion. Solvent debenzylation of the phosphotriester, which simultaneously accompanies the cyclization, leads to a benzyl phosphodiester stable to further reaction.

[184] H. W. Heine, *J. Am. Chem. Soc.* **78**, 3708 (1956).
[185] F. L. Scott, R. E. Glick, and S. Winstein, *Experientia* **13**, 183 (1957).

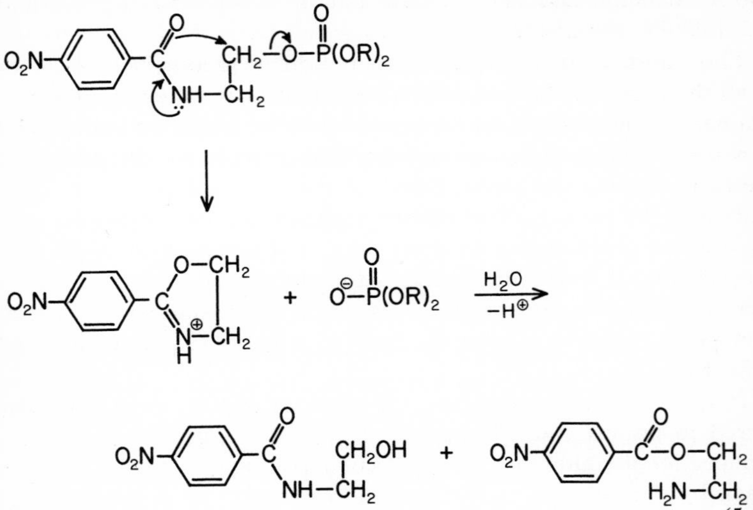

$$(5\text{-}52)$$

In addition to the phosphotriesters already cited, the neutral solvolysis of the following two compounds was studied. In compound I of (5-53) the p-nitrobenzoyl function is replaced by the peptide-like carbobenzoxy-

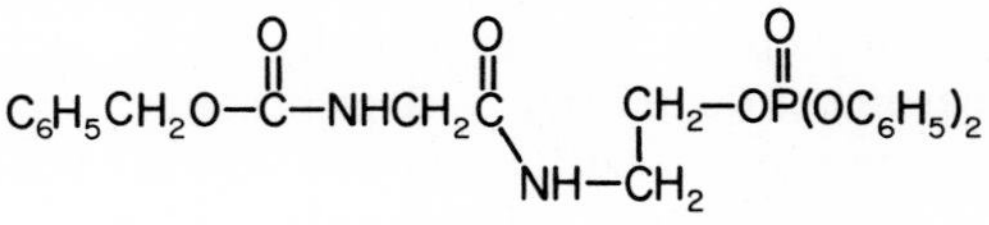

I

$$(5\text{-}53)$$

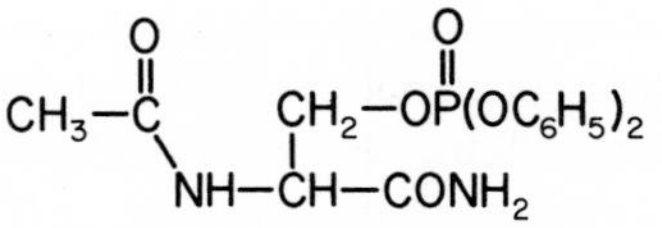

II

glycyl group, while compound II may be considered the prototype of phosphotriester derived from serine residues incorporated in peptides. The favored mechanism for their solvolysis is in complete analogy to the mechanism of (5-52). It is of interest to note that the formation of diphenyl phosphate ion from compound II in ethanol is 1200 times faster than the corresponding reaction of the related simple triester, ethyl diphenyl phosphate. The latter solvolysis also presumably involves attack at the alkyl carbon atom. The possibility of base catalyzed β-elimination of diphenyl phosphate ion from compound II is made extremely unlikely by the absence of acetamide and pyruvic acid amide in the solvolytic products, and the lack of evidence for an arylamide intermediate. As in the above compounds, there appears to be no participation by the amide nitrogen leading to a nucleophilic displacement on phosphorus of free phenol.

IV. GENERAL-BASE CATALYSIS

The aqueous hydrolysis of methyl ethylene phosphate [186] is catalyzed by heterocyclic bases with a deuterium solvent isotope effect, k^{H_2O}/k^{D_2O}, of about 2. Product analysis of the pyridine or imidazole catalyzed hydrolysis revealed that both ring opening and loss of methoxyl occurred, with the former pathway predominating. Ring opening and loss of methoxyl also are found in the hydrolysis of methyl ethylene phosphate in acid solution, for which the distribution of products parallels that observed in the acid catalyzed hydrolysis of ethylene hydrogen phosphate.[64] The reaction of methyl ethylene phosphate is extraordinarily fast for C—O cleavage, and both compounds are tentatively assumed to undergo hydrolysis with attack by water on phosphorus. In alkali the hydrolysis or methanolysis of methyl ethylene phosphate,[63a] like that for the monoanion of ethylene phosphate,[64] takes place exclusively with P—O fission and ring opening.

Table 5-6 *   *Hydrolysis of methyl ethylene phosphate* [a]

Base	k_2 (l. mole^{-1} min^{-1})	pK'_a
Pyridine	3.6	5.22
3-Picoline	5.3	5.63
4-Picoline	7.7	5.98
2,4-Lutidine	6.7	6.63
2,6-Lutidine	1.3	6.72
Imidazole	11.7	7.10
H_2O	0.07 (min^{-1})	—

* Ref. 186.
[a] H_2O; 30°.

[186] F. Covitz and F. H. Westheimer, *J. Am. Chem. Soc.* **85,** 1773 (1963).

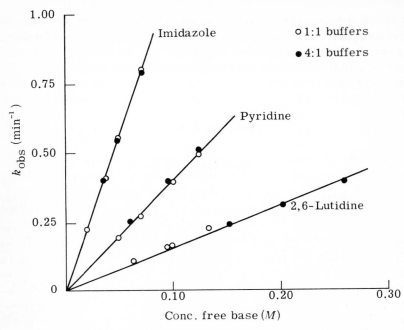

Fig. 5-5　　*Hydrolysis of methyl ethylene phosphate at 27°.*　　*(Ref. 186.)*

In Fig. 5-5 is graphically illustrated the dependence of the rate for the hydrolysis of methyl ethylene phosphate on the concentration of free base. Table 5-6 lists the second-order rate constants found for the various bases employed. It should be noted that the hydrolysis of methyl ethylene phosphate is subject to steric hindrance of moderate size, since 2,4-lutidine and especially 2,6-lutidine are less powerful catalysts (assuming a Brönsted relationship) than might be anticipated from consideration of base strength. The steric effects are comparable to those for mutarotation of glucose and inversion of menthone, the former reaction being a classic example of general-base catalysis,[187] and the latter subject to general-acid catalysis. This further serves to indicate that the hydrolysis of methyl ethylene phosphate is subject to general-base rather than to nucleophilic catalysis.

That general-base catalysis is affected by steric hindrance is not surprising, since the pK_a' reflects steric hindrance which accompanies addition of the proton and solvation of the cation $BH^\oplus$, whereas the catalytic rate constant reflects the interaction of the base and a large organic mole-

[187] J. N. Brönsted, *Chem. Rev.* **5**, 231 (1928).

cule which are exchanging a proton. Nucleophilic attack at both carbon (Chapter 1) and phosphorus (Chapter 6) is subject to steric effects of greater size. The pronounced catalytic effect of imidazole in the hydrolysis of methyl ethylene phosphate strongly suggests a role for this base in the action of ribonuclease.[188]

V. METAL-ION CATALYSIS

The study of metal-ion catalysis in "model" systems may be divided into two categories: (1) homogeneous aqueous catalysis, and (2) heterogeneous hydroxide gel catalysis. Examples of homogeneous aqueous catalysis, although preferred for mechanistic interpretation, are not numerous. In reality the investigator is confronted with the dilemma of desiring information in a pH region where the phosphate monoester is present as the dianion, and conceivably where catalysis by the metal ion would be most effective. Unfortunately, this is also a pH region where most metal ions will exist as separate hydroxide gels, greatly complicating any mechanistic formulations.

The ester salicyl phosphate, whose unique hydrolysis has been discussed in detail, is subject to homogeneous metal catalyzed hydrolysis.[189] The catalytic effects observed for various metal salts are listed in Table 5-7. The ineffectiveness of $MoO_2(VI)$ for this ester contrasts with the rate accelerations produced by this metal ion in the hydrolysis of phenyl phosphate, p-nitrophenyl phosphate, fructose-6-phosphate, adenosine-5-phosphate, phosphocreatine, and acetyl phosphate.[122, 190, 191] The order of increasing catalytic activity for metal salts, taking into account the rapid increase of catalytic activity with pH, is $Cu(II) < VO_2(VI) < VO(IV) < ZrO(IV) < Fe(III)$.

Significantly, equilibrium batch experiments with various tervalent-metal forms [192] (Al, Fe, Ti, In, Sc, Yb, Er, Nb, and La) of a strong cation-exchange resin and orthophosphoric acid have indicated a regular variation in the degree of complex formation with the ionic radius (nonhydrated) of the metal. With Al, Fe, Ti, and In a high degree of complex formation with orthophosphoric acid is found in the order $Ti > Fe > In > Al$. These results are substantially in agreement with

[188] F. H. Westheimer, *Advan. Enzymol.* **24,** 441 (1962).

[189] R. Hofstetter, Y. Murakami, G. Mont, and A. E. Martell, *J. Am. Chem. Soc.* **84,** 3041 (1962).

[190] L. Lutwak and J. Sacks, *J. Biol. Chem.* **200,** 565 (1953).

[191] F. Lipmann, *Advan. Enzymol.* **1,** 112 (1941).

[192] J. A. R. Genge and J. E. Salmon, *J. Chem. Soc.* 1459 (1959).

those obtained from pH titrations of the metal chloride solutions with phosphoric acid.

It is suggested for the ion-exchange experiments that the complexes are of a chelate type with the phosphate acting as a bidentate ligand.[193] Although in the pH range (1.0–3.0) used in the titration experiments the complex ions will tend to be cationic and multinuclear, uninuclear complexes are also expected.[194–196] These chelate complexes are essentially four-membered rings whose stability is directly related to the size of the metal ion. From their results, Genge and Salmon suggest that the ideal ionic radius for complexing is ca. 0.7 Å, with sharp departure from this radius leading to bridged, multinuclear structures or in the extreme case to precipitation. The use of ionic rather than covalent radius is justified on the basis that the interaction between M^{+3} and effectively HPO_4^{-2} involves bonds of a highly polar character. This postulate finds some experimental support in the crystal structure of heavy-metal phosphates which apparently have a high degree of ionic character.[197]

In connection with the metal-ion catalyzed hydrolysis of salicyl phosphate, the ionic radii (Å) of the ions [198, 199] employed are Fe(III) = 0.67, Ce(III) = 1.18, Cd(II) = 1.03, Th(IV) = 1.10, Ni(II) = 0.78, and Co(II) = 0.82. In an approximate manner the behavior of the ester in the presence of these metal ions is qualitatively predictable on the basis of the ionic radii (see Table 5-7). However, subtle nuances, such as the activity of Fe(III) contrasted to the inactivity of Ni(II), require the understanding of other factors.

The variation of Cu(II) and of VO(IV) catalysis of salicyl phosphate hydrolysis as a function of pH is restricted to a narrow range (pH 2–5), because of extensive metal ion hydrolysis above the higher pH value. Therefore it is not possible to determine if a maximum would exist at higher pH to give a rate profile similar to that observed in the absence of metal ions. Nevertheless the rate of hydrolysis appears to increase sharply with pH, as inspection of Table 5-7 and Fig. 5-6 reveals.

Chelation of the metal ions, as for example the Cu(II) chelates formed

[193] R. F. Jameson and J. E. Salmon, *J. Chem. Soc.* 28 (1954); 4013 (1954); 360 (1955).

[194] J. A. R. Genge and J. E. Salmon, *J. Chem. Soc.* 256 (1957).

[195] A. Holroyd and J. E. Salmon, *J. Chem. Soc.* 269 (1956); 959 (1957).

[196] A. Holroyd, J. E. Jameson, A. L. Odell, and J. E. Salmon, *J. Chem. Soc.* 3239 (1957).

[197] A. F. Wells, "Structural Inorganic Chemistry," 2nd Ed., *Oxford University Press*, London, 1950, p. 488.

[198] V. M. Goldschmidt, *Skrifter Norske Videnskaps-Akad. Oslo I Mat. Naturv. Kl.* **8,** 69 (1926).

[199] V. M. Goldschmidt, *Ber.*, **60,** 1263 (1927).

with dimethylethylenediamine, ethylenediamine, hydroxyethylethylene-diamine, and dihydroxyethylethylenediamine allowed pH studies to be extended into the alkaline range. All four Cu(II) chelates show an increase in the rate of reaction, as the pH is increased, to a maximum value, followed by a decrease in the more alkaline region (Fig. 5-6). The catalytic effects for the Cu(II) chelates as well as the vanadyl chelates are always equal or lower than that of the free metal ion. Metal ions which alone exhibited no catalytic activity are equally ineffective when chelated. Th(IV) complexes with ligands such as ethylenediamine-tetraacetic acid is no longer precipitated and does possess activity.

The mechanistic considerations for the metal-ion catalyzed hydrolysis require further elucidation of the nature and concentrations of the species involved. Nevertheless, it appears quite possible that the free metal ion is the most important catalytically active species even at high pH. The facts that the chelate and metal ion curves coincide at low pH where the chelates are highly dissociated, and diverge at high pH where the stability of the chelate is increased, are consistent with this view. It is possible, of course, that the chelates also function as Lewis acids and themselves possess some residual catalytic activity as long as the metal ion is not fully coordinated. The catalytic effect of the 2:1 ethylenediamine-Cu(II) system in which the Cu(II) is fully coordinated rapidly decreases to the

Table 5-7* *Catalytic effects of various metal ions on the hydrolysis of salicyl phosphate* [a]

Metal ions [b]	pH	$t_{1/2}$ (min)
None	3.4	768
	5.1	334
Cu(II)	3.4	768
	5.1	48
Fe(III)	2.2	~165
VO(IV)	3.3	130
	4.5	21
ZrO(IV)	3.3	~60
VO$_2$(VI)	3.3	~200

* Ref. 189.
[a] $T = 0°$; $\mu = 0.10$ (KNO$_3$).
[b] No effects with Co(II), Ni(II), Cd(II), and MoO$_2$(VI); precipitates obtained with Ce(III) and Th(IV); 1.0×10^{-3} M concentrations of metal ions and substrate.

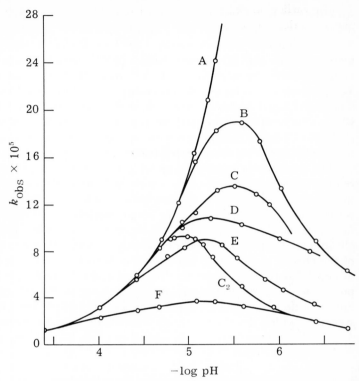

Fig. 5-6 *Rate profiles for 1.00×10^{-3} salicyl phosphate hydrolysis in the presence of 1.00×10^{-3} M Cu(II) nitrate, 0.100 M KNO₃, and the following concentrations of ligands: A, no ligand; B, 1.00×10^{-3} M dimethylethylenediamine; C_1, 1.00×10^{-3} M ethylenediamine; C_2, 2.00×10^{-3} M ethylenediamine; D, 1.00×10^{-3} M hydroxyethylethylenediamine; E, 1.00×10^{-3} M dihydroxyethylethylenediamine; F, no Cu(II) salt or ligand. (Ref. 189.)*

(metal ion-free) rate at high pH (Fig. 5-6). A tentative mechanism by Martell and co-workers for the hydrolysis of the dianion species of salicyl phosphate is depicted in (5-54). It should be pointed out that the reaction pathway actually involves a metal-ion induced ionization of the dianion to a complexed trianionic species, which is then made to undergo an intramolecular nucleophilic attack by the carboxyl anion. No expulsion of metaphosphate is anticipated. As has been seen, the presently favored mechanism for the non-metal-ion hydrolysis of salicyl phosphate depicts the carboxyl group as acting as an intramolecular proton donor facilitating metaphosphate expulsion; thus, the role tentatively assigned to the metal ions results in a change in mechanism. Alternatively the role of the metal ion may be similar to that of (5-55) but further speculation is groundless without additional experimental evidence.

The earliest work in hydroxide-gel promoted hydrolysis of phosphate esters was done by E. Bamann,[200–210] who discovered that the hydroxides

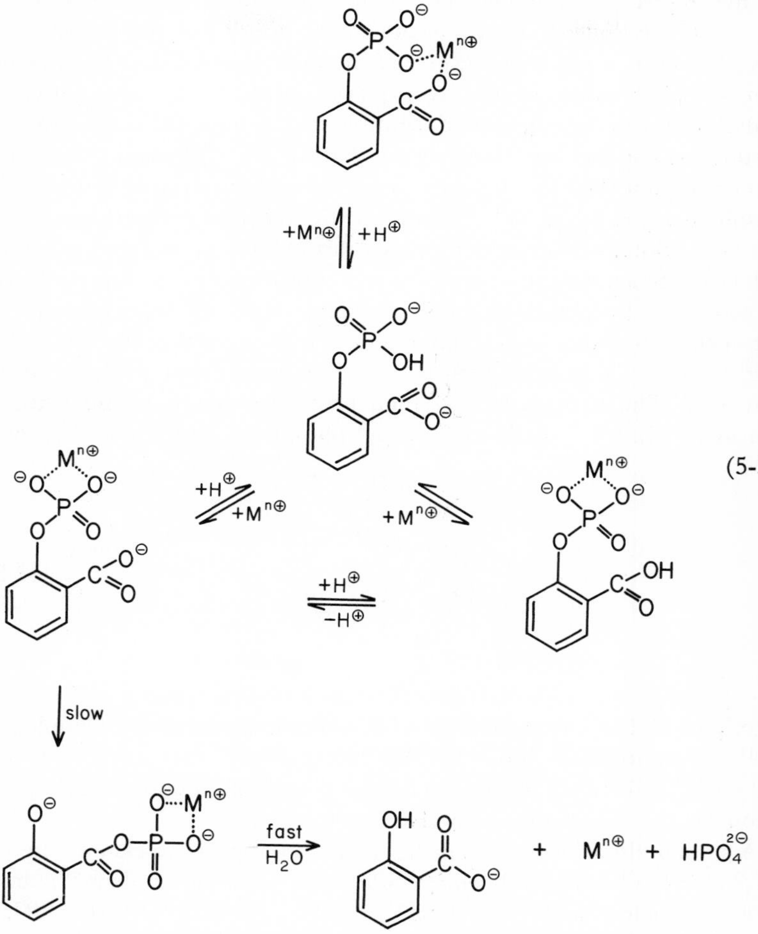

(5-54)

slow

fast
H_2O

[200] E. Bamann and M. Meisenheimer, *Ber.* **71,** 1711, 1980, 2086, 2233 (1938).

[201] E. Bamann, *Angew. Chem.* **52,** 186 (1939).

[202] E. Bamann and E. Nowotny, *Ber.* **81,** 451, 455, 463 (1948).

[203] E. Bamann, F. Fischler, and H. Trapmann, *Biochem. Z.* **325,** 413 (1954); **326,** 89 (1954).

[204] E. Bamann and H. Trapmann, *Biochem. Z.* **326,** 161, 237 (1955).

[205] E. Bamann and H. Trapmann, *Ber.* **88,** 199 (1955).

[206] E. Bamann and A. Schuegraf, *Biochem. Z.* **326,** 507 (1955).

[207] E. Bamann, H. Trapmann, and A. Schuegraf, *Ber.* **88,** 1726 (1955).

[208] E. Bamann, J. Riehl, and R. Nicolai, *Biochem. Z.* **328,** 12 (1956).

[209] E. Bamann, L. F. Sanchez, and H. Trapmann, *Ber.* **88,** 1846 (1955).

[210] E. Bamann and W. D. Mütterlein, *Ber.* **91,** 471, 1322 (1958).

of La(III), Ce(III) (IV), and Th(IV) were active catalysts. The experimental work by Bamann and his collaborators is very extensive, covering the hydrolysis of numerous phosphate compounds as affected by the hydroxide gels, mainly of the above metal ions. For mechanistic purposes, however, any interpretation of the experimental data is extremely complicated because of the two phases present. Consequently, the catalysis does not appear to be susceptible to a meaningful kinetic analysis. Westheimer and Butcher[11] have shown that La(III) hydroxide gel accounts for more than a 1000-fold increase in the rate of hydrolysis of hydroxyethyl phosphate at pH 8.5 at 78°. Moreover, the reaction proceeds exclusively with P—O bond scission as determined through tracer and stereochemical evidence. Since the rate is sensitive to a substituent in the β-position (the gel promoted hydrolysis of ethyl phosphate is 70–80 times slower than that of the β-hydroxy or β-amino ester), it is thought that the nitrogen or oxygen atom of this substituent is probably coordinated with the lanthanum ion. The hydrolysis may then proceed through an intermediate such as (5-55), for 1-methoxy-2-propyl phosphate, which may hydrolyze

(5-55)

directly to $H_2PO_4^{\ominus}$, or rearrange to a lanthanum phosphate complex, or expel metaphosphate ion. In the intermediate the lanthanum ion, $La(OH)^{\oplus 2}$, effectively substitutes for the proton of the monoanion species to convert the dianion to a reactive form.

A similar situation in which the metal ion appears to assume the role of a proton has been postulated to explain the metal-ion catalyzed hydrolysis of ribonucleic acid [211] by Pb(II), Cd(II), La(III), Ce(III), Bi(III), and Al(III) hydroxides. Isolation of the products from hydrolysis carried out near neutrality revealed the presence of compounds found only upon acid hydrolysis of ribonucleic acid. The course of the hydrolysis is peculiar in the sense that Al(III), Bi(III), Cd(II), Zn(II), and Fe(II) hydroxides catalyze a hydrolysis only to the phosphate monoester level, whereas Ce(III), Pb(II), and La(III) hydroxides catalyze complete hydrolysis of the ribonucleic acid to the various nucleosides. The latter three hydroxide gels are also active catalysts for the hydrolysis of glycerol-2-phosphate, while Cd(II), Zn(II), and Bi(III) are inactive. The gels

[211] K. Dimroth, H. Witzel, W. Hülsen, and H. Mirbach, *Ann.* **620,** 94 (1959).

of Ce(III), La(III), and Pb(II) seem equally effective against glycerol-1-phosphate, the optimum rate of hydrolysis for both esters for any of the three metal ions being about pH 7. It is thought in the case of the glycerol phosphates that the metal ion binds to the dianion species, although it appears likely that inactive chelates may exist since the catalytic activity of Pb(II) hydroxide is markedly inhibited by addition of inactive Cd(II) hydroxide.

It has been proposed [11, 29] that the mechanism for lanthanum hydroxide-gel promoted hydrolysis of phosphate esters might serve as a "model" of the enzymic reactions catalyzed by alkaline phosphatase. The similarity between the enzymic and nonenzymic systems can best be judged by considering in detail what is known about the reactions of the alkaline phosphatase isolated from *Escherichia coli*.

It has been presumed for some time that phosphate ester hydrolysis catalyzed by nonspecific phosphatases occurs in two catalytic steps.[212] The first step is the phosphorylation of the enzyme by the substrate with loss of the alcohol group; the second is the hydrolysis of the phosphoryl enzyme. This mechanism was advanced by R. K. Morton [213] to explain the phosphoryl transferase activity of the enzymes, and it may be surmised from observations that substrate hydrolysis by intestinal alkaline phosphatase proceeds with P—O bond cleavage [30] and that incubation of high concentrations of inorganic phosphate and alcohol with intestinal alkaline phosphatase [214] leads to ester formation. For the alkaline phosphatase from *E. coli*, the similarity in the maximal rates of hydrolysis of different substrates with varying substituents also supports a mechanism in which the rate-limiting reaction is the hydrolysis of the common intermediate, phosphoryl enzyme.[215, 216]

Phosphorylation of alkaline phosphatase from *E. coli* has recently been achieved with glucose-6-phosphate [219] and orthophosphoric acid, the latter having the same characteristics expected of a reaction at the active center of the enzyme. Comparison of the pH dependence of the maximal rate of hydrolysis of glycerol-2-phosphate at 30° to the equilibrium amount of phosphate fixed by alkaline phosphatase during incubation at 0° with saturating orthophosphate is shown graphically in Fig. 5-7 Degradation of the phosphate-fixed enzyme yields an *O*-phosphorylserine,[217—219] which

[212] J. H. Schwartz, *Proc. Natl. Acad. Sci. U.S.* **49,** 871 (1963).
[213] R. K. Morton, *Discussions Faraday Soc.* **20,** 149 (1955).
[214] O. Meyerhof and H. Green, *J. Biol. Chem.* **178,** 655 (1949).
[215] S. Horiuchi, *Japan. J. Med. Sci. Biol.* **12,** 429 (1959).
[216] L. A. Heppel, D. R. Harkness, and R. J. Hilmoe, *J. Biol. Chem.* **237,** 841 (1962).
[217] J. H. Schwartz and F. Lipmann, *Proc. Natl. Acad. Sci. U.S.* **47,** 1996 (1961).
[218] L. Engström, *Biochim. Biophys. Acta* **56,** 606 (1962).
[219] L. Engström, *Arkiv. Kemi* **19,** 129 (1962).

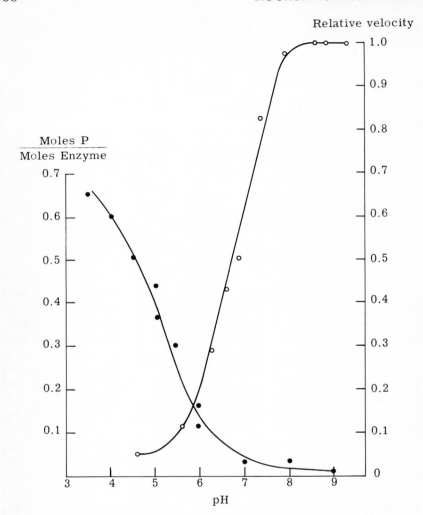

Fig. 5-7 *Phosphate fixation and enzymic activity of alkaline phosphatase as a function of pH. Phosphate fixation (—●—●—) is the mole ratio of phosphate to enzyme after incubation with 1 mM P³²-orthophosphate at 0° for 15 min in Tris-acetate buffers pH 4.6–9, and Tris-formate buffers pH 3.5–4.2. Relative velocity: the initial rate of hydrolysis of 0.01 M β-glycerol phosphate in 0.1 M Tris-acetate buffers was followed by the appearance of inorganic phosphate at 30°. The ratio of the maximal velocities obtained at the various values of pH to the velocity in the optimal pH range are plotted (—○—○—). (Ref. 212.)*

is surrounded by the amino acid sequence [220] Thr-Asp-SerP-Ala-Ala. This sequence closely resembles the sequence around the reactive serine in trypsin, chymotrypsin, and other esterases (see Chapter 2). The phosphorylation of alkaline phosphatase by orthophosphate is favored at low pH (Fig. 5-7), as is the acylation of the reactive serine in chymotrypsin by acyl esters. This evidence strongly suggests that serine is involved in the catalytic mechanism.

Phosphorylation of the enzyme under alkaline conditions, which is far from complete, is not increased by increasing the orthophosphate concentration above saturation. This finding suggests that orthophosphate is bound to the enzyme before the serine residue is phosphorylated, and that the binding site is different from the site of phosphorylation. This postulate is further supported by evidence that orthophosphate profoundly inhibits enzymic activity at alkaline pH,[221] where phosphorylation hardly occurs, and moreover is firmly bound under these conditions as revealed in equilibrium dialysis experiments.[222] The enzyme is known to contain $Zn(II)$,[223] which may serve as a binding site. It is surprising that, although orthophosphate binds at least as well as the phosphate ester at alkaline pH, its rate of turnover is much slower than the optimal rate of ester hydrolysis. This may reflect the possibility that orthophosphate at alkaline pH may, upon bonding, ionize to the trianionic species which is inactive.

Evidently ester phosphate and orthophosphate are bound to the enzyme at the same site, and form similar complexes. Both phosphorylate the same serine and behave equally as substrates. These considerations suggest that the process of phosphorylation by either ester or orthophosphate is similar mechanistically, with hydrolysis being the reversal of phosphorylation or vice versa. The normal enzymic hydrolysis of a phosphate ester, leading to phosphorylation of the enzyme followed by hydrolysis of the phosphoryl enzyme, may then be viewed as a reversal of the phosphorylation reaction of orthophosphate, due to the presence of water in high concentration. A plausible scheme summarizing these observations is given in Fig. 5-8. It must be emphasized, however, that steps 2 and 3, in which an apparent nucleophilic attack by serine on bound ester or orthophosphate occurs, represent only the actual reaction pathway and probably not the mechanistic one. There is as yet no

[220] J. H. Schwartz, A. M. Crestfield, and F. Lipmann, *Proc. Natl. Acad. Sci. U.S.* **49,** 722 (1963).

[221] A. Garen and C. Levinthal, *Biochim. Biophys. Acta* **38,** 470 (1960).

[222] C. Levinthal, E. R. Signer, and K. Fetherolf, *Proc. Natl. Acad. Sci. U.S.* **48,** 1230 (1962).

[223] D. J. Plocke, C. Levinthal, and B. L. Vallee, *Biochemistry* **1,** 373 (1962).

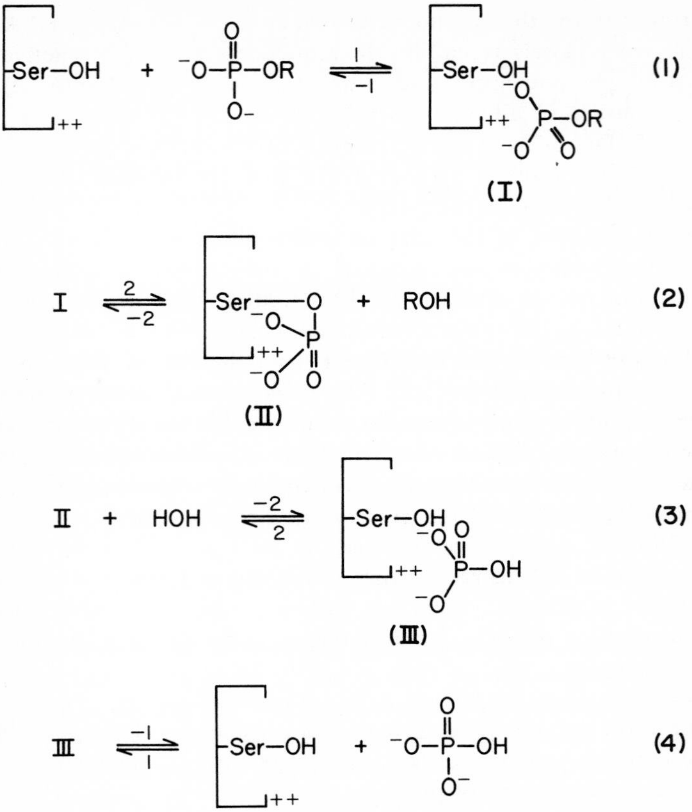

Fig. 5-8   *A plausible mechanism for the hydrolysis of phosphate esters by alkaline phosphatase.   (Ref. 212.)*

evidence for an unusual reactivity of the hydroxyl group of serine toward phosphate esters.[224]   The nucleophilicity of serine toward acyl compounds has been discussed (Chapter 1) and does not appear abnormal on the basis of its pK_a'.

Strictly speaking, it is of course unfair to consider the early hydroxide gel studies as "models" for what is presently known about the alkaline phosphatases.   Nevertheless the need for increasingly sophisticated or more detailed investigations is obvious.   The importance of metal ions for the activity of the phosphatases is widespread, for example, fructose-1,6-diphosphatase [225] from liver is activated by Mn(II) or Mg(II), yeast

[224] W. P. Jencks, *Ann. Rev. Biochem.* **32**, 639 (1963).
[225] J. Reis, *Enzymologia* **2**, 110 (1937).

alkaline phosphatase [226] activity is dependent on Fe(II), mannitol-1-phosphatase [227] is activated by Fe(II), Mn(II), and Mg(II), and kidney alkaline phosphatase [228] requires Zn(II) as a cofactor. This is in contrast to the lack of a requirement for, or stimulation by, a divalent metal ion in reactions that involve derivatives of orthophosphate catalyzed by phosphorylase, a fact which raises further interesting questions.

VI. PHOSPHORAMIDATES

Phosphoramidate (PA), the simplest member of this class of compounds, upon hydrolysis [127, 229, 244, 245] exhibits a pH-rate profile strikingly different at first glance from that observed for the exchange reaction of orthophosphoric acid or the hydrolysis of monoalkyl phosphates (Fig. 5-9). The rate equation which adequately describes this behavior is expressed by (5-56):

$$k_{obs} = k_h a_H[M_0] + k_0[M_0] + k_1[M_1] \qquad (5\text{-}56)$$

where M_0 and M_1 are the mole fractions of the neutral ($NH_2PO_2H_2$) and monoanionic species ($NH_2PO_2H^{\ominus}$), respectively, and k_h, k_0, and k_1 are their associated specific rate constants. Hydrolysis in acidic medium is described as an acid catalyzed hydrolysis of the neutral species rather than the kinetically indistinguishable spontaneous decomposition of the conjugate acid form of the neutral species. As is the case with the dianionic species of monoesters, PA dianion is stable in alkaline solution and is not represented in equation (5-56). It is obvious that the kinetic expressions describing monoester and phosphoramidate hydrolysis consist of the same collection of terms, and that the occurrence of an S-shaped rather than a bell-shaped curve is due to the relative magnitudes of the specific rate constants. Similar S-shaped pH-rate profiles have been observed in the aqueous hydrolysis of N-(phenyl)-, N-(p-chlorophenyl)-, and N-(p-methoxyphenyl)-phosphoramidates.[230] It is of interest to note that, whereas solvolysis of PA in 50% methanol-water does not affect the basic shape of the pH-rate profile (Fig. 5-9), hydrolysis of N-(p-chloro-

[226] J. Van Eys, M. M. Ciotti, and N. O. Kaplan, *J. Biol. Chem.* **231,** 571 (1958).

[227] H. Yamada, K. Okamoto, K. Kodama, and S. Tanaka, *Biochim. Biophys. Acta* **33,** 271 (1959).

[228] J. Mathies, *J. Biol. Chem.* **233,** 1121 (1958).

[229] T. Rathlev and T. Rosenberg, *Arch. Biochem. Biophys.* **65,** 319 (1956).

[230] J. D. Chanley and E. Feageson, *J. Am. Chem. Soc.* **80,** 2686 (1958).

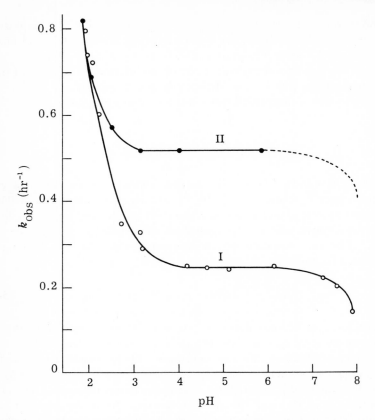

Fig. 5-9   *The observed solvolysis rate at 38.8°, $\mu = 0.2$, as plotted against pH for phosphoramidate: in water, I; in 50% methanol-water, II.   The solid lines are the theoretical curves; the symbols ○ and ⊕ represent the experimental points.   (Ref. 127.)*

phenyl)-phosphoramidate (ClPhPA) in 50% dioxane-water leads to a dramatic change in the shape of this profile (Fig. 5-10).

Analysis of the rate data for PA and ClPhPA allowed evaluation of the various rate constants, which are listed in Table 5-8.   A note of practical importance should be inserted at this point, cautioning against use of the analytical method of Fiske and SubbaRow as modified by Sobel [230a] for determination of free phosphoric acid.   The high acidity of the development medium and the catalysis by molybdate [229, 230, 246] preclude its use for the more reactive phosphoramidates.   Inspection of the rate values reveals that in water $k_0 > k_1$ for both phosphoramidates,

[230a] A. E. Sobel, *Ind. Eng. Chem.* (*Anal. Edition*) **17**, 242 (1945).

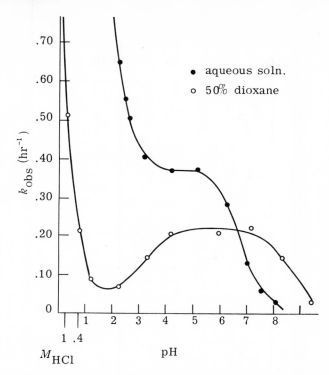

Fig. 5-10   *The observed hydrolysis rate at 20°, μ = 0.1, as plotted against pH for N-(p-chlorophenyl)phosphoramidate: in water, ●; in 50% dioxane-water mixture, O. (Ref. 230.)*

hence the absence of a maximum in the pH-rate profile.   It also should be noted that the rate of hydrolysis of the monoanionic species of these compounds is much faster $(10^3 – 10^4)$ than that of the comparable ionic species of an alkyl or aryl phosphate.

In order to gain further insight into the mechanism of this hydrolysis, Chanley and Feageson [127] studied the variation in product composition, monoalkyl phosphate/phosphoric acid, derived from the solvolysis of both phosphoramidate and N-(p-chlorophenyl)-phosphoramidate in various ethanol and methanol-water mixtures.   Their investigation was conducted over the acidity range 3 M HCl to pH 7 and correlated with the ionic species present.   This discussion, in turn, will treat each species separately.

In essence the solvolysis of the PA monoanion in methanol-water (0–60%) can be described by a two-term bimolecular rate equation (5-57), which correctly predicts the rate and product composition observed in

Table 5-8 *   Specific rate constants, heats and entropies of activation, for the various ionic species of phosphoramidate and N-(p-chlorophenyl)-phosphoramidate

Species	pK_a'	Solvent	k_h (liter mole^{-1} hr^{-1})	k_0 (hr^{-1})	k_1 (hr^{-1})	$T°$	$\Delta H^{\ddagger}$ (kcal mole^{-1})	$\Delta S^{\ddagger}$ (e.u.)
[H$_3$⊕][H$_2$NPO$_3$H$_2$]	—	H$_2$O	33.3 [a]	—	—	36.8	14.5 [f]	−21.1 [f]
[H$_3$⊕][p-ClC$_6$H$_4$NHPO$_3$H$_2$]	—	H$_2$O	0.88 [b]	—	—	0	—	—
[H$_2$NPO$_3$H$_2$]	3.00 [c]	H$_2$O	—	0.420 [a]	—	36.8	18.1 [f]	−18.2 [f]
[p-ClC$_6$H$_4$NHPO$_3$H$_2$]	ca. 1.6 [d]	H$_2$O	—	0.23 [b]	—	0	—	—
[H$_2$NPO$_3$H]⊖	8.15 [c]	H$_2$O	—	—	0.252 [a]	36.8	23.6 [g]	−1.6 [g]
[p-ClC$_6$H$_4$NHPO$_3$H]⊖	ca. 6.8 [e]	H$_2$O	—	—	0.03 [b]	0	19.8 [g]	−6.3 [g]

* Ref. 127, 230.

[a] $\mu = 0.2$.
[b] $\mu = 2.0$.
[c] $\mu = 0.2$, $T = 25°$.
[d] $\mu = 2.0$, $T = 0°$.
[e] $\mu = 0.1$, $T = 20°$.
[f] Evaluated at $T = 10.1°$.
[g] Evaluated at $T = 20°$.

74

the various solvent mixtures.   In ethanol-water mixtures the near identity

$$k_{obs} = 4.51 \times 10^{-3}[H_2O] + 3.17 \times 10^{-2}[CH_3OH] \qquad (5\text{-}57)$$

of the two rate constants precludes an accurate calculation of a similar equation.   Corresponding studies with the monoanions of simple aromatic phosphate esters, phenyl and p-nitrophenyl phosphate, revealed that the ratio of methyl phosphate/phosphoric acid is very nearly identical to the ratio methanol-water in the reaction mixtures, while in ethanol-water mixtures it is smaller.

It is presumed that the hydrolysis of the monoanions of these aromatic phosphate esters does proceed through formation of a highly reactive monomeric metaphosphate, as has been noted.   The solvolysis of such a species is anticipated as being indiscriminate toward the components of the solvent mixture, reacting equally rapidly with methanol, ethanol, or water.   The experimental data for the solvolysis of the phosphate ester in methanol-water mixtures are consistent with this view.   It is interesting to note, however, that some solvent "sorting" appears to exist for the metaphosphate ion in ethanol-water mixtures, which becomes even more pronounced in i-propyl and t-butyl alcohol-water mixtures for which no alkyl phosphate is detected.   Nevertheless, the finding of alkyl phosphate in greater proportion than the mole fraction of methanol in the reaction mixture for PA monoanion, predictable through equation (5-57), is consonant with the concept of attack of solvent molecules on phosphorus. The evidence is not as convincing for the solvolysis of the PA monoanion in ethanol-water mixtures.

The solvolysis of the monoanionic species of ClPhPA in methanol-water mixtures is presumably also bimolecular, yielding very nearly the same product distribution in various solvent mixtures as phosphoramidate. Unlike the monoanionic species of the latter, the rate of solvolysis of ClPhPA is decreased in 50% methanol-water and dioxane-water mixtures. A possible qualitative explanation is derived from the possibility that the phosphoramidates may exist in a zwitterion and nonzwitterion form.[231, 232] The amount in zwitterion form for a given species, as for example a monoanion, is given by

$$[RNH - PO_3H]^{\ominus} \underset{Z_n}{\overset{K_e}{\rightleftarrows}} [RH_2N^{\oplus} - PO_3^{\ominus}]^{\ominus} \qquad (5\text{-}58)$$

$$Z_w = M_1\left(\frac{K_e}{K_e + 1}\right)$$

[231] P. Oesper, *Arch. Biochem. Biophys.* **27**, 255 (1950).
[232] T. Hill and M. Morales, *J. Am. Chem. Soc.* **73**, 1656 (1951).

where $M_1 = Z_w + Z_n$. When $K_e \ll 1$, any change in K_e, as might be anticipated in changing to a less aqueous solvent, results in an equivalent change in Z_w, whereas when $K_e \gg 1$, a change in K_e would not substantially alter Z_w.

Insofar as it is applicable, support for the existence of a zwitterion form for the monoanion of PA stems from X-ray crystallographic studies,[233] which show the crystalline monoanion of PA to be zwitterionic. The possibility that K_e in solution is large for PA as compared to ClPhPA is suggested by the significantly larger pK'_{a_2} (8.2) [127] of PA relative to pK'_{a_2} (6.8) for ClPhPA. This latter value approaches in magnitude that of N-benzoylphosphoramidate (pK'_{a_2} 6.0, 6.42,[234] 5.67 [235]) and N-acetylphosphoramidate (pK'_{a_2} 6.0) where zwitterion formation is disfavored. The pK'_{a_2} values for the nonacylated phosphoramidate monoanions are also significantly larger than the corresponding pK'_{a_2} values for phenyl and acetyl phosphate (5.88 and 4.95, respectively), from which it may be inferred that a significant concentration of dipolar zwitterion exists in aqueous medium.[230] Thus, it is thought that in the various solvent mixtures employed, the monoanion zwitterion form of the phosphoramidate is present and that, in the case of PA and ClPhPA, this form predominates only for PA.[127, 236] Although it is probably true that the zwitterion species is important for phosphoramidates, acceptance of such arguments based on pK'_a values should be tempered by the fact that the less electronegative nitrogen will tend to increase the pK'_a relative to those compounds containing oxygen. The bimolecular mechanism postulated for monoanion hydrolysis by Chanley and Feageson is given in (5-59a).[127] Path (a) is considered the primary course of solvolysis of the phosphoramidates PA and ClPhPA, with the possibility that path (b) may be of some significance, especially for ClPhPA.

The above mechanism therefore features a departure from mechanisms usually postulated for the hydrolysis of phosphate ester monoanions. There is, as yet, no evidence as to whether a pentacovalent intermediate exists during the displacement. It should be noted, however, that the hydrolysis of the phosphoramidates in water is characterized by an entropy of activation near zero and also is little affected by change of solvent to D_2O. The solvent deuterium isotope effect k^{H_2O}/k^{D_2O} for PA and ClPhPA monoanions is 1.20 and 0.76, respectively. In addition, solvolysis of PA in ethanol-water mixtures does not clearly indicate a bimolecular solvolysis. It is possible therefore that the zwitterion form of the mono-

[233] E. Hobbs, D. E. C. Corbridge, and B. Raistrick, *Acta Cryst.* **6**, 621 (1953).
[234] C. Zioudrou, *Tetrahedron* **18**, 197 (1962).
[235] M. Halmann, A. Lapidot, and D. Samuel, *J. Chem. Soc.* 4672 (1960).
[236] W. D. Kumler and J. J. Eiler, *J. Am. Chem. Soc.* **65**, 2355 (1943).

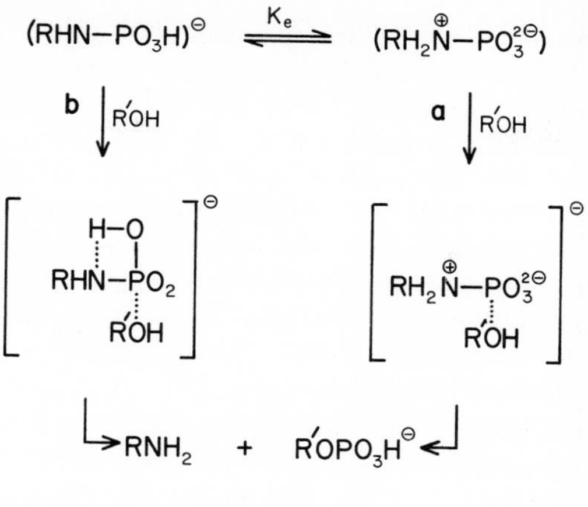

$$(RHN{-}PO_3H)^{\ominus} \overset{K_e}{\rightleftharpoons} (RH_2\overset{\oplus}{N}{-}PO_3^{2\ominus})$$

$$\mathbf{b} \downarrow R'OH \qquad\qquad \mathbf{a} \downarrow R'OH$$

$$\left[\begin{array}{c} H{-}O \\ \vdots | \\ RH\overset{\vdots}{N}{-}PO_2 \\ \vdots \\ R'OH \end{array}\right]^{\ominus} \qquad \left[\begin{array}{c} RH_2\overset{\oplus}{N}{-}PO_3^{2\ominus} \\ \vdots \\ R'OH \end{array}\right]^{\ominus} \qquad (5\text{-}59)$$

$$\overset{}{\underset{}{\text{L}}}{\to}RNH_2 \quad + \quad R'OPO_3H^{\ominus} {\leftarrow}\text{J}$$

$$\text{where} \quad R = H, \; p{-}ClC_6H_5$$
$$R' = H, \; CH_3, \; C_2H_5$$

anions of PA and ClPhPA may indeed still decompose to form a monomeric metaphosphate intermediate but, depending on the nucleophilicity of the alcohol, may also solvolyze through a competing bimolecular pathway. Although the solvolysis of PA in i-propyl and t-butyl alcohol mixtures gives no alkyl phosphate, perhaps due to steric hindrance, neither is alcoholysis of metaphosphate anticipated. An alternate mechanism, as in the case of PA, may involve a unimolecular path (a), analogous to phosphate monoester hydrolysis, and a competing bimolecular path (b)

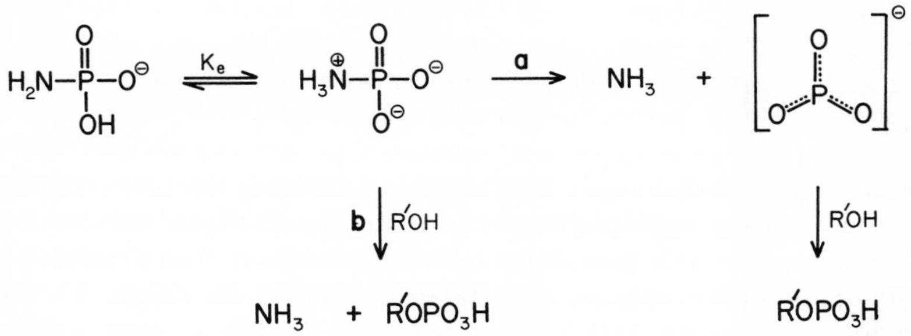

$$H_2N{-}\overset{\overset{\textstyle O}{\|}}{\underset{\underset{\textstyle OH}{|}}{P}}{-}O^{\ominus} \overset{K_e}{\rightleftharpoons} H_3\overset{\oplus}{N}{-}\overset{\overset{\textstyle O}{\|}}{\underset{\underset{\textstyle O^{\ominus}}{|}}{P}}{-}O^{\ominus} \overset{a}{\longrightarrow} NH_3 \; + \; \left[\begin{array}{c} \overset{\textstyle O}{\vdots} \\ O{\cdots}\overset{\vdots}{P}{\cdots}O \end{array}\right]^{\ominus}$$

$$\mathbf{b} \downarrow R'OH \qquad\qquad\qquad \downarrow R'OH$$

$$NH_3 \quad + \quad R'OPO_3H \qquad\qquad\qquad R'OPO_3H$$

$$(5\text{-}60)$$

whose importance depends on the nucleophilicity of R'OH. Other investigators have indicated the order of nucleophilicity toward phosphorus to be MeOH > EtOH > H_2O.[237]

[237] I. Dostrovsky and M. Halmann, *J. Chem. Soc.* 502 (1953).

Further support for the interpretation favoring the monoanion zwitterion as the reactive species arises from observations of the base catalyzed solvolysis of PA and ClPhPA. The rate of solvolysis of PA monoanion is directly proportional to the free base concentration of pyridine, 3- and 4-methylpyridine, and the anions of nicotinic and iso-nicotinic acids. The hydrolysis of ClPhPA monoanion is also catalyzed by the anion of nicotinic acid, the only base investigated. Effective catalysis by these bases is not found for *p*-nitrophenyl and phenyl phosphate. Evidence that this is an example of a nucleophilic displacement is also indicated by the absence of a solvent deuterium isotope effect. No catalysis of hydrolysis of phosphoramidate is observed with 2-methyl-pyridine, 2,6-dimethylpyridine, aniline, the anion of picolinic acid, or the dianion of phosphoric acid, illustrating the strict steric requirement imposed on the nucleophile.[238]   The base catalysis, as illustrated in (5-61) for

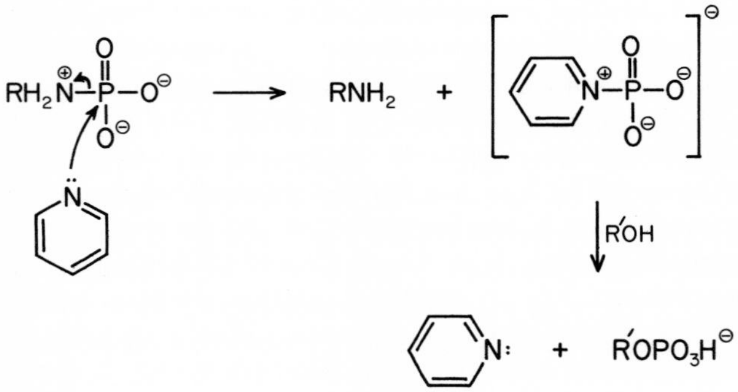

$$(5\text{-}61)$$

where   R = H, p–ClC$_6$H$_5$
R′ = H, CH$_3$, C$_2$H$_5$

pyridine, may be reasonably interpreted as a two-step reaction involving a rate-determining nucleophilic attack by free base on the monoanion, leading to a more unstable phosphoramidate monoanion. The latter may decompose unimolecularly or, as postulated, solvolyze bimolecularly. The product distribution found in the solvolysis of PA in methanol- and ethanol-water mixtures is not altered in the presence of nicotinic acid, requiring that only the relative rate of attack of alcohol and water on the intermediate be the same as that found for the uncatalyzed reaction.

[238] H. C. Brown and A. Cahn, *J. Am. Chem. Soc.* **77,** 1715 (1955); H. C. Brown and X. R. Mihm, *J. Am. Chem. Soc.* **77,** 1723 (1955); H. C. Brown and R. R. Holmes, *J. Am. Chem. Soc.* **77,** 1727 (1955).

The fast rate of hydrolysis of the neutral species of the phosphoramidates also may be ascribed to a zwitterion form $(RNH_2^{\oplus}\text{-}PO_3H^{\ominus})$. The presence of the zwitterion is suggested by the same arguments cited for the monoanion species, namely, a larger pK_{a_1}' value for the phosphoramidate than that for aromatic phosphate (i.e., ca. 1.6 for pK_{a_1}' ClPhPA versus pK_{a_1}' 1.0 for phenyl phosphate).[127] The pK_{a_1}' of 3.00 in water for PA sets it apart from other substituted phosphoramidates and implies that its neutral species exists primarily as a zwitterion.[127] In methanol-water solutions the neutral species of PA again solvolyzes with formation of a greater percentage of alkyl phosphate than the mole % of alcohol in the reaction mixture. However, the percentage is smaller than that observed for the monoanionic species, and alone is inconclusive in regard to the apparent molecularity of the reaction pathway.

As has been stated previously, the rate of solvolysis of the neutral species of ClPhPA is considerably decreased in 50% dioxane-water, a fact which may be ascribed to repression of zwitterion formation. In this solvent mixture the pH-rate profile can be accounted for by the rate terms associated with the monoanionic species and the acid catalyzed hydrolysis of the neutral species. Of interest then is the unresolved question whether dioxane selectively represses zwitterion formation of the neutral species of ClPhPA or whether the solvolysis of the nonzwitterion form of the monoanion is also important, as indicated in (5-59).

Acid catalyzes the hydrolysis of both PA and ClPhPA, possibly through different pathways. PA in acidified methanol-water systems yields practically no methyl phosphate, whereas ClPhPA in various strongly acidified alcohol-water mixtures yields alkyl phosphate in the same percentage as the mole % of alcohol present. Chanley and Feageson[127] suggest that solvolysis of protonated ClPhPA proceeds by way of a unimolecular breakdown of the protonated species with formation of the conjugate acid of metaphosphate, while protonated PA is preferentially attacked by water. To interpret the former as a bimolecular solvolysis, however, requires only that the protonated species of ClPhPA be equally reactive with water or alcohol, a possibility which has not yet been excluded.

Jencks and Gilchrist[238a] have recently demonstrated that the hydrolysis of PA monoanion is catalyzed by formaldehyde, hypochlorous acid, and nitrous acid. These reactions appear to be examples of electrophilic catalysis, in which the catalyst forms a covalent bond with the PA monoanion to give an intermediate with a better leaving group, as illustrated in (5-62), for the hypochlorite catalyzed reaction. From the above, the

[238a] W. P. Jencks and M. Gilchrist, *J. Am. Chem. Soc.* **86,** 1410 (1964).

$$Cl_2\overset{\oplus}{\underset{H}{N}}-\overset{\overset{O}{\|}}{\underset{\underset{O^{\ominus}}{|}}{P}}-O^{\ominus} \qquad (5\text{-}62)$$

solvolytic step may be formulated as occurring either by a unimolecular decomposition or by nucleophilic attack of solvent on phosphorus. Since pyridine and fluoride,[19, 229] which are effective nucleophilic reagents toward PA, do not participate in the formaldehyde or hypochlorite catalyzed reactions, the catalytic mechanism does not appear to involve simply an increase in the susceptibility of phosphoramidate toward nucleophilic attack. On the other hand, different yields of methyl phosphate are obtained when the formaldehyde and hypochlorite catalyzed reactions are conducted in the same methanol-water mixture, which in both cases are greater than that obtained with p-nitrophenyl phosphate. These results are especially significant in view of the above discussion and suggest that the apparently contradictory results found with the phosphoramidates may be due to a borderline situation in which the metaphosphate-like intermediate is not completely separated from the attacking and leaving groups.

In addition to the reaction of PA monoanion with heterocyclic tertiary nitrogenous bases leading to a catalyzed hydrolysis, Rathlev and Rosenberg [229] demonstrated that reaction occurs with the free base of imidazole, histidine, and histamine. The intermediate phosphorylated imidazole derivatives are stable in alkaline solutions and may be isolated. In addition they undergo a second phosphorylation leading to the diphosphorylated compounds.

Monophosphorylimidazole (MPI) and diphosphorylimidazole (DPI) are unusual in their reactivity when compared to other phosphoramidates. At neutral pH both are hydrolyzed readily, whereas in alkaline solution (pH 12, 100°) MPI is stable but DPI is completely hydrolyzed in ca. 15 min. The neutral hydrolysis of MPI and other monophosphorylated imidazole derivatives is not first-order but involves two molecules of MPI, leading to the formation of DPI and free imidazole. DPI also proves to be an effective phosphorylating agent for amines such as ethanolamine, α-alanine, β-alanine, serine, tyrosine, p-aminobenzoic acid, and proline. The N-phosphorylation occurs readily under mildly alkaline conditions at room temperature and yields no O-phosphorylated products, which is unusual. It should be recalled that nitrogenous bases presently appear to be conspicuously unreactive as nucleophiles toward phosphate esters, and that phosphoramidates, such as PA and ClPhPA, undergo attack only by select tertiary heterocyclic bases. With amines and amino acids, PA reacts very slowly if at all.[229]

Extensive studies [239, 240] with the mono- and diphenyl esters of mono-phosphorylimidazole have indicated their utility as phosphorylating agents. The generalized reactions are summarized in (5-63). Amines including benzylamine, cyclohexylamine, and aniline, and alcohols like

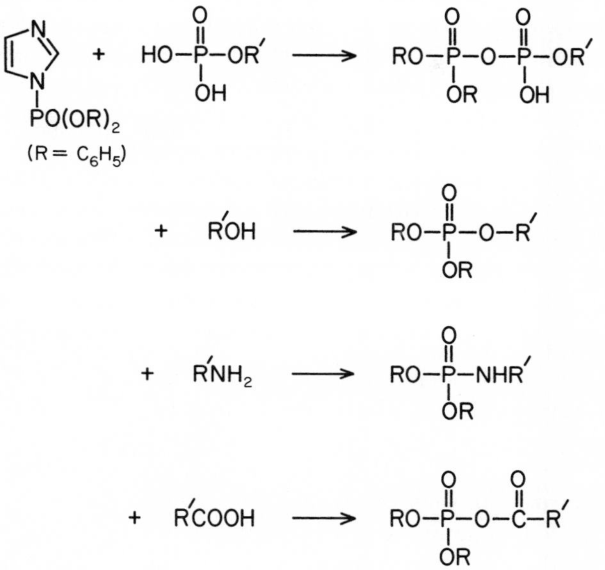

$$(5\text{-}63)$$

cyclohexanol have been phosphorylated in high yield. In the presence of acetic acid and inorganic phosphate, acetyl phosphate and pyrophosphate have been formed, respectively. The di-p-nitrobenzyl ester of MPI has been successfully employed for phosphorylation of benzyloxycarbonyl-L-serine-L-alanine benzyl ester.[241]

The reactivity of the phosphorylimidazoles has been attributed to the system —P—N—C=N—,[229, 239] which upon nucleophilic displacement yields a resonance-stabilized leaving group. The same structure exists in creatine phosphate, a well-known enzymic phosphorylating agent. The diphosphorylations and transphosphorylations of DPI may depend upon relief of the positive charge possessed by this molecule. Although reactions with the unsubstituted monophosphorylimidazole would have been preferred, the transphosphorylations already described may nevertheless serve as models for biological transphosphorylations in

[239] J. Baddiley, J. G. Buchanan, and R. Letters, *J. Chem. Soc.* 2812 (1956).
[240] H. A. Staab, H. Schaller, and F. Cramer, *Angew. Chem.* **71,** 736 (1959).
[241] D. Theodoropoulos, J. Gazopoulos, and I. Souchleris, *J. Chem. Soc.* 5257 (1960).

Table 5-9 *   *Hydrolysis of phosphoramidates*

Compound	$T°$	$10^4\ k$ (sec^{-1}) at pH 4	Acid catalysis	Ref.
$NH_2PO_3H_2$	25	0.15	Yes	229, 244, 245
$HO_2CCH_2NHPO_3H_2$	25	9.8 (pH 3)	Yes	246
$C_6H_5NHPO_3H_2$	20.0	0.99	Yes	230
$p\text{-}CH_3OC_6H_4NHPO_3H_2$	$\begin{cases}20.0\\25\end{cases}$	$\begin{cases}1.04\\1.91\end{cases}$	Yes	230
$C_6H_5CONHPO_3H_2$	$\begin{cases}25.0\\37.0\end{cases}$	$\begin{cases}0.36\\1.85\end{cases}$	(only in conc. acid)	242
$C_2H_5O_2CNHPO_3H_2$	$\begin{cases}26.7\\37.0\end{cases}$	$\begin{cases}0.435\\2.02\end{cases}$	No	243
$(C_6H_5O)_2PONHPO_3H$	37	0.059	No	242

* Ref. 242.

which a histidine residue is involved.[239]   Such transfers, usually ATP-requiring, will be considered in some detail in a subsequent chapter.

The N-acylphosphoramidates are hydrolyzed in aqueous solutions to phosphoric acid and an amide, with the rates being maximal at about pH 4.[235, 242, 243]   At this pH the compounds are predominantly in the monoanion form; thus their behavior is analogous to that of the phosphate monoesters.   The magnitude of the rate of hydrolysis is little affected by the nature of the substituting group; acyl and nonacyl derivatives hydrolyze at comparable rates, as revealed by inspection of Table 5-9.   This is opposed to the behavior of acyl phosphates which hydrolyze considerably faster than alkyl or aromatic phosphates, possibly through a cyclic mechanism (5-17).

A rather complete study of the hydrolysis of the monoanion of phosphourethane,[243] $C_2H_5O_2CNHPO_3H^{\ominus}$, has shown that (1) the rate of solvolysis is not altered in D_2O; (2) no appreciable oxygen exchange occurs between the phosphoryl group and O^{18}-enriched water; and (3) the entropy of activation is positive, $\Delta S^{\ddagger} = +14.4$ e.u.   In addition the pH-rate profile in this region is not altered by conducting the hydrolysis in dioxane-water mixtures, implying the relative unimportance of a zwitterion form.   Similarly, no change in the rate of hydrolysis is noted in the presence of added urethane.   Consequently, scheme (5-2) for the

[242] M. Halmann, A. Lapidot, and D. Samuel, *J. Chem. Soc.* 3158 (1961).
[243] M. Halmann and A. Lapidot, *J. Chem. Soc.* 419 (1960).
[244] K. M. Moller, *Biochim. Biophys. Acta* **16**, 162 (1955).
[245] O. T. Quimby, A. Narath, and F. H. Lohman, *J. Am. Chem. Soc.* **82**, 1099 (1960).
[246] T. Winnick and E. M. S. Scott, *Arch. Biochem. Biophys.* **12**, 201 (1947).

hydrolysis of the monoanions of phosphate monoesters appears equally applicable for phosphourethane. Subsequent studies have revealed similar characteristics for the hydrolysis of N-benzoylphosphoramidate,[242] although the observation of a small solvent deuterium isotope effect (k^{H_2O}/k^{D_2O} 0.82) might indicate that the solvolysis does not proceed via metaphosphate as a free intermediate.

The most striking difference between the various phosphoramidates is that the hydrolysis of some of them is acid catalyzed. Those not susceptible to acid catalysis have a carbonyl or phosphoryl group adjacent to the nitrogen atom which, Halmann and co-workers[242] suggest, acts to lower the electron density on nitrogen, decreasing its susceptibility to protonation. This interpretation is supported by the observation that the acidic hydrolysis of phosphourethane and diphenyl N-dihydroxyphosphinylphosphoramidate is not subject to a solvent deuterium isotope effect in contrast to N-benzoylphosphoramidate. Halmann and co-workers[235] have recently shown that N-benzenesulfonylphosphoramidate, possessing a highly polar acyl group, is not subject to acid catalyzed hydrolysis.

The reactivity of N-acylphosphoramidates toward various nucleophilic reagents has not been thoroughly investigated. However, Halmann and Lapidot[243] have found that fluoride, di-n-butylamine, and butane-1-thiol do not change the rate of hydrolysis of phosphourethane monoanion.

Zioudrou[234] has demonstrated, however, that N-benzoylphosphoramidate and its p-methyl- and p-nitro-substituted derivatives react with alcohols in the presence of organic bases to give the phosphorylated alcohols. Ethanol, benzyl alcohol, cyclohexanol, phenol, and the hydroxyl group of ethanolamine undergo phosphorylation in good yield. The rate of ethanolysis of N-benzoylphosphoramidate as a function of triethylamine concentration is maximal where N-benzoylphosphoramidate is present as the monoanion, but does not become negligible where the predominant species is the dianion. The rate of ethanolysis of the same compound in the presence of equimolar concentration of bases other than triethylamine is not changed by a factor of more than 4. The variation in pK_a' for these bases ranges from 5.2 for pyridine to 11.2 for piperidine.[247] These results may be rationalized on the grounds that metaphosphate is generated by both the mono- and dianion species of the N-benzoylphosphoramidate. Phosphorylation of ethanol by N-benzoylphosphoramidate also occurs in 2.51 N HCl, possibly through a bimolecular rather than a metaphosphate pathway. Attempts to phosphorylate amines under conditions where N-benzoylphosphoramidate is present as the monoanion

[247] A. Gero and J. J. Markham, *J. Org. Chem.* **16,** 1835 (1951).

resulted only in the recovery of the amine salts of these acids. The reaction of phosphourethane [243] with aniline also results in salt formation.

Halmann and co-workers [243] report attempts to accelerate the rate of phosphourethane monoanion hydrolysis through the addition of metal ions. Ag(I), Cu(II), Ce(III), and La(III) were inactive as catalysts, at pH's where they are not present as hydroxide gels.

There is not sufficient information to allow a meaningful comparison of the reactivity of phosphoramidates with esters of orthophosphoric acid. However, a few points are worthy of mention, such as (1) the sensitivity of PA and ClPhPA monoanions to nucleophilic attack by tertiary heterocyclic bases comparable to that observed for acetyl phosphate monoanion, (2) the inactivity of fluoride ion toward phosphourethane monoanion in contrast to its high nucleophilicity toward acetyl phosphate and PA monoanion, and (3) the possibility of zwitterion formation, which may significantly alter the hydrolytic mechanism of the monoanion as compared to the monoanions of phosphate monoesters. Also significant are the phosphorylating properties of DPI, which structurally must exist in a zwitterion form, further substantiating the claim that the zwitterion of PA and ClPhPA is the reactive species in hydrolysis.

VII. CARBAMYLPHOSPHATE

Interest in carbamylphosphate, $H_2NCO_2PO_3H_2$, is generated by its varied role in enzymic reactions. Biologically, carbamylphosphate appears to be the universal donor [248] of the carbamyl moiety in the biosynthesis of citrulline (5-65) [249] and carbamylaspartate (5-64).[250–252] These two amino acids are essential for the synthesis of arginine and uridylic acid, and therefore, the biosynthesis of protein and nucleic acid.[248] Degradation of citrulline,[253] creatinine,[254] (5-66), and allantoin [255] by microbial enzymes utilizes carbamyl-transfer reactions for energy production yielding ATP, with carbamylphosphate being the first high-energy phosphate intermediate formed. Also of interest is the biological synthesis

[248] M. E. Jones, *Science*, **140**, 1373 (1963).

[249] P. Reichard, *Acta Chem. Scand.* **11**, 523 (1957).

[250] P. Reichard, *Acta Chem. Scand.* **8**, 795 (1954).

[251] J. M. Lowenstein and P. P. Cohen, *J. Am. Chem. Soc.* **76**, 5571 (1954).

[252] M. E. Jones, L. Spector, and F. Lipmann, *Proc. 3rd Intern. Congr. Biochem. Brussels 1955*, p. 278.

[253] M. E. Jones, L. Spector, and F. Lipmann, *J. Am. Chem. Soc.* **77**, 819 (1955).

[254] J. Szulmajster, *Biochim. Biophys. Acta* **44**, 173 (1960).

[255] R. C. Valentine and R. S. Wolfe, *Biochim. Biophys. Acta* **45**, 389 (1960).

$$
\underset{\text{H}_2\text{N}-\overset{\overset{\text{O}}{\|}}{\text{C}}-\text{OPO}_3^{2\ominus}}{} \;+\; \underset{\overset{\oplus}{\text{H}_3\text{N}}-\overset{\overset{\text{COO}^{\ominus}}{|}\,\overset{\text{CH}_2}{|}}{\text{CH}}-\text{COO}^{\ominus}}{} \;\;\xrightleftharpoons{\;\text{aspartate transcarbamylase}\;}\;\; \underset{\text{HN}-\overset{\overset{\text{H}_2\text{N}\ \ \text{COO}^{\ominus}}{}\,\overset{\text{O}=\text{C}\ \ \text{CH}_2}{}}{\text{CH}}-\text{COO}^{\ominus}}{} \;+\;
$$

$$
\text{HPO}_4^{2\ominus} \;+\; \text{H}^{\oplus} \tag{5-64}
$$

$$
\text{H}_2\text{N}-\overset{\overset{\text{O}}{\|}}{\text{C}}-\text{OPO}_3^{2\ominus} \;+\; \overset{\oplus}{\text{H}_3\text{N}}-\overset{\overset{\text{NH}_3^{\oplus}}{|}\,\overset{(\text{CH}_2)_3}{|}}{\text{CH}}-\text{COO}^{\ominus} \;\;\rightleftharpoons\;\; \overset{\text{ornithine transcarbamylase}}{}
$$

$$
\begin{array}{c}\text{NH}_2\\ \text{C}=\text{O}\\ \text{NH}\\ (\text{CH}_2)_3\\ \overset{\oplus}{\text{H}_3\text{N}}-\text{CH}\\ \text{COO}^{\ominus}\end{array} \;+\; \tag{5-65}
$$

$$
\text{HPO}_4^{2\ominus} \;+\; \text{H}^{\oplus}
$$

$$
\begin{array}{c}\text{HN}\\ \text{C}\!-\!\text{NH}\\ \text{CH}_3\!-\!\text{N}\quad\text{C}=\text{O}\\ \text{CH}_2\end{array} \;+\; \text{HPO}_4^{2\ominus} \;\xrightarrow{\text{(enzymes not known)}}\; \longrightarrow\; \text{H}_2\text{N}-\overset{\overset{\text{O}}{\|}}{\text{C}}-\text{OPO}_3^{2\ominus} \;+\; \text{NH}_3
$$

$$
+
$$

$$
\text{CH}_3\text{NH}-\text{CH}_2\text{COO}^{\ominus}
$$

<u>Eubacterium sarcosinogenum</u> (5-66)

of carbamylphosphate, which in microorganisms, plants, and animals proceeds with three entirely different enzyme systems.[248] In uroetelic vertebrates, for example, the enzymic synthesis [256–258] employs the substrate ammonium bicarbonate,[259] and requires 2-moles of ATP and an essential catalytic cofactor, N-acylglutamate.[260] The detailed mechanism is unknown.

[256] S. Grisolia and P. P. Cohen, *J. Biol. Chem.* **198,** 561 (1952).

[257] R. L. Metzenberg, M. Marshall, and P. P. Cohen, *J. Biol. Chem.* **233,** 1560 (1958).

[258] R. L. Metzenberg, M. Marshall, P. P. Cohen, and W. G. Miller, *J. Biol. Chem.* **234,** 1534 (1959).

[259] M. E. Jones and L. Spector, *J. Biol. Chem.* **235,** 2897 (1960).

[260] L. M. Hall, R. L. Metzenberg, and P. P. Cohen, *J. Biol. Chem.* **230,** 1013 (1958).

$$\text{NH}_4\text{HCO}_3 \quad + \quad 2 \text{ ATP}^{4\ominus} \quad \underset{\xleftarrow{\hspace{2cm}}}{\xrightarrow[\text{AGA, Mg(II)}]{\substack{\text{carbamylphosphate} \\ \text{synthetase}}}} \quad \underset{\text{NH}_2\text{COPO}_3^{2\ominus}}{\overset{\overset{\text{O}}{\|}}{}}$$

$$+ \quad 2 \text{ ADP}^{3\ominus} \quad + \quad \text{HPO}_4^{2\ominus} \quad + \quad 2 \text{ H}^{\oplus}$$

$$(5\text{-}67)$$

Nonenzymically, the synthesis of carbamylphosphate by Jones, Spector, and Lipmann [252] is accomplished through condensation of potassium cyanate and potassium dihydrogen phosphate. For example, if a molar solution of the two salts is kept at 30° for half an hour, ca. 50% of the phosphate is in the form of the condensation product, carbamylphosphate. It may be easily isolated by alcohol fractionation as the water-soluble dilithium salt.

Preliminary experiments showed that the nonenzymic decomposition in aqueous solution of carbamylphosphate proceeded through (1) a reversible elimination to produce cyanate and phosphate, and (2) hydrolysis to ammonia, carbon dioxide, and inorganic phosphate.[261] Later a more detailed investigation was conducted by Halmann, Lapidot, and Samuel,[262] but it now appears that many of their major conclusions are probably incorrect due to experimental errors as to the position of bond fission. In (5-68) are summarized the pertinent results obtained by Allen and Jones,[263] and the following discussion generally will present their conclusions ($\mu = 0.6$; 25°).

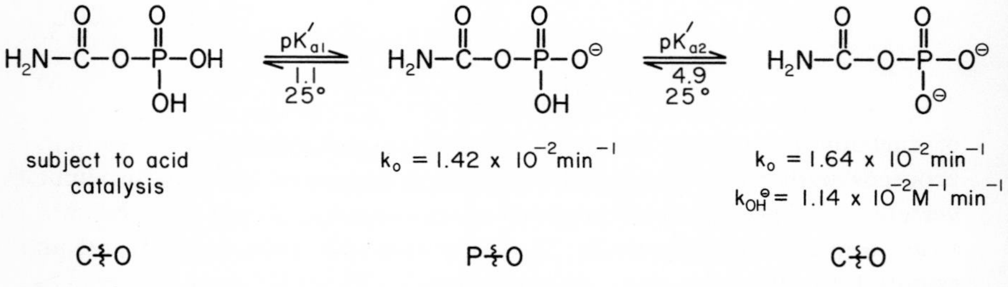

subject to acid catalysis

$k_0 = 1.42 \times 10^{-2} \text{min}^{-1}$

$k_0 = 1.64 \times 10^{-2} \text{min}^{-1}$

$k_{\text{OH}}^{\ominus} = 1.14 \times 10^{-2} \text{M}^{-1}\text{min}^{-1}$

C$\cancel{\ }$O   P$\cancel{\ }$O   C$\cancel{\ }$O

$$(5\text{-}68)$$

The decomposition of the monoanion is proposed as proceeding via unimolecular elimination of carbamic acid to form monomeric meta-

[261] M. E. Jones and F. Lipmann, *Proc. Natl. Acad. Sci. U.S.* **46**, 1194 (1960).
[262] M. Halmann, A. Lapidot, and D. Samuel, *J. Chem. Soc.* 1944 (1962).
[263] C. M. Allen, Jr., and M. E. Jones, *Biochemistry* **3**, 1238 (1964).

phosphate, both species reacting rapidly with water (5-69). It is possible that a cyclic concerted proton transfer occurs, as postulated for acetyl

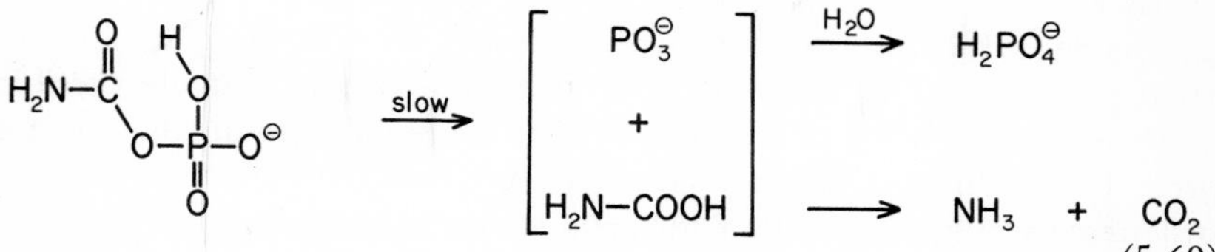

$$(5\text{-}69)$$

phosphate. On the other hand, the decomposition of the dianion very likely proceeds by a unimolecular elimination of cyanic acid and orthophosphate (5-70). The intermediacy of cyanic acid can be demonstrated

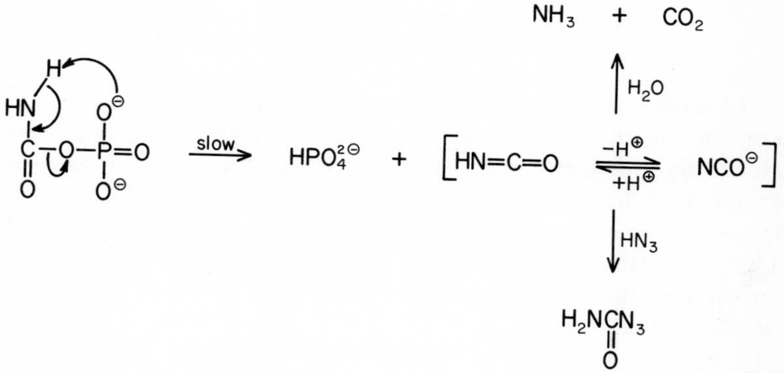

$$(5\text{-}70)$$

by the lag in ammonia release at pH > 4 and its quantitative trapping by azide between pH 2.8 and 6.3. The extent of carbamylazide formation from carbamylphosphate reflects quantitatively the amount of carbamylphosphate dianion present. At more alkaline pH, hydroxide ion abstraction may effectively compete with the intramolecular proton abstraction by phosphate dianion or may displace orthophosphate by direct attack at the carbonyl carbon. The mechanisms by which the neutral species may hydrolyze have not been elucidated, but the limited evidence suggests that the carbamyl product may be either carbamic acid or the carbamyl cation.[262–264]

Various reagents are without effect on the hydrolytic rate of the monoanion at pH 4, including Cu(II), Li(I), CO_2, $F^\ominus$, methylamine

[264] H. K. Hall, *J. Am. Chem. Soc.*, **77**, 5993 (1955).

hydrochloride, and succinate.[262]   Imidazole buffers at pH 7 are simi-larly ineffective toward the dianion.[263]   Molybdate, however, is a signifi-cant catalyst.

In essence, the unusual feature of the decomposition of carbamyl-phosphate is that the dianion hydrolyzes via C—O rather than P—O bond cleavage.   This different mode of decomposition is made possible by the ease of removal of a hydrogen from the amide group which is not present in other acyl phosphates.   The fact that the dianion is the ab-stracting species suggests that the monoanion is not sufficiently basic to do so.   What relevance this may assume in the enzymic reactions is unknown.   Perhaps the most unusual aspect of carbamylphosphate chem-istry at present is its apparent stability toward nucleophilic reagents in nonenzymic systems, whereas the enzymic reactions seemingly involve simple bimolecular displacements.

VIII. OXIDATIVE PHOSPHORYLATION

The great biochemical interest in this area demands at least a cursory survey of the possible phosphorylated derivatives which may serve as high energy intermediates.   No attempt will be made to place these compounds in a mechanistic scheme; let us hope that a future text will take advantage of the furious, at times bewildering, research being pres-ently conducted.   It should prove interesting, however, to examine the known properties of these phosphorylated derivatives, especially in the context of this chapter.

In oversimplified terms, mitochondrial oxidative phosphorylation involves the generation of the pyrophosphate bonds of ATP from inorganic phosphate through operation of enzymic mechanisms for electron transfer to oxygen from pyridine nucleotides or from metabolites such as succi-nate.[265]   A profusion of hypothetical intermediates which are high-energy phosphorylated and nonphosphorylated derivatives of the respiratory chain carriers has been formulated.   Nevertheless, there is at present direct evidence for the existence of only three such intermediates, the first implicating pyridine nucleotides,[266, 267] the second quinones,[268] and the third the amino acid histidine.[269]

[265] J. S. Fruton and S. Simmonds, "General Biochemistry," Wiley, New York, 1958, p. 381.

[266] G. B. Pinchot and M. Hormanski, *Proc. Natl. Acad. Sci. U.S.* **48,** 1970 (1962).

[267] J. L. Purvis, *Biochim. Biophys. Acta* **38,** 435 (1960).

[268] A. F. Brodie and P. J. Russell, *Proc. Intern. Cong. Biochem. 5th Moscow 1961* **5,** 89.

[269] P. D. Boyer, D. E. Hultquist, J. B. Peter, G. Kreil, R. A. Mitchell, M. DeLuca, J. W. Hinkson, L. G. Butler, and R. W. Moyer, *Federation Proc.* **22,** 1080 (1963).

The role of NAD, nicotinamide-adenine dinucleotide, as the functional pyridine nucleotide in oxidative phosphorylation is now firmly established and the evidence has recently been reviewed by Racker [270] and by Slater.[271] Present evidence indicates that one site of oxidative phosphorylation lies between reduced NAD and cytochrome b, and various high-energy derivatives of NAD, formulated as DPN $\sim$ I, DPNH $\sim$ I, and DPNH $\sim$ P, have been postulated as being involved.[270] The first direct evidence for the existence of these derivatives of NAD in mitochondria resulted from the work of Purvis,[267] who reported the presence of a phosphorylated form of NAD which has the properties expected of DPN $\sim$ I.[268, 272] It is not known if the compound is a derivative of the oxidized or the reduced form of NAD. The existence of this form of NAD has been confirmed by Slater et al.[272] and Snoswell.[273] Evidence for a nonphosphorylated high-energy derivative of NAD has also been obtained by Pinchot and Hormanski,[266] but this discussion will center on the phosphorylated intermediate.

Griffiths [274] has recently reported the separation and purification of an NAD from sheep heart mitochondria, which satisfies the biochemist's requirements for a phosphorylated intermediate in oxidative phosphorylation, i.e., it is a phosphorylated derivative of an oxidoreduction component in the respiratory chain, whose formation is dependent on electron transport and from which ATP is formed in an oligomycin-sensitive reaction. The stability or lack of it is indicated by the compound's lability even at neutral pH in the cold (80% decomposition in 5 hr at 0°) and its rapid decomposition in acid and in alkali (35% decomposed in 5 min at pH 1 at 15°, 60% decomposed in 5 min at pH 13 at 15°). The compound decomposes at 0°, yielding NAD and inorganic phosphate as estimated by alcohol dehydrogenase and the Fiske-SubbaRow method. Measurements of the inorganic phosphate and NAD released during the decomposition do not correlate and suggest that other phosphorylated forms of NAD are formed during the nonenzymic breakdown.

Spectral changes during the decomposition of the compound suggest that a modification of the nicotinamide has taken place, the most likely position being the 2-, 4-, or 6-position with the 6-position preferred. However, spectral interpretations leading to the structure of an unknown NAD derivative are rather tenuous (see Chapter 9), consequently the

[270] E. Racker, *Advan. Enzymol.* **23,** 323 (1961).
[271] E. C. Slater, *Rev. Pure Appl. Chem.* **8,** 221 (1958).
[272] E. C. Slater, M. J. Bailie, and J. Bouman, *Biol. Struct. Function Proc. IUB/IUBS Intern. Symp. 1st Stockholm 1960,* p. 207.
[273] A. M. Snoswell, *Biochim. Biophys. Acta* **60,** 143 (1962).
[274] D. E. Griffiths, *Federation Proc.* **22,** 1064 (1963).

fact that 6-amino-NAD is a good inhibitor of the phosphorylated compound [275] constitutes the strongest evidence for modification at the 6-position.

General reaction mechanisms of oxidative phosphorylation involving the phosphorylated 6-position of the nicotinamide ring of NAD have been postulated [276] and involve structures such as (5-71I) and (5-71II). The identity of the discussed intermediate with either of the above awaits further evidence but on the basis of the available data a phosphorylated derivative of $NADH_2$ is indicated. For studies of the addition of anions to N-substituted dihydronicotinamides, the reader is referred to Chapter 9.

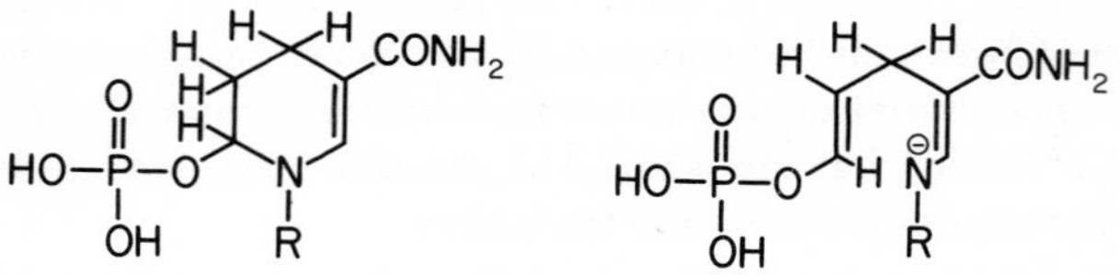

$$(5\text{-}71)$$

The only direct evidence for a phosphorylated quinone intermediate stems from the work of Brodie and Russell [268, 277, 278] on the *Mycobacterium phlei* system. Extracts incubated anaerobically with malate and labeled inorganic phosphate form a compound whose spectrum is similar to that of a chromanol derivative of dihydrovitamin K_1. On nonenzymic decomposition of this compound, the final spectrum obtained is that of the quinone form of vitamin K_1. Although the P^{32}-labeled intermediate, incubated aerobically with ADP and the extract, leads to the synthesis of labeled ATP, its specific activity is only a small fraction of that expected. It cannot yet be concluded that the material is a direct intermediate in oxidative phosphorylation.[279]

Brodie and co-workers [280] have carried their study a step further by synthesizing a 6-chromanol phosphate derivative of vitamin K_1. This

[275] Unpublished results; see ref. 273.
[276] N. O. Kaplan, in P. D. Boyer, H. Lardy, and K. Myrbäck (eds.) "The Enzymes," Academic Press, New York, 1960, Vol. III, Part B, p. 105.
[277] P. J. Russell, Jr., and A. F. Brodie, *Ciba Found. Symp. Quinones Electron Transport 1960*, p. 205.
[278] P. J. Russell, Jr., and A. F. Brodie, *Biochim. Biophys. Acta* **50**, 76 (1961).
[279] A. L. Lehninger and C. L. Wadkins, *Ann. Rev. Biochem.* **31**, 47 (1962).
[280] A. Asano, A. F. Brodie, A. F. Wagner, P. E. Wittreich, and K. Folkers, *Federation Proc.* **21**, 54 (1962).

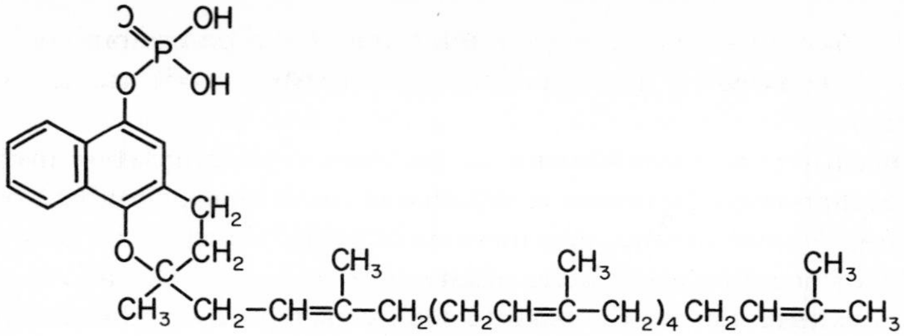

(5-72)

compound in substrate amounts, incubated anaerobically with cyto-chrome c, bacterial extract, and a phosphoryl acceptor, will give rise to ATP formation. The rate of reduction of cytochrome c directly depends on the concentration of the chromanol, the latter being oxidized to vita-min K_1. The activity of this synthetic compound approaches the theo-retical $P/2e^\ominus$ ratio, but its structural identity with that isolated from the bacteria extract still must be confirmed.

Other quinones, suggested as candidates for intermediary roles in oxi-dative phosphorylation, include ubiquinone (coenzyme Q), and α-tocoph-erol. The role of these is open to speculation but the participation of phosphate derivatives of the corresponding cyclized chroman forms appears possible.[281] An example is the above-mentioned vitamin K_1; other similar cyclized forms may be written for the remaining quinones through involvement of the side chain.

Some fascinating "model" studies have been done in the area of quinone phosphates. Clark, Todd, and collaborators[282] and Wieland and Patterman[283] have demonstrated that a variety of quinone phos-phates, while stable to hydrolysis, are quickly decomposed in the presence of oxidizing agents. The 4-hydroxy-3-methyl-1-naphthyl phosphate (5-73) hydrolyzes in aqueous solution, pH 6.8, with a $t_{1/2}$ of $\sim$4 days but undergoes immediate oxidation with aqueous bromine or Ce(III) in

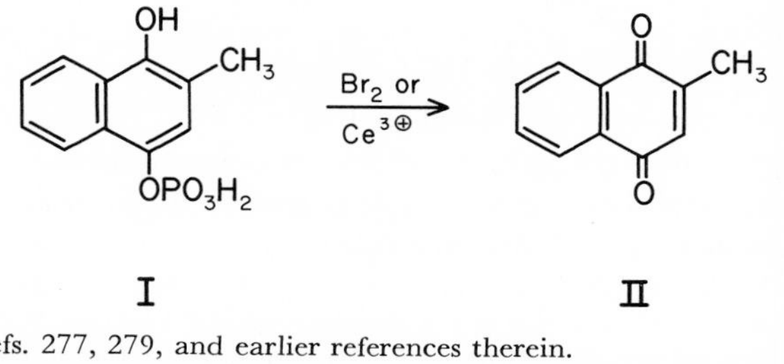

(5-73)

I   II

[281] See refs. 277, 279, and earlier references therein.

[282] V. M. Clark, D. W. Hutchinson, G. W. Kirby, and A. R. Todd, *J. Chem. Soc.* 715 (1961).

[283] T. Wieland and F. Patterman, *Ber.* **92**, 2917 (1959).

$3 N$ H_2SO_4 to give the corresponding quinone.   The bromine oxidation can be carried out in aqueous solution over a wide pH range.   In the presence of added orthophosphate or acetic acid the oxidation leads to the formation of pyrophosphate and acetyl phosphate, respectively. Bromination of the acetylated derivative of (5-73 I) leads to the 2-bromo-3-methyl-1,4-naphthaquinone, in contrast to the behavior of compound I and the corresponding bisphosphate.

It now appears that the oxidative conversion of hydroquinone mono-phosphates occurs via two pathways involving C—O and P—O bond fission, respectively.   The predominant pathway in aqueous or methanolic solution is (5-74b) or (5-74c), which does not involve the generation of metaphosphate.   Tracer studies by Samuel and Lapidot [284] on the bromi-nation of 4-hydroxy-2,3-dimethyl-1-naphthyl phosphate have revealed that P—O bond cleavage accounts for only 35% of the hydrolytic oxida-tion reaction at pH 4 and ca. 60% of the normal hydrolytic reaction. Moreover, Dürckheimer and Cohen [285] have found that oxidation of hydroquinone monophosphate with ceric ion in methanol leads to the dimethyl ketal of p-quinone, path (5-74a) being less than 5% under these reaction conditions.   Furthermore, repetition of the bromine oxida-tion of 3-methyl-1-naphthyl bisphosphate in the presence of added $H_3P^{32}O_4$ indicates that the pyrophosphate product does not have P^{32} incorporated, suggesting an intramolecular reaction between the two phosphate moieties [286] rather than the generation of free metaphosphate as a precursor for pyrophosphate synthesis.

Studies of hydroquinone phosphate oxidations in nonaqueous solvents such as dimethylformamide (DMF) have produced several interesting results.[287, 288]   The bromine oxidation of the above bisphosphate in DMF leads to the synthesis of pyrophosphate and condensed phosphates includ-ing tripolyphosphate, trimetaphosphate, and possibly tetrametaphosphate (ca. 70% of the total phosphate formed).   Moreover, in the presence of added P^{32}-orthophosphate, all of these compounds are radioactive.[287, 288] The incorporation of P^{32}-orthophosphate into these compounds cannot be explained by attack of orthophosphate on metaphosphate, since tri-metaphosphate may not be formed in this manner.   Trimetaphosphate can be generated only via polymerization of metaphosphate or dehydra-tion of tripolyphosphate; the latter does not occur under the reaction conditions.   It also can be demonstrated that the incorporation of P^{32}

[284] A. Lapidot and D. Samuel, *Biochim. Biophys. Acta* **65,** 164 (1962).
[285] W. Dürckheimer and L. A. Cohen, *Biochemistry* **3,** 1948 (1964).
[286] G. E. Tomasi, J. W. Hamilton, and R. D. Dallam, *Federation Proc.* **21,** 53 (1962).
[287] G. E. Tomasi and R. D. Dallam, *J. Biol. Chem.* **239,** 1604 (1964).
[288] A. Lapidot and D. Samuel, *J. Am. Chem. Soc.* **86,** 1886 (1964).

(5-74)

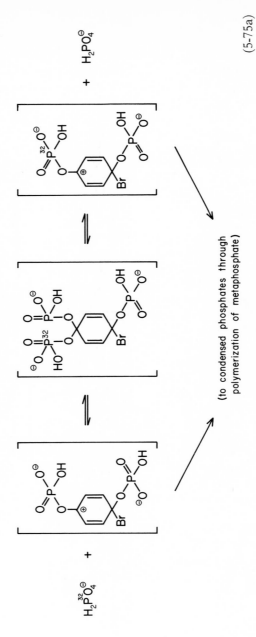

$$(5\text{-}75a)$$

94

(5-75b)

and the formation of condensed phosphates depend on the presence of
DMF in the solvent (in dioxane, no condensed phosphates are found).
These observations suggest the two mechanistic schemes, (5-75a) and
(5-75b), or a combination of both to be operative. In (5-75a) exchange
of orthophosphate takes place at the phosphorylated site of the highly
reactive carbonium ion intermediate, whereas in (5-75b) DMF serves
as the phosphate carrier, exchange taking place at that level. Precedent
for phosphorylated DMF stems from the studies of Cramer and Winter,[289]
who postulate such an addition compound arising from the reaction of
phosphorochloridates with DMF. The addition product reacts with
alcohols, phosphoric acid, and amines to yield esters, pyrophosphate, and
amides, respectively. The exchange of (5-75a), which does not appear
to occur in water, would be favored by the increased nucleophilicity of
anions in DMF.[290] On the basis of present evidence a clear distinction
between these two mechanisms is not possible.

The bromine oxidation in DMF is also of synthetic utility, for example,
oxidation of 4-hydroxy-2,3-dimethyl-1-naphthyl phosphate in DMF in
the presence of adenosine-5'-phosphate, or of the phosphate diester of the
naphthaquinone and 2',3'-O-isopropylideneadenosine in the presence of
inorganic phosphate, gives ADP.[291] Related oxidation reactions are the
later mentioned iodine activation of thiolphosphates and a corresponding
activation of phosphoryl hydrazides.[292] In the latter a diphenylphos-
phoryl hydrazide most likely decomposes in the presence of iodine to a
phosphoryl cation which is then subject to nucleophilic solvolysis.

Another interesting example in quinone chemistry that may have
some bearing on oxidative phosphorylation is the novel cyclization reaction encountered by Folkers and co-workers.[293, 294] They have shown
that the reaction of vitamin K_1 with acetyl chloride in the presence of
water, strong acids, or dihydrovitamin K_1 yields the 5-chloromethyl
derivative (5-76 II). The same product (II) arises from the action of
acetyl chloride on the hydroxyquinone (I). A reasonable explanation
for compound II involves the 1,4-addition of acetyl chloride to the
quinone methine, which may be derived from the acid catalyzed, non-
reductive cyclization of vitamin K_1. Addition of inorganic phosphate

[289] F. Cramer and M. Winter, *Ber.* **94,** 989 (1961).

[290] A. J. Parker, *Quart. Rev. (London)* **16,** 163 (1962).

[291] V. M. Clark, D. W. Hutchinson, and A. R. Todd, *J. Chem. Soc.* 722 (1961).

[292] D. M. Brown and N. K. Hamer, *Proc. Chem. Soc.* 212 (1960).

[293] A. F. Wagner, A. Lusi, C. H. Shunk, B. O. Linn, D. E. Wolf, C. H. Hoffman,
R. E. Erickson, B. Arison, N. R. Trenner, and K. Folkers, *J. Am. Chem. Soc.* **85,** 1534
(1963).

[294] R. E. Erickson, A. F. Wagner, and K. Folkers, *J. Am. Chem. Soc.* **85,** 1535 (1963).

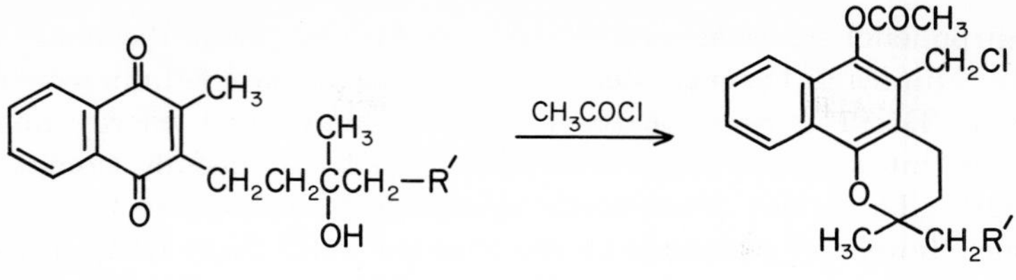

I

II   (5-76)

where $R' = -(CH_2CH_2\overset{CH_3}{\underset{}{CH}}-CH_2)_3H$

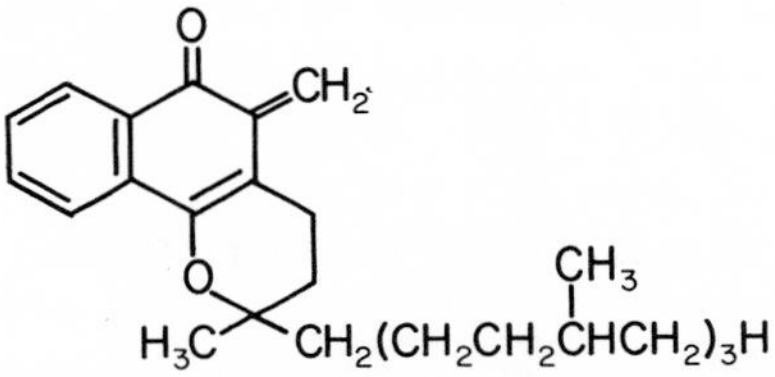

(5-77)

to a quinone methine intermediate, followed then by oxidation of the resulting 6-hydroxy-5-phosphomethyl derivative to give active phosphate, may be of some significance in the biochemical phosphorylation sequence.

Interest in a phosphorylated imidazole group in phosphorylation has been raised by Boyer [269] and his associates. Their studies have indicated the amount of phosphorylated imidazole, present as protein-bound phosphohistidine, to be of the order of 1 part in 500, an estimate derived from the appearance of added labeled orthophosphate in phosphohistidine from intact bovine liver mitochondria. Furthermore, it may be estimated that if the bound phosphohistidine participates in the labeling of all the intramitochondrial ATP by labeled inorganic phosphate, then the phosphorylated imidazole group must have a turnover of roughly 1000 min^{-1}. Boyer *et al.* also suggest that the phosphorylated imidazole may be formed from an activated imidazole structure, possibly an acyl imidazole. The intriguing possibility that the phosphorylated imidazole group may be a high energy intermediate awaits further clarification,[294a] but the unique aspects of reactions of mono- and diphosphorylimidazoles should be recalled.

In connection with the topic of oxidative phosphorylation, it is of interest to briefly mention the phosphate ester of 2,4-dinitrophenol.

[294a] The phosphorylhistidine has been identified as the 3-isomer; however, it does not appear to be involved in oxidative phosphorylation (D. E. Hultquist, R. W. Moyer, and P. D. Boyer, *Biochemistry* 5, 322 (1966)).

2,4-Dinitrophenol serves as an uncoupling agent inhibiting the synthesis of ATP. Hunter [295] has suggested that the formation of 2,4-dinitrophenyl phosphate (DNPP), from the reaction of an active high-energy phosphorylated intermediate with 2,4-dinitrophenol, successfully competes with ADP. The DNPP would then be rapidly hydrolyzed to DNP and inorganic phosphate, arresting in this manner ATP formation without intervening directly in electron transport. Many attempts have been made to isolate DNPP, all without success.[296-298] Recently, however, DNPP has been prepared as the biscyclohexylamine salt by Fendler and Bunton,[298a] who have shown the compound not to be as reactive chemically as previously suggested (see Phosphomonoesters).[299] Nevertheless the precise role of DNP in uncoupling oxidative phosphorylation remains unsettled.[300]

IX. PHOSPHOROTHIOATES

Monoesters of thiols and orthophosphoric acid have been suggested by Walsh [301] as "models" for intermediates in enzymic phosphoryl transfers but evidence for their existence in enzymic systems is weak. S-phosphoryl-CoA has been reported as an intermediate in the enzymic conversion of succinate to succinyl-S-CoA, [302, 303] although attempts to confirm the formation of S-phosphoryl-CoA have been unsuccessful.[304] S-phosphoryl-CoA also has been implicated in acetate activation (5-78) and synthesis of ATP from ADP.[303] However, as pointed out by Jencks,[305] the postulation of such an intermediate (5-78 II) does not aid in elucidating the mechanism of such thiophorase reactions, because the carboxylate group (I) must still undergo, for reaction, loss of one of its oxygen atoms. There is no reason to suppose that the thiolphosphate

[295] F. E. Hunter, Jr., in W. D. McElroy and B. Glass (eds.) "Phosphorus Metabolism," Johns Hopkins Press, Baltimore, 1951, Vol. I, p. 297.

[296] R. Wittmann, *Ber.* **96,** 2116 (1963).

[297] V. H. Parker, *Biochem. J.* **69,** 306 (1958).

[298] P. D. Boyer, *Proc. Intern. Symp. Enzyme Chem. Tokyo Kyoto 1958*, p. 301.

[298a] E. J. Fendler and C. A. Bunton, private communication.

[299] R. Azerad, D. Gautheron, and M. Vilkas, *Bull. Soc. Chim. France* 2078 (1963).

[300] R. H. Eisenhardt and O. Rosenthal, *Science* **143,** 476 (1964).

[301] E. O' F. Walsh, *Nature* **169,** 546 (1952).

[302] R. A. Smith, I. F. Frank, and I. C. Gunsalus, *Federation Proc.* **16,** 251 (1957).

[303] M. Wollemann and G. Feuer, *Proc. Intern. Symp. Enzyme Chem. Tokyo Kyoto 1958*, p. 191.

[304] R. Nordlie and H. Lardy, in P. D. Boyer, H. Lardy, and K. Myrbäck (eds.) "The Enzymes," Academic Press, New York, 1962, Vol. VI, p. 19.

[305] W. P. Jencks, *Ann. Rev. Biochem.* **32,** 663 (1963).

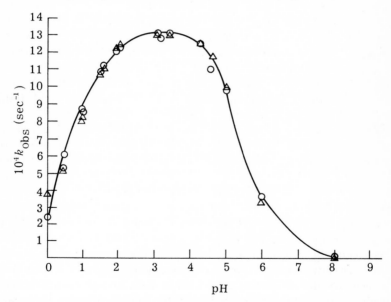

$$CH_3-\overset{\overset{\displaystyle O}{\|}}{C}-O^{\ominus} \quad + \quad CoA-S-\overset{\overset{\displaystyle O}{\|}}{\underset{\underset{\displaystyle O^{\ominus}}{|}}{P}}-O^{\ominus} \quad \rightleftharpoons \quad CH_3-\overset{\overset{\displaystyle O}{\|}}{C}-SCoA \quad + \quad PO_4^{3\ominus}$$

$$\qquad\quad I \qquad\qquad\qquad\quad II \qquad\qquad\qquad\qquad\qquad\qquad\quad (5\text{-}78)$$

intermediates are any more effective as dehydrating agents than the ATP from which they were formed. Other mono S-phosphoryl derivatives may be involved in the enzymic reduction of amino acids.[306] Consequently for our purposes this discussion will be restricted principally to thiolphosphate monoesters.

Among the earlier studies in this area was the establishment of the pH-rate profile for the hydrolysis of *S-n*-butylphosphorothioate by Koshland and Herr.[307] Their results are essentially in agreement with a later profile developed by Dittmer and co-workers [308] (Fig. 5-11). The bell

Fig. 5-11 *pH rate profile for the hydrolysis of S-n-butylphosphorothioate at 37.1°, 1 M ionic strength:* ○, *observed;* △, *calculated.* (*Ref. 308.*)

[306] T. Stadtman, P. Elliott, and L. Tiemann, *J. Biol. Chem.* **231,** 961 (1958).

[307] E. B. Herr, Jr., and D. E. Koshland, Jr., *Biochim. Biophys. Acta* **25,** 219 (1957).

[308] D. C. Dittmer, O. B. Ramsay, and R. E. Spalding, *J. Org. Chem.* **28,** 1273 (1963).

shape of the profile is similar to that observed for other phosphate monoesters for which the monoanion is the most reactive species. A similar
maximal behavior, ca. pH 4, has been observed in the hydrolysis of
S-(2-aminoethyl)phosphorothioate,[318] S-(1-carboxyethyl)- and S-(2-car-
boxyethyl)phosphorothioate,[309] cysteamine S-phosphate,[310] and phosphorothioic acid.[311] The hydrolysis of each species of S-n-butylphos-
phorothioate represented in (5-79) will be treated separately, and should
adequately serve to illustrate the general characteristics of thiolphosphate
ester hydrolysis:

$$n\text{-BuSPO}_3\text{H}_2 \xrightleftharpoons{K'_{a_1}} n\text{-BuSPO}_3\text{H}^{\ominus} + \text{H}^{\oplus} \xrightleftharpoons{K'_{a_2}} n\text{-BuSPO}_3{}^{\ominus} + \text{H}^{\oplus} \quad (5\text{-}79)$$

The pK'_{a_1} of S-n-butylphosphorothioate is somewhat smaller than the
pK'_{a_1} of the corresponding oxygen esters (1.0 versus 1.9 at 25°), although
the measurements are not at identical ionic strength. The assumption
of a greater acidity for the thiolester derives additional support from a
comparison of pK'_{a_2} values (5.5 versus 6.8 for the oxygen ester), but the
generality of this assumption awaits further data.

In contrast to the oxygen esters of orthophosphoric acid, the neutral
species of this particular thiolester hydrolyzes with only P—S bond
cleavage. Similar results are found in the acid and alkaline hydrolysis
of tri-(S-ethyl)phosphorotrithioate[312] and of di-(S-isopropyl)-methyl-
phosphonodithioate.[313] Likewise the hydrolysis of the neutral species
of S-(2-aminoethyl)phosphorothioate in 1 M perchloric acid results
strictly in a P—S bond fission.[314] Dittmer has surmised that this apparently general selective cleavage of the P—S bond may arise from the
absence of resonance in the sulfur derivatives in contrast to an electron
distribution in oxygen esters which may predispose them to C—O bond

$$\text{ROPO}_3\text{H}_2 \leftrightarrow \text{R}\overset{\oplus}{\text{O}}=\overset{\ominus}{\text{PO}}_3\text{H}_2 \quad (5\text{-}80)$$

cleavage.

The rate of hydrolysis of the neutral species of S-n-butylphosphoro-
thioate decreases in increasing acidic medium (3-10 M HCl or HClO$_4$).
In contrast, the rate of hydrolysis of phosphorothioic acid is increased
with increasing acidity. For both compounds there is experimental
evidence that the addition of salts, LiCl or KCl, at a given acidity qualitatively causes a directional change in the hydrolytic rates identical to

[309] S. Akerfeldt, *Acta Chem. Scand.* **15,** 575 (1961).
[310] S. Akerfeldt, *Acta Chem. Scand.* **14,** 1980 (1960).
[311] D. C. Dittmer and O. B. Ramsay, *J. Org. Chem.* **28,** 1268 (1963).
[312] E. Thain, *J. Chem. Soc.* 4694 (1957).
[313] R. F. Hudson and L. Keay, *J. Chem. Soc.* 3269 (1956).
[314] S. Akerfeldt, *Acta Chem. Scand.* **13,** 1479 (1959).

that observed upon increasing the acid concentration. The salt LiCl, for example, accelerates the rate of hydrolysis in strong acid of phosphoro-thioic acid and retards that of S-n-butylphosphorothioate. Therefore, although conversion to a conjugate acid species may be also postulated, Dittmer and collaborators prefer a rationale based on ionic strength effects.   Intervention of the conjugate acid in the case of S-n-butylphos-phorothioate requires an unusually low ionization constant ($pK'_a = 1.3$) in order to fit the experimental data to such an assumption.   It should be realized that for the solution temperatures at which hydrolysis of the oxygen esters is experimentally feasible, the acidic hydrolysis of phosphates is   extremely   rapid.   The   hydrolysis   of S-n-propyl-phosphorothioate in normal HCl at 100° is complete in 7 minutes.

Hydrolysis of the monoanions of the thiolphosphates also is extremely rapid in relation to their oxygen counterparts.   For S-n-butylphosphoro-thioate the specific rate constant for the monoanion is 1.31×10^{-3} sec^{-1} ($T = 37.1°$, $\mu = 1.0$).   This may be due in part to the smaller P—S bond energy (P—S, 45–50 kcal mole^{-1}; P—O, 95–100 kcal mole^{-1}),[311] which is then reflected in a lower energy of activation, E_a for S-n-butyl-phosphorothioate being 23.8 kcal mole^{-1}, $\Delta S^{\ddagger} = +3.08$ e.u.   Yet in the alkaline hydrolysis of triethylphosphorotrithioate, which is 1500 times faster than triethyl phosphate, the difference is solely in $\Delta S^{\ddagger}$.[312]   While there is no reason to propose a unique new mechanism for thiol monoester hydrolysis some attention should be focused on a bimolecular postulation in addition to the aforementioned monoester mechanisms involving monomeric metaphosphate.   The following mechanism, originally postu-lated for the S-n-butylphosphorothioate monoanion by Herr and Kosh-land, features a concerted acid-base catalysis activating both nucleophile and substrate [307] in order to rationalize the unusual velocity of the reac-tion.   Such a mechanism can be equally employed for monoesters of

$$H_2O \; + \; RSPO_3H^{\ominus} \; \longrightarrow \; \longrightarrow \qquad (5\text{-}81)$$

$$RSH \; + \; H_2PO_4^{\ominus}$$

orthophosphoric acid, although undeniably the available data are strongly in favor of a metaphosphate mechanism.   However, the possibility that the mechanism is actually a borderline situation cannot be excluded on the basis of present evidence.

In the dianion region, S-n-butylphosphorothioate and S-(1-carboxy-ethyl)- and S-(2-carboxyethyl)phosphorothioates, like other phosphate esters, are unreactive.   In contrast, the dianion of phosphorothioic acid does show reactivity, albeit small, 3.81×10^{-5} sec^{-1} at 37° or one fifth of that for the corresponding monoanion.   The hydrolysis is ascribed to a specific hydration of the acid which orients a water molecule for attack on the phosphorus atom.   The reported alkaline lability of S-(2-amino-ethyl)phosphorothioate probably is in error.[308, 315]

S-n-Butylphosphorothioate under acid and neutral conditions in the presence of methanol, ethanol, n-butanol, i-butanol, and phenol will transfer its phosphoryl group, forming the corresponding phosphorylated alcohol.[316]   Similar transfers have been effected to acetic acid [316] and inorganic phosphate,[317] yielding acetyl phosphate and pyrophosphate, respectively.   Whether these reactions (in nonaqueous media) are direct nucleophilic displacements on phosphorus, or represent trapping a meta-phosphate intermediate, has not been elucidated.   Other reagents, namely, the nitrogenous bases pyridine, 2,6-lutidine, and imidazole, do not appear to react with the ester in aqueous solution.   At pH 3.25, $\mu = 1$, addition of Mn(II), Ni(II), Mg(II), and Zn(II) has a negligible effect on the rate.[308]

A further aspect of thiolphosphates appears in the phosphorylation of alcohols by S-n-butylphosphorothioate in alkaline solution, which will not occur unless iodine is added.[316]   Activation of thiolesters by either bromine [318] or iodine is an interesting example of oxidative activation. Cysteamine S-phosphate [310] and the two isomeric S-carboxyethylphos-phorothioic acids are similarly oxidized by iodine to the corresponding disulfides.   The reaction between a 1:1 ratio of molar equivalents at pH ca. 2 is almost instantaneous.   At pH's below ca. 1, complete decolor-ization of the iodine requires more than 2.5 hours.   The proposed scheme [316, 318] for this process is illustrated in (5-82) for the bromine oxidation of cysteamine S-phosphate, for which all of the above com-pounds, excluding the sulfenyl bromide, have been detected through paper chromatographic analysis.

It is also meaningful to point out that C—S bond cleavage may indeed be possible in the presence of properly oriented nucleophilic groups.   The hydrolysis of S-(2-ethylthioethyl)dimethylphosphorothioate (I) results in the appearance of phosphorothioate ion and probably a cyclic sulfonium ion (5-83).   Identical products are formed from the hydrolytic decom-

[315] Experimental evidence which indicates that neighboring amino groups are unreactive toward thiolphosphates may be found in S. Akerfeldt, *Acta Chem. Scand.* **17,** 319 (1963).

[316] T. Wieland and R. Lambert, *Ber.* **89,** 2476 (1956).

[317] D. C. Dittmer and O. Silverstein, *J. Org. Chem.* **26,** 4706 (1961).

[318] S. Akerfeldt, *Acta Chem. Scand.* **16,** 1897 (1962).

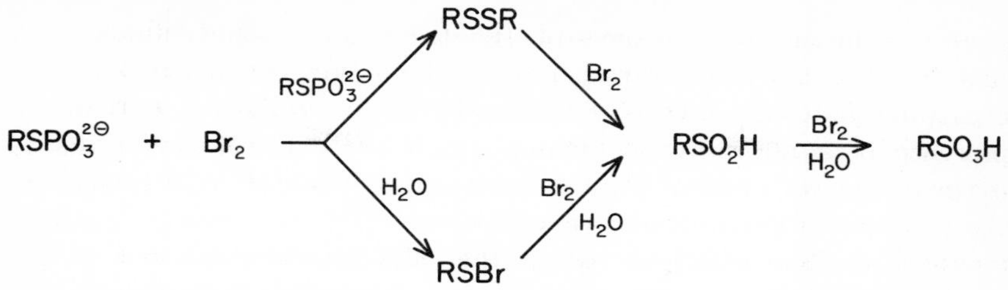

$$\text{RSPO}_3^{2\ominus} + \text{Br}_2 \quad \underset{H_2O}{\overset{RSPO_3^{2\ominus}}{\nearrow}} \quad \overset{RSSR}{\underset{Br_2}{}} \quad \overset{Br_2}{\searrow} \quad RSO_2H \xrightarrow[\text{H}_2\text{O}]{Br_2} RSO_3H$$

where $R = \overset{\oplus}{N}H_3CH_2CH_2-$

$$(5\text{-}82)$$

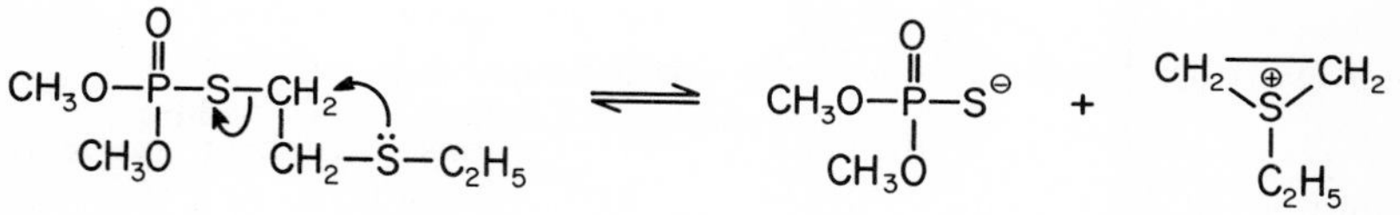

I

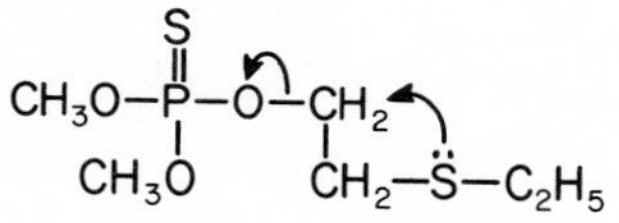

II

$$(5\text{-}83)$$

position of (2-ethylthioethyl)dimethylphosphorothionate (II). The above equilibrium lies to the left, favoring synthesis of I. An analogous intramolecular nucleophilic displacement is visualized for the S-(2-diethylaminoethyl)diethylphosphorothioate.[319] Intramolecular nucleophilic attack might be an explanation for the reported instability of S-phosphoryl-CoA, at least in alkaline solutions.[320]

X. ENOL PHOSPHATES [321]

In view of the biochemical interest in phosphoenol pyruvate (PEP), some consideration is due this class of phosphates. Several of the important enzymic reactions of PEP include (1) condensations with sugar phos-

[319] J. I. G. Cadogan and L. C. Thomas, *J. Chem. Soc.* 2248 (1960).
[320] G. Feuer and M. Wollemann, *Acta Physiol. Acad. Sci. Hung.* **10,** 1 (1956).
[321] F. W. Lichtenthaler, *Chem. Rev.* **61,** 607 (1961).

phates such as D-erythrose-4-phosphate [322] and D-arabinose-5-phosphate [323] to yield the corresponding 2-keto-3-deoxyaldonic acid and orthophosphate; (2) reversible carboxylation to oxaloacetic acid in the presence of a nucleoside polyphosphate; [324-326] and (3) conversion to pyruvic acid with concomitant transphosphorylation of ADP to ATP in the presence of the enzyme pyruvate kinase.[327] Nonenzymic "models" for these reactions will be stressed in the following discussion.

The hydrolysis of various dialkyl vinyl phosphates has been examined in strongly alkaline and acidic solutions. In 0.5 N potassium hydroxide at 80° or in barium hydroxide at 100°, hydrolysis proceeds with cleavage of only the enol ester linkage. Exact measurements of rates of

$$
(RO)_2\overset{O}{\underset{\|}{P}}-O-C=C \quad \xrightarrow{OH^{\ominus}} \quad (RO)_2\overset{O}{\underset{\|}{P}}-O^{\ominus} \quad + \quad \underset{O}{C}-CH \qquad (5\text{-}84)
$$

hydrolysis at varying hydroxyl-ion concentrations have been made for a number of dialkyl vinyl phosphates,[328-332] and are listed in Table 5-10.

A possibly related hydrolysis is that of dimethylphosphoacetoin in the pH range 7.7–8.3, which gives acetoin and dimethyl hydrogen phosphate and proceeds at least 10,000 times faster than that of triethyl phosphate. Although Ramirez and co-workers suggest that this reaction might be

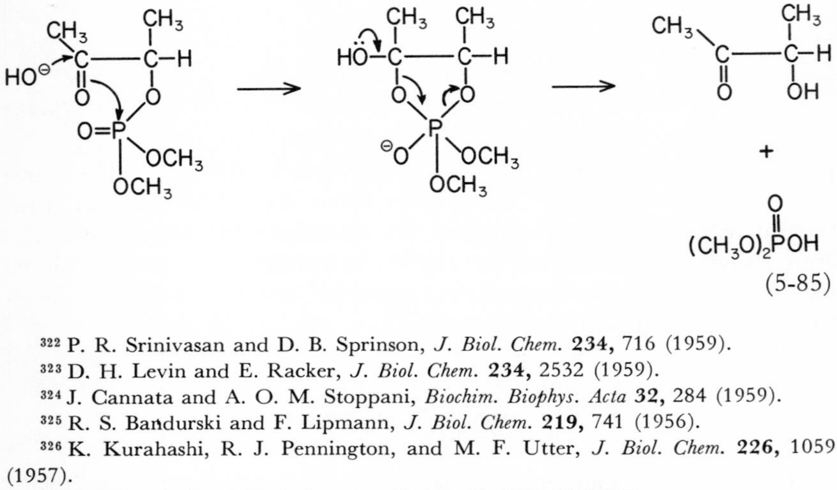

$$(5\text{-}85)$$

[322] P. R. Srinivasan and D. B. Sprinson, *J. Biol. Chem.* **234,** 716 (1959).

[323] D. H. Levin and E. Racker, *J. Biol. Chem.* **234,** 2532 (1959).

[324] J. Cannata and A. O. M. Stoppani, *Biochim. Biophys. Acta* **32,** 284 (1959).

[325] R. S. Bandurski and F. Lipmann, *J. Biol. Chem.* **219,** 741 (1956).

[326] K. Kurahashi, R. J. Pennington, and M. F. Utter, *J. Biol. Chem.* **226,** 1059 (1957).

[327] O. Meyerhof and K. Lohmann, *Biochem. Z.* **293,** 60 (1934).

[328] B. W. Arthur and J. E. Casida, *J. Agr. Food Chem.* **5,** 186 (1957).

[329] J. E. Casida, *Science* **122,** 597 (1955).

[330] J. E. Casida, *J. Agr. Food Chem.* **4,** 772 (1956).

[331] J. E. Casida, *J. Econ. Entomol.* **52,** 270 (1959).

[332] H. C. Chapman, *Mosquito News* **15,** 204 (1955).

Table 5-10 *   *Hydrolysis of dialkyl vinyl phosphates* [a]

	$t_{1/2}$ (hr)	
Ester	Trans [b] isomer	Cis isomer
$(CH_3O)_2P(O)OC(CH_3)=CHCOOCH_3$	1.8	3.0
$(C_2H_5O)_2P(O)OC(CH_3)=CHCOOC_2H_5$	3.4	8.9
$(C_2H_5O)_2P(O)OCH=CHCl$	6.0	11.0
$(CH_3O)_2P(O)OCH=CCl_2$	0.2	0.2

* Ref. 321.
[a] pH 11, 28°.
[b] Trans refers to

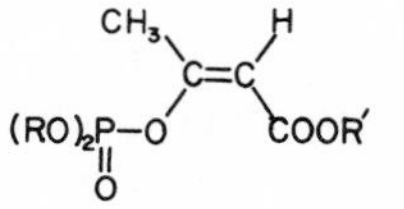

an example of oxyphosphorane participation,[333] they emphasize the possibility that an intervening enol phosphate may be responsible for the hydrolytic acceleration which is probably the case from the observed products (5-86). Evidence for expulsion of dimethyl phosphate anion by

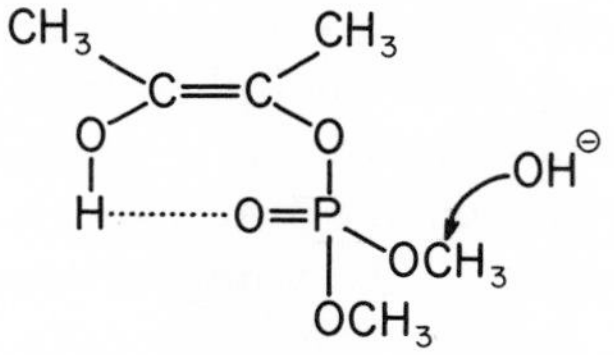

(5-86)

backside attack on the α-carbon by the oxyanion formed by addition of $OH^{\ominus}$ to $>C=0$ (5-86a) has been recently reported.[333a] Dialkyl vinyl phosphates display a remarkable stability toward water. Diethyl

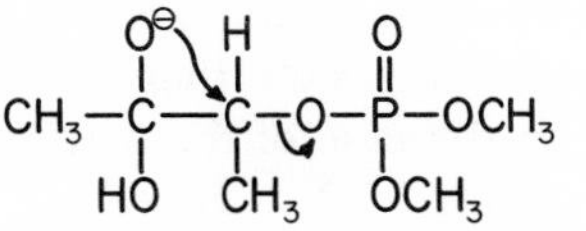

(5-86a)

1-phenylvinyl phosphate, for example, is only 11% hydrolyzed after 20 hr at 100° in 30% aqueous ethanol.[334] An exception is the ketene acylal,

[333] F. Ramirez, B. Hansen, and N. B. Desai, *J. Am. Chem. Soc.* **84,** 4588 (1962).
[333a] H. Witzel, A. Botta, and K. Dimroth, *Ber.* **98,** 1465 (1965).
[334] A. N. Pudovik, *Zh. Obshch. Khim.* **25,** 2173 (1955).

diethyl 2-carbethoxy-1-ethoxyvinyl phosphate, which undergoes spontane-ous hydrolysis at room temperature.[335]

The course of acid hydrolysis of the dialkyl vinyl phosphate is de-pendent upon the strength of the acid used. With hydrochloric acid (1:1) [334, 336] and 30% sulfuric acid,[334, 337—339] total hydrolysis of all ester groups occurs, forming mainly alkyl chloride, phosphoric acid, and the corresponding ketone. Under milder conditions, however, selective

$$
\underset{(RO)_2\,\overset{O}{\underset{\|}{P}}-O}{\diagup}C=C\diagup \quad \xrightarrow{\text{HCl}} \quad RCl \;+\; H_3PO_4 \;+\; \diagup C-\overset{\diagup}{\underset{O}{C}}H \quad (5\text{-}87)
$$

hydrolysis of the enol ester group can be accomplished, yielding the dialkyl hydrogen phosphate and the corresponding carbonyl compound. Table 5-11 lists the rates of hydrolysis of various diethyl vinyl phosphates under mild acidic conditions revealing, with the exception of diethyl 2-carbethoxy-1-ethoxyvinyl phosphate, that none of the investigated diethyl vinyl phosphates is expected to be hydrolyzed to an appreciable extent at room temperature. Nevertheless the rate of hydrolysis of the non-enolic triethyl phosphate is considerably less than that of the most unreactive vinyl phosphate. Inspection of Table 5-11 also reveals that substitution on the vinyl groups at the 1-position accelerates the rate of hydrolysis in the order $CH_3 > C_6H_5 > COOC_2H_5 > H$. The first and fourth phosphates of Table 5-11 are classified as ketene acylals, which may be regarded as the most reactive enol phosphates.

Other than the pseudo-first-order rate constants already mentioned, further quantitative studies on the hydrolytic reactions of this class of compounds are not numerous. Quantitative determination of the second-order rate constants for acid catalysis is complicated by the susceptibility of certain enol phosphates to autocatalysis by the liberated diethyl hydro-gen phosphate.[335] Yet the detection of pyrophosphates formed during the acidolysis indicates strongly that cleavage occurs at the phosphorus-oxygen bond of the enol ester group. Furthermore, comparison of the relative rates of hydrolysis of ethyl and vinyl acetates [340, 341] and triethyl and diethyl vinyl phosphates shows that there are more pronounced differences in reactivity in the case of the diethyl phosphates than in the corresponding acetates (Table 5-12). Since the hydrolysis of both of the

[335] F. W. Lichtenthaler and F. Cramer, Ber. **95**, 1971 (1962).
[336] P. I. Alimov and I. V. Cheplanova, Chem. Abstr. **54**, 6520 (1960).
[337] A. N. Pudovik and V. P. Avery'anova, Zh. Obshch. Khim. **26**, 1426 (1956).
[338] A. N. Pudovik and L. G. Biktimirova, Zh. Obshch. Khim. **28**, 1496 (1958).
[339] A. N. Pudovik and T. M. Moshkina, Zh. Obshch. Khim. **27**, 1611 (1957).
[340] A. Skrabal and A. Zahorka, Monatsh. Chem. **48**, 459 (1927).
[341] A. Skrabal and A. Zahorka, Monatsh. Chem. **53/54**, 562 (1929).

Table 5-11 *   *Rates of hydrolysis of diethyl vinyl phosphates in 0.1 N hydrochloric acid–40% ethanol at 85°*

Diethyl vinyl phosphate	$k \times 10^3$ (min^{-1})	$t_{1/2}$ (hr)
$(C_2H_5O)_2POC$=$CHCOOC_2H_5$ $\quad\ \overset{\|}{O}\ \ \overset{\|}{OC_2H_5}$	130	0.1
$(C_2H_5O)_2POC$=CH_2 $\quad\ \overset{\|}{O}\ \ \overset{\|}{CH_3}$	14.88	0.78
$(C_2H_5O)_2POC$=CH_2 $\quad\ \overset{\|}{O}\ \ \overset{\|}{C_6H_5}$	6.46	1.79
$(C_2H_5O)_2POC$=CCl_2 $\quad\ \overset{\|}{O}\ \ \overset{\|}{OC_2H_5}$	3.77	3.06
$(C_2H_5O)_2POC$=CH_2 $\quad\ \overset{\|}{O}\ \ \overset{\|}{COOC_2H_5}$	2.38 [a]	4.86
$(C_2H_5O)_2POCH$=CCl_2 $\quad\ \overset{\|}{O}$	1.34	8.56
$(C_2H_5O)_2POCH$=$CHCOOC_2H_5$ $\quad\ \overset{\|}{O}$	0.99 [a]	11.71
$(C_2H_5O)_2POC_2H_5$ $\quad\ \overset{\|}{O}$	0.037	308.7

* Ref. 335.

[a] k is probably high for these esters due to simultaneous hydrolysis of —$COOC_2H_5$.

Table 5-12 *   *Comparative rates of hydrolysis of ethyl and vinyl acetates*

Ester	$k \times 10^{-3}$ (min^{-1})	Relative rate	Ref.
$(C_2H_5O)_2P(O)OCH_2CH_3$	0.037	12.45	335
$(C_2H_5O)_2P(O)OCH$=CH_2	0.46		335
$CH_3C(O)OCH_2CH_3$	6.58	1.23	342
$CH_3C(O)OCH$=CH_2	8.13		341

* Ref. 321.

acetates involves acyl-oxygen bond scission, the unexpected large difference in the rates of hydrolysis of the corresponding phosphates suggests
that hydrolysis of the diethyl vinyl phosphate proceeds with phosphorus-
oxygen bond rupture.   It should be recalled that uncatalyzed hydrolysis
of triethyl phosphate involves cleavage of only the carbon-oxygen bond.
These observations have led Lichtenthaler and Cramer to postulate the
following possible mechanism for acid hydrolysis of the dialkyl vinyl
phosphates [335]:

$$ (RO)_2 \overset{\overset{O}{\|}}{P}-O \underset{H^{\oplus}}{\overset{\diagdown}{C}=C\diagup} \qquad \qquad \text{(5-88)} $$
$$ R'O^{\ominus} $$

where R' = H, PO(OR)$_2$, C(O)R

The hydrolysis in either alkaline or acid medium of secondary phosphates containing a vinyl ester group has received scant attention, although it appears that cleavage of the enol ester group in acid medium
is easier than in the corresponding dialkylated compound.   A similar
situation prevails for the vinyl dihydrogen phosphates, although the
pseudo-first-order rate constant for the hydrolysis of PEP in 1 N hydrochloric acid at 100° has been determined by many investigators [342, 343]
as 3.5×10^{-3} ($t_{1/2} = 8.6$ min).

As indicated in the proposed mechanism for the acid hydrolysis of
dialkyl vinyl phosphates, reaction with carboxylic acids and substituted
phosphoric acids should lead to the respective acyl phosphates and pyrophosphates.   The most acid-labile enol phosphate, diethyl 2-carbethoxy-
1-ethoxyvinyl phosphate, reacts easily at room temperature, with carboxylic acids giving the corresponding acyl phosphates.[344–346]   Reaction
of the same compound with adenosine monophosphate for 12–15 hr at
37° gives a 90% yield of O,O-diethyl adenosine diphosphate isolated as
the sodium salt.[344, 345]   Such reactions with other enol phosphates and
various alkyl dihydrogen phosphates may serve as "models" for the
enzymic transphosphorylation reactions.   Replacement of the proton
of (5-88) with I$^{\oplus}$ [327] or Br$^{\oplus}$,[181] causing phosphate release and formation
of the halogenated carbonyl derivative, has been cited as a "model" for

[342] E. Cherbuliez and J. Rabinowitz, *Helv. Chim. Acta* **39,** 1461 (1956).
[343] W. Kiessling, *Ber.* **68,** 597 (1935).
[344] F. Cramer, *Angew. Chem.* **72,** 239 (1960).
[345] F. Cramer and K. G. Gärtner, *Ber.* **91,** 704 (1958).
[346] F. Cramer and R. Wittmann, *Angew. Chem.* **72,** 628 (1960).

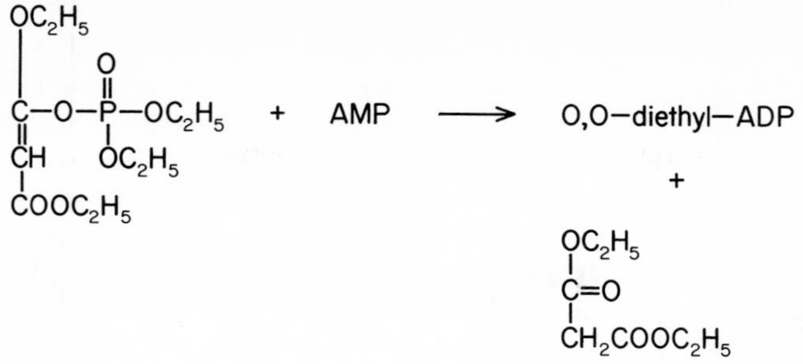

$$
\begin{array}{c}
\overset{\displaystyle OC_2H_5}{\underset{\displaystyle \underset{\displaystyle COOC_2H_5}{\overset{\displaystyle \|}{CH}}}{\overset{\displaystyle |}{\underset{\displaystyle \|}{C}}}\text{—O—}\overset{\displaystyle O}{\underset{\displaystyle OC_2H_5}{\overset{\displaystyle \|}{P}}}\text{—}OC_2H_5
\end{array}
\quad + \quad AMP \quad \longrightarrow \quad O,O\text{—diethyl—}ADP
$$

$$+$$

$$
\begin{array}{c}
OC_2H_5 \\
| \\
C=O \\
| \\
CH_2COOC_2H_5
\end{array}
$$

(5-89)

the enzymic carboxylation of PEP in which the electrophilic reagent is carbon dioxide and the phosphate acceptor is a nucleoside diphosphate, inorganic phosphate, or water.[326, 347, 348, 349]

[347] R. S. Bandurski and C. M. Greiner, *J. Biol. Chem.* **204**, 781 (1953).

[348] P. M. L. Siu, H. G. Wood, and R. L. Stjernholm, *J. Biol. Chem.* **236**, 21PC (1961).

[349] After this chapter was completed, two reviews appeared which are worthy of mention; the first emphasizes mechanisms of nucleophilic displacements on phosphorus: J. R. Cox, Jr., and O. B. Ramsay, *Chem. Rev.* **64**, 317 (1964); the second the design of phosphorylating agents: V. M. Clark, D. W. Hutchinson, A. J. Kirby, and S. G. Warren, *Angew. Chem. Intern. Ed. Engl.* **3**, 678 (1964).

chapter
six

Phosphoro- and Phosphonohalides

I. INTRODUCTION

In this chapter, mechanistic studies will be discussed which deal with compounds of the general formula:

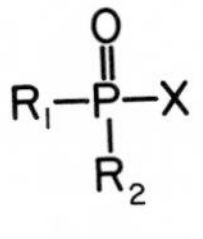

$$R_1-\overset{\displaystyle O}{\underset{\displaystyle R_2}{\overset{\|}{\underset{|}{P}}}}-X \qquad (6\text{-}1)$$

where R_1 and R_2 are alkyl, alkoxy, alkylthio, or alkylamino groups, and X is fluoride, chloride, or cyanide. Representative of this class are isopropyl methylphosphonofluoridate (R_1 = Me-, R_2 = i-PrO-, X = F; Sarin), diisopropyl phosphorofluoridate (R_1 = R_2 = i-PrO-, X = F; DFP), diisopropyl phosphorochloridate (R_1 = R_2 = i-PrO-, X = Cl; DClP) and ethyl N,N-dimethylphosphoramidocyanidate (R_1 = (Me)$_2$N-,

$R_2 = $ EtO-, $X = $ CN; Tabun). Surveys of the chemistry and toxicology of these and related compounds are available.[1-5]

Organophosphorus compounds of the structure (6-1) are in general very toxic because of their inhibitory effect on the cholinesterases, and the more potent members are commonly referred to as "nerve gases." As cited in a preceding chapter, cholinesterases, chymotrypsin, trypsin, liver esterase, milk lipase, and thrombin are inhibited as a result of chemical reaction with DFP.[6-11] For cholinesterase, chymotrypsin, and trypsin, an O-phosphorylserine was isolated upon degradation of the enzyme [12, 13] (Volume I, Chapter 2). Sarin, N,N,N',N'-tetramethylphosphorodiamidic fluoride ($R_1 = R_2 = (CH_3)_2N$, $X = F$), Tabun, and their analogs likewise are potent inhibitors of esterases; a more complete listing of various enzymes and their respective inhibitors has been given by Aldridge.[14] It is interesting to note that compounds in which $X = Cl$ are of negligible toxicity *in vivo*. Several theories, whose common features were summarized by Saunders,[2] have been offered to explain the structural requirement of compounds (6-1) for antiesterase activity, but no single one proves completely satisfactory.

The reaction of reagents of type (6-1) with an enzyme representative of the class of serine esterases has been discussed (Chapter 2); thus we will confine our considerations to the general mechanisms of displacement reactions on these compounds. Such studies have led, for example, to the elaboration of suitable methods for reactivation of the inhibited enzyme, to the implication of the possible functional groups at the "active

[1] G. Schrader, "Die Entwicklung neuer Insektizide auf Grundlage organischer Fluor-und Phosphor-Verbundungen," 2 Aufl. Verlag Chemie, Weinheim, 1952.

[2] B. C. Saunders, "Phosphorus and Fluorine. The Chemistry and Toxic Action of their Organic Compounds," Cambridge University Press, Cambridge, 1957.

[3] G. M. Kosolapoff, "Organophosphorus Compounds," Wiley, New York, 1950.

[4] T. R. Fukuto in R. L. Metcalf (ed.) "Advances in Pest Control Research," Interscience, New York, 1957, Vol. I, p. 147.

[5] R. D. O'Brien, "Toxic Phosphorus Esters-Chemistry, Metabolism and Biological Effects," Academic Press, New York, 1960.

[6] E. F. Jansen, M. D. F. Nutting, R. Jang, and A. K. Balls, *J. Biol. Chem.* **179,** 189 (1949).

[7] E. F. Jansen and A. K. Balls, *J. Biol. Chem.* **194,** 721 (1952).

[8] A. Mazur and O. Bodansky, *J. Biol. Chem.* **163,** 261 (1946).

[9] E. C. Webb, *Biochem. J.* **42,** 96 (1948).

[10] K. Bailey and F. R. Bettelheim, *Biochim. Biophys. Acta* **18,** 495 (1955).

[11] J. A. Gladner and K. Laki, *Arch. Biochem. Biophys.* **62,** 501 (1956).

[12] N. K. Schaffer, S. C. May, and W. H. Summerson, *J. Biol. Chem.* **202,** 67 (1953); **206,** 201 (1954).

[13] R. A. Oosterbaan, P. Kunst, and J. A. Cohen, *Biochim. Biophys. Acta* **16,** 299 (1955).

[14] W. N. Aldridge, *Ann. Rept. Progr. Chem. (Chem. Soc. London)* **53,** 294 (1957).

site," and to a knowledge of the stability of the organophosphorus compounds in aqueous solutions. Moreover, for our purposes investigations on these compounds are the major source of data for nucleophilic displacements on phosphorus.

II. HYDROLYSIS

Compounds (6-1) undergo hydrolysis catalyzed by acid and base species and generally exhibit a neutral water rate. In water at a given pH, assuming all processes to be kinetically important,

$$k_{\text{obs}} = k_{\text{H}}a_{\text{H}} + k_{\text{HA}}[\text{HA}] + k_{\text{OH}}\ominus[\text{OH}^{\ominus}] + k_{\text{A}}\ominus[\text{A}^{\ominus}] + k_0 \quad (6\text{-}2)$$

where k_{obs} is the experimental pseudo-first-order rate constant. In the absence of added buffer, (6-2) reduces to

$$k_{\text{obs}} = k_{\text{H}}a_{\text{H}} + k_{\text{OH}}\ominus[\text{OH}^{\ominus}] + k_0 \quad (6\text{-}3)$$

By suitable manipulation of pH, all three constants may be determined separately (Chapter 1).

A. Acid Catalyzed Hydrolysis

The pioneering work performed by Kilpatrick and Kilpatrick [15] revealed that DFP is subject to acid catalysis. Experiments in aqueous hydrochloric acid solutions of varying concentration indicate that the observed pseudo-first-order rate constants for the hydrolysis of DFP are less than directly proportional to the acid concentration. The same exceptional behavior had been observed earlier by Euler [16] in the acid catalyzed hydrolysis of acetamide and later by Nylen [17] in the acid catalyzed hydrolysis of dialkylphosphites. The experimental data of all three investigators can be accommodated by the following kinetic scheme, proposed originally by Euler, which involves a pre-equilibrium protonation of the substrate:

$$\text{S} + \text{H}_3\text{O}^{\oplus} \underset{K_{a'}}{\rightleftarrows} \text{H}_2\text{O} + \text{SH}^{\oplus}$$

$$\text{SH}^{\oplus} \underset{\text{slow}}{\overset{k'}{\longrightarrow}} \text{P} \quad (6\text{-}4)$$

[15] M. Kilpatrick, Jr., and M. L. Kilpatrick, *J. Phys. Colloid Chem.* **53**, 1371, 1385 (1949).

[16] H. von Euler and A. Olander, *Z. Physik. Chem.* (*Leipzig*) **131**, 107 (1927).

[17] P. Nylen, *Svensk Kem. Tidskr.* **49**, 29 (1937).

followed by a rate-determining cleavage of $SH^{\oplus}$. The pseudo-first-order rate constant (k_{obs}) is then satisfied by the equation (6-5):

$$k_{obs} = \frac{k' a_H}{K_a' + a_H} \qquad (6\text{-}5)$$

where a_H is the hydronium ion activity, and K_a' the acid dissociation constant of the substrate. Rearrangement of equation (6-5) leads to (6-6):

$$\frac{k_{obs}}{a_H} = -\left(\frac{1}{K_a'}\right) k_{obs} + \frac{k'}{K_a'} \qquad (6\text{-}6)$$

Thus a plot of k_{obs}/a_H versus k_{obs} should be linear and have a slope equal to $-K_a'^{-1}$. The data of Euler, Nylen, Kilpatrick, and Kilpatrick obey equation (6-6). It should be recalled that leveling of the rate at high acid concentrations may be explained on the basis of activity coefficient effects on water and the substrate. Waters and de Worms [18] independently verified the fact that DFP is subject to acid catalysis, and firmly established that the hydrolysis proceeds with only P-F bond fission.

Removal of several of the ambiguities surrounding the above reaction mechanism was sought by Halmann,[19] who measured the rate of the acid catalyzed hydrolysis of DFP in HCl-H_2O and DCl-D_2O solutions. A k^{D_2O}/k^{H_2O} value of 0.94 ± 0.03 was found, whose magnitude is not in accord with the specific-acid catalyzed scheme of (6-4), but a mechanism involving a rate-determining proton transfer [20, 21] or, more speculatively, a hydrogen-bonded complex. It should be noted, however, that a k^{D_2O}/k^{H_2O} value of 0.94 is similar to those obtained for alkyl halide solvolysis, which can be rationalized strictly in terms of solvent effects.[22] In addition, the ratio of k^{D_2O}/k^{H_2O} is similar to that obtained for hydrolysis in water (see p. 117). Consequently, the deuterium solvent isotope effect may not be mechanistically significant.

Halmann also observed that the acid catalyzed hydrolysis of DFP in H_2O^{18} does not result in appreciable back incorporation of O^{18} into the phosphoryl group of remaining unhydrolyzed compound. This contrasts with the observations of O^{18} incorporation during the acid catalyzed hydrolysis of methyl dihydrogen and ethylene hydrogen phosphate (Chapter 5, p. 18) and may be interpreted with certain reservations (see p. 117) to preclude the addition of water to the phosphoryl group in a

[18] W. A. Waters and C. G. M. de Worms, *J. Chem. Soc.* 926 (1949).
[19] M. Halmann, *J. Chem. Soc.* 305 (1959).
[20] F. A. Long, *Ann. N.Y. Acad. Sci.* **84**, 596 (1960).
[21] F. A. Long and D. Watson, *J. Chem. Soc.* 2019 (1958).
[22] P. M. Laughton and R. E. Robertson, *Can. J. Chem.* **37**, 1491 (1959).

pre-equilibrium step.   However, before considering a revised reaction mechanism it is pertinent to review the findings of Aksnes.

The study of Aksnes is based on the known relation between the basicity of solvents and their ability to form hydrogen bonds.[23]   The frequency of the O—D stretching band of D_2O in different basic solvents is proportional to the pK_b' of the solvents, where $\Delta\mu$ is the frequency shift of the O—D band[24, 25]:

$$\Delta\mu = 0.0175 \log K_b' + 0.297 \qquad (6\text{-}7)$$

The K_b' value for DFP determined by this method is in good agreement with that calculated from earlier data through equation (6-6) where $K_b' = 1/K_a'$.   Moreover, no pH change was detected upon dissolving DFP in aqueous solution, which might be expected from (6-4).   This, of course, would occur only if considerable $DFPH^{\oplus}$ were formed.   Presumably hydrogen-bonding equilibrium would not exert a measurable influence upon the hydronium ion activity.   Consistent with the collective present data are the acid catalyzed displacement mechanisms (6-8a,b), in which the number of water molecules complexed with the proton is not specified.   The two are similar to those favored by Aksnes and Halmann,

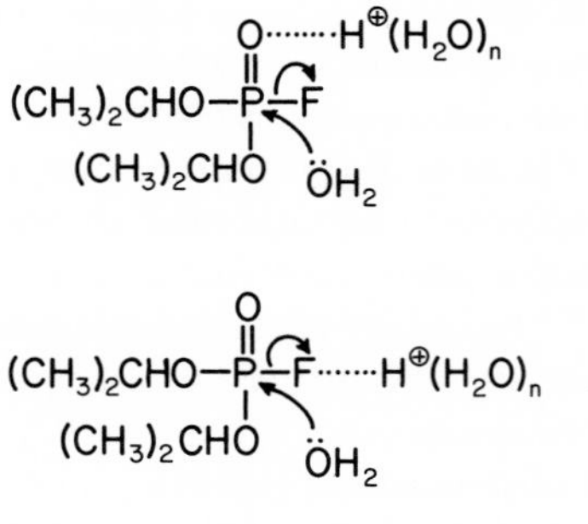

$$(6\text{-}8)$$

respectively.   It is conceivable that, for certain cases where the phosphoryl compound is of greater basicity, the already fine "distinction" separating hydrogen bonding and preprotonation mechanisms may disappear.   The precedent for hydrogen bond formation with phosphoryl compounds of this form had been previously established by infrared experiments,[26] in which the thermodynamic functions of the hydrogen-bond equilibrium

[23] G. Aksnes, *Acta Chem. Scand.* **14,** 1526 (1960).
[24] W. J. Gordy and S. C. Stanford, *J. Chem. Phys.* **9,** 204 (1941).
[25] W. J. Gordy, *J. Chem. Phys.* **9,** 215 (1941).
[26] G. Aksnes and T. Gramstad, *Acta Chem. Scand.* **14,** 1485 (1960).

reaction between phenol and a series of organophosphorus compounds were determined. However, the infrared experiments were carried out in carbon tetrachloride and not in aqueous solutions. Mechanisms based on such extrapolation to aqueous solutions are rather tenuous.

The acid catalyzed hydrolysis of dimethyl phosphorofluoridate, methyl ethylphosphonofluoridate, and diethylphosphinic fluoride in dilute aqueous hydrochloric acid solutions exhibits the same kinetic behavior as DFP.[27] The kinetically determined values for K_b' parallel the tendency of the particular substrate to hydrogen bond with phenol.[26] The values of k_H at 25° and 0.04 N in HCl are 0.437, 0.476, and 2.06 liter mole^{-1} min^{-1}, respectively. The insensitivity of k_H to substituent effects is in contrast to the ca. 50-fold spread in $k_{OH}\ominus$ for the same compounds. In this respect the acid catalyzed hydrolysis of organophosphoryl fluorides manifests the same general tendency as esters of carboxylic acids [28] (see Chapter 1).

On the other hand, DCIP does not show acid catalysis. The rate of hydrolysis for DCIP at 0° in 10% EtOH-H_2O is the same in the absence or presence of 0.13 N sulfuric acid.[29] Isolation of the reaction products indicates only P—Cl bond fission. Thus, the pattern of reactivity in acidic solutions for the fluoro- and chlorophosphorus compounds is similar to that found for the fluoro- and chloroacyl derivatives.[30]

Replacement of the isopropoxy groups by isopropylamino, as in N,N'-diisopropylphosphorodiamidic fluoride, results in both P—N and P—F bonds being split simultaneously in acid solution (the relative rates are 1.67/1 at 25°). The overall rate of hydrolysis is about half that of DFP.[31] With N,N,N',N'-tetramethylphosphorodiamidic fluoride only P—N splitting is observed under acidic conditions.[31] Loss of the amino group also has been found in the acid catalyzed hydrolysis of ethyl N,N-diethyl-phosphoramidochloridate [32] and of Tabun.[33, 34] In the chloridate, P—Cl fission precedes deamination. The facile acid-catalyzed P—N bond rupture is typical of phosphoramidates.

The mechanism of the acid catalyzed hydrolysis of these amino group-containing compounds is probably akin to that proposed for Tabun[35]:

[27] G. Aksnes and S. I. Snaprud, *Acta Chem. Scand.* **15**, 457 (1961).

[28] L. P. Hammett, "Physical Organic Chemistry," McGraw-Hill, New York, 1940, p. 211.

[29] I. Dostrovsky and M. Halmann, *J. Chem. Soc.* 502, 516 (1953).

[30] C. W. L. Bevan and R. F. Hudson, *J. Chem. Soc.* 2187 (1953).

[31] D. F. Heath and P. Casapieri, *Trans. Faraday Soc.* **47**, 1093 (1951).

[32] E. W. Crunden and R. F. Hudson, *J. Chem. Soc.* 3591 (1962).

[33] L. Larsson, *Acta Chem. Scand.* **6**, 1470 (1952).

[34] L. Larsson, *Acta Chem. Scand.* **7**, 306 (1953).

[35] L. Larsson, *Svensk Kem. Tidskr.* **70**, 405 (1958).

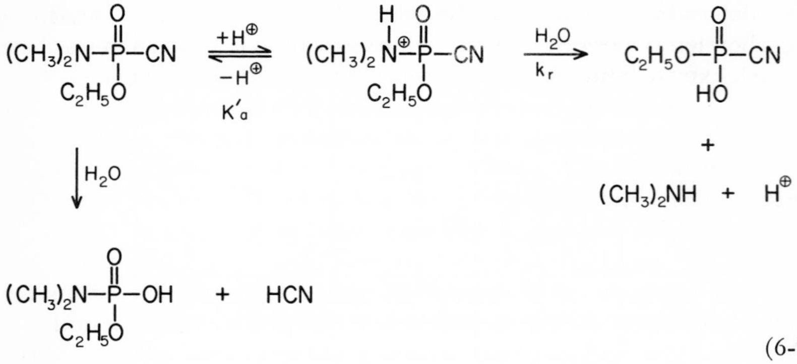

$$(CH_3)_2N-\underset{\underset{C_2H_5O}{|}}{\overset{\overset{O}{\|}}{P}}-CN \quad \underset{-H^{\oplus}}{\overset{+H^{\oplus}}{\rightleftharpoons}} \quad (CH_3)_2\overset{\overset{H}{|}}{\underset{\underset{C_2H_5O}{|}}{N}}\overset{\overset{O}{\|}}{\underset{}{P}}-CN \quad \xrightarrow{\underset{k_r}{H_2O}} \quad C_2H_5O-\underset{\underset{HO}{|}}{\overset{\overset{O}{\|}}{P}}-CN$$

$$K'_a$$

$$\Big\downarrow H_2O \qquad\qquad\qquad\qquad\qquad\qquad\qquad + $$

$$(CH_3)_2NH \; + \; H^{\oplus}$$

$$(CH_3)_2N-\underset{\underset{C_2H_5O}{|}}{\overset{\overset{O}{\|}}{P}}-OH \quad + \quad HCN$$

$$(6\text{-}9)$$

Addition of the hydronium ion in the pre-equilibrium step may act to inhibit the $p\pi$-$d\pi$ conjugation which stabilizes the ground state, thereby making the phosphorus atom more vulnerable to nucleophilic attack [35] and simultaneously converting the amino nitrogen into a good leaving group. Attack by water is most likely a simple rate-determining nucleophilic displacement. If $K'_a \gg a_H$ then k_H is proportional to a_H, which has been observed for Tabun and N,N,N',N'-tetramethylphosphorodiamidic fluoride.[31] Whether the loss of cyanide is also acid catalyzed is unresolved.

B. Spontaneous Hydrolysis [35a]

A direct reaction with water has been observed for a number of compounds of type (6-1). Table 6-1 lists the hydrolytic rate constants for several fluoro derivatives.

The scant data do not allow generalizations to be drawn concerning the effect of substituents on the magnitude of k_0. Nevertheless, it appears doubtful that simple inductive effects are solely operative. For instance, the importance of resonance has been implied by infrared studies.[26] The stretching vibrational frequency of the P=O bond for various fluoro and chloro compounds is displaced upon formation of the hydrogen-bonded complex with phenol. This frequency shift has been interpreted as a measure of the polarizability of substituents in the compound with the amino and alkoxy groups giving rise to the greatest shifts. As a result,

---

[35a] The term spontaneous hydrolysis should not be interpreted as synonymous with a general-base catalyzed mechanism, which is observed with the acyl activated esters (Chapter 1).

Table 6-1   *Rates of spontaneous hydrolysis for compounds having the structure* R, R′ POF

Compound	$T°$	k_0 (min^{-1})	Ref.
$(i\text{-}C_3H_7O)_2POF$	25	1.2×10^{-4}	15
$(i\text{-}C_3H_7NH)_2POF$	25	2.3×10^{-6} [a]	36
$[(CH_3)_2N](i\text{-}C_3H_7NH)POF$	100	1.5×10^{-3}	36
$[O(CH_2CH_2)_2N](C_2H_5O)POF$	25	4×10^{-7}	36
$(i\text{-}C_3H_7O)(CH_3)POF$	25	2×10^{-4} [b]	37

[a] Proceeds with P—F and P—N bond cleavage.
[b] Average value from extrapolations at several pH values.

the following resonance form is considered an important contributor to the resonance hybrid of compounds possessing these groups:

$$R-\overset{\oplus}{O}=\overset{\overset{\textstyle O^{\ominus}}{|}}{\underset{\underset{\textstyle R'}{|}}{P}}-X \qquad (6\text{-}10)$$

An identical conclusion may be reached through analysis of the decrease in k_0 upon replacement of one or both alkoxy groups by amino groups.[32] Implicit is the requirement of a phosphorus π orbital capable of overlap with the unshared electron pair of R.   Lastly, steric effects by R and R′ should of course influence k_0.

The spontaneous hydrolysis of the fluoro derivatives may be viewed as a bimolecular S_N2 displacement of fluoride anion by a water molecule on the grounds that (1) no appreciable O^{18} exchange into the P=O bond occurs during the hydrolysis of DFP and dimethylphosphinic fluoride,[19] (2) the rate constant, k_0, for dimethylphosphinic fluoride is ca. 400-fold greater than that for DFP, which may be attributed to the loss of the electron-donating alkoxy groups, and (3) k^{D_2O}/k^{H_2O} for diisopropyl phosphorofluoridate is 0.87 ± 0.06 at 40°.   The lack of O^{18} incorporation in any of the experimental cases discussed is subject, however, to two qualifications: (1) partitioning of a pentacovalent addition intermediate in H_2O^{18} would not be observed if the ratio of the partitioning constants exceeds $1:100$ (see Chapter 1), and (2) addition of water may give rise to an intermediate or transition state in which the entering oxygen atom is not equivalent to the phosphoryl oxygen atom.   Moreover, it may be

[36] D. F. Heath, *J. Chem. Soc.* 3804 (1956).
[37] J. Epstein, V. E. Bauer, M. Saxe, and M. M. Demek, *J. Am. Chem. Soc.* **78**, 4068 (1956).

Table 6-2 *   *Solvolysis of* DClP *in various media*

T°	HCO₂H [a]	100% CH₃OH	% C₂H₅OH—H₂O (v/v) 100%	95%	90%	80%	60%	10%	H₂O	D₂O
63.8	—	—	—	—	—	37.1	84	—	—	—
39.60	0.06	—	1.78	—	5.53	9.5	—	—	—	—
25.14	0.008	2.44	0.61	1.41	2.03	3.0	5.8	—	81	65
10.08	—	—	0.19	—	0.65	—	—	—	—	—
0.0	—	—	0.97	—	—	—	0.63	8.6	8.6	—

* Ref. 29.

[a] These values should be regarded as upper limits.   No reaction could be detected in *t*-butyl alcohol after 7 days at 40°

argued that the above deuterium solvent kinetic isotope effect is indicative of a solvent-assisted spontaneous hydrolysis rather than a nucleophilic attack by water.   Consequently, it is more profitable to consider the chloro derivatives, for which more data have been amassed, before attempting definite mechanistic formulations.

Reactions of phosphorochloridates and phosphinic chlorides were first investigated kinetically by Dostrovsky and Halmann.[29]   The media effect on the rate of solvolysis was examined thoroughly through experiments conducted in dry methanol, dry ethanol, a number of aqueous-ethanolic media, water, deuterium oxide, and wet formic acid.   The effects of various solvents on the rate of disappearance of DClP are recorded in Table 6-2.   The changes in solvent affect primarily the entropy of activation in a manner which leads to a net increase in rate for the more aqueous medium.

Change of solvent from a less to a more aqueous medium accelerates solvolytic reactions proceeding by both unimolecular and bimolecular mechanisms.   However, solvent effects on a unimolecular pathway are more pronounced.[38, 39]   Solvent effects also have been treated on a semi-quantitative basis by Winstein *et al.*[40]   Analysis of the data in Table 6-2 by either approach leads to the conclusion that the solvolysis in aqueous ethanolic media is bimolecular.   Application of the Winstein-Grunwald relationship yielded an m of 0.33, almost identical with that obtained for the solvolysis of ethyl bromide ($m = 0.34$).   For S_N1 reactions, the value of m is ca. 1.0.   The value of k^{D_2O}/k^{H_2O} (0.80) does not, however, allow an

[38] E. D. Hughes, *Trans. Faraday Soc.* **37**, 603 (1941).
[39] I. Dostrovsky and E. D. Hughes, *J. Chem. Soc.* 166 (1946).
[40] S. Winstein, E. Grunwald, and H. W. Jones, *J. Am. Chem. Soc.* **73**, 2700 (1951).

unequivocal decision as to whether the displacement of $Cl^{\ominus}$ is general base assisted.

Further support for the bimolecular hypothesis was derived from the comparison of the rates of solvolysis in formic acid and aqueous ethanol of equal ionizing capacity—ca. 40% ethanol. Little change in the rate of solvolysis should attend the passage from aqueous ethanol to formic acid for a truly unimolecular solvolysis.[40–42] On the other hand, a marked reduction in rate is expected for a mainly bimolecular solvolysis, because of the considerable difference in nucleophilicity between the two solvents. For DClP a 2000-fold decrease in rate results. It is of interest to note that the alkoxy groups are removed in addition to chloride during the formolysis of DClP.

A similar investigation of solvent effects in the solvolysis of the related phosphonochloridates further confirms the probable bimolecularity of the solvolysis.[43] 1-Methylheptyl methylphosphonochloridate is 1840 times more reactive in 40% ethanol than in moist formic acid. Unlike DClP, the solvolysis proceeds with only P—Cl bond fission in both solvents. Application of the Winstein-Grunwald relationship to the solvolysis of isopropyl methylphosphonochloridate in solvents of varying water concentration gives an m value of 0.43. Moreover, the importance of steric hindrance is demonstrated by the rapid decrease in the rate of alcoholysis in the series MeOH > EtOH > i-PrOH > t-BuOH. Introduction of bulkier alkyl groups in the phosphonochloridate also serves to reduce the rate of solvolysis.[44]

An attempt was made to differentiate between steric and electronic effects in the solvolysis by comparing the reactivities of compounds of similar configuration.[44] The compounds diethylphosphinic chloride, methyl ethylphosphonochloridate, and dimethyl phosphorochoridate were employed because their entropies of activation for the solvolytic reaction are nearly identical. The contention is that the entropy term serves as an index of steric hindrance. The solvolytic data obtained are summarized in Table 6-3. Inspection of Table 6-3 reveals that substituents, which inductively act to decrease the electron density around the phosphorus atom and which should, therefore, accelerate a bimolecular solvolysis, actually decrease the observed rates. The most likely explanation for this trend is the increasing importance of π bonding between the phosphorus and oxygen atoms which opposes the negative inductive effect.[44] Such an opposition of effects may be present even

[41] L. C. Bateman and E. D. Hughes, *J. Chem. Soc.* 940 (1940).
[42] I. Dostrovsky and E. D. Hughes, *J. Chem. Soc.* 171 (1946).
[43] R. F. Hudson and L. Keay, *J. Chem. Soc.* 1865 (1960).
[44] R. F. Hudson and L. Keay, *J. Chem. Soc.* 1859 (1960).

Table 6-3 *   *The effect of methoxy groups on the rate of hydrolysis in 5%
aqueous acetone*

	$(C_2H_5)_2POCl$	$(CH_3O)(C_2H_5)POCl$	$(CH_3O)_2POCl$
$10^3 k_1$ (sec^{-1}) at 0°	1500	98	1.75
E_a (kcal mole^{-1})	7.3	8.4	10.6
log PZ	5.9	5.7	5.7

* Ref. 44.

when the substituent is a second chlorine atom.[45]   Yet it appears that
bonding of the substituent to P=O is considerably weaker than π bonding
to >C=O.   For example, acetyl chloride is hydrolyzed ca. 10^4 times
more rapidly than ethyl chloroformate,[46, 47] while diethylphosphinic
chloride hydrolyzes only 15 times more rapidly than methyl ethylphos-
phorochloridate.   Such data indicate that considerable caution should
be exercised before assigning the high relative rates of cyclic phosphate
hydrolysis to inhibition of π overlap.   Furthermore, measurements of the
ultraviolet[48] and infrared[49] spectra of phenylphosphonic acid and its
derivatives reveal only negligible conjugation between the phenyl group
and the phosphorus atom.   Sensitivity to changes in conjugation, therefore, should be small in organophosphorus compounds.   This is in contrast to the alkaline hydrolysis of aromatic esters, in which resonance
effects are more pronounced.[50]   The above considerations apply in general
to nucleophilic displacements on phosphorus compounds of structure (6-1).
It is noteworthy in conjunction with the bimolecular solvolysis of phosphoryl chlorides that no O^{18} incorporation into the intact halide is found
either in the hydrolysis of diethyl phosphorochloridate[51] or in the three
stages involving hydrolysis of $POCl_3$ to H_3PO_4.[51a]

At this point it is of interest to relate the solvolytic reactions of organophosphorus compounds to their sulfur and carbon analogs.[19]   Results for
some fluoro and chloro derivatives are compared in Table 6-4.   In the
few reactions for which activation energies have been determined, the

[45] R. F. Hudson and G. E. Moss, *J. Chem. Soc.* 1040 (1964).

[46] G. Zimmerman and C. Yuan, *J. Am. Chem. Soc.* **77**, 332 (1955).

[47] H. Bohme and W. Schurhoff, *Ber.* **84**, 28 (1951).

[48] H. H. Jaffé, *J. Chem. Phys.* **22**, 1430 (1954).

[49] J. V. Bell, J. Heisler, H. Tannenbaum, and J. Goldenson, *J. Am. Chem. Soc.* **7 6**, 5185 (1954).

[50] C. K. Ingold, "Structure and Mechanism in Organic Chemistry," Cornell University Press, Ithaca, New York, 1953, p. 758.

[51] I. Dostrovsky and M. Halmann, *J. Chem. Soc.* 1004 (1956).

[51a] M. Halmann and L. Kugel, *J. Chem. Soc.* 3733 (1964).

Table 6-4 *   *Hydrolysis of fluorides and chlorides of phosphorus, sulfur, and carbon at 25°*

Acid halide	Solvent	10^4 k_1 (sec^{-1})	E_a (kcal mole^{-1})	$\Delta S^{\ddagger}$ (kcal deg^{-1})	k_{RCl}/k_{RF}	Ref.
$(CH_3)_2POF$	H_2O	4	—	—	—	19
$(CH_3)_2POCl$	EtOH($-8.5°$)	60	—	—	—	29
$(i$-$C_3H_7O)_2POF$	H_2O	0.017	21.8	-12.7	$\sim$5000	19
$(i$-$C_2H_7O)_2POCl$	H_2O	81	14.4	-20.6		29
$C_6H_5SO_2F$	50% COMe$_2$	$<5 \times 10^{-4}$	—	—	$\sim$5000	52
$C_6H_5SO_2Cl$	50% COMe$_2$	2.4	14	-29		
CH_3COF	75% COMe$_2$	1.1	—	—	$\sim$8000	52
CH_3COCl	75% COMe$_2$	8600	14	-14		
$(C_6H_5)_3CF$	85% COMe$_2$	0.027	22.6	-10	$\sim$1 $\times$ 10^6	52
$(C_6H_5)_3CCl$	85% COMe$_2$	27,000	12.5	-17		

* Ref. 19.

lower rate of solvolysis of the fluoro compound is due to a more unfavorable E_a, which is only partially compensated by a more favorable $\Delta S^{\ddagger}$.   The larger E_a may be connected with the greater bond energy of fluorine,[53] but interpretations of activation energies usually do not lend themselves to simple statements.   Inspection of Table 6-4 suggests that the magnitude of the ratio k_{RCl}/k_{RF} may reflect a change from an S_N2 to an S_N1 mechanism.   Triphenylmethyl halides most certainly solvolyze via an S_N1 pathway and exhibit a k_{RCl}/k_{RF} ratio substantially larger than the others.[52]

The spontaneous hydrolysis of phosphoramidochloridates has been a subject of some controversy.   It originally was thought that the hydrolysis of N,N,N',N'-tetramethylphosphorodiamidic chloride occurred though an S_N1 mechanism.[54]   This postulate was based, first, on the similarity of k_0 for the above compound and DClP, in spite of the steric hindrance imposed by the dialkylated amino groups; second, on the absence of a rate increase upon the addition of hydroxide, m-cresol, or pyrrolidine.   However, a later kinetic investigation [32] of a series of substituted phosphorodiamidic chlorides uncovered the following information: (1) k_0 decreases with an increase in the basicity of the alkylamino group; (2) the ratio of the rate of solvolysis in 65% aqueous acetone to that in formic acid for several phosphorodiamidic chlorides is ca. 100; (3) a plot of the

[52] C. G. Swain and C. B. Scott, *J. Am. Chem. Soc.* **75,** 246 (1953).
[53] G. Wittig and M. Rieber, *Ann.* **562,** 187 (1949).
[54] H. K. Hall, *J. Org. Chem.* **21,** 248 (1956).

Grunwald-Winstein equation, although nonlinear, has $m = 0.58$ as the upper limit. Collectively the data support the conclusion that the solvolysis of phosphorodiamidic chlorides proceeds via a bimolecular mechanism,[54a] yet it is apparent that bond breaking is probably more important here than in the solvolysis of the phosphorochloridates. Westheimer and Samuel earlier had theorized that the solvolytic reaction was most likely bimolecular on the basis of salt effects.[55]

C. Hydroxide-Ion Catalyzed Hydrolysis

The most extensive work on the hydrolysis of compounds (6-1) has been performed in alkaline solutions. Strictly speaking, this is not a true catalysis, but a nucleophilic displacement reaction resulting in hydrolysis of the compound. An investigation of the alkaline hydrolysis of Sarin is typical of experiments conducted in this area.[56]

The pH profile of Sarin hydrolysis was obtained in water at 25° over the pH range 8.00–9.80, and at 35° over the pH range 8.30–9.13. At these acidities, equation (6-3) should simply reduce to

$$k_{obs} = k_{OH}\ominus[OH\ominus] \qquad (6\text{-}11)$$

since k_0 is negligible for Sarin. Equation (6-11) can be rewritten [56] in logarithmic form as

$$\log k_{obs} = \log k_{OH}\ominus - pOH \qquad (6\text{-}12)$$

Plots of the experimental data according to equation (6-12) are linear and can be expressed by

$$\log k_{obs} = 1.519 - 0.995 \, pOH \quad 25°$$
$$\log k_{obs} = 1.731 - 0.955 \, pOH \quad 35° \qquad (6\text{-}13)$$

The error in the determined coefficients of pOH is ± 0.013 and ± 0.021, respectively. Thus, these coefficients are within the limits of error equal to 1.00, confirming the validity of the proposed equation (6-12). In view of these results it is difficult to explain the saturation effect observed by Martell et al. in the hydrolysis of Sarin within the same pH region.[57]

Experiments at varying ionic strengths through the addition of KCl appeared to indicate that $k_{OH}\ominus$ increased with increasing ionic strength. However, if a correction is applied for the change in the activity coefficient of hydroxyl ion, $k_{OH}\ominus$ is independent of ionic strength at least to 0.5, the

[54a] See P. S. Traylor, Ph.D. Thesis, Harvard University (1963) for recent data in mixed solvents in support of this mechanism.

[55] D. Samuel and F. H. Westheimer, Chem. Ind. (London) 51 (1959).

[56] L. Larsson, Acta Chem. Scand. 11, 1131 (1957).

[57] R. L. Gustafson and A. E. Martell, J. Am. Chem. Soc. 84, 2309 (1962).

upper experimental limit. The addition of fluoride ion does not alter $k_{OH^\ominus}$.[56]

Analysis of the hydrolysis products by means of paper chromatography showed that only one phosphorus compound was present. Other techniques revealed that 2 equivalents of acid are formed per equivalent of Sarin hydrolyzed, and that fluoride is in the spent reaction mixture. All observations therefore indicate that only P—F rupture occurs.

The direct proportionality of $k_{OH^\ominus}$ to $[OH^\ominus]$, the negligible effect of ionic strength, and the absence of a common ion effect support an S_N2 type of mechanism:

$$HO^\ominus \;+\; (CH_3)_2CHO-\underset{\underset{CH_3}{|}}{\overset{\overset{O}{\|}}{P}}-F \longrightarrow \left[\begin{array}{c} \overset{O}{\overset{\|}{}} \\ HO\overset{\delta\ominus}{---}P\overset{\delta\ominus}{---}F \\ (CH_3)_2CHO \qquad CH_3 \end{array} \right] \longrightarrow$$

$$HO-\underset{\underset{(CH_3)_2CHO}{|}}{\overset{\overset{O}{\|}}{P}}-CH_3 \;+\; F^\ominus$$

$$(6\text{-}14)$$

The values of $k_{OH^\ominus}$, E_a, and $\Delta S^\ddagger$ for a number of fluoro derivatives are listed in Table 6-5.[35] Qualitative predictions concerning the effect of substituents on the magnitude of $k_{OH^\ominus}$ follow from consideration of electronic, steric, and electrostatic influences upon a bimolecular nucleophilic displacement in which bond making appears to be more important in the transition state. Anomalous behavior is seen, however, in compound 5 of Table 6-5. Substitution of a less electronegative alkylthio for the alkoxy group should lower $k_{OH^\ominus}$, whereas $k_{OH^\ominus}$ is actually increased by a factor of ca. 1000. An explanation for this phenomenon, implicating the polarizability of the sulfur atom,[58] has been proposed. The approach of the hydroxyl ion may polarize the P—S bond in the sense

$$\overset{\delta+}{P}—\overset{\delta-}{S}$$

thus facilitating the formation of the transition state. The E_a for the reaction of compound 5 of Table 6-5 is considerably lower than the others.[59] A decrease in E_a has been viewed by Aksnes as associated with

[58] D. F. Heath, *J. Chem. Soc.* 3796 (1956).

[59] The $k_{OH^\ominus}$ for Tabun [60] is larger than anticipated, perhaps due to a polarizability of the cyanide group.

[60] L. Larsson, *Acta Chem. Scand.* **12**, 783 (1958).

Table 6-5 * Values of $k_{OH^{\ominus}}$, E_a, and $\Delta S^{\ddagger}$ for compounds of the structure R_1R_2POF (25°)

	R_1	R_2	X	$k_{OH^{\ominus}}$ (liter mole^{-1} sec^{-1})	E_a (kcal mole^{-1})	$\Delta S^{\ddagger}$ (e.u.)	Ref.
(1)	CH$_3$	CH$_3$O	F	106	10.5	-16	56
(2)	CH$_3$	C$_2$H$_5$O	F	60.7	11.2	-15	56
(3)	CH$_3$	n-C$_3$H$_7$O	F	54.0	10.4	-18	56
(4)	CH$_3$	(CH$_3$)$_2$CHO	F	25.8	9.1	-24	56
(5)	CH$_3$	C$_2$H$_5$S	F	1.95×10^4	6.2	-22	60
(6)	CH$_3$	BrC$_2$H$_4$O	F	162	11.3	-13	60
(7)	CH$_3$	(CH$_3$)$_3\overset{\oplus}{N}$C$_2$H$_4$O	F	935	9.0	-17	60
(8)	CH$_3$	(CH$_3$)$_3\overset{\oplus}{N}$C$_3$H$_6$O	F	305	11.6	-10	60
(9)	CH$_3$	(CH$_3$)$_3$NCH$_2$CH$_2$CH(CH$_3$)O	F	381	10.1	-15	60
(10)	(CH$_3$)$_2$CH	(CH$_3$)$_2$CHO	F	2.03	9.2	-28	60
(11)	(CH$_3$)$_2$CHO	(CH$_3$)$_2$CHO	F	0.83	—	—	15
(12)	(CH$_3$)$_2$N	(CH$_3$)$_2$N	F	5.7×10^{-5}	14.7	-31	31

* Ref. 35.

124

an increase in the residual positive charge on the phosphorus atom for compounds (6-1).[61] Inspection of Table 6-5 also serves to illustrate the compensation between E_a and $\Delta S^{\ddagger}$ which has been noted for other reactions proceeding via similar pathways.[62, 63] A considerable part of the entropy term has been attributed to the difference in the orientation of the solvent molecules.

The chlorine analog of Sarin (isopropyl methylphosphonochloridate) is 5000 times more reactive than Sarin, even though replacement by the less electronegative chlorine should lower $k_{\mathrm{OH}\ominus}$. The high reactivity of the chlorine analog, as in the case of spontaneous hydrolysis, may again be related to a lower P—Cl bond energy,[64, 65] although undoubtedly solvation and differences in the pK_a' of the leaving groups, etc., are of significance. It is of interest that the higher reactivity of the above mentioned thio-substituted relative to the oxo-substituted fluorides, and the greater instability of chloro vs. fluoro derivatives may be qualitatively related to one parameter, a decreasing tendency for these substituents to partake in $p\pi$—$d\pi$ bonding with phosphorus, thereby lowering E_a.

A considerable accumulation of rate data is available for the alkaline hydrolysis of phosphoramidates.[55, 58, 66] Table 6-6 records some values of interest. The decrease in $k_{\mathrm{OH}\ominus}$ for compounds 1 through 7 can be rationalized readily by invoking the usual electronic and steric argument applicable to a bimolecular reaction. Similar explanations do not suffice to explain the large difference (ca. 10^3) in $k_{\mathrm{OH}\ominus}$ between groups 1 through 7, and 8 through 12. The latter group is almost completely resistant to alkaline hydrolysis.

With this arbitrary division it is apparent that the more reactive group possesses a hydrogen atom on at least one of the nitrogens, whereas the less reactive group is completely N-alkylated. From this viewpoint, a possible mechanism was first suggested by Westheimer[67]:

$$R_2N-\overset{\overset{\displaystyle O}{\|}}{\underset{\underset{\displaystyle NHR'}{|}}{P}}-F \;+\; OH^{\ominus} \;\xrightarrow[\substack{-H_2O, \\ -F^{\ominus}}]{\text{slow}}\; \left[\overset{\overset{\displaystyle O}{\|}}{\underset{\displaystyle R_2N \quad NR'}{P}} \right] \;\xrightarrow[+H_2O]{\text{fast}}\; R_2N-\overset{\overset{\displaystyle O}{\|}}{\underset{\underset{\displaystyle HNR'}{|}}{P}}-OH$$

$$(6\text{-}15)$$

[61] G. Aksnes, *Acta Chem. Scand.* **14,** 1515 (1960).

[62] E. Whalley, *Trans. Faraday Soc.* **55,** 798 (1959).

[63] F. A. Long, J. G. Pritchard, and F. E. Stafford, *J. Am. Chem. Soc.* **79,** 2362 (1957).

[64] E. Neale, L. T. D. Williams, and V. T. Moores, *J. Chem. Soc.* 422 (1956).

[65] L. Larsson and P. E. Bergner, *Arkiv Kemi* **13,** 143 (1958).

[66] E. W. Crunden and R. F. Hudson, *Chem. Ind.* (*London*) 1478 (1958).

[67] F. H. Westheimer, *Chem. Soc.* (*London*) *Spec. Publ.* **8,** 181 (1957).

Table 6-6 *   *Alkaline hydrolysis of phosphorodiamidic fluorides*

	R	R'	$T°$	$k_{OH}{}^{\ominus}$ (liter mole^{-1} min^{-1})	E_a (kcal mole^{-1})	Ref.
(1)	$CH_2{=}CHCH_2NH$	$CH_2{=}CHCH_2NH$	16	$\sim$1000	—	58
(2)	$i\text{-}C_3H_7NH$	$i\text{-}C_3H_7NH$	25.09	48.9	11.2 ± 0.5	58
(3)	CH_3NH	$(CH_3)_2N$	25.08	17.6	11.2 ± 0.5	58
(4)	C_2H_5NH	$(CH_3)_2N$	25.0	12.3	11.4 ± 0.3	58
(5)	$n\text{-}C_4H_9NH$	$(CH_3)_2N$	25.0	11.1	11.4 ± 0.5	58
(6)	$i\text{-}C_3H_7NH$	$(CH_3)_2N$	25.0	8.43	11.9 ± 0.5	58
(7)	CH_3NH	$(C_2H_5)_2N$	25.0	1.69	—	58
(8)	$O(CH_2CH_2)_2N$	$(CH_3)_2N$	25.0	9.0×10^{-3}	—	58
(9)	$(CH_3)_2N$	$(CH_3)_2N$	28.9	4.70×10^{-3}	14.7 ± 0.5	31
(10)	$O(CH_2CH_2)_2N$	$(C_2H_5)_2N$	25.0	1.0×10^{-3}	16.58 ± 0.02	58
(11)	$(C_2H_5)_2N$	$(CH_3)_2N$	25.0	2.87×10^{-4}	—	58
(12)	$(C_2H_5)_2N$	$(C_2H_5)_2N$	25.2	2.5×10^{-5}	17.1 ± 1.0	58

* Ref. 58.

126

The ionization of the amine in base would then be essential to the mechanism; consequently, only those phosphoramidates possessing at least one partially alkylated nitrogen would be hydrolyzed rapidly. The postulated monomeric metaphosphate derivative is analogous to those encountered in the preceding chapter. Other workers established that 2,6-lutidine increases the rate of hydrolysis of N,N'-diethylphosphorodiamidic chloride but has no effect on diethylphosphorochloridate.[32, 66] In view of the similar stereochemistry of the two compounds, it is unlikely that the catalytic effect is a result of a direct displacement at the phosphorus atom, but rather a removal of a proton which is not subject to steric control.[67a]

III. NUCLEOPHILIC DISPLACEMENTS AT PHOSPHORUS

A. Oxyanions

It has been found that oxyanions such as nitrite,[32] ethoxide,[68] and methoxide [32] act as nucleophiles toward compounds (6-1). Fluoride [68] and azide [55] anions also are effective nucleophilic reagents, forming stable derivatives which can be isolated.

Additional mechanistic evidence for the S_N2 type of mechanism arises from stereochemical studies. Theoretically and experimentally, S_N2 bimolecular displacement reactions should lead to inversion of an optical center.[69] Experiments on the reaction between optically active phosphinic acid derivatives and anions suggested that certain of the displacements involve predominant inversion of configuration.[70, 71] Unfortunately no definite conclusions could be stated, as the products were not isolated owing to extensive racemization and decomposition upon distillation. Furthermore, the assumption in these experiments, that similar

[67a] In a recent article by P. S. Traylor and F. H. Westheimer, *J. Am. Chem. Soc.* **87,** 553 (1965), it is reported that 2,6-lutidine does not catalyze the hydrolysis of N,N'-dipropylphosphorodiamidic chloride in 50% dimethoxyethane-water, although pyridine functions effectively as a nucleophile. These investigators also have determined that the alkaline hydrolysis of dipropylphosphorodiamidic chloride is at least 4 million times faster than that of tetramethylphosphorodiamidic chloride under identical conditions. The extraordinary effect is presumably produced by mechanism (6-15) being operative for the former compound.

[68] I. Dostrovsky and M. Halmann, *J. Chem. Soc.* 508 (1953).

[69] W. A. Cowdrey, E. D. Hughes, C. K. Ingold, S. Masterman, and A. D. Scott, *J. Chem. Soc.* 1252 (1937).

[70] H. S. Aaron, R. T. Uyeda, H. F. Frack, and J. I. Miller, *J. Am. Chem. Soc.* **84,** 617 (1962).

[71] M. Green and R. F. Hudson, *Proc. Chem. Soc.* 227 (1959).

reactions proceed with similar stereochemical changes, must be used with caution in view of recent observations by Michalski and Ratajczak (6-16).[72]

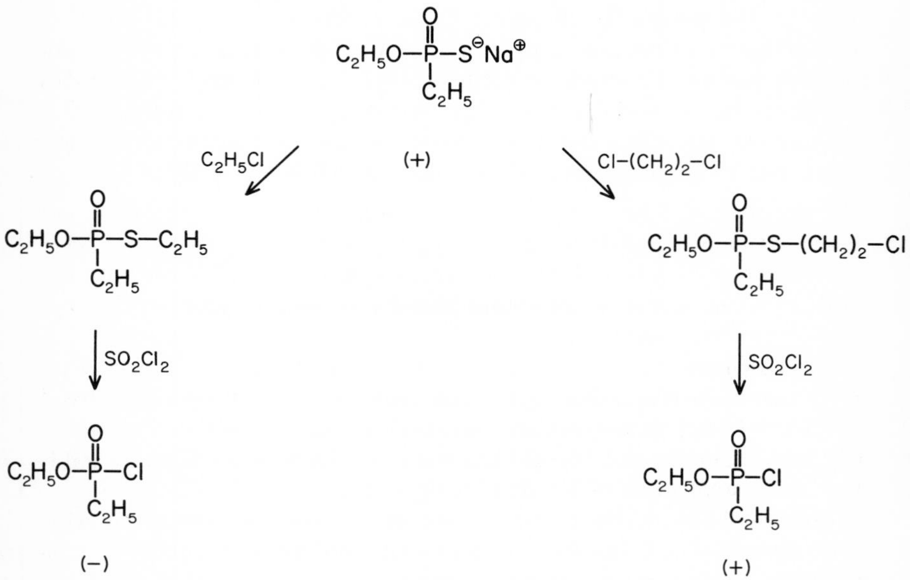

$$(6\text{-}16)$$

A more definitive approach was employed by Hudson et al.,[73] who prepared the optically active O-methyl ester of phenylethylphosphinic acid. The rate of racemization of this ester by sodium methoxide in methanol was carefully measured, and a characteristic rate constant (k_1) calculated, assuming that each displacement involved stereochemical inversion. An independent check on k_1 was obtained by measuring the rate of exchange of labeled ester under identical conditions. The values of k_1 determined by either method were identical within limits of experi-

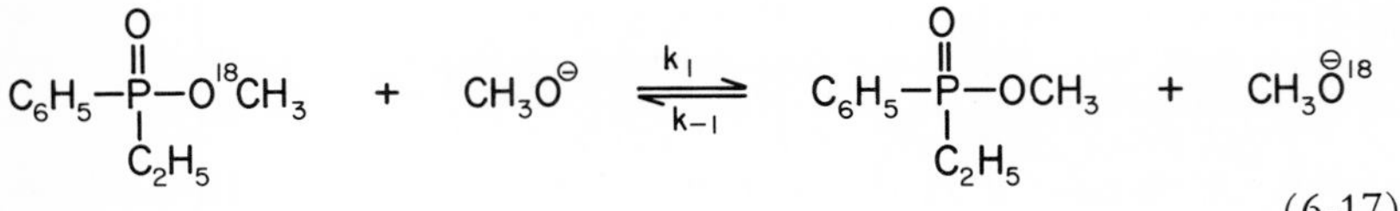

$$(6\text{-}17)$$

[72] J. Michalski and A. Ratajczak, Chem. Ind. (London) 1241 (1960).
[73] M. Green and R. F. Hudson, J. Chem. Soc. 540 (1963).

mental error. The proposed transition state (6-18a) for the reaction is akin to the S_N2 transition state of a saturated carbon atom with the axial bonds (p or pd) weaker than the sp^2 bonds in the basal plane:

$$
\left[\begin{array}{c} R \quad R' \\ X\text{----}P\text{----}X \\ | \\ O \end{array}\right]^{\ominus}
\qquad
\left[\begin{array}{c} X \quad X \\ O\text{---}P\text{---}R' \\ | \\ R \end{array}\right]^{\ominus}
\qquad (6\text{-}18)
$$

a   b

The structure (6-18b), which is indistinguishable from (6-18a), was suggested by Haake and Westheimer [74] as a possible transition state structure for the acid hydrolysis of cyclic phosphates. In (6-18b) the entering and leaving groups lie in the basal plane, these bonds being weaker because of sp^3d hybridization.

Certain ions greatly facilitate the rate of hydrolysis of organophosphorus compounds. Among the most effective catalysts is perhydroxyl ion,[75, 76] which reacts with Sarin in a fashion analogous to hydroxyl ion. The rate ($k_{A\ominus}$) for perhydroxyl ion attack on Sarin is 1340 liter mole^{-1} sec^{-1} as compared to $k_{OH\ominus}$ of 25.8 liter mole^{-1} sec^{-1} for the alkaline hydrolysis of Sarin, both at 25°. Epstein [77] has postulated that the facilitation of P—X bond cleavage is acquired through formation of a hydrogen bond between the perhydroxyl ion and the oxygen atom in the P=O group. The basic hydrolysis of Paroxon is also markedly accelerated by the perhydroxyl ion.[77] Scheme (6-19) may be written for this process which features a unimolecular decomposition of the peroxy acid intermediate.[78] Evidence for this pathway derives from the rate of oxygen evolution, followed volumetrically, which is first-order and independent of peroxide concentration. Thus, the decomposition of peroxy acid is slower than its formation, and mediated perhaps by solvent or the walls of the vessel. The pH profile of oxygen evolution is sigmoid with pK_a' of ca. 8.0. Everett et al.[79] have found that pK_a' values for the dissociation of peroxy fatty acids lie in the range 7.1–8.3. From the pH-rate profile the species undergoing decomposition is presumably the anion (6-19 I).

[74] P. C. Haake and F. H. Westheimer, *J. Am. Chem. Soc.* **83,** 1102 (1961).

[75] L. Larsson, *Acta Chem. Scand.* **12,** 723 (1958).

[76] B. Gehauf, J. Epstein, G. B. Wilson, B. Witten, A. Sass, V. E. Bauer, and W. H. C. Rueggeberg, *Anal. Chem.* **29,** 278 (1957).

[77] J. Epstein, M. M. Demek, and D. H. Rosenblatt, *J. Org. Chem.* **21,** 796 (1956).

[78] G. Aksnes, *Acta Chem. Scand.* **14,** 2075 (1960).

[79] A. J. Everett and G. J. Minkoff, *Trans. Faraday Soc.* **49,** 410 (1953).

Hypochlorite ion also is a potent catalyst, as demonstrated by Epstein *et al.* in their studies of the chlorine catalyzed hydrolysis of Sarin [37] and O,O,S-triethyl thiolphosphate in aqueous solution.[80] As in the case of perhydroxyl ion, the reactivity of hypochlorite is ascribed to a bifunctional attack that polarizes the P=O bond, thus facilitating displacement of the fluoride ion. The proposed reaction pathway does not depart from the basic scheme postulated for perhydroxyl ion. In these and later

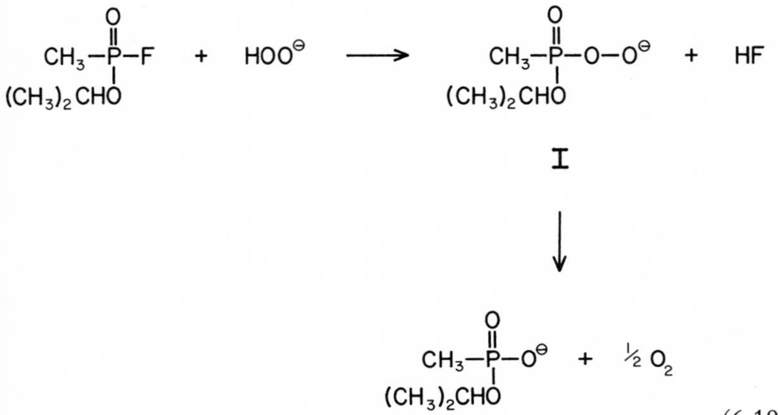

$$
\underset{(CH_3)_2CHO}{\overset{O}{\underset{\|}{CH_3-\overset{}{P}-F}}} \;+\; HOO^{\ominus} \;\longrightarrow\; \underset{(CH_3)_2CHO}{\overset{O}{\underset{\|}{CH_3-\overset{}{P}-O-O^{\ominus}}}} \;+\; HF
$$

$$\mathbf{I}$$

$$\downarrow$$

$$
\underset{(CH_3)_2CHO}{\overset{O}{\underset{\|}{CH_3-\overset{}{P}-O^{\ominus}}}} \;+\; \tfrac{1}{2}\,O_2
$$

(6-19)

studies,[37, 81] it was observed that the thiosulfate ion does not catalyze the hydrolysis of Sarin or Tabun. Thus in terms of Edwards' treatment [82] of nucleophilicity the basicity of the anion and not the polarizability appears as the dominant factor in determining the rate of a nucleophilic displacement on these (6-1) compounds. In addition, the importance of the "α-effect" is suggested by the enhanced reactivity of perhydroxyl and hypochlorite ion. Therefore, bifunctionality of the catalyst is not strictly required. Consequently, the gross parameters that govern nucleophilicity toward carbonyl compounds also appear to be important in nucleophilicity toward phosphorus compounds (6-1) (see Chapter 1).

B. Amines and Amino Acids

The reaction between DFP or DClP and amines or amino acid derivatives is of considerable biochemical importance because of their anti-

[80] N. G. Lordi and J. Epstein, *J. Am. Chem. Soc.* **80**, 509 (1958).

[81] K. B. Augustinsson, *Acta Chem. Scand.* **12**, 1286 (1958).

[82] J. O. Edwards, *J. Am. Chem. Soc.* **76**, 1540 (1954).

cholinesterase activity. Attempts to phosphorylate amino acids with DFP in a slightly alkaline aqueous medium were without success.[83] Use of DClP which, as discussed, is more reactive than DFP [84] gave the desired diisopropylphosphorylated amino acid derivatives. Glycine ethyl ester, glycinamide, and methyl esters of serine and DL-threonine are converted in nonaqueous solvents, e.g., chloroform, benzene, and ethyl acetate, at room temperature to the corresponding N-phosphorylated compound. As expected, the reaction of DClP occurs with other amines such as benzylamine and cyclohexylamine. Preliminary experiments also indicated that both the α-amino group and the phenolic hydroxyl of tyrosine ethyl ester are phosphorylated by DClP in the presence of triethylamine.

Ashbolt and Rydon [85] carefully reinvestigated the reactions between DClP and DFP and a series of amino acids in aqueous solutions, pH 7.8, 37–38°. No reaction products were detected after 30 hr for serine, lysine, cysteine, hydroxyproline, arginine, tryptophan, and asparagine. Diisopropylphosphorylation of the α-amino groups of phenylalanine and tyrosine happens to a slight extent with both DFP and DClP. However, the reaction of DFP with tyrosine results in diisopropylphosphorylation in ca. 50% yield of the phenolic hydroxyl group. No reaction was detected for DClP.

The search for "model reactions" of the enzyme process continued with a study of the interaction of imidazole, pyridine, and several of their derivatives with DFP.[86] In the presence of bicarbonate–carbon dioxide buffers, phosphorylation is characterized by the evolution of 1 mole of CO_2 per mole of DFP disappearing through nucleophilic attack:

$$(RO)_2POF + R'NH_2 + NaHCO_3 \rightarrow$$
$$(RO)_2PONHR' + NaF + H_2O + CO_2 \quad (6\text{-}20)$$

whereas 2 moles of CO_2 would be formed per mole of DFP hydrolyzed:

$$(RO)_2POF + 2NaHCO_3 \rightarrow (RO)_2PO_2Na + NaF + H_2O + 2CO_2$$
$$(6\text{-}21)$$

[83] T. Wagner-Jauregg, J. J. O'Neil, and W. H. Summerson, *J. Am. Chem. Soc* **73,** 5202 (1951).

[84] B. C. Saunders and G. J. Stacey, *J. Chem. Soc.* 695 (1948).

[85] R. F. Ashbolt and H. N. Rydon, *Biochem. J.* **66,** 237 (1957).

[86] T. Wagner-Jauregg and B. E. Hackley, Jr., *J. Am. Chem. Soc.* **75,** 2125 (1953).

No increase in the rate of hydrolysis of DFP at pH 7.6 was found for
serine, serine methyl ester, tryptophan, lysine, arginine, proline, creatine,
and creatinine, reconfirming portions of the work by Ashbolt and Rydon.[85]
The rate is accelerated by the following nitrogenous bases in the
order N-methylimidazole, 4-hydroxymethylimidazole, histidine methyl
ester, histamine, carnosine, histidine, and imidazole > benzimidazole
and 3,5-dimethylpyrazole > tetrazole, morpholine, and 2-methyloxazo-
line. The bases 2-methylimidazole, 2-mercaptoimidazole, ergothioneine,
pyrazine, and 2-methyloxazolidine are inactive as catalysts. Assays
established that neither histidine nor imidazole is consumed during the
reaction.

The hydrolysis of DFP in the presence of pyridine is 2-fold slower, in
terms of half-life, than in the presence of an equal concentration of
imidazole. 2-Picoline is as effective a nucleophile as pyridine, in contrast to the inactivity of 2-methylimidazole. Surprisingly, 2-hydroxy-
pyridine is inactive whereas 3-hydroxypyridine is a potent catalyst. The
velocity of the reaction of DFP with 3-hydroxypyridine is much faster
than that of DFP in the presence of a corresponding equimolar mixture
of phenol and pyridine. Thus 3-hydroxypyridine was suggested to be
acting as a bifunctional catalyst in a complete reversal of roles from the
catalysis of the mutarotation of tetramethylglucose, where 2-hydroxy-
pyridine was proposed as the bifunctional catalyst.[87]

The mechanism of these reactions is most likely similar to those already
discussed. The N-phosphorylated intermediates are highly unstable, as
was demonstrated for diisopropylphosphorylimidazole (DPI). DPI, isolated from the reaction of imidazole with DClP in chloroform, is ca. 50%
hydrolyzed in bicarbonate buffer, pH 7.6 at 30°, after 3 hours. Under
comparable conditions DFP hydrolyzed ca. 25 times slower.

The reactivity of a particular nitrogenous base is apparently a function of its basicity and configuration. Steric hindrance could be a reason
for the ineffectiveness of 2-substituted imidazoles, which are likewise
unable to bind hemin [88, 89] and show a much smaller rate of reaction with
p-nitrophenyl acetate (see Chapter 1). The importance of basicity
and configuration also has been demonstrated in the reaction of
several phosphorochloridates with aliphatic amines in nonaqueous
solutions.[90]

An interesting consequence of amine catalysis was observed by

[87] C. G. Swain and J. F. Brown, *J. Am. Chem. Soc.* **74,** 2538 (1952).
[88] W. Langenbeck and H. Schubert, *Naturwissenschaften* **39,** 211 (1952).
[89] R. W. Cowgill and W. M. Clark, *J. Biol. Chem.* **198,** 33 (1952).
[90] I. Dostrovsky and M. Halmann, *J. Chem. Soc.* 511 (1953).

Tammelin,[91] as represented in (6-22). Compound (6-22 I) upon storage underwent conversion to isomer II with a half-life at pH 6 at room temperature of ca. 7 minutes. The structure of (6-22 II) was later corroborated through spectroscopic evidence.[92]

$$
\begin{array}{cc}
\underset{\underset{F}{\overset{\parallel}{\underset{O}{\overset{}{\text{P}}}}}}{\overset{\text{CH}_3}{\diagdown}} \text{O---CH}_2\text{CH}_2\text{N(CH}_3)_2
& \longrightarrow
\left[\begin{array}{c}
\text{CH}_3 \diagdown \quad \text{O---CH}_2 \\
\text{P} \\
O \diagdown \overset{\oplus}{N}\text{---CH}_2 \\
(\text{CH}_3)_2
\end{array} \right] \text{F}^{\ominus}
\end{array} \qquad (6\text{-}22)
$$

$$
\text{I} \qquad\qquad\qquad\qquad \text{II}
$$

C. Hydroxylamine and Hydroxylamine Derivatives

In the search for reagents which can react rapidly to neutralize the toxicity of compounds (6-1) or possibly serve as reactivators for the inhibited enzyme,[93-96] extensive studies have been performed with hydroxylamine, hydroxamic acids, and oximes.

Jandorf[97] found that the reaction of Sarin with hydroxylamine under pseudo-first-order conditions in bicarbonate buffer liberates 2 moles of gas per mole of Sarin. Substitution of a phosphate for the bicarbonate buffer showed that the reaction, in addition to acid formation, is accompanied by the simultaneous liberation of a mole of nitrogen per mole of hydrolyzed Sarin. A second experiment manifested the rapid disappearance of hydroxylamine in the presence of excess Sarin. Thus, the action of hydroxylamine is not restricted to catalysis of the spontaneous hydrolysis of Sarin, which would have resulted in the evolution specifically of 2 moles of CO_2 per mole of Sarin and no net loss of hydroxylamine.

Other information forthcoming from the reaction of excess Sarin with hydroxylamine is the absence of gas evolution in phosphate buffer, but the presence of a mole of gas per mole of Sarin hydrolyzed in bicarbonate buffer. Close scrutiny of the amount of acid formation in view of the overall reaction led to the discovery that a mole of ammonia also is pro-

[91] L. E. Tammelin, Acta Chem. Scand. 11, 859 (1957).
[92] L. Larsson, Acta Chem. Scand. 12, 587 (1958).
[93] D. R. Davies and A. L. Green, Biochem. J. 63, 529 (1956).
[94] I. B. Wilson, S. Ginsberg, and E. K. Meislich, J. Am. Chem. Soc. 77, 4286 (1955).
[95] I. B. Wilson and E. K. Meislich, J. Am. Chem. Soc. 75, 4628 (1953).
[96] I. B. Wilson, J. Am. Chem. Soc. 77, 2383 (1955).
[97] B. J. Jandorf, J. Am. Chem. Soc. 78, 3686 (1956).

duced per mole of Sarin destroyed. The overall scheme deduced from these observations is as follows:

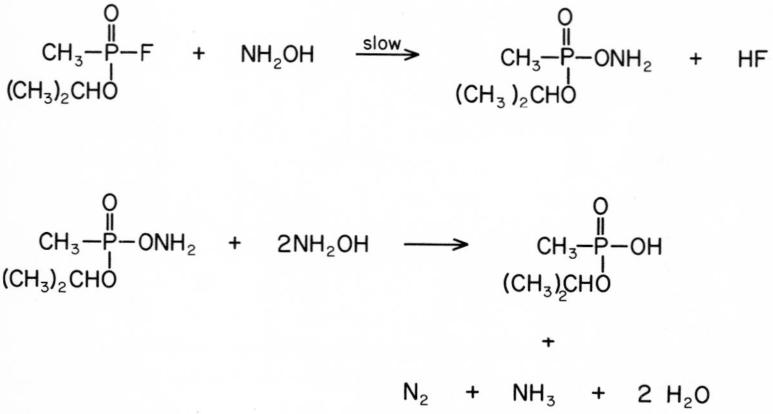

$$CH_3-\overset{\overset{O}{\|}}{\underset{\underset{(CH_3)_2CHO}{|}}{P}}-F \ + \ NH_2OH \ \xrightarrow{\text{slow}} \ CH_3-\overset{\overset{O}{\|}}{\underset{\underset{(CH_3)_2CHO}{|}}{P}}-ONH_2 \ + \ HF$$

$$CH_3-\overset{\overset{O}{\|}}{\underset{\underset{(CH_3)_2CHO}{|}}{P}}-ONH_2 \ + \ 2NH_2OH \ \longrightarrow \ CH_3-\overset{\overset{O}{\|}}{\underset{\underset{(CH_3)_2CHO}{|}}{P}}-OH$$

$$+$$

$$N_2 \ + \ NH_3 \ + \ 2 \ H_2O$$

$$(6\text{-}23)$$

The first step appears rate-limiting since the rates of acid and nitrogen production are identical. O rather than N attack is favored because substitution at O greatly lowers or abolishes the reactivity of the nucleophile. Other experiments indicate that DFP and Tabun are also readily attacked by hydroxylamine, with Tabun presumably undergoing P—N bond cleavage rather than loss of cyanide ion.

Reactions between compounds (6-1) and hydroxamic acids were first observed by Hackley et al.[98] Later, elucidation of the reaction mechanism was undertaken in a detailed kinetic study of the reaction between Sarin and benzohydroxamic acid in aqueous solution.[99] Preparative reactions had resulted in the postulation that initial acylation of the hydroxamic acid by the phosphoryl halide was followed by a Lossen rearrangement.[100] The overall rate constant for (6-24) was determined by following the rate of acid production. That k_1 was rate-limiting was established by showing that the rate constant for the appearance of fluoride ion was identical to the rate constant for total acid production. The overall stoichiometry of acid production was also determined. In the net reaction the total quantity of acid produced, Q_{acid}, at constant pH per mole of Sarin, is

[98] B. E. Hackley, Jr., R. Plapinger, M. A. Stolberg, and T. Wagner-Jauregg, J. Am. Chem. Soc. 77, 3651 (1955).

[99] R. Swidler and G. M. Steinberg, J. Am. Chem. Soc. 78, 3594 (1956).

[100] M. A. Stolberg, R. C. Tweit, G. H. Steinberg, and T. Wagner-Jauregg, J. Am. Chem. Soc. 77, 765 (1955).

(6-24)

135

defined by

$$Q_{acid} = 2 + \left[\frac{K'_{a_2}}{K'_{a_2} + a_H}\right] - 2\left[\frac{K'_{a_1}}{K'_{a_1} + a_H}\right] \quad (C_6H_5CONHOH) \quad (6\text{-}25)$$

where K'_{a_2} and K'_{a_1} are the dissociation constants for (6-24 I) and benzohydroxamic acid, respectively.   Correction for the side reaction of Sarin
and phenyl isocyanate with solvent brought Q_{acid} into agreement with
the experimental value of acid production.   Further proof that k_1 is
rate-limiting derived from independent study of step (6-24d), in which
phenyl isocyanate was found to react with water or benzohydroxamate
ion at an immeasurably fast rate.   Other experiments at differing pH
and reactant concentrations described a second-order dependence of the
rate upon Sarin and benzohydroxamate ion.   Thus the kinetic data
clearly support the above reaction series.   It is noteworthy that the
phosphorylated hydroxamic acid is extremely unstable in contrast to the
acylated hydroxamic acids.[101, 102]

The originally proposed mechanism attributed the enhanced reac-
tivity ($k_{A^\ominus} = 17.0$ liter mole^{-1} sec^{-1} at 25°) to the possible bifunctionality
of the catalyst.[103]   The same view was adopted by Swidler et al.,[104] who

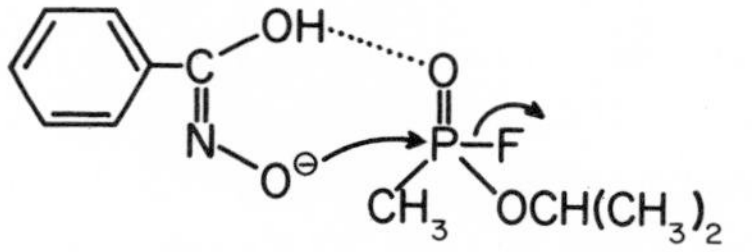

$$(6\text{-}26)$$

investigated the reaction of a series of p-substituted benzohydroxamic
acids with Sarin.   The experimental data fit a conventional Hammett
plot [105] with a ρ of -0.77 and the more general free-energy Brönsted
relationship [106] with an α of $+0.80$ (Fig. 6-1).   The value of ρ is consistent
with a gross mechanism involving attack by an anion on a neutral mole-
cule and far less than a rate step involving a Lossen rearrangement
(ρ ca. -2.6).[107]   The adherence to the Brönsted catalysis law and the
high value of α further stress the importance of the nucleophile's basicity
as a significant factor in these reactions.

[101] W. B. Renfrow and C. R. Hauser, J. Am. Chem. Soc. 59, 2308 (1937).

[102] R. D. Bright and C. R. Hauser, J. Am. Chem. Soc. 61, 618 (1939).

[103] T. Wagner-Jauregg, Arzneimittel-Forsch. 6, 194 (1956).

[104] R. Swidler, R. E. Plapinger, and G. M. Steinberg, J. Am. Chem. Soc. 81, 3271 (1959).

[105] L. P. Hammett, "Physical Organic Chemistry," McGraw-Hill, New York, 1940, p. 185.

[106] J. N. Brönsted and K. Pedersen, Z. Physik. Chem. (Leipzig) 108A, 185 (1924).

[107] H. H. Jaffé, Chem. Rev. 53, 191 (1953).

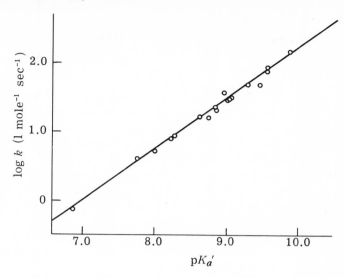

Fig. 6-1   *Relationship between log $k_A^\ominus$ (liter mole^{-1} sec^{-1}) and pK$_a'$ for the reaction between Sarin and the anions of a variety of hydroxamic acids.   (Ref. 104.)*

Research aimed at discovering more efficacious hydroxamic acids led first to the synthesis of a series of o-substituted benzohydroxamic acids and vicinal dihydroxamic acids.[108, 109]   Rate enhancements produced by either o-substitution or vicinal groups have been reported frequently in the literature.[87, 110, 111]   Other investigators [112] undertook preparation of hydroxamic acids possessing (1) negatively charged sites at varying distances from the hydroxamate ion, as in N-hydroxyoxalamic acid and N-hydroxysuccinamic acid; (2) groups capable of hydrogen bonding, e.g., D-gluconohydroxamic acid; and (3) a second electrophilic group at the opposite end of the molecule sterically able to attack either phosphorus or fluorine, as in $H_2NCO(CH_2)_8CONHOH$ (9-carboxamidopelargonohydroxamic acid) and $HO(CH_2)_9CONHOH$ (10-hydroxycaprohydroxamic acid).   In no instance did the $k_A^\ominus$ determined for a particular compound in either study show significant deviation from the Brönsted plot of Fig. 6-1.

[108] M. A. Stolberg and W. A. Mosher, *J. Am. Chem. Soc.* **79**, 2618 (1957).

[109] M. A. Stolberg, W. A. Mosher, and T. Wagner-Jauregg, *J. Am. Chem. Soc.* **79**, 2615 (1957).

[110] L. P. Hammett, "Physical Organic Chemistry," McGraw-Hill, New York, 1940, p. 204.

[111] D. E. Pearson and W. E. Cole, *J. Org. Chem.* **20**, 488 (1955).

[112] C. F. Endres and J. Epstein, *J. Org. Chem.* **24**, 1497 (1959).

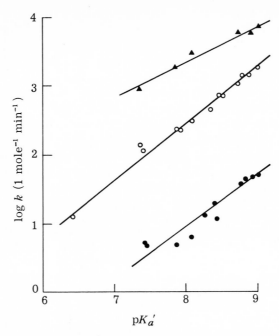

Fig. 6-2   *Reaction of hydroxamic acids at 25° and in collidine buffer with Tabun* (▲) *(1 + log k), Sarin* (○), *or DFP* (●).   *(Ref. 113.)*

Extension of the studies of the reactions of hydroxamic acids to include various substrates of type (6-1) yielded a distinct Brönsted plot (Fig. 6-2) for each individual substrate.[113]   Unfortunately little can be said on the basis of these data concerning the sensitivity of these compounds to basicity and polarizability, due to change in the leaving group and structural alterations which may sterically influence the attack by the nucleophile. It is sufficient to note that the Brönsted α remains relatively the same for the three compounds with the main difference in rate arising from dissimilar intercepts.

The inability to synthesize more efficacious bifunctional hydroxamic acid catalysts is clarified by the finding of Green et al. that N-hydroxyphthalimide (6-27 I), which cannot tautomerize to the hydroximic acid (6-27 II), reacts with Sarin in accord with its basicity.   This jeopardizes the theory of bifunctional catalysis as a reason for the high reactivity of hydroxamic acids and indicates that the reaction, at least for these

[113] A. L. Green, G. L. Sainsbury, B. Saville, and M. Stansfield, *J. Chem. Soc.* 1583 (1958).

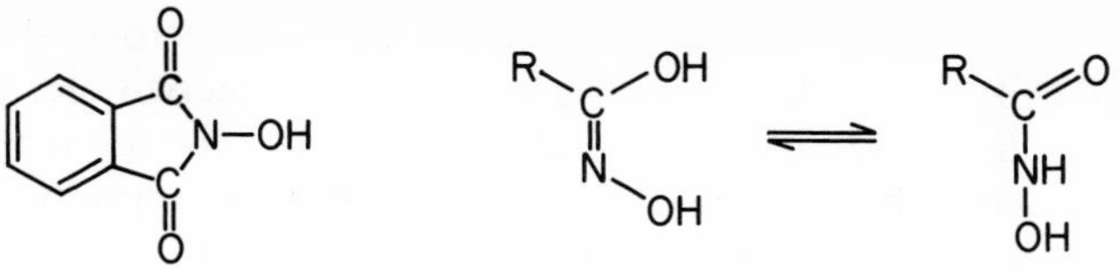

Equation (6-27):

I (phthalimide N-OH structure)

$$R-C(OH)=N-OH \rightleftharpoons R-C(=O)-NH-OH \quad (6\text{-}27)$$

I   II

catalysts, is simply a nucleophilic displacement. It appears that hydroxylamine, hydroxamic acids, and oximes capable of exerting an "α-effect" owe their enhanced reactivity to this phenomenon.

The reaction between Sarin and 1,2-dionemonoximes, the more active oximes studied, is formulated as involving a rate-determining O-phosphorylation of the oxime anion, followed by rapid decomposition of the oxime phosphonate to the observed products.[114] The equally rapid forma-

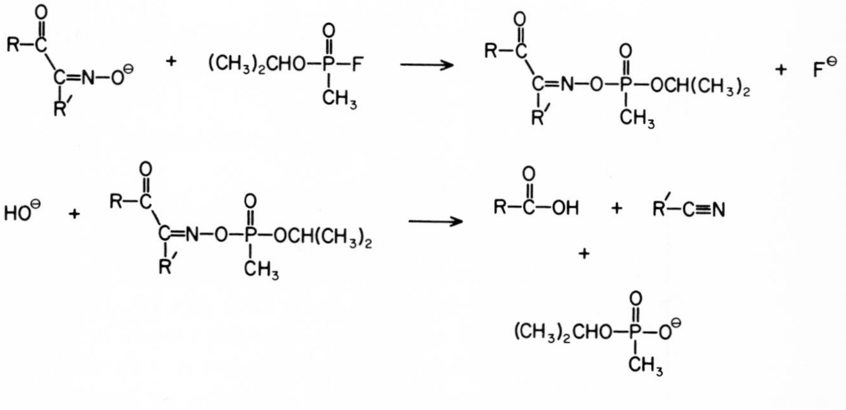

$$R-C(=O)-C(R')=N-O^{\ominus} + (CH_3)_2CHO-P(=O)(CH_3)-F \longrightarrow R-C(=O)-C(R')=N-O-P(=O)(CH_3)-OCH(CH_3)_2 + F^{\ominus}$$

$$HO^{\ominus} + R-C(=O)-C(R')=N-O-P(=O)(CH_3)-OCH(CH_3)_2 \longrightarrow R-C(=O)-OH + R'-C{\equiv}N + (CH_3)_2CHO-P(=O)(CH_3)-O^{\ominus}$$

(6-28)

tion of 3 moles of acid per mole of Sarin with either 2-oxo-aldoximes ($R' = H$) or ketoximes ($R' = $ alkyl) makes it unlikely, but does not exclude the possibility, that 2-oxo-aldoxime phosphonates decompose by initial elimination of isopropyl methylphosphonic acid to give an acyl cyanide. The acylating properties of the postulated oxime phosphonate have been shown by carrying out the reaction between Sarin and hydroxyiminoacetone ($R = CH_3$, $R' = H$) in the presence of aniline and isolating acetanilide.

[114] A. L. Green and B. Saville, J. Chem. Soc. 3887 (1956).

The reaction of Sarin with hydroxyiminoacetylacetone ($R = CH_3$, $R' = CH_3CO$), in which the oxime group is flanked by two acyl groups instead of one, is more complicated.   Pyruvic acid was found among the reaction products.   A reasonable mechanism for the decomposition of Sarin in the presence of this oxime may include a Beckmann rearrangement.

It is now appropriate to discuss briefly the reactivation of DFP or tetraethylpyrophosphate (TEPP)-inhibited acetylcholinesterase by nucleophiles similar to those already mentioned in this section.   The active site of acetylcholinesterase may be conveniently considered as consisting of two subsites: (a) an anionic site which contributes to the catalytic activity by binding and orienting substituted ammonium structures, and (b) an esteratic site which is postulated to contain an acidic and a basic group, both of which are necessary for activity.[94, 118]   During enzymic hydrolysis, attack by groups of the esteratic site on the substrate results in acylation of a basic group which is rapidly deacylated, regenerating free enzyme (6-28a).   Substitution of the organophosphorus compound

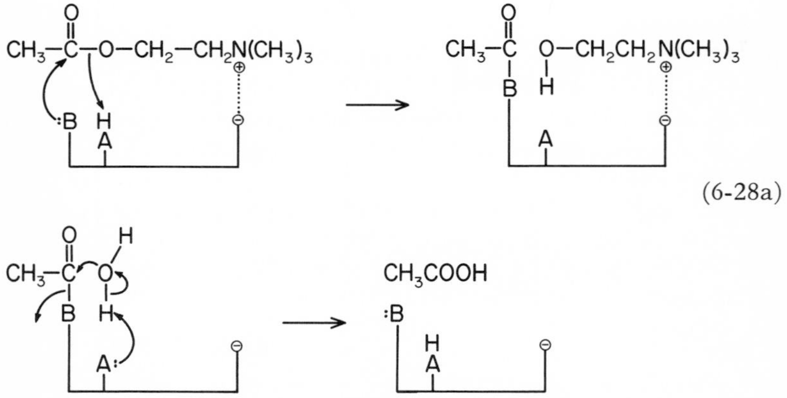

$$CH_3-\overset{\overset{O}{\|}}{C}-O-CH_2-CH_2\overset{\oplus}{N}(CH_3)_3 \qquad \longrightarrow \qquad CH_3-\overset{\overset{O}{\|}}{C}\quad O-CH_2CH_2\overset{\oplus}{N}(CH_3)_3$$

$$(6\text{-}28a)$$

$$CH_3-\overset{\overset{O}{\|}}{C}\overset{H}{\underset{O}{\diagup}} \qquad \longrightarrow \qquad CH_3COOH$$

for the normal ester substrate leads to a dialkylphosphoryl enzyme which does not reaily deacylate.

It would then appear possible to restore enzymic activity by means of a bimolecular nucleophilic displacement on the phosphorylated enzyme, yielding free enzyme.[95, 115, 116]   Experiments by Wilson have indicated that the anionic site is still functional in TEPP-inhibited enzyme, although with an affinity only $1/60$ that in the normal enzyme.[115]   The anionic site does not appear to be functional in DFP-inhibited enzyme, possibly being shielded by the larger isopropyl groups.   Thus, it is suggested that the ability of a nucleophile to serve as a reactivator at least for the TEPP-

[115] I. B. Wilson, *J. Biol. Chem.* **190**, 111 (1951).
[116] I. B. Wilson, *J. Biol. Chem.* **199**, 113 (1952).

inhibited enzyme may be enhanced by incorporation of a quaternary nitrogen structure into the same molecule.[94, 95]

It was found that nucleophiles without a cationic center, such as nicotinohydroxamic acid, pyridine, imidazole, hydroxylamine, monoisonitrosoacetone, and acethydroxamic acid, and those with cationic centers, such as nicotinohydroxamic acid methiodide, isonicotinohydroxamic acid methiodide, betaine hydroxamic acid, choline, and trimethylamine oxide, can serve as reactivators [93, 117] for inhibited acetylcholinesterase. Those with cationic sites definitely promote the rate of reactivation over that expected on the basis of their pK_a'.[117] In addition, Wilson [94] observed for the hydroxamic acids and phosphorylated acetylcholinesterase a saturation effect which was interpreted as due to an enzyme reactivator complex. The pH dependence of reactivation of phosphorylated acetylcholinesterase by hydroxamic acids and oximes describes a bell-shaped profile in which the pH optima follow the order of the pK_a' of the reactivators.[93, 94]

D. Catechols

Phenolic hydroxyl groups, as previously mentioned, are phosphorylated by DFP or DClP. Phenyl diisopropylphosphate was isolated after the reaction of DClP with phenol in benzene buffered by triethylamine.[119] Phenol also could be phosphorylated to a small extent by DFP in aqueous potassium carbonate solution.

The reactivity of the phenolic hydroxy group with DFP was increased markedly by the introduction of a second hydroxyl group in the o-position.[119, 120] Catechol reacts readily with DFP at pH 9 in aqueous solution (6-29):

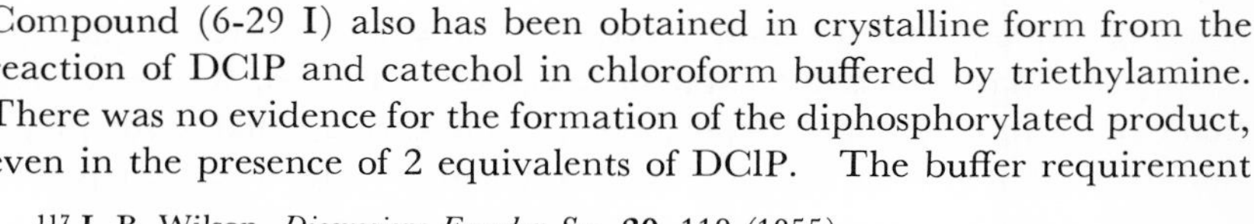

$$(6\text{-}29)$$

Compound (6-29 I) also has been obtained in crystalline form from the reaction of DClP and catechol in chloroform buffered by triethylamine. There was no evidence for the formation of the diphosphorylated product, even in the presence of 2 equivalents of DClP. The buffer requirement

[117] I. B. Wilson, Discussions Faraday Soc. 20, 119 (1955).

[118] I. B. Wilson and F. Bergmann, J. Biol. Chem. 185, 479 (1950).

[119] B. J. Jandorf, T. Wagner-Jauregg, J. J. O'Neil, and M. Stolberg, J. Am. Chem. Soc. 74, 1521 (1952).

[120] K. B. Augustinsson, Acta Chem. Scand. 6, 959 (1952).

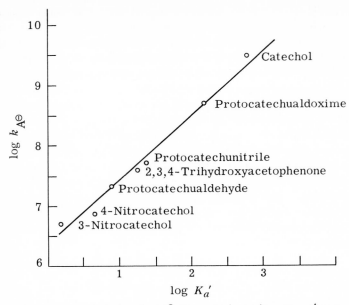

Fig. 6-3   *Relationship between log $k_A\ominus$ (liter mole^{-1} min^{-1}) and log K_a' in the reactions between Sarin and a series of catechols.   (Ref. 121.)*

in conjunction with preliminary kinetic studies implicates the catecholate ion as the probable reactive species.

The requirement of *o*-hydroxyl groups was further demonstrated by the lack of reactivity under comparable conditions of resorcinol, hydroquinone, *o*-nitrophenol, *o*-methoxyphenol, salicylic acid, and *o*-hydroxybenzylalcohol.   On the other hand, phenols with three vicinal hydroxyl groups exhibited a reactivity toward DFP ca. 5 times that of catechol. Pyrogallol and DFP in equimolar amounts gave a monophosphorylated product; excess DFP and pyrogallol yielded a diphosphorylated, presumably 1,3 product.

A kinetic investigation of the reaction between Sarin and a series of catechols in aqueous solution more rigorously demonstrated that the monocatecholate ion is the catalytic species.[121]   Indeed, further ionization cancels its reactivity.   As before, $k_A\ominus$ is linearly related to the pK_a' of the nucleophile.   This is illustrated graphically in Fig. 6-3, the equation of the plot being

$$k_A\ominus = 2.57 \times 10^{-6}/K_a'^{0.89} \qquad (6\text{-}30)$$

[121] J. Epstein, D. H. Rosenblatt, and M. M. Demek, *J. Am. Chem. Soc.* **78,** 341 (1956).

The α value of 0.89 reflects an almost complete dependency on basicity for reactivity and a high degree of bond formation in the critical transition state. In view of the ability of Sarin to hydrogen bond catechol,[122] the most probable mechanism is depicted as involving an intermediate complex which collapses in a rate-determining step to product:

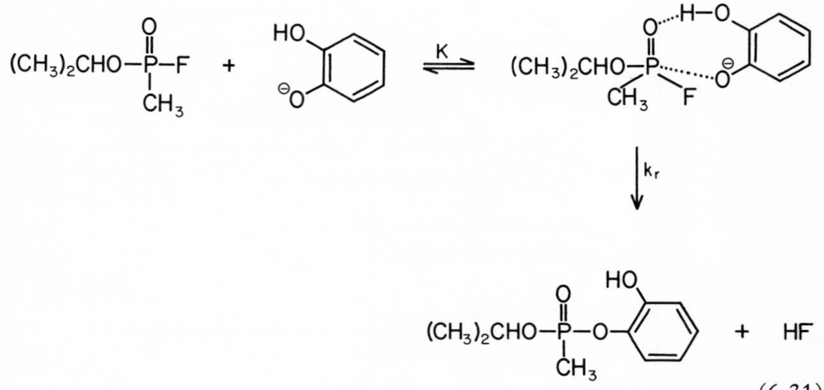

$$(6\text{-}31)$$

The high reactivity of the catecholate ion relative to its basicity can be readily seen through comparison with hydroxyl ion: $k_{A^\ominus} = 9.82$, $pK_a' = 9.48$ vs. $k_{OH^\ominus} = 25.8$, $pK_a' \cong 14$ at 25°.

The mechanism proposed by Epstein et al. lends itself quite readily to a mathematical treatment designed to elucidate the extent of intermediate complex formation and, therefore, allow comparison of the binding strength of different compounds.[123] It can be formulated kinetically as

$$S + C \underset{k_{-1}}{\overset{k_1}{\rightleftarrows}} SC \overset{k_2}{\to} P \qquad (6\text{-}32)$$

where S is substrate, C is catalyst, and SC is substrate-catalyst complex. Let $[S_0]$ and $[C_0]$ be the initial substrate and catalyst concentrations, respectively; $[S]$ and $[SC]$ the concentration of substrate and complex at any time, t; and set $K = k_1/k_{-1}$. When $k_2 \ll k_{-1}$, then

$$[SC] = K[S][C]$$
$$[S] = [S_0] - [SC] \qquad (6\text{-}33)$$
$$[C] = [C_0] - [SC]$$

[122] L. Larsson, Arkiv Kemi 13, 259 (1958).

[123] T. Higuchi, Progress Report submitted to Armed Forces Chemical Center, Maryland (May 20, 1959).

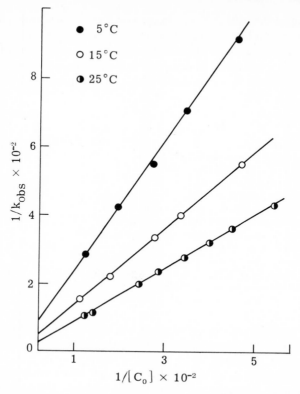

Fig. 6-4   *Reciprocal plots for reaction of Sarin with CDMA.*   *(Ref. 123.)*

If $[C_0] \gg [S_0]$, then $[C] \cong [C_0]$ and

$$[SC] = K[C_0]\{[S_0] - [SC]\}$$

$$[SC] = \frac{K[C_0][S_0]}{1 + K[C_0]} \tag{6-34}$$

The initial rate for the disappearance of substrate can then be defined in terms of k_{obs}, the pseudo-first-order rate constant as

$$k_{obs} = \frac{k_2 K[C_0]}{1 + K[C_0]} \tag{6-35}$$

or in reciprocal form as

$$1/k_{obs} = 1/k_2 K[C_0] + 1/k_2 \tag{6-36}$$

Thus a plot of $1/k_{obs}$ *vs.* $[C_0]^{-1}$ should be linear with a slope equal to

Table 6-7 *   *Rate and equilibrium constants for the reaction of Sarin
with a series of catechols*

Catechol	pK_a'	k_2 (sec^{-1})	K (liter mole^{-1})	k_2K (liter mole^{-1} sec^{-1})
3-Nitrocatechol	6.66	0.005	12	0.060
4-Nitrocatechol	6.89	0.008	11	0.088
Protocatechualdehyde	7.23	0.02	9	0.18
3,6-Bis(dimethylaminomethyl)catechol dihydrochloride (CDMA)	6.35	0.063	22.5	1.42
3,6-Bis(piperidinomethyl)catechol dihydrochloride (CDPM)	6.39	0.037	36	1.33
2-Morpholinomethyl-4-methoxyphenol hydrochloride (PMPM)	6.84	0.035	2.5	0.088
Propyl 2-diethyl-aminomethyl-galliate hydrochloride (GME)	6.78	0.043	38.3	1.65
Propyl 2-dimethyl-aminomethyl-galliate hydrochloride (GMM)	6.82	0.039	38.5	1.50

* Ref. 123.

$1/k_2K$ and an intercept equal to $1/k_2$.   A test of the validity of (6-35)
is represented in Fig. 6-4, for the reaction of CDMA with Sarin.   The
calculated values of k_2 and K so obtained for the reaction of Sarin with
a series of catechols are recorded in Table 6-7.

The pH dependence of k_{obs} for the reaction between Sarin and CDMA
suggested a singly dissociated active species.   Spectrophotometric evidence for a bathochromic shift at pH 7 and an increase in absorption over
that at pH 1 is typical of phenolic behavior upon ionization.   The predominant species is probably the zwitterion:

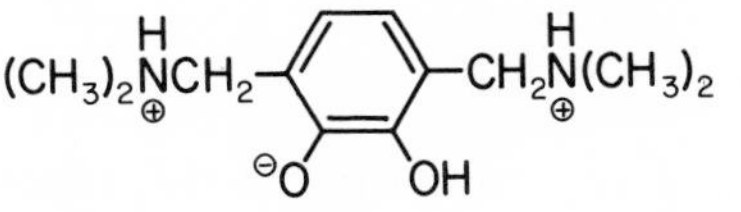

$$(CH_3)_2\overset{H}{\underset{\oplus}{N}}CH_2\text{---}\!\!\!\!\underset{\underset{\ominus O \quad OH}{}}{\text{---}}\!\!\!\!\text{---}CH_2\overset{H}{\underset{\oplus}{N}}(CH_3)_2 \qquad (6\text{-}37)$$

The same type of pH dependence was observed for the other Mannich-
base type catechols of Table 6-7.

The k_2 values for catechols of the Mannich-base variety are greater
than those for other catechols of comparable basicity.   This is probably
due to the presence of the cationic site in the phenolic nucleus, which
increases the reactivity of the anion relative to its basic strength.[123a]

[123a] J. Epstein, H. O. Michel, D. H. Rosenblatt, R. E. Plapinger, R. A. Stephani,
and E. Cook, *J. Am. Chem. Soc.* **86,** 4958 (1964).

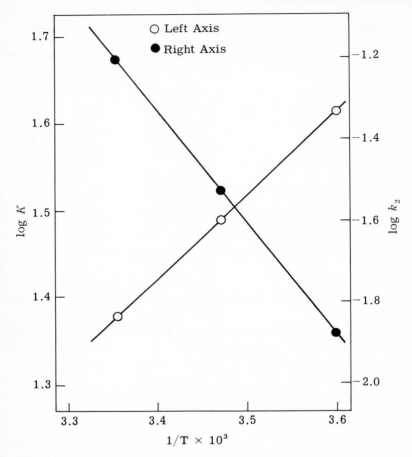

Fig. 6-5   *Temperature dependence of equilibrium and rate constants for reaction of Sarin with CDMA. $\Delta H_{eq} \sim -5\ kcal/mole;\ \Delta H_{act} \sim 13\ kcal/mole.   (Ref. 123.)*

Indeed, Epstein *et al.* have demonstrated this effect to be additive; that is, each cationic site contributes to an increase in reactivity, the magnitude of the increase being related to the distance of separation of the cationic and anionic sites in the phenol.   Thus, for the Mannich-base type catechols, it is quite possible that an electrostatic interaction other than hydrogen bonding is responsible for the observed complexing.

Values of k_2 and K at various temperatures plotted in the Arrhenius manner allowed evaluation of E_a for the equilibrium and rate-determining step.   The results for CDMA and Sarin interaction, illustrated in Fig. 6-5, complete a convincing kinetic argument favoring intermediate

Table 6-8 *   *Rate constants for the reaction of Sarin with some
nucleophilic reagents (25°)*

Catalyst	pK_a'	$k_{A^{\ominus}}$ (liter mole^{-1} sec^{-1})	Ref.
3-Nitrocatechol	6.66	0.025	121
Isonitrosoacetylacetone	7.38	1.3	114
ClO$^{\ominus}$	7.40	10	37
Salicylhydroxamic acid	7.43	1.9	113
2,3,4-Trihydroxyacetophenone	7.62	0.295	121
Pyruvaldoxime	8.30	4.2	114
Benzhydroxamic acid	8.75	17.0	113
Diacetylmonoxime	9.30	6.8	114
Catechol	9.48	9.82	121
Pyridine-2-aldoxime	10.10	28.2	114
H$_2$O$_2$	11.53	1340	75

* Ref. 35.

complex formation for the reaction of organophosphorus compounds with catechols.

Rate constants for the reaction of Sarin with nucleophilic reagents are given in Table 6-8.

IV. METAL-ION CATALYZED HYDROLYSIS

Studies of the catalytic properties of a variety of metal salts and chelates revealed that MoO_4^{-2} markedly accelerates the hydrolysis of DFP and Sarin.[124, 125] Hydrolysis of Sarin in water is catalyzed also by Ce(III), Mn(II), Cu(II), WO_4^{-2}, and CrO_4^{-2} ions.[125, 126] The hydrolysis of Tabun is accelerated by Cu(II), Ni(II), Co(II), Ag(I), Au(III), and Pd(II) salts.[127] Yet in aqueous solution at pH 7, La(III), Pd(II), Cr(III), Co(II), Fe(II), and Ni(II) show little if any catalytic activity toward the hydrolysis of DFP.[125] The absence of catalytic activity by metal salts of the rare earths is in contrast to their rapid acceleration of the hydrolysis of organophosphates in general (see Chapter 5). Cu(II) also proved to be a potent accelerator for the hydrolysis of DFP.[125]

[124] L. Larsson, *Acta Chem. Scand.* **12**, 1226 (1958).
[125] T. Wagner-Jauregg, B. E. Hackley, Jr., T. A. Lies, O. O. Owens, and R. Proper, *J. Am. Chem. Soc.* **77**, 922 (1955).
[126] J. Epstein and D. H. Rosenblatt, *J. Am. Chem. Soc.* **80**, 3596 (1958).
[127] K. B. Augustinsson and G. Heimbürger, *Acta Chem. Scand.* **9**, 383 (1955).

Table 6-9 *   *Efficient copper(II) chelate catalysts for* DFP *hydrolysis* [a]

Complexing agent	Half-life (min)	Complexing agent	Half-life (min)
(no catalyst)	(>2500)	Threonine	13
Catechol [b]	29	Ethylenediamine	16
β-Alanine	29	o-Phenanthroline	14
Glycine	27	Imidazole	14
Aspartic acid	26	4,4'-Dimethyl-2,2'-bipyridyl	9
Glutamic acid	25	L-Histidine	8
Arginine	23	Gallic acid [b]	7
Lysine	23	α,α'-Dipyridyl	4.5

* Ref. 125.

[a] At 38° in bicarbonate-CO_2 buffer, pH 7.6 ($4.5 \times 10^{-3} M$ DFP; $22.8 \times 10^{-3} M$ complexing agent + $CuSO_4$ 1:1).

[b] For the purpose of comparison.

The effect of Cu(II), at a pH above 7, can be greatly enhanced through complex formation with certain nitrogen-containing bases. The most efficient Cu(II) chelates are given in Table 6-9.[125] Chelates of Ni(II), Co(II), Fe(II), and Mn(II) were found to lack significant catalytic activity.

With monodentate donors, such as imidazole, maximum reactivity is reached at the Cu(II): imidazole ratio 1:2, and remains at that level upon further addition of imidazole. In the case of bidentate donor groups, such as dipyridyl, the 1:1 chelates are the most effective catalysts. Use of a tetradentate ion, such as ethylenediaminetetraacetic acid, results in a poor hydrolytic Cu(II) chelate catalyst, perhaps by occupying coordination sites needed for binding the organophosphorus compound.

Several of the above observations were substantiated and expanded by an extensive study of the catalytic effects of various metal chelates on the hydrolysis of DFP and Sarin.[128] In this work some of the characteristics necessary for Cu(II) chelates to function as catalysts were established, several of which may be generalized to include other metal ions.

The charge of the Cu(II) complex appears to exert an important influence on the activity of the particular chelate as a hydrolytic catalyst. Since the degree of polarization and neutralization of negative charge is directly proportional to the magnitude of the effective positive charge on the metal ion, this property of the metal ion is probably its most impor-

[128] R. C. Courtney, R. L. Gustafson, S. J. Westerback, H. Hyytianinen, S. C. Chaberek, Jr., and A. E. Martell, *J. Am. Chem. Soc.* **79,** 3030 (1957).

tant aspect.[128a] From a mechanistic standpoint there are two general ways by which these chelates may act as catalysts in the hydrolysis of Sarin and DFP. One involves combination of the metal chelate with the substrate, followed by attack on this complex by hydroxide ion. The more electropositive the Cu(II) atom, the greater will be the facilitation of the nucleophilic attack through lowering of electron density on the phosphorus atom. An alternate mechanism analogous to a "push-pull mechanism" pictures the Cu(II) chelate acting amphoterically. The chelate would

$$
\underset{\substack{A\\A}}{\overset{A}{\diagdown}}\,\overset{2\oplus}{Cu}\overset{O^{\ominus}}{\underset{OH_2}{\diagup}} \quad + \quad \underset{\substack{|\\R_2}}{\overset{O}{\overset{\|}{R_1-P-F}}} \quad \longrightarrow \quad \underset{\substack{A\\A}}{\overset{A}{\diagdown}}\,\overset{2\oplus}{Cu}\overset{O}{\underset{F}{\diagup}}\,\overset{R_1}{\underset{R_2}{\overset{|}{P-O^{\ominus}}}} \quad \longrightarrow \quad \text{Product}
$$

(6-38)

therefore have two functions: (1) as an electrophile in accepting the fluoride ion, and (2) as a nucleophile through $>M-O^{\ominus}$ species. In this case the more positive the metal ion, the greater will be its ability to accept fluoride. However the effect on the $>M-O^{\ominus}$ species is difficult to predict since the lower pK'_a of the complexed hydroxyl is compensated by an increase in the concentration of this species. Experiments with Cu(II) chelates showed their catalytic activity in the hydrolysis of Sarin to decrease with the increasing negative charge of the chelate, consistent with the lowering of the effective positive charge on the metal ion.

As noted earlier, the number of donors in a ligand also exerts a pronounced effect on the catalytic activity of the chelate. The highest catalytic activity of Cu(II) chelates is obtained with bidentate donors, with additional donor groups per mole of ligand reducing their effectiveness as catalysts. Of the bidentate chelate compounds, those containing two water molecules bound directly to the metal ion apparently possess the most favorable structure for producing catalytic activity in Cu(II) chelates. Systems containing monodentate ligands unfortunately were not sufficiently stable to prevent precipitation of Cu(II) hydroxides at pH 7 and were not studied.

The importance of steric factors also enters into the stability of the 1:1 Cu(II) chelate. The stability of the chelate is controlled by the tendency to disproportionate to the 2:1 chelate and copper hydroxide, as well as by its own intrinsic stability constant. Thus a 1:1 chelate with a high stability constant may be unstable in solution, if the 2:1 chelate is also very stable. Since Cu(II) chelates are square planar, the substitution of alkyl groups in place of the amino hydrogen atoms in a ligand

[128a] M. L. Bender, "Reactions of Coordinated Ligands and Homogenous Catalysis," American Chemical Society Advances in Chemistry Series **37**, 19–35 (1963).

would help to prevent their disproportionation by destabilizing the $2:1$ chelate through steric repulsion between the substituents. This effect was observed in the case of substituted ethylenediamines such as N,N,N',N'-

$$
\begin{array}{c}
\text{R}\quad\text{R}\;\;\text{R}\quad\text{R} \\
\diagdown\,\diagup\quad\diagdown\,\diagup \\
\text{N}\quad\;\;\text{N} \\
\;\;\;^{2\oplus}\!\!\diagdown\text{Cu}\diagup \\
\text{N}\quad\;\;\text{N} \\
\diagup\,\diagdown\quad\diagup\,\diagdown \\
\text{R}\quad\text{R}\;\;\text{R}\quad\text{R}
\end{array}
\qquad\qquad (6\text{-}39)
$$

tetramethylethylenediamine and N,N'-dimethylethylenediamine and thereby is helpful in obtaining a stable aqueous $1:1$ Cu(II) chelate.

Lastly, the experimental evidence seems to indicate that the catalytic activity generally decreases with increasing stability of the metal chelate compound. For example, in a series of $1:1$ Cu(II) chelates formed by N-substituted ethylenediamines, the chelate stability constants decrease in the order ethylenediamine $>$ N,N'-dimethylethylenediamine $>$ N,N,N',N'-tetramethylethylenediamine. The order of catalytic activity is exactly the reverse. In view of this correlation with stability, the least stable metal chelate should have a maximum catalytic activity although a limit is imposed by the stability needed to keep the metal ion in solution.

The above study also demonstrated that a number of stable aqueous metal chelates of the Fe(III), Cr(III), Ti(IV), Sn(IV), Zn(II), Cd(II), Co(II), Fe(II), Ni(II), and Pb(II) ions had no interesting catalytic properties. On the other hand, a number of metal chelate compounds of oxo-metal ions such as ZrO(IV), UO_2(VI), and MoO_2(VI) markedly accelerated the hydrolysis of Sarin. Cu(II), N,N,N',N'-tetramethylenediamine chelate was found to be the most active catalyst for both Sarin and DFP hydrolysis. One may anticipate a direct correlation between the stability constants of the metal chelates and their catalytic properties when the chelate approximates the transition state. In this case it appears, however, that the metal chelates may be acting to stabilize the ground state of the organophosphorus compound, and owe their primary effect to solubilizing the metal ion at high pH's.

The catalytic activities of the aforementioned Cu(II) chelates were placed on a quantitative basis in a kinetic investigation by Gustafson and Martell [57] and Fowkes et al.[129] The possible catalytic metal species for the hydrolysis of Sarin [57] in the presence of a Cu(II) chelate are (1) the diaquo chelate CuL^{2+}; (2) the monohydroxo chelate, $Cu(OH)L^{\oplus}$; (3) the dihydroxo chelate, $Cu(OH)_2L$; (4) a binuclear diolated species $(Cu[OH]L)_2^{2+}$; and (5) the unbound or aquo copper(II) ion. The

[129] F. M. Fowkes, G. S. Ronay, and L. B. Ryland, J. Phys. Chem. 62, 867 (1958).

dimeric copper chelate should have negligible catalytic activity since it is shielded by two ligand molecules. The validity of this hypothesis was also demonstrated experimentally. Inclusion of the hydroxide-ion catalysis and spontaneous catalysis terms allows the following general expression to be written for the rate of disappearance of Sarin (where k_{obs} is the experimental pseudo-first-order rate constant):

$$k_{obs} = k_{ML}[CuL^{2+}][OH^{\ominus}] + k_{M(OH)L}[Cu(OH)L^{\oplus}]$$
$$+ k'_{M(OH)L}[Cu(OH)L^{\oplus}][OH^{\ominus}] + k_{M(OH)_2L}[Cu(OH)_2L]$$
$$+ k_M[Cu^{2+}][OH^{\ominus}] + k_{OH}\ominus[OH^{\ominus}] + k_0 \quad (6\text{-}40)$$

Since the concentration of the monohydroxo species is proportional to that of the diaquo chelate according to the equilibrium

$$CuL^{2+} \rightleftharpoons Cu(OH)L^{\oplus} + [H^{\oplus}]$$

$$K_{M(OH)L} = \frac{[Cu(OH)L^{\oplus}][H^{\oplus}]}{[CuL^{2+}]} \quad (6\text{-}41)$$

the quantities $k_{ML}[CuL^{2+}][OH^{\ominus}]$ and $k_{M(OH)L}[Cu(OH)L^{\oplus}]$ are kinetically indistinguishable. Similarly it is impossible to distinguish between the quantities $k'_{M(OH)L}[Cu(OH)L^{\oplus}][OH^{\ominus}]$ and $k_{M(OH)_2L}[Cu(OH)_2L]$. Thus the first two terms (as well as the third and fourth terms) on the right-hand side of equation (6-40) may be combined and equation (6-40) rewritten as (6-42):

$$k_{obs} = k_L[CuL^{2+}][OH^{\ominus}] + k_B[Cu(OH)_2L] + k_M[Cu^{2+}][OH^{\ominus}]$$
$$+ k_{OH}\ominus[OH^{\ominus}] + k_0 \quad (6\text{-}42)$$

where

$$k_L = \left(k_{ML} + \frac{k_{M(OH)L}K_{M(OH)L}}{K_W}\right)$$

$$k_B = \left(k_{M(OH)_2L} + \frac{K_W k_{M(OH)L}}{K_{M(OH)_2L}}\right)$$

Here k_L is a rate constant which represents catalysis by the diaquo chelate and/or the monohydroxo compound. Similar considerations apply to k_B.

Separate measurements of the rate of hydrolysis of Sarin in the absence of the metal chelate enabled the determination of $k_{OH\ominus}$ and k_0. The constant k_M was enumerated by rate measurements of Sarin hydrolysis in the presence of cupric nitrate. Thus it is possible to describe the total rate in terms of only two unknown quantities, k_L and k_B. Values assigned to k_B and k_L are summarized in Table 6-10.

Table 6-10 *   *Values of k_L and k_B in Sarin hydrolysis* [a]

Ligand	k_L (liter^2 mole^{-2} sec^{-1})	k_B (liter mole^{-1} sec^{-1})
N,N,N',N'-Tetramethylethylene- diamine	1.0×10^8	—
N,N'-Dimethylethylenediamine	3.2×10^7	2.2×10^2
N-Hydroxyethylethylenediamine	9.3×10^6	5.5
Dipyridyl	3.10×10^7	—
N,N'-Dihydroxyethylethylenediamine	5.2×10^6	9.0×10^{-1}

* Ref. 53.
[a] 25.0°, H$_2$O.

The favoring of k_L over k_B appears to be caused by a lower enthalpy of activation. For example, $\Delta H^{\ddagger}$ for N,N,N',N'-tetramethylethylene-diamine ligand has a value of 0.9 kcal mole^{-1} for k_L as compared to 10.0 kcal mole^{-1} for k_B. Martell [57] postulates that the more favorable free energy of activation is expected if the monohydroxo chelate were the predominant catalytic species because of its ability to facilitate a "push-pull" mechanism. On the basis of this assumption the rate constant for the latter species may be calculated from the observed rates in a pH region where the contribution from $k_B[\text{Cu(OH)}_2\text{L}]$ is negligible, allowing a more meaningful comparison than is accessible from either k_B or k_L. Under these conditions the most reactive chelate (N,N,N',N'-tetramethylethyl-enediamine) is ca. 20-fold more effective than hydroxide ion when both are present at identical concentrations in spite of the latter's probably higher pK_a'. This underscores the effects possible through interaction of metal ions with organophosphorus compounds.

chapter	Polyphosphates	
seven		

I. INTRODUCTION

In addition to the phosphoryl group-transferring enzymes already mentioned, enzymes such as kinases, pyrophosphokinases, phosphomutases, and certain of the pyrophosphorylases exhibit a similar ability. Although nucleotides are not directly involved in the phosphomutase catalyzed reactions, which appear superficially to consist of an intramolecular phosphoryl transfer between sites in the same molecule, all others involve direct participation by a nucleoside di- or triphosphate.[1] Consequently, a discussion of the properties of these polyphosphates is of interest.

The kinases constitute the largest class of known phosphoryl group-transferring enzymes, and their reactions may be thought of as involving nucleophilic attack by the acceptor molecule on the terminal phosphorus atom of the nucleotide (7-1).[1] Among those enzymes promoting phosphoryl transfer to a hydroxyl group are hexokinases from various sources which catalyze the phosphorylation of glucose, mannose, fructose, 2-de-

[1] R. Nordlie and H. Lardy, in P. D. Boyer, H. Lardy, and K. Myrbäck (eds.) "The Enzymes," Academic Press, New York, 1962, Vol. VI, p. 7.

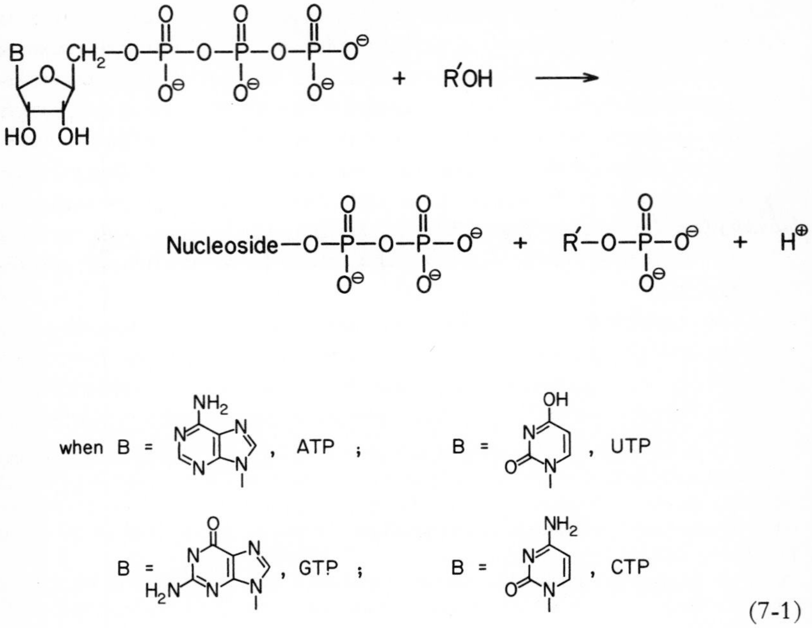

$$(7\text{-}1)$$

oxyglucose, glucosamine, galactose, etc., as well as the pentokinases which act on ribose, 2-deoxyribose, L-ribulose, D-xylulose, and other sugars.[1, 2] These are discussed in detail by Crane.[2] The hydroxyl group of other compounds, namely pantetheine,[3] hydroxymethylpyrimidine,[4] pyridoxal,[5] diphosphopyridine nucleotide,[6-8] choline,[9] 5-amino-4-imidazole carboxamide,[10] and homoserine,[11] also undergo phosphorylation in the presence of ATP and the respective kinase.

Other functional groups which undergo kinase promoted phosphoryla-

[2] R. K. Crane, in P. D. Boyer, H. Lardy, and K. Myrbäck (eds.) "The Enzymes," Academic Press, New York, 1962, Vol. VI, p. 47.

[3] L. Levintow and G. D. Novelli, *J. Biol. Chem.* **207,** 761 (1954).

[4] G. W. Camiener and G. M. Brown, *J. Biol. Chem.* **235,** 2404 (1960).

[5] A. F. Trufanov and V. A. Krisanova, *Chem. Abstr.* **41,** 7485c (1947).

[6] A. Kornberg, *J. Biol. Chem.* **182,** 805 (1950).

[7] B. Katchman, J. J. Betheil, A. I. Schepartz, and D. R. Sanadi, *Arch. Biochem. Biophys.* **34,** 437 (1951).

[8] T. P. Wang and N. O. Kaplan, *J. Biol. Chem.* **206,** 311 (1954).

[9] J. Wittenberg and A. Kornberg, *J. Biol. Chem.* **202,** 431 (1953).

[10] G. R. Greenberg, *J. Biol. Chem.* **219,** 423 (1956).

[11] Y. Watanabe and K. Shimura, *J. Biochem.* (*Tokyo*) **42,** 181 (1955).

tion are the thiol of CoA[12]; the carboxyl of 3-phosphoglycerate,[13] acetate,[14] and carbamate[15]; inorganic phosphate,[19] and the terminal phosphates of nucleoside mono- and diphosphates.[16, 17]   A complete discussion of several of these particular reactions and their respective enzymes can be found elsewhere.[18]   Other substrates which also serve as phosphoryl group acceptors are pyruvate,[20] forming phosphoenolpyruvic acid,[21] and a number of guanidines including creatine,[22] arginine,[23] glycocyamine,[24] and lombricine [24-26] which yield the corresponding N-phosphorylated guanidine or phosphagen.   It is obvious, even from this incomplete survey of kinase catalyzed reactions, that their important activity is widespread.

The existence of pyrophosphokinases, catalyzing the transfer of pyrophosphoryl groups from ATP to an acceptor molecule, has been demonstrated in the formation of ribose-5-phosphate-1-pyrophosphate from ribose-5-phosphate [26, 27] and thiamine pyrophosphate from thiamine.[28, 29]

[12] The existence of a thiolphosphate derivative of CoA has been questioned (see Chapter 5); recent experiments, however, reveal a CoA-dependent ATP-P_i exchange, although the intermediary of a thiolphosphate derivative is as yet only one of several possible explanations: K. G. Reid and R. A. Smith, *Arch. Biochem. Biophys.* **109,** 358 (1965).

[13] B. G. Malstrom and M. Larsson-Raznikiewicz, in P. D. Boyer, M. Lardy, and K. Myrbäck (eds.) "The Enzymes," Academic Press, New York, 1962, Vol. VI, Chap. 5.

[14] I. A. Rose, in P. D. Boyer, M. Lardy, and K. Myrbäck (eds.) "The Enzymes," Academic Press, New York, 1962, Vol. VI, Chap. 7.

[15] P. P. Cohen, in P. D. Boyer, M. Lardy, and K. Myrbäck (eds.) "The Enzymes," Academic Press, New York, 1962, Vol. VI, Chap. 29.

[16] L. Noda, in P. D. Boyer, M. Lardy, and K. Myrbäck (eds.) "The Enzymes," Academic Press, New York, 1962, Vol. VI, Chap. 10.

[17] R. Weaver, in P. D. Boyer, M. Lardy, and K. Myrbäck (eds.) "The Enzymes," Academic Press, New York, 1962, Vol. VI, Chap. 11.

[18] See refs. 13–17.

[19] A. Kornberg, S. R. Kornberg, and E. S. Simms, *Biochim. Biophys. Acta* **20,** 215 (1956).

[20] P. D. Boyer, in P. D. Boyer, M. Lardy, and K. Myrbäck (eds.) "The Enzymes," Academic Press, New York, 1962, Vol. VI, Chap. 6.

[21] M. F. Utter, in P. D. Boyer, M. Lardy, and K. Myrbäck (eds.) "The Enzymes," Academic Press, New York, 1961, Vol. V, p. 319.

[22] S. A. Kuby and E. A. Noltmann, in P. D. Boyer, M. Lardy, and K. Myrbäck (eds.) "The Enzymes," Academic Press, New York, 1962, Vol. VI, Chap. 31.

[23] O. Meyerhof and K. Lohmann, *Biochem. Z.* **196,** 49 (1928).

[24] N. V. Thoai and J. Roche, *Chem. Abstr.* **51,** 11420a (1957).

[25] N. V. Thoai and Y. Robin, *Biochim. Biophys. Acta* **14,** 76 (1954).

[26] A. Kornberg, I. Lieberman, and E. S. Simms, *J. Biol. Chem.* **215,** 389 (1955).

[27] C. N. Remy, W. T. Remy, and J. M. Buchanan, *J. Biol. Chem.* **217,** 885 (1955).

[28] Y. Kajiro, *J. Biochem. (Tokyo)* **46,** 1523 (1959).

[29] Y. Kajiro and N. Shimazono, *J. Biochem. (Tokyo)* **46,** 963 (1959).

In both cases the transfer involves the middle and terminal phosphates of ATP.[30]

Other enzymes, among the many that catalyze phosphoryl-group transfer, include (1) UDP-6 pyrophosphorylase, which catalyzes a reversible reaction involving the transfer of uridylyl monophosphate from UTP to glucose-1-phosphate [3] (7-2),[31] (2) uridyl transferase, which catalyzes the transfer of uridylyl monophosphate from UDP-glucose to galactose-1-phosphate [32, 33] (7-3), (3) phosphoramidic hexose transphosphorylase, which promotes the formation of a hexose-6-phosphate from phosphoramidate and hexose,[34] (4) adenylyl transferase, which involves the transfer of AMP from ADP to sulfate,[35] and (5) CDP-choline pyrophosphorylase, which catalyzes the transfer of a cytidine monophosphoryl group from CTP to phosphorylcholine (7-4).[36] It must be re-emphasized that the reactions cited in the introduction only repre-

$$\text{UTP} + \alpha\text{-D-glucose-1-P} \rightleftharpoons \text{UDP-glucose} + \text{P—P} \qquad (7\text{-}2)$$

$$\text{UDP-glucose} + \alpha\text{-galactose-1-P} \rightleftharpoons \text{UDP-galactose} + \alpha\text{-glucose-1-P}$$
$$(7\text{-}3)$$

$$\text{CTP} + \text{phosphorylcholine} \rightleftharpoons \text{CDP-choline} + \text{P—P} \qquad (7\text{-}4)$$

sent a much larger number of known reactions which occur with all or nearly all of the known nucleotides and numerous other substrates. For a detailed discussion of the enzymes involved in phosphoryl-group transfer, the reader is referred to Ref. 36a. Some mechanistic aspects of the above reactions, however, will be introduced when appropriate.

II. HYDROLYSIS

For the nonenzymic reactions, precise knowledge of the hydrolytic chemistry of polyphosphates is scanty. Mechanistic studies are complicated by the fact that pyrophosphates are subject to "reorganization"

[30] H. G. Khorana, J. F. Fernandes, and A. Kornberg, *J. Biol. Chem.* **230**, 941 (1958).

[31] A. Munch-Petersen, H. M. Kalckar, E. Cutolo, and E. E. B. Smith, *Nature* **172**, 1036 (1953).

[32] H. M. Kalckar, B. Braganca, and A. Munch-Petersen, *Nature* **172**, 1038 (1953).

[33] E. E. B. Smith and G. T. Mills, *Biochim. Biophys. Acta* **18**, 152 (1955).

[34] R. A. Smith, *J. Am. Chem. Soc.* **81**, 4758 (1959).

[35] M. Cohn, in P. D. Boyer, M. Lardy, and K. Myrbäck (eds.) "The Enzymes," Academic Press, New York, 1961, Vol. V, p. 179.

[36] J. Imsande and P. Handler, in P. D. Boyer, M. Lardy, and K. Myrbäck (eds.) "The Enzymes," Academic Press, New York, 1961, Vol. V, Chap. 5.

[36a] "The Enzymes," P. D. Boyer, M. Lardy, and K. Myrbäck (eds.), Academic Press, New York, 1960, Vol. II; 1962, Vol. VI.

into complex mixtures of phosphate esters.[37]   Values available for the
rates of hydrolysis of various polyphosphate species are listed in Table 7-1.
On the basis of these data alone, it is of course not possible to convincingly
regard the hydrolysis of the monoanion $(H_3P_2O_7)^{-1}$ as proceeding via
the formation of monomeric metaphosphate (7-5).   The hydrolytic rates
for the di- and trianionic pyrophosphate species are smaller in comparison,
as anticipated in analogy with the resistance to hydrolysis of the dianionic
species of phosphomonoesters, but one can only speculate as to whether
the hydrolytic pathways for these pyrophosphate species are mono- or
bimolecular.   It is of interest that the solvolysis of the dianionic species
of the unsymmetrical diethyl pyrophosphate may readily be interpreted
as monomolecular.   The latter, which can exist only in an unsymmetrical
ionized form and moreover can expel a diesterified leaving group, solvolyzes at a rate too fast to measure (see 7-11).   The hydrolysis of the
conjugate acid and, with less certainty, the neutral pyrophosphate species
may be reasonably viewed as a displacement by water of a phosphate
moiety (converted by protonation to a better leaving group), as is presented in (7-6).   It is also plausible that the apparently more reactive

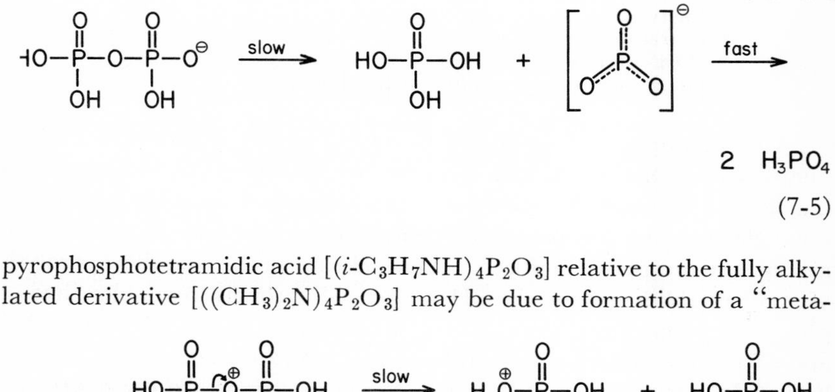

$$2 \quad H_3PO_4$$

$$(7\text{-}5)$$

pyrophosphotetramidic acid $[(i\text{-}C_3H_7NH)_4P_2O_3]$ relative to the fully alkylated derivative $[((CH_3)_2N)_4P_2O_3]$ may be due to formation of a "meta-

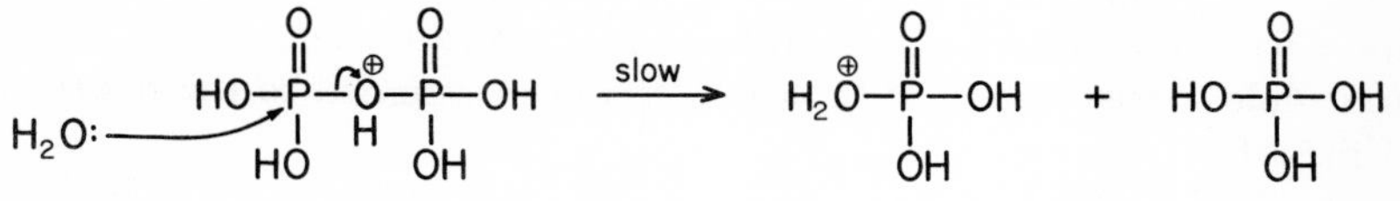

$$(7\text{-}6)$$

phosphate type" species, although the values in Table 7-1 cannot be
directly compared.   As expected, hydrolysis of these latter compounds
involves P–O bond cleavage, the P–N bond being split only in acidic
medium.[38]

[37] E. Schwarzmann and J. R. Van Wazer, *J. Am. Chem. Soc.* **83,** 365 (1961).
[38] D. F. Heath and P. Casapieri, *Trans. Faraday Soc.* **47,** 1093 (1951).

Table 7-1   *Hydrolysis rates of polyphosphates* [a]

Species	$T°$	k (sec^{-1})	Ref.
$H_5P_2O_7^{\oplus}$	70	ca. 7×10^{-4} [a]	39
$H_4P_2O_7$	70	6.6×10^{-4} [b]	39
$H_3P_2O_7^{\ominus}$	70	9.6×10^{-4} [b]	39
$H_2P_2O_7^{\ominus}$	70	9.25×10^{-6} [c]	39
$HP_2O_7^{-3}$	70	1.23×10^{-6} [c]	39
$P_2O_7^{-4}$	70	—	39
$(CH_3O)_4P_2O_3$	25	4.16×10^{-4} [c]	41
$(C_2H_5O)_4P_2O_3$	25	2.66×10^{-5} [c]	40
$(i\text{-}C_3H_7O)_4P_2O_3$	25	ca. 1.5×10^{-6} [c]	41
$(C_2H_5O)_4P_2O_3$	25	2.63 [d]	40
$[(CH_3)_2N]_4P_2O_3$	100	7.8×10^{-5}	42
$(i\text{-}C_3H_7NH)_4P_2O_3$	25	2.18×10^{-3} [d]	42
$H_4P_3O_{10}^{\ominus} + H_3P_3O_{10}^{\ominus}$	60	1.14×10^{-4} [e]	43
$H_4P_3O_{10}^{\ominus} + H_3P_3O_{10}^{\ominus}$	49	2.69×10^{-5} [e]	44

[a] From E. M. Kosower, "Molecular Biochemistry," McGraw-Hill, New York (1962), p. 255.
[b] Observed pseudo-first-order constants at $(H_3O^{\oplus}) = 1\ M$.
[c] Neutral water rates.
[d] $k(OH^{\ominus})$ (sec^{-1}).
[e] Rate constants corresponding to principle species.

A pyrophosphate of significant biological import is adenosine diphosphate, whose nonenzymic hydrolysis has been examined by Holbrook and Ouellet.[45]   The overall hydrolysis of this compound proceeds with P—O bond cleavage, no pyrophosphate being found in the hydrolyzed reaction mixture at the pH's employed.   The pH-rate profile for the hydrolysis of ADP established over the pH region 3–8 strongly resembles that of phosphate monoesters, approaching a maximum in the pH range 3–4 and decreasing rapidly with increasing pH.   A rate value of 2.07×10^{-7} liter mole^{-1} sec^{-1} at 92.6°, $\mu = 0.1$, has been assigned to the hydrolysis of the ADP^{-3} species.

Table 7-1 also includes values for the rates of hydrolysis of mixtures of linear triphosphate ions.   Without regard to the molecular species, at

[39] D. O. Campbell and M. L. Kilpatrick, *J. Am. Chem. Soc.* **76,** 893 (1954).
[40] J. A. A. Ketelaar and A. H. Bloksma, *Rec. Trav. Chim.* **67,** 665 (1948).
[41] A. D. F. Toy, *J. Am. Chem. Soc.* **70,** 3882 (1948).
[42] D. F. Heath, *J. Chem. Soc.* 3796 (1956).
[43] J. R. Van Wazer, E. J. Griffith, and J. F. McCullough, *J. Am. Chem. Soc.* **77,** 287 (1955).
[44] S. L. Friess, *J. Am. Chem. Soc.* **74,** 4027 (1952).
[45] K. A. Holbrook and L. Ouellet, *Can. J. Chem.* **35,** 1496 (1957).

pH 1 triphosphate hydrolyzes about 9 times faster than pyrophosphate and in alkaline medium roughly 20–100 times faster. In neutral solutions the triphosphate hydrolyzes somewhat less than 3 times faster than the pyrophosphate. Van Wazer and co-workers [43] suggest that if the P—O—P linkages of pyro- and triphosphate were identical in reactivity, statistically the equivalent rate constants for triphosphate should be twice that of pyrophosphate. The slower rate for the pyrophosphate degradation is ascribed to its symmetry in both charge and atomic position in strongly basic or acidic solution, a symmetry which disappears in the neutral region where the trianionic species of pyrophosphate is most abundant. Hydrolysis of the triphosphate also appears to be catalyzed by hydronium ion. Mechanistically, a metapyrophosphate can be postulated, in analogy with other phosphate esters, as being involved in the hydrolysis of appropriately charged species of triphosphate, but this hypothesis is only speculative.

In connection with the linear triphosphate moiety, it is appropriate to mention the cyclic isomer trimetaphosphate [46] that has been detected in the free acid or an ester form as a product arising from reactions including (1) hydrolysis of phenyl hydrogen phosphate in a warm aqueous solution of disodium hydrogen phosphate,[47] (2) treatment of methyl hydrogen N-cyclohexylphosphoramidate with pyridine at 100° (7-7),[48] (3) oxidation

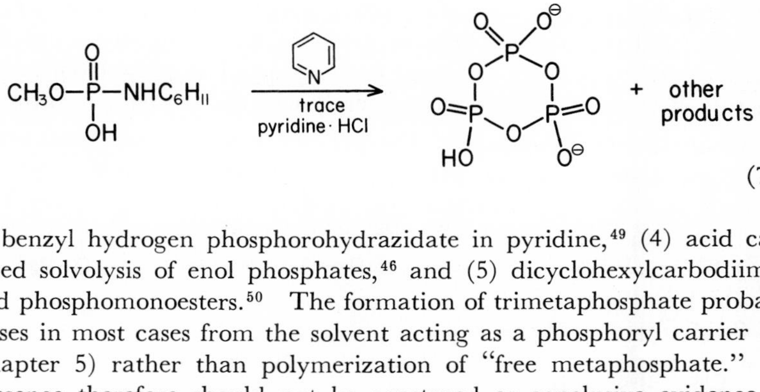

(7-7)

of benzyl hydrogen phosphorohydrazidate in pyridine,[49] (4) acid catalyzed solvolysis of enol phosphates,[46] and (5) dicyclohexylcarbodiimide and phosphomonoesters.[50] The formation of trimetaphosphate probably arises in most cases from the solvent acting as a phosphoryl carrier (see Chapter 5) rather than polymerization of "free metaphosphate." Its presence therefore should not be construed as conclusive evidence for formulating a metaphosphate mechanism.

[46] F. Cramer and H. Hettler, *Ber.* **91**, 1181 (1958).
[47] D. M. Brown and N. K. Hamer, *J. Chem. Soc.* 1155 (1960).
[48] N. K. Hamer, *J. Chem. Soc.* 46 (1965).
[49] D. M. Brown, J. A. Flint, and N. K. Hamer, *J. Chem. Soc.* 326 (1964).
[50] H. G. Khorana and G. Weimann, *J. Am. Chem. Soc.* **84**, 4329 (1962).

III. NUCLEOPHILIC AND GENERAL-BASE CATALYSIS

Of considerable importance in the elucidation of enzymic mechanisms, especially those involving phosphoryl-group transfers, is an understanding of the action of nucleophilic groups toward pyrophosphates. A significant study in this area was carried out by Dudek and Westheimer[51] on the solvolysis of tetrabenzylpyrophosphate. This ester reacts with 1-propanol in the presence of tribenzylamine or 2,6-N,N'-tetramethylaniline to yield mostly benzyl propyl ether and salts of tribenzylpyrophosphate. The

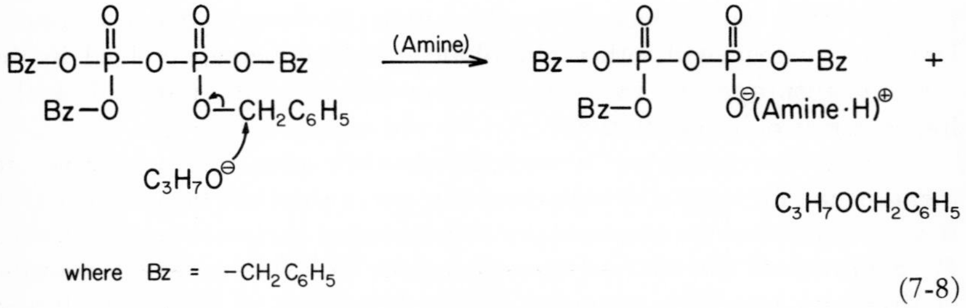

where Bz = $-CH_2C_6H_5$

$$(7\text{-}8)$$

solvolytic reaction when carried out in the absence of added base is strongly autocatalytic, an experimental finding that will be developed more completely in a succeeding paragraph. In the presence of less sterically hindered amines, lutidine or collidine, the solvolysis proceeds largely with P—O bond cleavage, forming dibenzyl propyl phosphate. The rate of the solvolysis increases linearly with increasing concentration

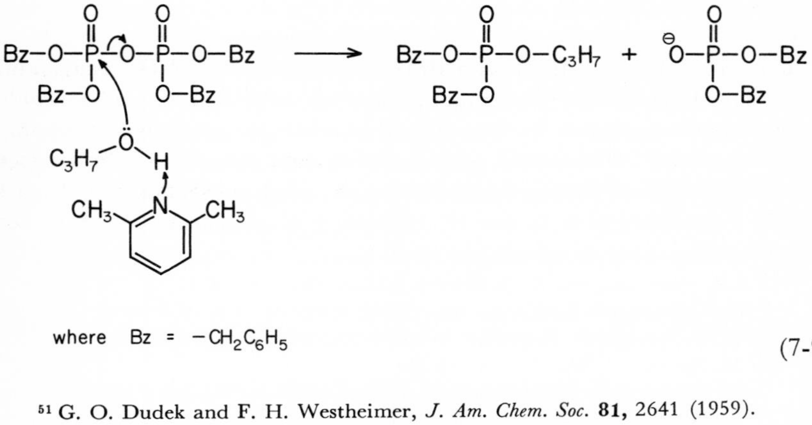

where Bz = $-CH_2C_6H_5$

$$(7\text{-}9)$$

[51] G. O. Dudek and F. H. Westheimer, *J. Am. Chem. Soc.* **81,** 2641 (1959).

of lutidine or collidine, and is subject to a deuterium solvent kinetic isotope effect of ca. 3.3.   These findings suggest that the lutidine and collidine catalyzed solvolyses are probably a general-base assisted attack by
propanol upon the P—O bond.

It is of interest to compare the rates of C—O bond cleavage for tetrabenzylpyrophosphate and other benzyl esters to assess the efficiency of
a triesterified pyrophosphate as a "leaving group."   The rate constant
of solvolysis of tetrabenzylpyrophosphate, with C—O cleavage, in propanol at 50° is about 4×10^{-5} sec^{-1}; the rate constant in ethanol at 50°
is ca. 5×10^{-5} sec^{-1}.   The corresponding constant for benzyl chloride
at 50° in absolute ethanol is 3×10^{-7} sec^{-1},[52] that for benzyl bromide at
77° in 80% aqueous alcohol is ca. 20×10^{-5} sec^{-1},[53] that for benzyl
tosylate in absolute ethanol at 25° is 5×10^{-5} sec^{-1},[52] and that for
benzyl nitrate at 50° in 60% aqueous dioxane is 0.16×10^{-5} sec^{-1}.[54]
Comparison of the rates for the tetrabenzylpyrophosphate and benzyl
tosylate, when allowance is made for the difference in temperature, indicates that the rate of solvolysis of the pyrophosphate is probably a fifth
as great as that for the tosylate.   Assuming a similar mechanism for all
the solvolyses, the tribenzylpyrophosphate is then a remarkably efficient
"leaving group."[51]   However, Kosower [55] estimates that chloride ion is
a better leaving group than the dianion of the unsubstituted pyrophos-
phoric acid by a factor of 10^3, which he obtains by comparison of the
hydrolysis of 3,3-dimethylallyl chloride and geranyl pyrophosphate.
The latter pyrophosphate derivative serves as precursor for the synthesis
of squalene, lanosterol, cholesterol, and other steroids and is itself derived
from isopentyl pyrophosphate.   It might be anticipated, then, from the
model studies that the pyrophosphate in the biological system would
possess a low net charge to facilitate its expulsion, possibly attained
through complexation with a metal ion or positively charged functional
groups on the enzyme.   Consideration of the biological process will serve
to demonstrate the utilization of pyrophosphate ion in biological systems.

The fascinating biopolymerization of isopentenyl pyrophosphate,
ultimately responsible for steroid and triterpenoid biosynthesis, has been
reviewed.[56, 57]   Formation of geranyl pyrophosphate has been treated
as an example of carbon-to-carbon bond formation through nucleophilic

[52] S. Winstein, E. Grunwald, and H. W. Jones, *J. Am. Chem. Soc.* **73,** 2700 (1951).
[53] J. B. Shoesmith and R. H. Slater, *J. Chem. Soc.* 214 (1926).
[54] G. R. Lucas and L. P. Hammett, *J. Am. Chem. Soc.* **64,** 1928 (1942).
[55] E. M. Kosower, "Molecular Biochemistry," McGraw-Hill, New York, 1962,
p. 55.
[56] F. Lynen and U. Henning, *Angew. Chem.* **72,** 820 (1960).
[57] L. Ruzicka, *Proc. Chem. Soc.* 341, (1959).

displacement of pyrophosphate monoanion by a carbon-to-carbon double bond.[58]   The driving force for the reaction has been postulated as partially arising from lactone formation, as represented in (7-10).[59]   Condensation of geranyl pyrophosphate with a second isopentyl pyrophosphate

Geranyl pyrophosphate

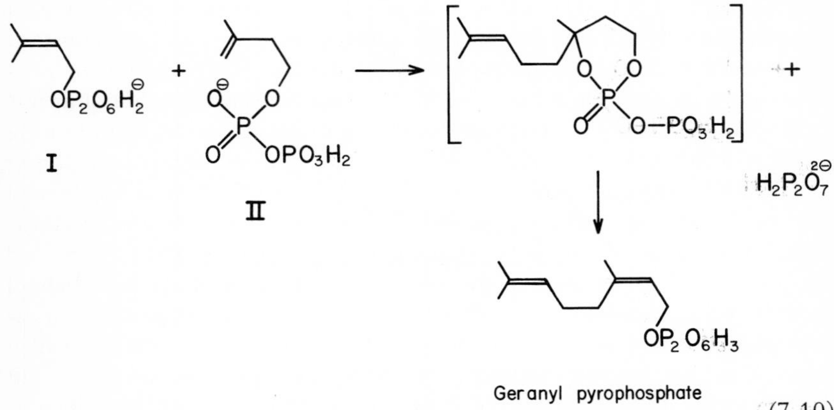

(7-10)

yields farnesyl pyrophosphate, which tracer and isolation studies also have demonstrated as a natural precursor of squalene.   The ready interconvertibility of I and II has been shown enzymically.[60]   It is important to realize that although allylic systems under polar conditions are known to solvolyze primarily via a carbonium ion, the enzymic formation of terpenes appears to be highly position-specific, occurring only through reaction at the primary carbon atom.   For that reason one might favor a bimolecular displacement mechanism,[55] although a carbonium ion mechanism on an enzyme surface probably would be position-specific. The acidic hydrolysis of isopentyl pyrophosphate does appear to occur via a carbonium ion.[60]

   Brown and Hamer [47] in their study of the hydrolysis of tetraethyl pyrophosphate also encountered a strong catalytic effect on the rate of hydrolysis with added orthophosphate.   The effect of this salt and others is revealed graphically in Fig. 7-1.   Experiments on the variation in the hydrolytic rate in the presence of added orthophosphate at varying pH's implicated the $HPO_4^{\ominus}$ anion as the catalytically active species.   Inspection of Fig. 7-1 shows that sulfite anion ($HSO_3^{\ominus}$) and pyridine have an effect very similar to $HPO_4^{\ominus}$, whereas lutidine, the stronger of the two nitrogen

[58] P. D. Bartlett, *Ann.* **653**, 45 (1962).
[59] W. S. Johnson and R. A. Bell, *Tetrahedron Letters* **12**, 27 (1960).
[60] H. Eggerer, *Ber.* **94**, 174 (1961).

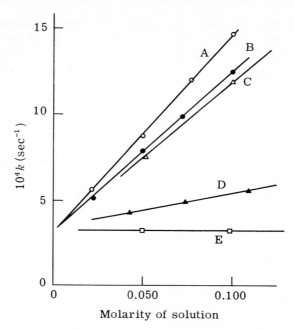

Fig. 7-1 *Effect of added salts on the hydrolysis of tetraethyl pyrophosphate at 57.0° and pH 8.80. (A) Na_2SO_3. (B) Na_2HPO_4. (C) Pyridine. (D) Na_2MePO_4. (E) 2,6-Lutidine. (Ref. 47.)*

bases, has virtually none. In all cases the sole phosphorus-containing product is diethyl phosphate. Brown and Hamer also found that, if the hydrolysis were conducted in a saturated solution of disodium hydrogen phosphate in 50% methanol or 75% ethylene glycol, the presence of the respective methyl dihydrogen phosphate and 2-hydroxyethyl dihydrogen phosphate could be detected. The proposed mechanism thus involves an intermediate $P'P'$-dialkyl pyrophosphate anion formed through nucleophilic attack by $HPO_4^{\ominus}$ on a phosphorus atom of the pyrophosphate. Avison [61] earlier had invoked a similar scheme for the phosphate catalyzed hydrolysis of tetramethyl pyrophosphate. The $P'P'$-dialkyl pyrophosphate anion, once formed, could then hydrolyze via an S_N1 or S_N2 mechanism. Samuel and Silver [62] confirmed this hypothesis by following the hydrolysis of tetraethyl pyrophosphate with the aid of $H_3PO_4^{18}$. Their results and the probable mechanism of the reaction are shown in (7-11). The dehydration of benzaldoxime by tetraethyl pyrophosphate has been

[61] A. W. D. Avison, *J. Chem. Soc.* 732 (1955).
[62] D. Samuel and B. Silver, *J. Chem. Soc.* 4321 (1961).

shown to proceed through an analogous intermediate, diethyl benzal-
diminophosphate, formed by a nucleophilic attack of the oxime on
phosphorus.[63] Thus it appears that pyrophosphates are susceptible to

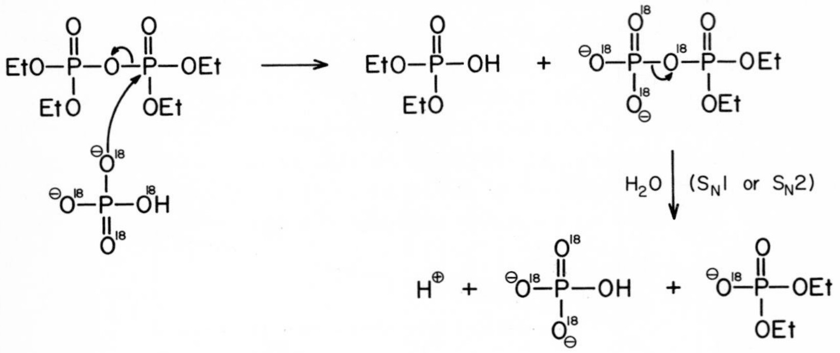

$$(7\text{-}11)$$

nucleophilic attack by oxyanions and most likely heterocyclic nitrogenous
bases (i.e., pyridine, excepting those sterically hindered). Sterically
hindered amines impose a change in mechanism to one of general-base
catalysis of P—O bond cleavage, and in the limiting case direct the
solvolyses to proceed with C—O bond fission. The solvolysis reactions,
of course, can be considered as models for transphosphorylations with the
solvent serving as the acceptor.

One might expect that the tetraesterified pyrophosphates would be
subject to nucleophilic attack by a larger number of reagents than phosphate esters, since the former possess a better leaving group. An interesting consequence of leaving group stability is manifested in studies on
synthetic methods of phosphorylation.[64] If an unsymmetrical pyrophosphate A–B, derived from two different phosphodiesters A and B, is brought
into contact with a salt of a third phosphodiester, C, then, provided the
order of ion stability is B > C > A, the exchange reaction (7-12) is
observed.

$$A\text{—}B + C \rightarrow A\text{—}C + B \qquad (7\text{-}12)$$

Moreover, under normal conditions of phosphorylation in the presence of
base and with C now representative of an alcohol, a mixed pyrophosphate
appears to yield predominantly a phosphate derived from the weaker of
the two acids.

[63] T. Mukaiyama and T. Fujisawa, *Bull. Chem. Soc. Japan* **34**, 812 (1961).
[64] A. R. Todd, *Proc. Nat. Acad. Sci. U.S.* **45**, 1389 (1959).

An additional but fascinating example of cleavage of a pyrophosphate linkage occurs with cyclodextrins. Hennrich and Cramer [65] have demonstrated that a phosphoryl group of the symmetrical diphenylpyrophosphate is transferred to a hydroxyl of the cyclodextrin in aqueous solution in the presence of Ca(II). The proposed reaction sequence involves two steps: (1) approximately one half of the pyrophosphate molecule forms an inclusion compound with the cyclodextrin and is attacked with the loss of phenyl phosphate by a cyclodextrin hydroxyl group (7-13a), (2) a second cyclodextrin hydroxyl group displaces phenol, forming a cyclic phosphate which under the conditions of the reaction (pH 12) rapidly hydrolyzes (7-13b). The fact that the inside phosphoryl group, which is adjacent to

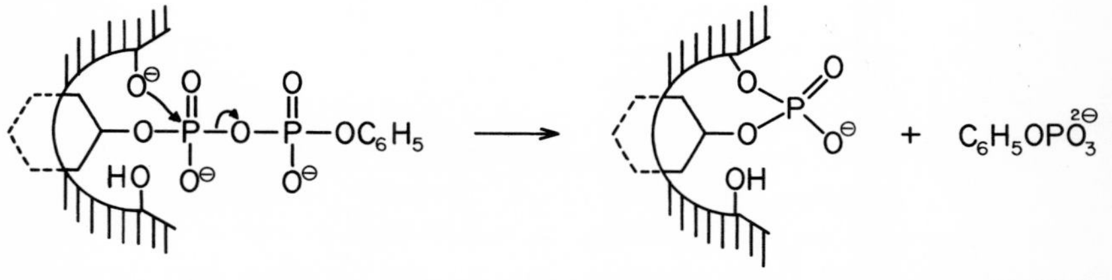

$$I \longrightarrow II + C_6H_5OPO_3^{2\ominus} \qquad (7\text{-}13a)$$

$$II \xrightarrow{-C_6H_5OH} \longrightarrow \text{Dextrin}-OPO_3^{2\ominus} \qquad (7\text{-}13b)$$

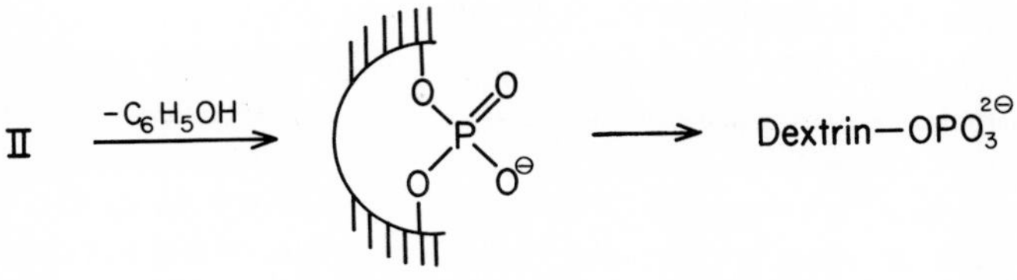

the enclosed phenyl group, phosphorylates the dextrin was shown by employing an unsymmetrical pyrophosphate, which would lead to different products depending on the relative affinity of the substituents for the cyclodextrin cavity. Cleavage of P^1-chlorophenyl P^2-ethyl phosphate (it is assumed the phenyl ring will have the greater affinity) in the presence of Ca(II) and cyclodextrin yields only ethyl phosphate, 4-chlorophenol, and phosphorylated dextrin. This is in contrast to the formation of 4-chlorophenyl phosphate and ethyl phosphate in equal proportions in the presence of Ca(II) but no cyclodextrin. Adequate evidence is not avail-

[65] N. Hennrich and F. Cramer, *J. Am. Chem. Soc.* **87**, 1121 (1965).

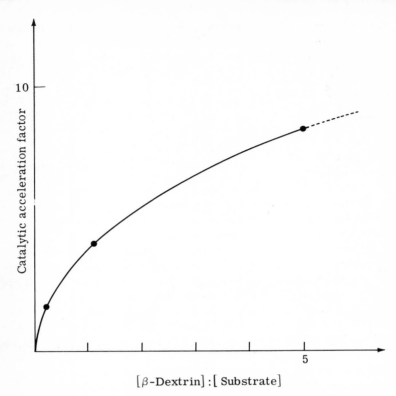

Fig. 7-2   *Concentration of pyrophosphate* $= [CaCl_2] = 3.125 \times 10^{-3}$ *M, pH 12, 40°; catalytic acceleration factors relative to substrate and Ca(II) in the absence of cyclodextrin.   (Ref. 65.)*

able to delineate the possible role of other cyclodextrin hydroxyl groups or of Ca(II) in the catalysis.   Cleavage is found with concentrations 3.125×10^{-3} *M* in cyclodextrin and 3.12×10^{-4} *M* in Ca(II) but not in the presence of such Ca(II) concentrations alone.

It is also of considerable interest that the catalytic dependency of the catalysis on cyclodextrin concentration exhibits a saturation effect, typical of an enzymic reaction (Fig. 7-2).   At high cyclodextrin concentrations, when all substrate molecules have occupied the inclusion cavity, a further addition of catalyst will have little effect.   Moreover, at low cyclodextrin concentrations, it was shown that the rate of pyrophosphate cleavage drops off rapidly with time, since the phosphorylated cyclodextrin is no longer as active a catalyst and also the reaction product, phenyl phosphate, functions as an "inhibitor" forming an inclusion compound.

IV. METAL IONS

The requirement for a divalent metal ion is found in most enzymatic reactions of nucleoside triphosphates.[66] Moreover, the known reactions of nucleoside triphosphates belong mainly to one of two classes involving (1) the cleavage of the γ-P–O bond of the nucleoside triphosphate in kinase reactions [67] (phosphotransferases), including hexokinase, 3-phosphoglycerate kinase, adenylate kinase, and creatine kinase; and (2) the cleavage of the α-P–O bond in pyrophosphorylase reactions [67, 68] (nucleotidyltransferases), including acetate and amino acid activation, adenylic and pantothenic acid formation, and some hydrolytic reactions. Of significance then are several nonenzymic reactions of adenosine di- and triphosphate in the presence of bivalent metal ions, which have been extensively studied by Lowenstein and co-workers.[69]

In acetic acid–sodium acetate buffer the bivalent metal ions,[70] with the exception of Ba(II) and Mg(II), which are rate-retarding, accelerate the rate of hydrolysis of ATP (all experimental at 80°) in the order Cu(II) > Zn(II) > Cd(II) > Mn(II) > Be(II). There is no obvious relationship between the effectiveness of the metal and its ionic radius (see Chapter 5). The ratio ADP formed/AMP formed for the four most effective ions is 8.0, 14.8, 52.5, and 16.2, respectively. In the absence of bivalent metal ions this ratio is 10. Since very little pyrophosphate is formed at pH 5 the differences in this ratio are due primarily to differences in the rates of hydrolysis of ADP as compared to ATP. On the alkaline side, at pH 9 in diethanolamine-HCl buffer, all of the bivalent metal ions employed accelerate the rate of hydrolysis of ATP in the order Ca(II) > Mn(II) > Cu(II) > Cd(II) > Zn(II) > Co(II). The maximum rate of hydrolysis which was obtained in the presence of Ca(II) ions at pH 9 is only one twenty-eighth of the maximum at pH 5 in the presence of Cu(II) ions. In turn, the hydrolysis of ATP in the presence of Cu(II) is 57 times faster than in its absence. The ratio ADP formed/AMP formed for the four most effective ions at pH 9 is 9.2, 5.6, 3.2, and 6.6, respectively. In the absence of bivalent metal ions this ratio is 39. Thus at pH 9 there appears to be a lessened selectivity of ATP hydrolysis relative to ADP hydrolysis by the metal ion, although the ratio values are subject to some qualification because of a small amount of pyrophosphate forma-

[66] M. Cohn, *Biochemistry* **2**, 623 (1963).
[67] M. Cohn, *Biochim. Biophys. Acta* **37**, 344 (1960).
[68] P. D. Boyer, *Ann. Rev. Biochem.* **29**, 15 (1960).
[69] M. Tetas and J. M. Lowenstein, *Biochemistry* **2**, 350 (1963).
[70] C. Liebecq and M. Jacquemotte-Louis, *Bull. Soc. Chim. Biol.* **40**, 67 (1958).

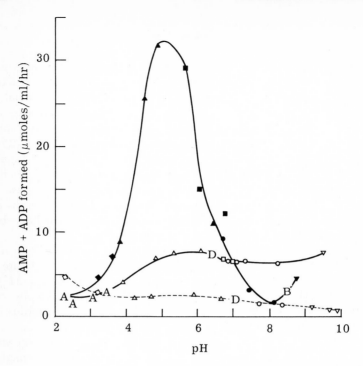

Fig. 7-3   *The effect of pH on the hydrolysis of ATP in the presence and absence of Mn(II) or Zn(II) ions.   Each tube contained 20 mM ATP (sodium salt), 20 mM bivalent metal chloride, and 100 mM buffer, as follows:* ▽, *diethanolamine; B, borate;* ○, *Tris; D, imidazole;* □, *dimethylglutarate;* △, *acetate; A, alanine; and* ◇, *formate.   Solid symbols for Zn(II), hollow symbols and solid line for Mn(II), hollow symbols and broken line for absence of bivalent metal ion.   Cu(II) not shown exhibits the same effect as Zn(II) but at higher ordinate values. (Ref. 69.)*

tion.   No formation of a 3′, 5′-cyclic AMP was detected, which has been reported in the degradation of ATP in saturated barium hydroxide.[71]

The most effective bivalent metal ions in the hydrolysis of ADP at pH 5 are Cu(II) and Zn(II), which are also the most effective with ATP. However, the least effective are Cd(II) and Mn(II), which are the third and fourth most effective ions in the hydrolysis of ATP at pH 5, a fact which is reflected in the ADP/AMP ratio.   At pH 9 the order of effectiveness of metal ions in promoting ADP hydrolysis is Cu(II) > Zn(II) > Cd(II) > Ba(II) > Mn(II).   Therefore Cu(II) and Zn(II) remain the most effective ions in the case of ADP hydrolysis at both pH values but not for ATP.

[71] D. Lipkin, R. Markham, and W. H. Cook, *J. Am. Chem. Soc.* **81,** 6075 (1959).

The effect of pH on the rate of hydrolysis of ATP in the presence and absence of metal ions is depicted in Fig. 7-3.[69, 70]   Compared to the control, the presence of Mn(II) ions retards the rate of hydrolysis of ATP between pH 2.2 and 3.3.   The pH-rate profile shows a broad maximum at about 5.5–6.   Likewise Cu(II) and Zn(II) ions retard the rate of hydrolysis at acidic pH's but promote a rapid increase in rate above pH 3 with a pH optimum at 5.   Both Cu(II) and Zn(II) ions affect the hydrolytic rate to a lesser extent than Mn(II) at alkaline pH values.

The influence of the concentration of Cu(II) and Mn(II) ions on the rate of ATP hydrolysis at pH 5 causes an increase in rate with increasing metal ion concentration.   However, an optimum concentration of bivalent metal ion cannot be attained before precipitation occurs.   Nevertheless it appears that the maximum rate of hydrolysis is attained when the ATP/metal ion ratio is less than 1.   Similar considerations apply to the influence of the concentration of Ca(II) and Mn(II) ions on the rate of hydrolysis of ATP at pH 9.

The effect of pH on the rate of hydrolysis of ADP in the presence and absence of metal ions is depicted in Fig. 7-4.   In contrast to its behavior toward ATP, Mn(II) retards the rate of hydrolysis of ADP between pH 3.7 and 7.3.   There is a rapid increase in the rate of hydrolysis between pH 8 and 9.5.   The maximum in the rate of hydrolysis of ATP catalyzed by Mn(II) ions, which occurs at about pH 6, is entirely absent in the case of the hydrolysis of ADP.   Cu(II) ions appear to be catalytically most effective at *ca.* pH 6 for ADP as well as ATP.[71a]   The influence of the concentration of these metal ions on the rate of ADP hydrolysis is similar to the case for ATP hydrolysis.

The foregoing discussion was necessarily detailed to demonstrate the complexities encountered in the metal-ion catalyzed hydrolyses of these biologically important entities.   There appears to be no simple means of correlating their activity with a single parameter.   Although the highly effective ions of Cu(II), Zn(II), Mn(II), and Ca(II) are all members of the 4th period of the periodic table, further subdivision into groups IIA and IIB leads to certain anomalies.   Group IIA, which includes the ions of Be and Ca(II) that are highly effective under certain conditions, also includes Mg ions that are conspicuous by their ineffectiveness under

---

[71a] C. A. Bunton and H. Chaimovich (private communication) have shown that the dependence of the rate of ADP hydrolysis on Cu(II) is complex.   When the Cu(II) concentration is equal to or less than that of ADP there is simple relation between reaction rate and reagent concentration, but in the pH region 4–6 with Cu(II) in excess over ADP the latter is converted wholly into the Cu(II)-ADP complex, which is readily hydrolyzed.   In these saturation conditions the pH-rate profile has a bell shape similar to that of Fig. 7-4 with a maximum at pH 5.2, and the reaction rate is then the rate of decomposition of the complex.

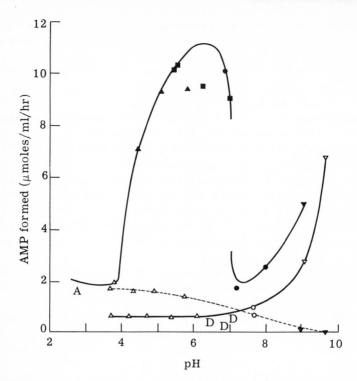

Fig. 7-4   *The effect of pH on the hydrolysis of ADP in the presence and absence of Mn(II) or Zn(II) ions.   Each tube contained 20 mM ADP (sodium salt), 20 mM bivalent metal chloride, and 100 mM buffer.   The same symbols are used as in Fig. 7-3.   The effect of Cu(II) resembles that of Zn(II), exhibiting a sharper pH maximum at higher ordinate values.   (Ref. 69.)*

all the experimental conditions described above. Yet, biologically, Mg(II) ions are of particular interest since they are encountered most frequently in enzymic reactions.   The order in which the ions occur in group IIA is Be(II), Mg(II), Ca(II), Sr(II), and Ba(II) which, however, correlates with a decrease in the stability of the ATP-metal ion chelates.[72, 73] This is not the same sequence as the order of the effectiveness of group IIA metal ions in catalyzing the hydrolysis of ATP and ADP.

The stability sequence generally observed with chelates of the bivalent transition ions is Mn(II) < Co(II) < Ni(II) < Cu(II) > Zn(II),[74–76]

[72] L. B. Nanninga, *Biochim. Biophys. Acta* **54,** 330 (1961).

[73] M. M. T. Khan and A. E. Martell, *J. Phys. Chem.* **66,** 10 (1962).

[74] D. P. Mellor and L. Maley, *Nature* **159,** 370 (1947).

[75] H. Irving and R. J. P. Williams, *Nature* **162,** 746 (1948).

[76] R. J. P. Williams, in P. D. Boyer, H. Lardy, and K. Myrbäck (eds.) "The Enzymes," Academic Press, New York, 1959, Vol. I, Chap. 9.

Table 7-2 *   *Stability constants of metal-nucleotide complexes*

Complex	Method used to determine value	Conditions	K (liter mole^{-1})
CaATP^{2-}	pH titration (calculated on IBM 1620 computer)	0.1 M (C$_2$H$_5$)$_4$NBr (30°)	32,000
	Spectral changes of 8-hydroxyquinoline	0.1 M N-ethylmorpholine (pH 8.0, 30°)	31,000
CaADP$^-$	Spectral changes of 8-hydroxy-quinoline	0.1 M N-ethylmorpholine (pH 8.0, 30°)	2,200
MnADP$^-$	Spectral changes of catechol-3,5-disulfonic acid (at 325 mμ)	0.1 M N-ethylmorpholine (pH 8.0, 30°)	25,000
	Electron paramagnetic resonance, 27°		30,000
NaATP^{3-}	Effect on apparent stability constant of MgATP^{2-} and CaATP^{2-} using spectral changes of 8-hydroxy-quinoline	0.1 M N-ethylmorpholine (pH 8.0, 30°)	15
KATP^{3-}	Effect on apparent stability constant of MgATP^{2-} using spectral changes of 8-hydroxy-quinoline	0.1 M N-ethylmorpholine (pH 8.0, 30°)	14

* Ref. 78.

but the order of Mn is changed for the corresponding ATP-metal ion chelates, with their stability increasing in the order Co(II) < Mn(II) < Ni(II) < Cu(II) > Zn(II).[73, 77] For these metal ions the order of effectiveness in the hydrolysis of ATP and ADP is Cu(II) > Zn(II) > Ni(II) ≈ Co(II). The Mn(II) ion, which alters its position in the ATP chelates, does not fall into a set sequence, being unusually effective in ATP hydrolysis at pH 9 and ineffective toward ADP at pH 5. An idea of the overall stability of metal-nucleotide complexes (the concentrations of the various structural forms that the 1:1 chelate may assume are unknown) may be gained through examination of Table 7-2.[78] These stability constants are the center of some scientific controversy (the reader is referred to Ref. 78 in order to appreciate the problem).

Other considerations in metal-ion catalysis include the metal ion-substrate ratio, the position of metal-substrate binding, and the ionization state of the chelate. Lowenstein and Tetas assume a 1:1 chelate of substrate and metal ion, which experiments have indicated as being the

[77] H. Brintzinger and S. Fallab, *Helv. Chim. Acta* **43**, 43 (1960).
[78] W. J. O'Sullivan and D. D. Perrin, *Biochemistry* **3**, 18 (1964).

predominant ATP-metal ion chelate in solution, although 2:1 chelates also have been postulated.[69, 79]   A number of different structures have been proposed for this chelate, being essentially the various structures allowed by utilizing the three phosphate moieties and the nitrogen of the purine ring as binding sites.[80–84]   Lowenstein and Tetas favor structure I of equation (7-14) as the most likely structure for $(ATP\text{-metal})^{-2}$ chelates, and also propose structure II for $(ATP\text{-metal})^{-2}$ chelates.   Cohn and Hughes,[85, 86] employing nuclear magnetic resonance spectroscopy, have found that the ions of Mg, Ca, and Zn bind predominantly to the β- and γ-phosphates of ATP, that of Cu predominantly to the α- and β-phosphates, and that of Mn appears to bind to all three.   Evidence also has been provided for an interaction between Cu(II), Zn(II), and Mn(II), and the adenine ring which is absent [87] with Mg(II) and Ca(II).   In review, the above considerations imply therefore that ions which interact with the adenine ring (Cu, Zn, Mn) or do not fit into the expected order of stability (Mn) are particularly active in ATP hydrolysis. [88]

Mechanistically the routes shown in (7-14) have been postulated for ATP-metal ion catalyzed hydrolysis.   Essentially they are analogous to the bimolecular and unimolecular mechanisms prevalent in phosphate hydrolyses (see Chapter 5).

Mechanisms I, II, III, and V depict a bimolecular nucleophilic attack by solvent on the chelate species, and differ only in the site undergoing attack.   The role of the metal ion may be envisaged as partially neutral-

[79] R. M. Bock, in P. D. Boyer, H. Lardy, and K. Myrbäck (eds.) "The Enzymes," Academic Press, New York, 1960, Vol. II, p. 3.

[80] H. Brintzinger, *Helv. Chim. Acta* **44**, 935 (1961).

[81] H. Brintzinger, *Helv. Chim. Acta* **44**, 1199 (1961).

[82] M. Cohn, W. D. McElroy, and B. Glass (eds.), "The Mechanism of Enzyme Action," Johns Hopkins Press, Baltimore, 1954, p. 542.

[83] J. M. Lowenstein, *Biochem. J.* **70**, 222 (1958).

[84] N. C. Melchior, *J. Biol. Chem.* **208**, 615 (1954).

[85] M. Cohn and T. R. Hughes, *J. Biol. Chem.* **235**, 3250 (1960).

[86] M. Cohn and T. R. Hughes, *J. Biol. Chem.* **237**, 176 (1962).

[87] G. G. Hammes, G. E. Maciel, and J. S. Waugh, *J. Am. Chem. Soc.* **83**, 2394 (1961).

[88] Although this discussion has emphasized the results of the more numerous thermodynamic investigations of metal-ion ligands which would appear to be meaningful in relation to the nonenzymic study under consideration, the reader should be aware of an alternative approach to the problem of metal-ion specificity in enzyme reactions. This involves investigation of the kinetic properties of various metal ions made possible through the temperature-jump method.   In such studies the actual rates of association and dissociation of various metal-ATP complexes are measured.   The results clearly indicate that both equilibrium and kinetic properties should be considered in assessing the role of metal ions in biological systems.   (G. G. Hammes and S. A. Levison, *Biochemistry* **3**, 1504 (1964) and earlier references therein.)

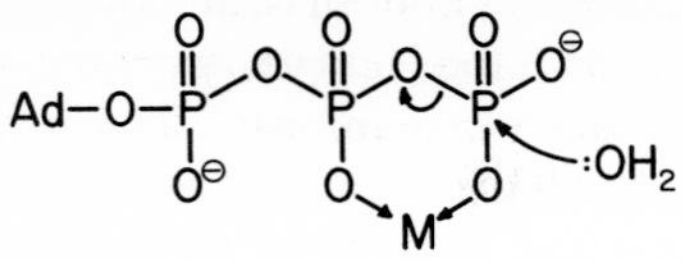

I

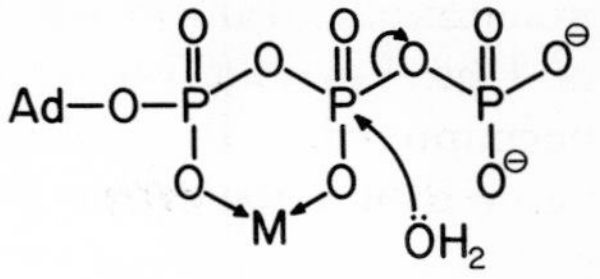

II [88a]

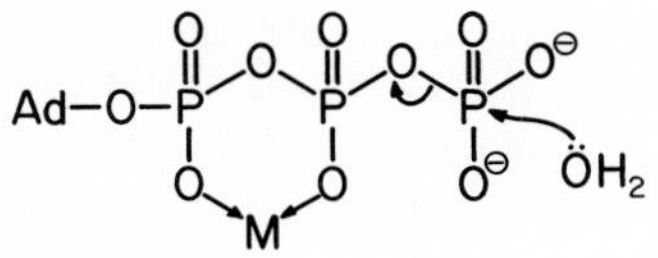

III

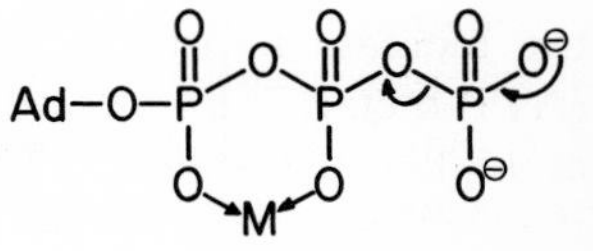

IV

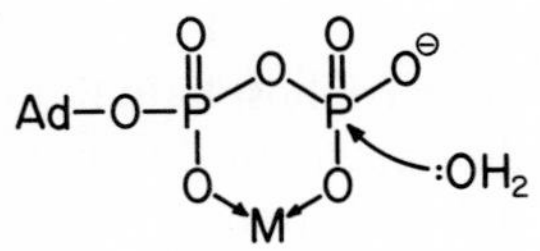

V

(7-14)

izing the net negative charge of the ionized phosphate groups, thereby facilitating the approach of the nucleophile. It may be argued, especially for I, II, and V, that chelation decreases the electron density on phosphorus, increasing its susceptibility to nucleophilic attack. The chelated species also may form a better leaving group than the more highly ionized pyrophosphate. Consequently the differences in the rates of hydrolysis of ATP and ADP may be attributed to differences in rate constants for (7-14 II or III) as compared to (7-14 V).

A second possibility may serve to rationalize the differences in the behavior of ATP- and ADP-metal ion catalyzed hydrolyses. This is illustrated by mechanism IV, which involves a unimolecular decomposition of the ATP chelate, forming the intermediate monomeric metaphosphate. Production of this highly reactive species, which is anticipated to undergo rapid nucleophilic attack, would be of special significance in enzymic and

[88a] The possible importance of mechanism (7-14 II) in the Cu(II) catalyzed hydrolysis of ATP is diminished by the finding that O^{18} from the aqueous medium enters the terminal phosphate group: H. Moll, P. W. Schneider, and H. Brintzinger, *Helv. Chim. Acta* **47**, 1837 (1964).

nonenzymic transphosphorylations. The experimental pH-rate profiles of Figs. 7-3 and 7-4 possess the familiar bell-shaped curve, previously encountered in the hydrolysis of phosphate ester monoanions. The pK_a' value for the ionization of

$$(\text{H-ATP metal})^{-1} \rightleftarrows (\text{ATP-metal})^{-2} + \text{H}^{\oplus}$$

is somewhat smaller than pK_{a2}' values for phosphate monoesters.[89] A similar value may be expected for the other metals. Thus, it appears that the increase in rate is associated with increasing concentration of the $(\text{ATP-metal})^{-2}$ species, although a plateau or constant rate is anticipated at higher pH values. The fact that the rates of hydrolysis decrease on the alkaline side of the pH optima for Cu(II) and Zn(II) may be caused by a change in the chelate structure to perhaps that involved in mechanism I or a change in the solvation of the metal ion of the chelate. Above pH 8 the observed increase in ATP and ADP hydrolysis in the presence of Cu(II) and Zn(II) may be caused by nucleophilic attack of hydroxide ion on a chelate structure, as in mechanism (7-14 I). If this occurs at the β-phosphate, it would account for the pyrophosphate found in the alkaline region. The ions of Mn(II) would appear to promote a bimolecular mechanism because of the absence of a bell-shaped pH-rate profile. In the above discussion it should be realized that the apparent binding of the metal ion to the adenine moiety has not as yet been assigned a role in the catalytic process. Perhaps this binding is of importance in the ADP-metal ion catalyzed hydrolysis, for which an ADP chelate may be proposed that might eliminate monomeric metaphosphate:

$$(7\text{-}15)$$

Replacement of water by various other acceptors, such as orthophosphate, acetate, glycine, and β-alanine, serves in the presence of bivalent metal ions to yield the corresponding phosphorylated derivatives. With orthophosphate the reaction product is pyrophosphate [83] and the most effective metal ions are Ca(II), Sr(II), and Ba(II) followed by Mn(II), Cd(II), and Zn(II). The nonenzymic transphosphorylation resembles the enzymic system in that (1) the reaction requires bivalent metal ion, (2) the reaction is inhibited by a nucleoside triphosphate:metal ratio greater

[89] A. E. Martell and G. Schwarzenbach, *Helv. Chim. Acta* **39,** 653 (1956).

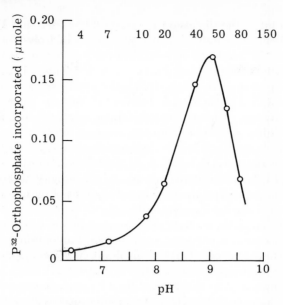

Fig. 7-5   *Effect of pH on transphosphorylation.   The complete reaction mixture contained 0.5 ml 0.10 M-ATP (pH 7.0), 0.1 ml 0.45 M-MnCl₂, 0.10 ml 0.05 M-P³²-orthophosphate (5.0 × 10⁴ counts/min), and 2-amino-2-hydroxymethylpropane-1,3-diol (free base) to give the pH indicated.   Figures above the experimental points of the curve indicate the amount of base added to the tube in question (in μmoles/ml).   The final volume was 1.0 ml, T 38°, and time of incubation 5 hr.   (Ref. 83.)*

than 1, and (3) the shape of the pH-rate profile, established at the physiological temperature of 38°, approaches that for a majority of the phosphotransferases.   The most reactive species is thought to be an $(ATP\text{-metal})^{-2}$ chelate, consistent with the pH optimum of the reaction being at 9.0 (Fig. 7-5).   With acetate, the product is presumably acetyl phosphate [83] (the presence of an activated acyl ester, not isolated, was demonstrated by its reaction with hydroxylamine), whose formation is catalyzed by the following ions in decreasing order of effectiveness, Be(II) > Ni(II) > Co(II) > Zn(II) > Mn(II).   The pH optimum [90] is 5.2.   Similarly with glycine, the acyl phosphate is again formed with the catalytic order being Be(II) > Zn(II) > Mn(II) > Ca(II) > Cd(II).   The pH optimum is 5.0.   Thus the pH optima for these three reactions occur at a pH where the concentration of $(ATP\text{-metal})^{-2}$ chelate is most abundant and may involve nucleophilic attack on a metaphosphate.   The other possibility is, of course, a bimolecular attack by the nucleophile on the γ-phosphate.

[90] J. M. Lowenstein and M. N. Schatz, *J. Biol. Chem.* **236,** 305 (1961).

At this point in the discussion the study by Martell and Hofstetter [91] of the metal-chelate catalysis of pyrophosphate hydrolysis is worthy of comment.   At 70° and pH 6.29 no catalysis was found for the divalent metal ions such as Cu(II) and Zn(II) or with MoO_2(VI) and Th(IV). This is in sharp contrast to the catalytic activity of these bivalent metal ions in ADP hydrolysis and transfer, and serves to emphasize the importance of the adenine moiety, at least in the metal-ion catalyzed hydrolysis.   Elements of higher oxidation number, in the form of water-soluble chelates, namely MoO_2(VI)-2,4-disulfopyrocatechol $<$ UO_2(VI)-2,4-disulfopyrocatechol $<$ Zr(IV)-EDTA $<$ ZrO(IV)-2,4-disulfopyrocatechol $<$ ZrO(IV)-EDTA, exhibit increasing catalytic activity in the order indicated.   The latter chelate increases the hydrolysis of pyrophosphate by a factor of 21 over the noncatalytic rate.

Besides the apparent catalytic role assumed by the metal ion, a second function for metal ions has some experimental foundation.   Westheimer and Dudek [51] found not only that the solvolysis of tetrabenzylpyrophosphate is accelerated in the presence of Mg(II) and Ca(II) ions, but that the position of bond cleavage is mediated by the nature of the metal ion present.   In the absence of Mg(II), the reaction proceeds according to equation (7-8) in contrast to the P-O and C-O cleavage observed in its presence. On the enzymic level the hydrolysis of ATP in the presence of muscle proteins and H_2O^{18} leads to exchange in the γ-phosphate with Mg(II) [92, 93] but no exchange with Ca(II). [92]   Consequently the metal ion appears to possess a directional effect on the mode of bond cleavage, preferentially lowering the free energy barrier for a particular mode.

V. FREE ENERGY OF HYDROLYSIS

The "energy rich" bond concept has had a profound influence upon the entire field of biochemistry.   This theory essentially states that the free energy necessary as a chemical driving force for unfavorable metabolic reactions is stored in the form of compounds possessing high free energies of hydrolysis, including ATP, acetyl phosphate, phosphoenol pyruvate, and others.   Hydrolysis of these compounds when coupled to an endergonic process may act to reverse the direction of the equilibrium. The reader should note, however, that this concept may be criticized on the

[91] R. Hofstetter and A. E. Martell, *J. Am. Chem. Soc.* **81**, 4461 (1959).

[92] H. M. Levy and D. E. Koshland, Jr., *J. Am. Chem. Soc.* **80**, 3164 (1958).

[93] D. E. Koshland, Jr., Z. Budenstein, and A. Kowalsky, *J. Biol. Chem.* **211**, 279 (1954).

grounds that the behavior of dynamic biological systems is only approximated by thermochemical considerations, since thermodynamic equilibrium is probably very rarely, if ever, attained in the intact system. Apart from this objection, examination of the free energy of hydrolysis or the "group potential" characteristic of a particular compound or class of compounds may be useful, since on occasion the kinetic process or rates associated with certain chemical transformations may parallel the thermodynamic behavior. For example, the susceptibility of activated acyl groups (amides, thiolesters, acyl phosphates) to nucleophilic attack is largely a function of the positive charge on the carbonyl carbon and generally closely parallels the "group potential" of the acyl group, since substituents affect both these properties in a similar manner.[94] Consequently, it is of interest to briefly consider the free energies of hydrolysis of the phosphates presently being reviewed.

Recent years have seen the de-evaluation of the free energy of hydrolysis for the most common "high-energy" phosphate compound, adenosine triphosphate (ATP). Early estimates [95-98] of $\Delta F^{0\prime}$ at 25° for the reaction (7-16):

$$ATP^{-4} + H_2O \rightleftarrows ADP^{-3} + P_i^{-2} + H^{\oplus} \qquad (7\text{-}16)$$

set a value of ca. -11 kcal mole^{-1} which recent measurements [99-101] have reduced to ca. -7 kcal mole^{-1}. Therefore ATP falls at the lower limit of compounds considered "energy-rich," which have been defined as substances possessing a $-\Delta F^{0\prime}$ of hydrolysis (physiological pH) of some 7–14 kcal mole^{-1}.[94] This is an apparent free energy change referring only to the specified pH and to a total of unity for the sum of the activities (or, to an approximation, the concentrations) of all the ionic and nonionic forms of each reactant and product which are present at the given pH, i.e., stoichiometric concentration of reactants + products equals $1M$. The activity of water is taken as unity. As such, the pH 7 convention is of considerable use in establishing a scale of group potentials (Fig. 7-6) at conditions approximating those in biological systems (subject to the

[94] W. P. Jencks, in P. D. Boyer, H. Lardy, and K. Myrbäck (eds.) "The Enzymes," Academic Press, New York, 1962, Vol. VI, pp. 339–361.

[95] F. Lipmann, *Advan. Enzymol.* **1**, 99 (1941).

[96] O. Meyerhoff, *Ann. N.Y. Acad. Sci.* **45**, 377 (1944).

[97] P. Oesper, in W. D. McElroy and B. Glass (eds.) "Phosphorus Metabolism," Johns Hopkins Press, Baltimore, 1951, p. 523.

[98] K. Burton and H. A. Krebs, *Biochem. J.* **54**, 94 (1953).

[99] L. Levintow and A. Meister, *J. Biol. Chem.* **209**, 265 (1954).

[100] R. J. Podolsky and M. F. Morales, *J. Biol. Chem.* **218**, 945 (1956).

[101] M. R. Atkinson, E. Johnson, and R. K. Morton, *Nature* **184**, 1925 (1959).

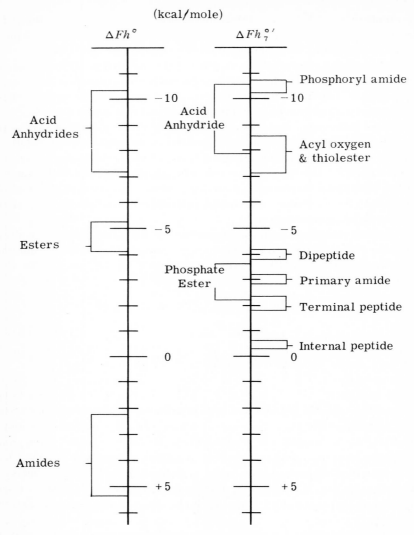

Fig. 7-6   *A scale of group potentials according to the nonionized compound convention* (ΔFh^0) *and the pH 7 convention* $(\Delta Fh^{0'}_{pH7})$. *(Ref. 102.)*

qualification already mentioned). However, it is obvious that the equilibrium constant of (7-16) will vary as the pH is changed and, therefore, it is of interest to evaluate $\Delta F^{0'}$ as a function of pH.

Any approach to this difficult problem involves a definition of a standard free energy of hydrolysis. For our purposes it is useful to employ the

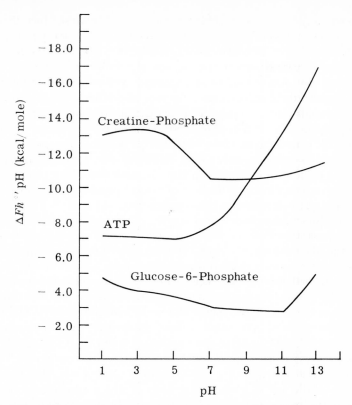

Fig. 7-7 *The free energy change on hydrolysis of several phosphate compounds as a function of pH.* *(Ref. 102.)*

"nonionized compound convention" proposed by Carpenter,[102] in which the standard free energy change, ΔFh^0, is defined as the increment of free energy involved in the hydrolysis of nonionized reactant by water in the liquid state to nonionized product in water at a specified temperature, both reactant and product being at unit activity in water. Since in a formal sense the free energy change involved in hydrolysis at a fixed pH value can be divided into two components: (1) the contribution from ΔFh^0, and (2) the contributions arising from ionization-neutralization reactions, $\Delta Fhi_{pH}^{0\prime}$, it is possible in theory to calculate $\Delta F_{pH}^{0\prime}$ providing that $\Delta Fhi_{pH}^{0\prime}$ may be accurately evaluated (7-17):

$$\Delta F_{pH}^{0\prime} = \Delta Fhi_{pH}^{0\prime} + \Delta Fh^0 \tag{7-17}$$

[102] F. H. Carpenter, *J. Am. Chem. Soc.* **82,** 1111 (1960).

Furthermore, the values of the latter term are of interest, since they provide a direct assessment of the importance of ionization-neutralization reactions in $\Delta F_{\mathrm{pH}}^{0'}$. The term $\Delta Fhi_{\mathrm{pH}}^{0'}$ is formally defined as the increment in free energy arising from the conversion of nonionized compounds to the mixture of ions determined by the specified pH value and temperature, and subject to the condition that the sum of the activities of compounds and ions equals unity. Without further detail, this may be accomplished by employing the appropriate acid dissociation constants. Unfortunately these constants are often very difficult to determine, particularly in the case of compounds which exist as zwitterions, and this approach is subject to criticism on these grounds. Nonetheless, the variation of the free energy change upon hydrolysis of several phosphate compounds as a function of pH calculated in this manner may be found in Fig. (7-7).

For ordinary phosphate esters at pH 7, the contribution of ionization-neutralization reactions is a positive value ($\Delta Fhi_{\mathrm{pH7}}^{0'} = +2.0$ kcal mole^{-1}), but as the pH is decreased below 7 it approaches ΔFh^0 as a limit (-5.4 for glucose-6-phosphate). This is due to the smaller pK_a values of the ester relative to orthophosphoric acid. For the pyrophosphates it would appear that ionization-neutralization reactions make relatively little contribution to the overall free energy change in hydrolysis at pH 7; ΔFh^0 and $\Delta Fh_{\mathrm{pH7}}^{0'}$ have about the same value. However, with increasing pH values above 7, $\Delta Fhi_{\mathrm{pH}}^{0'}$ decreases rapidly, as noted for ATP (ΔFh^0 -6.8), and appears to exert a profound influence on the "energy rich" properties of this compound. With creatine phosphate, the hydrolysis yields an acidic and a basic group, both of which contribute to $\Delta Fhi_{\mathrm{pH}}^{0'}$, although the magnitude of $\Delta Fhi_{\mathrm{pH}}^{0'}$ is in doubt due to difficulty in the assignment of pK_a values to the ionizing groups. In Fig. 7-6 two scales of group potentials are presented which may be directly compared to assess the importance of $\Delta Fhi_{\mathrm{pH7}}^{0'}$. It must be emphasized that the magnitude of $\Delta Fhi_{\mathrm{pH}}^{0'}$ depends on the choice of standard states. Moreover, the overall free energy changes, in particular for the phosphate compounds, should be influenced by the presence of metal ions, a factor which has not been incorporated in these scales.[103, 104]

[103] K. Burton, *Biochem. J.* **71**, 388 (1959).

[104] T. H. Benzinger, C. Kitzinger, R. Hems, and K. Burton, *Biochem. J.* **71**, 400 (1959).

Thiamine Pyrophosphate and Pyridoxal-5'- Phosphate

chapter
eight

I. INTRODUCTION

A. Type Reactions Catalyzed

Thiamine diphosphate (8-1) and pyridoxal- or pyridoxamine-5'-phosphoric acids (8-2) are requisite cofactors for a host of enzymic reac-

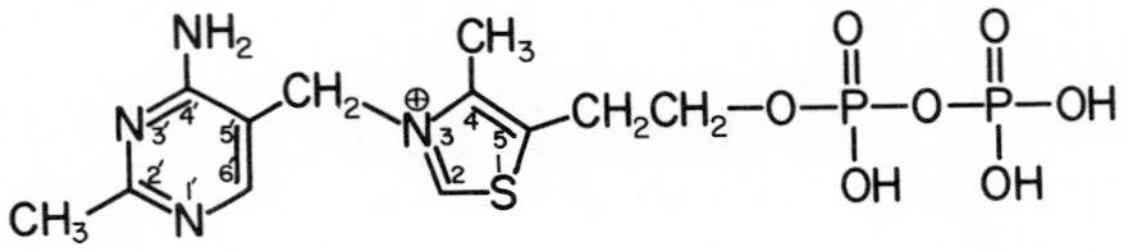

$$(8\text{-}1)$$

$$(8\text{-}2)$$

tions. We shall, unconventionally, consider both cofactors more or less together, since the early organic chemical studies of rudimentary model systems associated with the two coenzymes have a common basis and the most acceptable mechanisms for their action bear a broad similarity.

Both pyridoxal and thiamine may be considered to play their roles by stabilizing or obviating the necessity to stabilize carbanions. Perusal of the enzymic reactions for which thiamine diphosphate is required as a cofactor reveals that they involve the breaking of bonds immediately adjacent to carbonyl groups (acyloins, α-diketones, α-keto acids). If one were simply presented with the various chemical transformations for which thiamine serves as a cofactor the most rational organic mechanism, not including the cofactor, for all the reactions would be of a type necessitating the involvement of an improbable acyl anion (8-3)[1–7]:

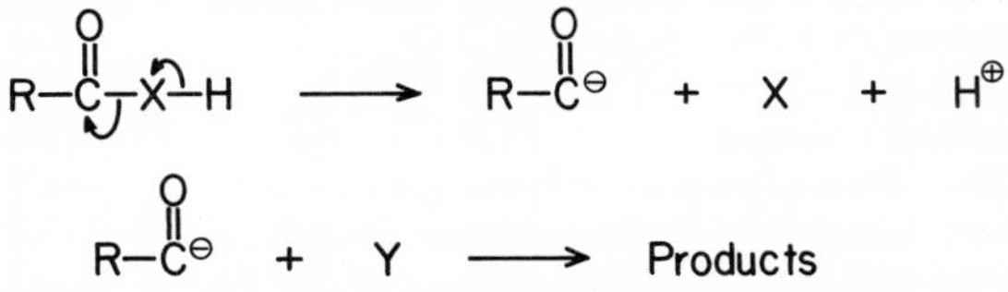

$$(8\text{-}3)$$

[1] I. C. Gunsalus, B. L. Horecker, and W. A. Wood, *Bacteriol. Rev.* **19,** 79 (1955).

Some specific examples follow.

(1) α-Keto acids [carboxylase reactions, requiring divalent metal ion, Mg(II), Mn(II), Co(II), Cd(II), Ca(II), Zn(II), Fe(II)]:

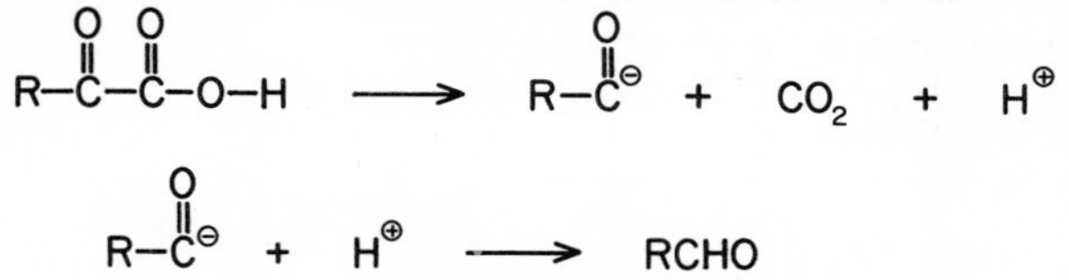

$$R-\overset{O}{\overset{\|}{C}}-\overset{O}{\overset{\|}{C}}-O-H \longrightarrow R-\overset{O}{\overset{\|}{C}}{}^{\ominus} + CO_2 + H^{\oplus}$$

$$R-\overset{O}{\overset{\|}{C}}{}^{\ominus} + H^{\oplus} \longrightarrow RCHO$$

$$\text{(8-4)}$$

(α-keto acid oxidase)

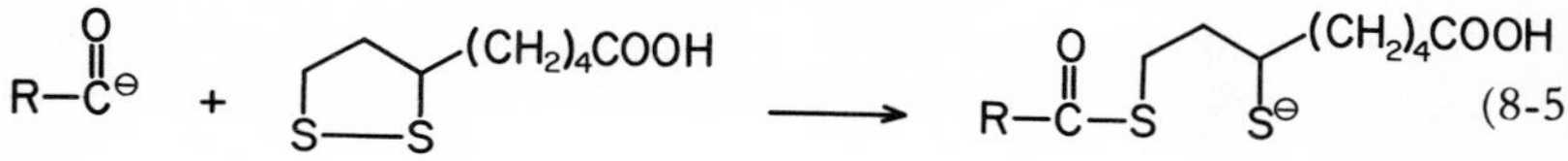

$$\text{(8-5)}$$

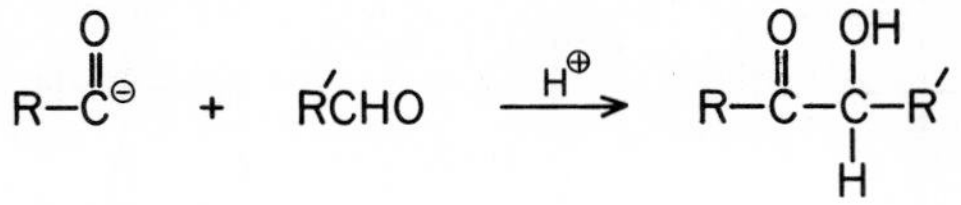

$$R-\overset{O}{\overset{\|}{C}}{}^{\ominus} + R'CHO \xrightarrow{H^{\oplus}} R-\overset{O}{\overset{\|}{C}}-\overset{OH}{\underset{H}{\overset{|}{C}}}-R' \qquad \text{(8-6)}$$

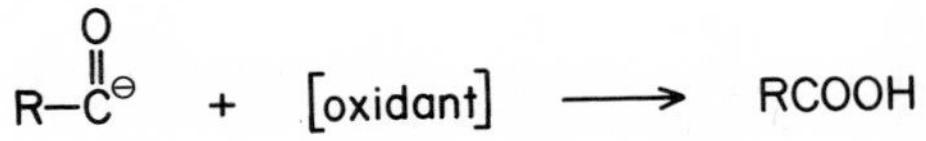

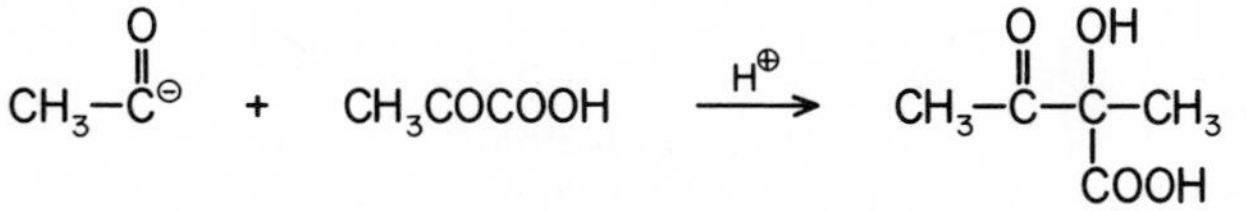

$$R-\overset{O}{\overset{\|}{C}}{}^{\ominus} + [\text{oxidant}] \longrightarrow RCOOH \qquad \text{(8-7)}$$

$$CH_3-\overset{O}{\overset{\|}{C}}{}^{\ominus} + CH_3COCOOH \xrightarrow{H^{\oplus}} CH_3-\overset{O}{\overset{\|}{C}}-\overset{OH}{\underset{COOH}{\overset{|}{C}}}-CH_3 \qquad \text{(8-8)}$$

(2) α-Diketones:

$$CH_3-\overset{O}{\overset{\|}{C}}-\overset{O}{\overset{\|}{C}}-CH_3 + H_2O \rightleftharpoons CH_3-\overset{O}{\overset{\|}{C}}-\overset{O-H}{\underset{OH}{\overset{|}{C}}}-CH_3 \longrightarrow$$

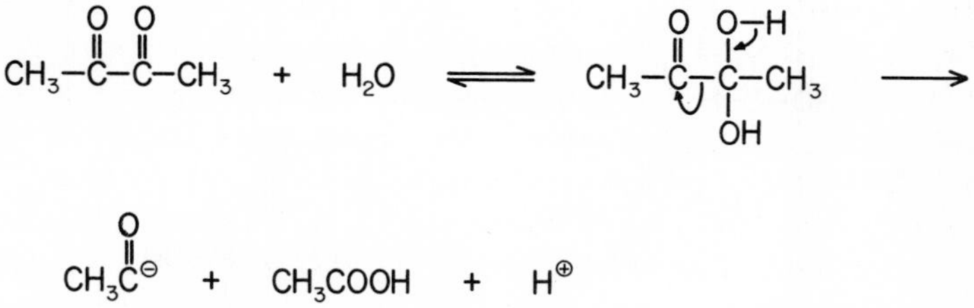

$$\text{(8-9)}$$

$$CH_3\overset{O}{\overset{\|}{C}}{}^{\ominus} + CH_3COOH + H^{\oplus}$$

---

[2] I. C. Gunsalus, in W. D. McElroy and B. Glass (eds.) "The Mechanism of Enzyme Action," Johns Hopkins Press, Baltimore, 1954, p. 547.

[3] L. L. Campbell, *J. Bacteriol.* **68,** 598 (1954).

[4] D. E. Green, D. Herbert, and V. Subrahmanyan, *J. Biol. Chem.* **138,** 327 (1941).

[5] A. Meister, "Biochemistry of Amino Acids," Academic Press, New York, 1957.

[6] B. L. Horecker, *J. Cellular Comp. Physiol.* **54,** Suppl. 1, 89 (1959).

[7] D. E. Metzler, in P. D. Boyer, H. Lardy, and K. Myrbäck (eds.) "The Enzymes," Academic Press, New York, 1960, Vol. II, p. 295.

(3) α-Hydroxyketones (transketolase):

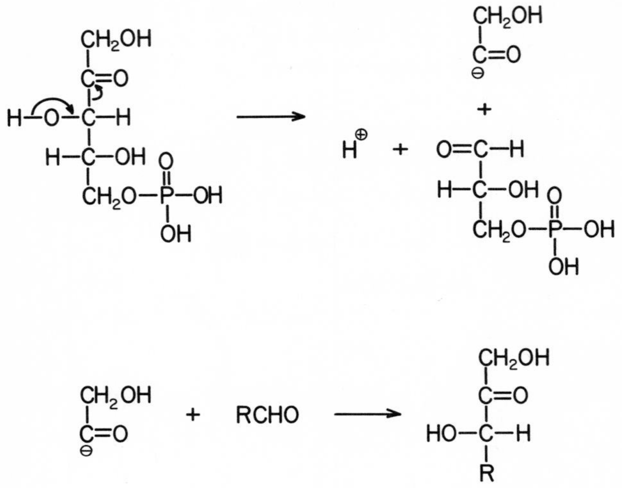

$$(8\text{-}10)$$

The reaction is represented with D-xylulose-5-phosphate as the substrate. D-Fructose-6-phosphate or seduheptulose-7-phosphate also may serve as substrate.

(phosphoketolase)

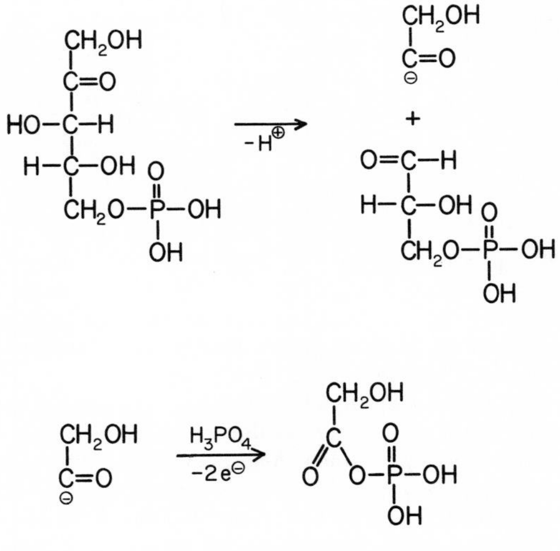

$$(8\text{-}11)$$

The question then arises as to how the employment of thiamine diphosphate in the enzymic mechanism obviates the necessity for the intermediate formation of the acyl anions of equations (8-3) to (8-11).

The various enzymic reactions for which pyridoxal-5′-phosphate is required as a cofactor have recently been summarized.[8-10] If these enzymic reactions involving pyridoxal phosphate are examined, it is found that their nonenzymic counterparts might be grouped as requiring stabilization of a carbanion at the α- or β-position of an α-amino acid:

(1) Reactions which require carbanion formation at the α-position of the amino acid.

(a) α-Amino acid racemases:

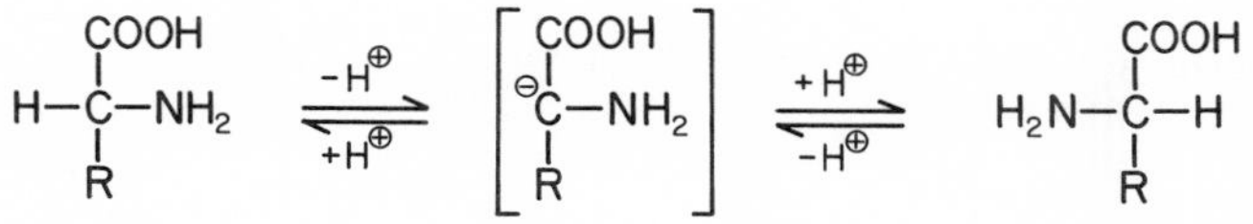

$$
\underset{R}{\overset{COOH}{H-C-NH_2}} \underset{+H^{\oplus}}{\overset{-H^{\oplus}}{\rightleftharpoons}} \left[\underset{R}{\overset{COOH}{{}^{\ominus}C-NH_2}}\right] \underset{-H^{\oplus}}{\overset{+H^{\oplus}}{\rightleftharpoons}} \underset{R}{\overset{COOH}{H_2N-C-H}} \qquad (8\text{-}12)
$$

(b) Amino acid α-decarboxylases:

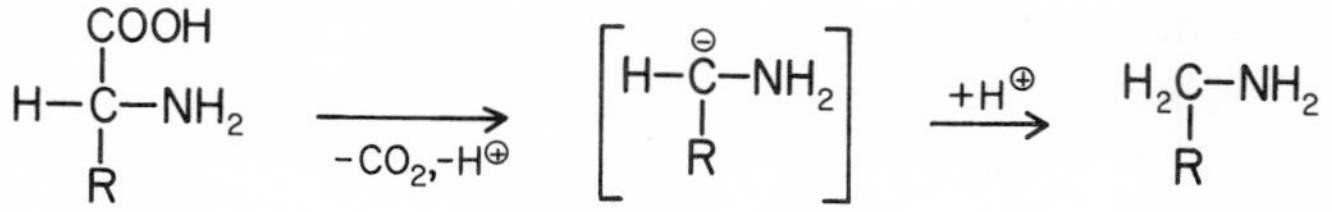

$$
\underset{R}{\overset{COOH}{H-C-NH_2}} \xrightarrow[-CO_2,-H^{\oplus}]{} \left[\underset{R}{\overset{H-\overset{\ominus}{C}-NH_2}{}}\right] \xrightarrow{+H^{\oplus}} \underset{R}{\overset{H_2C-NH_2}{}} \qquad (8\text{-}13)
$$

(c) Serine and threonine aldolases:

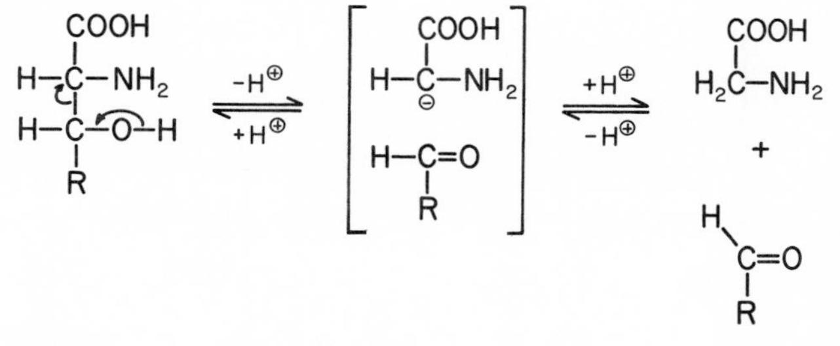

$$
\begin{matrix}COOH \\ H-C-NH_2 \\ H-C-O-H \\ R\end{matrix} \underset{+H^{\oplus}}{\overset{-H^{\oplus}}{\rightleftharpoons}} \left[\begin{matrix}COOH \\ H-\overset{\ominus}{C}-NH_2 \\ H-C=O \\ R\end{matrix}\right] \underset{-H^{\oplus}}{\overset{+H^{\oplus}}{\rightleftharpoons}} \begin{matrix}COOH \\ H_2C-NH_2 \\ + \\ \overset{H}{\underset{R}{\diagdown}}C=O\end{matrix} \qquad (8\text{-}14)
$$

[8] A. E. Braunstein, in P. D. Boyer, H. Lardy, and K. Myrbäck (eds.) "The Enzymes," Academic Press, New York, 1960, Vol. II.
[9] A. E. Braunstein, in E. E. Snell, P. M. Fasella, A. Braunstein, and A. R. Fanelli (eds.) "Chemical and Biological Aspects of Pyridoxal Catalysis," Pergamon, New York, 1963, p. 579.
[10] E. E. Snell and W. T. Jenkins, J. Cellular Comp. Physiol. 54, Suppl. 1, 161 (1959).

(d) Amino acid α,β-eliminases:

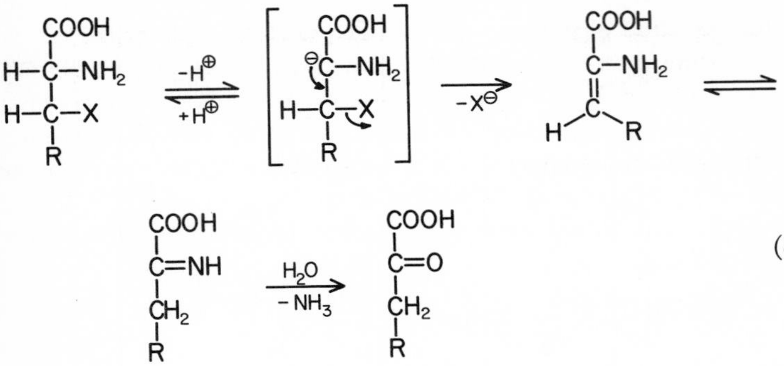

$$(8\text{-}15)$$

where X = −SH, −SR, −OH, −Cl, β−indolyl

(2) Reactions which involve stabilization of a negative charge at the β-position of the amino acid.

(a) α-Amino acid β-decarboxylases:

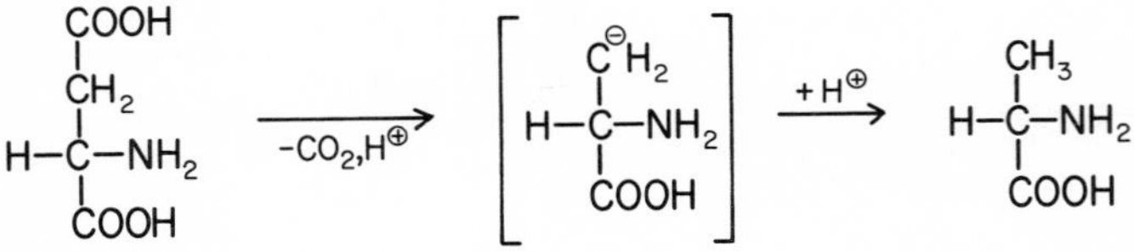

(b) Kynureninase:

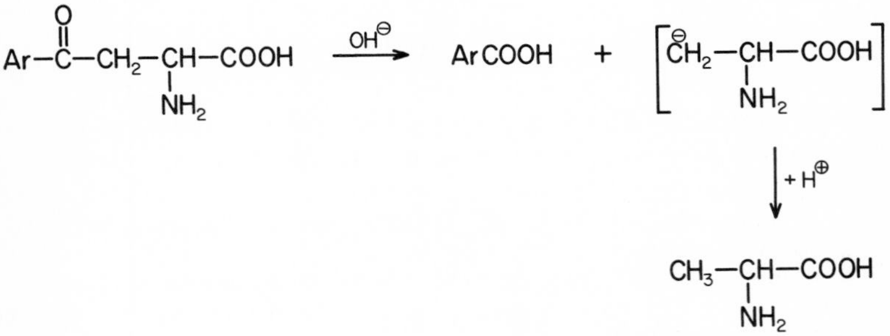

$$(8\text{-}17)$$

(c) Cystathionase, methionine lyase:

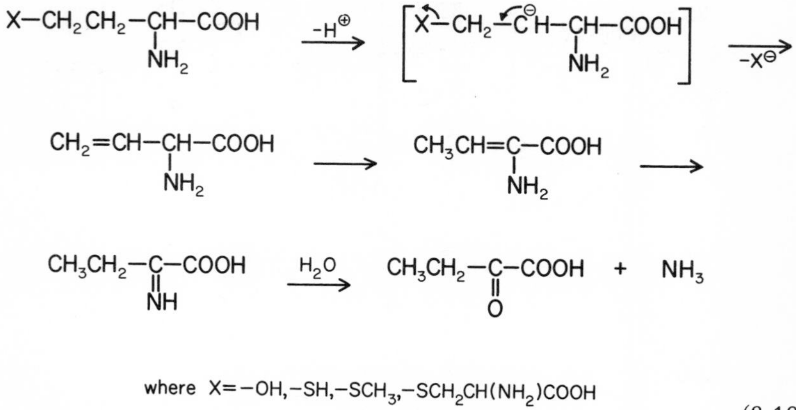

$$X-CH_2CH_2-\underset{\underset{NH_2}{|}}{CH}-COOH \quad \xrightarrow{-H^{\oplus}} \quad \left[X-CH_2-\overset{\ominus}{C}H-\underset{\underset{NH_2}{|}}{CH}-COOH \right] \quad \xrightarrow{-X^{\ominus}}$$

$$CH_2=CH-\underset{\underset{NH_2}{|}}{CH}-COOH \quad \longrightarrow \quad CH_3CH=\underset{\underset{NH_2}{|}}{C}-COOH \quad \longrightarrow$$

$$CH_3CH_2-\underset{\underset{NH}{\|}}{C}-COOH \quad \xrightarrow{H_2O} \quad CH_3CH_2-\underset{\underset{O}{\|}}{C}-COOH \quad + \quad NH_3$$

where $X = -OH, -SH, -SCH_3, -SCH_2CH(NH_2)COOH$

(8-18)

(3) Reactions involving transamination, transaminases:

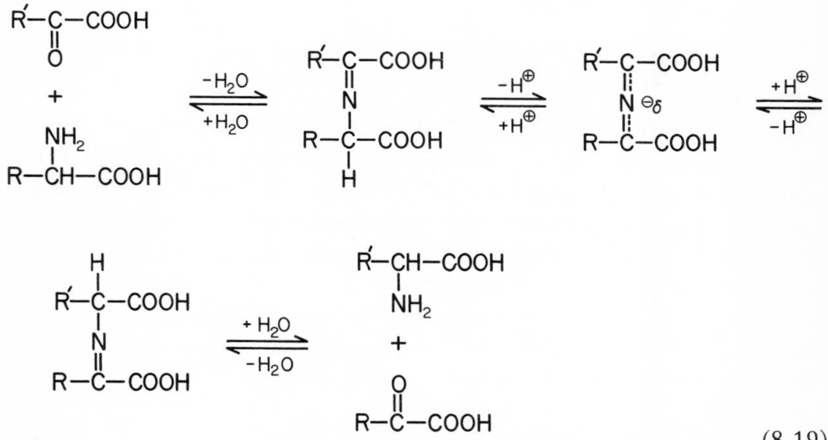

$$\underset{\overset{\|}{O}}{R'-C-COOH}$$
$$+$$
$$\underset{\overset{|}{NH_2}}{R-CH-COOH}$$
$$\underset{+H_2O}{\overset{-H_2O}{\rightleftharpoons}}$$
$$\underset{\overset{|}{H}}{\overset{R'-C-COOH}{\underset{R-C-COOH}{\overset{\|}{N}}}}$$
$$\underset{+H^{\oplus}}{\overset{-H^{\oplus}}{\rightleftharpoons}}$$
$$\overset{R'-C-COOH}{\underset{R-C-COOH}{\overset{\|}{N}\overset{\ominus}{\underset{\|}{\delta}}}}$$
$$\underset{-H^{\oplus}}{\overset{+H^{\oplus}}{\rightleftharpoons}}$$

$$\underset{\overset{\|}{N}}{\overset{\overset{H}{|}}{R'-C-COOH}}$$
$$\underset{R-C-COOH}{\overset{\|}{}}$$
$$\underset{-H_2O}{\overset{+H_2O}{\rightleftharpoons}}$$
$$\underset{\overset{|}{NH_2}}{R'-CH-COOH}$$
$$+$$
$$\underset{R-C-COOH}{\overset{O}{\overset{\|}{}}}$$

(8-19)

As in the case of thiamine, pyridoxal as a cofactor must also function in obviating the formation of carbanions. It will be seen that the two co-factors perform their catalytic roles by conjugating the center of the incipient carbanion with an unsaturated system terminating in a positive nitrogen.

B. Amines as Models

Before the discovery of either thiamine or pyridoxal, chemists had studied so-called model enzymes which catalyzed the decarboxylation and

Table 8-1   *Relative efficiencies of amines in the catalysis of the decarboxylation of phenylglyoxylic acid*

Catalyst	Approximate rel. rates
$C_2H_5NH_2$	1.0
Glycine	20
$C_6H_5CH(NH_2)COOH$	30
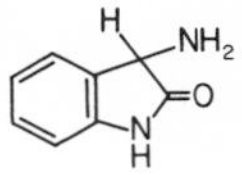	650
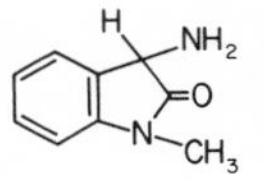	200
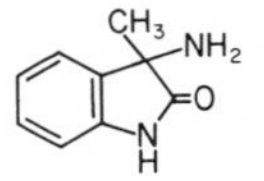	<u>ca.</u> 0

transamination of α-keto acids.   Both reactions are catalyzed by amines and the two processes are differentiated by the solvent employed.   For the decarboxylation studies phenol or phenol-cresol mixtures were used, whereas for the transamination reactions aqueous solutions were employed. These topics will be considered in this section beginning with those carried out in phenolic solvents.

1. AMINE CATALYZED DECARBOXYLATION OF α-KETO ACIDS   Langenbeck, his co-workers, and others [11–19] have extensively studied the amine catalysis of the decarboxylation of α-keto acids:

$$R-\overset{O}{\underset{\|}{C}}-\overset{O}{\underset{\|}{C}}-OH \quad \xrightarrow[\text{50–170°}]{\text{RNH}_2 \text{ in } C_6H_5OH,} \quad R-\overset{O}{\underset{\|}{C}}-H \quad + \quad CO_2 \qquad (8\text{-}20)$$

[11] W. Langenbeck, "Die Organischen Katalysatoren," 2nd Ed., Springer, Berlin, 1949.
[12] For a review see M. G. J. Beets, *Chem. Weekblad* **43,** 147 (1947).
[13] W. Langenbeck, *Ergeb. Enzymforsch.* **2,** 314 (1933).
[14] K. G. Stern and J. L. Melnick, *J. Biol. Chem.* **131,** 597 (1939).
[15] W. Dirscherl and H. Nahm, *Z. Physiol. Chem.* **264,** 41 (1940).
[16] R. E. Schachat, E. I. Becker, and A. D. McLaren, *J. Org. Chem.* **16,** 1349 (1951).
[17] R. E. Schachat, E. I. Becker, and A. D. McLaren, *J. Phys. Chem.* **56,** 722 (1952).
[18] A. S. Endler and E. I. Becker, *J. Am. Chem. Soc.* **77,** 6608 (1955).
[19] A. S. Endler and E. I. Becker, *J. Phys. Chem.* **61,** 747 (1957).

generally through measurement of CO_2 evolution with time. The kinetics of the reactions are complicated, displaying an initial burst of CO_2 evolution which subsides due to the conversion of the catalysts to inactive products. The efficiency of the catalysts has been expressed in various ways, and in Table 8-1 are compared the approximate relative efficiencies of various amines in the decarboxylation of phenylglyoxylic acid.

For the simple amines, the reaction undoubtedly proceeds through the formation of an imine, followed by prototropic rearrangement and de-

(a)
$$
\begin{array}{c} C_6H_5 \\ | \\ C{=}O \\ | \\ COOH \end{array}
\;+\; C_6H_5OH \;\rightleftharpoons\;
\begin{array}{c} C_6H_5 \\ | \\ \overset{\oplus}{C}{=}OH \\ | \\ COOH \end{array}
\;+\; C_6H_5O^{\ominus}
$$

$$
\begin{array}{c} C_6H_5 \\ | \\ \overset{\oplus}{C}{=}OH \\ | \\ COOH \end{array}
\;+\; R{-}CH_2NH_2 \;\rightleftharpoons\;
\begin{array}{c} \quad\quad C_6H_5 \\ \overset{\oplus}{\;} \quad | \\ R{-}CH_2{-}NH_2{-}C{-}OH \\ | \\ COOH \end{array}
\;\rightleftharpoons\;
$$

$$
\begin{array}{c} \quad\quad C_6H_5 \\ \quad | \\ R{-}CH_2{-}NH{-}C{-}\overset{\oplus}{O}H_2 \\ | \\ COOH \end{array}
\;\rightleftharpoons\;
\begin{array}{c} \quad\quad C_6H_5 \\ \overset{\oplus}{\;}\; | \\ R{-}CH_2{-}NH{=}C \\ | \\ COOH \end{array}
\;+\; H_2O
$$

(b)
$$
\begin{array}{c} \quad\quad C_6H_5 \\ \quad\;| \\ R{-}CH_2{-}N{=}C \quad HOC_6H_5 \\ \;\;| \quad\quad | \\ \;\;H \quad\quad COOH \\ C_6H_5O^{\ominus} \end{array}
\;\rightleftharpoons\;
\begin{array}{c} \quad\quad C_6H_5 \\ \quad\;\; | \\ R{-}CH{=}N{-}C{-}H \\ + \quad\quad | \\ \quad\quad COOH \\ C_6H_5OH \end{array}
\;+\; {}^{\ominus}OC_6H_5
$$

(c)
$$
\begin{array}{c} C_6H_5\;\;\;\;H \\ \;\;\;\diagdown\,C\,\diagup \\ N\;\;\;\;\;C{=}O \\ \| \quad\quad | \\ R{-}CH \quad CO \\ \;\;\;\;\;\;H \end{array}
\;\longrightarrow\;
\begin{array}{c} \quad\quad C_6H_5 \\ \;\;\;\;\; | \\ R{-}CH_2N{=}CH \end{array}
\;+\; CO_2
$$

(d)
$$
\begin{array}{c} \quad\quad C_6H_5 \\ \quad\;\; | \\ R{-}CH_2N{=}C{-}H \end{array}
\;+\;
\begin{array}{c} C_6H_5 \\ | \\ C{=}O \\ | \\ COOH \end{array}
\xrightarrow{\text{several steps}}
\begin{array}{c} \quad\quad C_6H_5 \\ \quad\;\; | \\ R{-}CH_2N{=}C \\ \quad\quad | \\ \quad\quad COOH \end{array}
\;+\;
$$

$$
C_6H_5CHO
$$

$$
(8\text{-}21)
$$

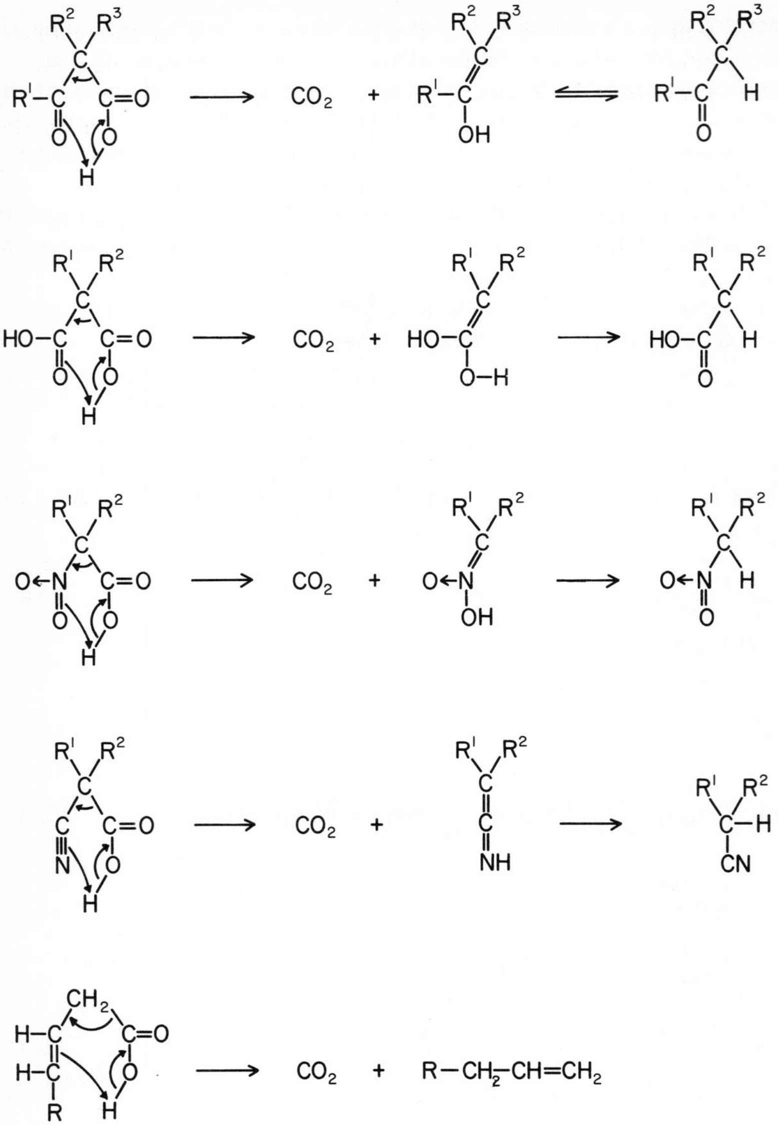

$$(8-22)$$

carboxylation. The phenolic solvent must act as either a specific-acid or general-acid catalyst in the formation of intermediate imine, and as a general-base and general-acid catalyst in the ensuing prototropic shift. Details of the catalysis of imine formation and prototropic shifts in aqueous solutions will be discussed under Section III-A and B of this chapter. The details of the mechanisms presented in (8-21) are only probable.

The catalytically important step in (8-21) is the prototropic shift (b), which converts the relatively stable α-unsaturated acid to a readily decarboxylated β-unsaturated acid. The prototropic shift and the obtainment of β-unsaturated carboxylic acids are of singular importance in the mechanisms of catalysis of decarboxylation by both pyridoxal and thiamine. The ability to obtain a β-unsaturated system readily insures decarboxylation, as exemplified by many examples (8-22).

The presentation of the decarboxylation reactions for β-unsaturated carboxylic acids as a cyclic shift of electrons is employed merely to indicate a formal similarity in the compounds undergoing decarboxylation. The decarboxylations may proceed via the cyclic process or via a stable carbanion mechanism.[20–22] Thus, the ammonium salt of $(-)$-2-cyano-2-phenylbutanoic acid decarboxylates in t-butanol solvent with partial retention of configuration (8-23).[22] A cyclic mechanism involving the

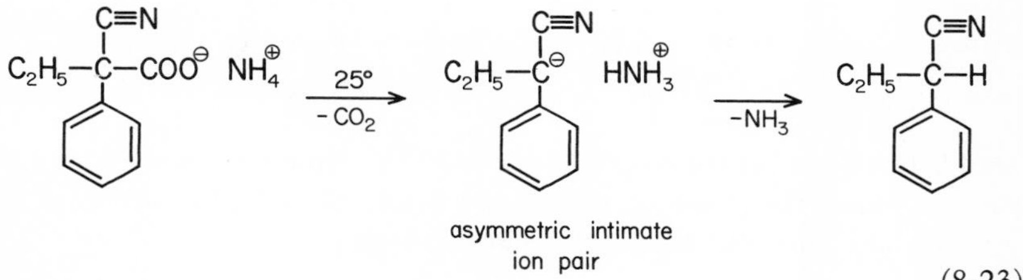

asymmetric intimate
ion pair

(8-23)

cyano group would, of course, have led to racemization.

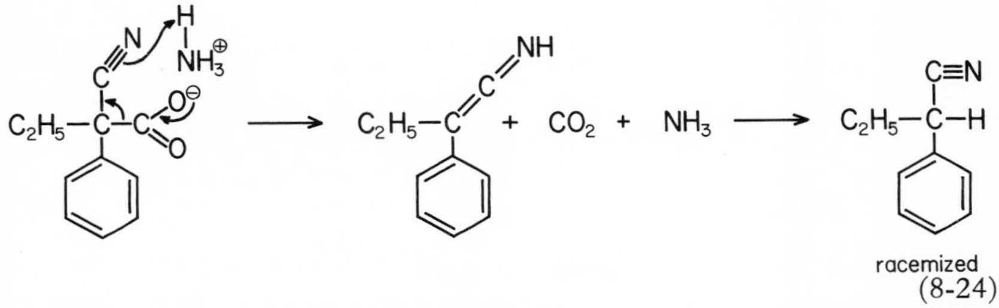

racemized
(8-24)

In the enzymic decarboxylations for which pyridoxal-5′-phosphate is a cofactor, β-unsaturation [i.e., $-CH{=}N-CH(R)COOH$] is essential but,

[20] C. G. Swain, R. F. W. Bader, R. M. Esteve, and R. N. Griffin, *J. Am. Chem. Soc.* **83**, 1951 (1961).

[21] F. H. Westheimer and W. A. Jones, *J. Am. Chem. Soc.* **63**, 3283 (1941).

[22] D. J. Cram and P. Haberfield, *J. Am. Chem. Soc.* **83**, 2354, 2363 (1961).

as in (8-23), retention of configuration is maintained.   In both instances collapse of carbanion intermediate to optically active product may be ascribed to the asymmetric character of their environment.   In certain instances the necessity of the formation of an intermediate, arising from the shift of the β-unsaturated center, to stabilize the carbanion may be demonstrated.[23]

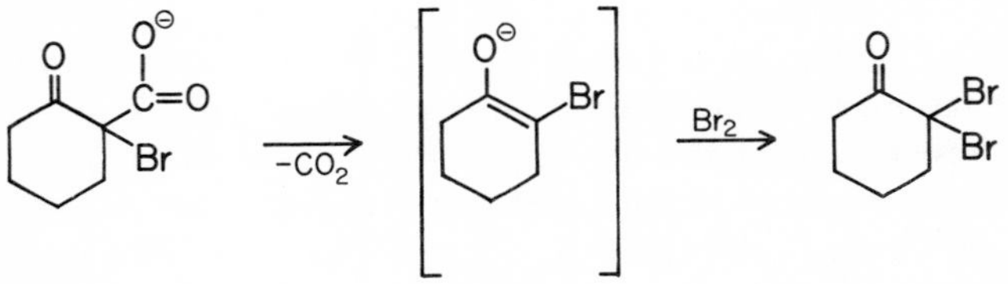

(8-25)

In the case of camphenoic and ketopinic acids (8-26 I, II) decarboxylation does not occur due to the impossibility of forming the enol

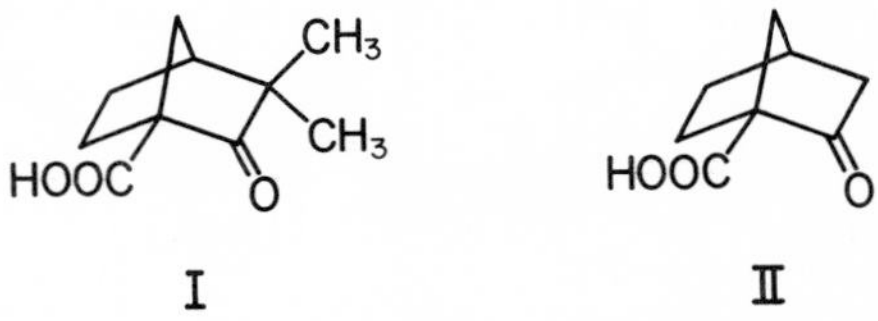

(8-26)

I   II

double bond at a bridge head (Bredt's rule).[24]   However, expansion of the ring decreases the strain at the bridge head, allowing formation of the intermediate enol and resultant decarboxylation.

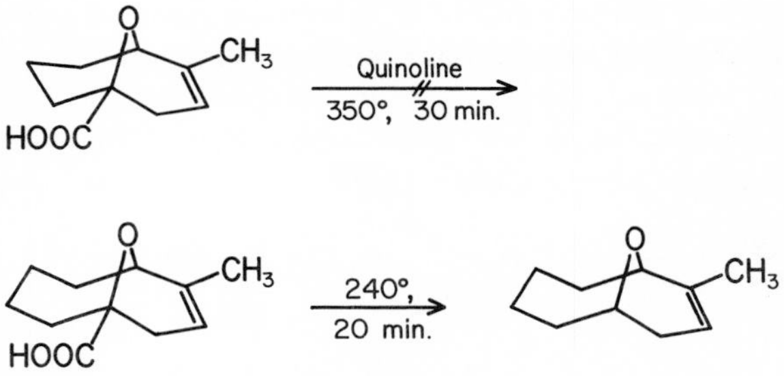

(8-27)

With the above considerations in mind, it is seen that the amines of Table 8-1 which possess a carbonyl group in the α-position have enhanced activity as catalysts for decarboxylation, and that the 3-amino-2-oxindoles are particularly effective.   The imines formed from the latter would be expected to undergo a prototropic shift with special ease.   Here, the

[23] E. J. Corey, J. Am. Chem. Soc. 75, 3297 (1953).
[24] V. Prelog, L. Ruzicka, P. Barman, and L. Frenkiel, Helv. Chim. Acta 31, 92 (1948).

benzylic α-carbon is held planar to both the benzene ring and the neighboring carbonyl group, both factors contributing to the resonance stabilization of the intermediate carbanion or the transition state for the prototropic shift which has carbanion character.

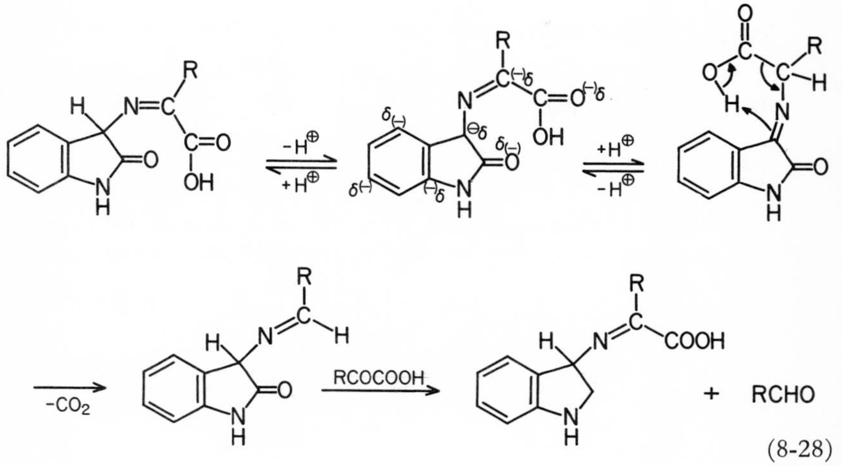

(8-28)

Support for the importance of the tautomeric shift in the rate of catalysis, as well as the importance of resonance stabilization of the intermediate carbanion, is seen in the inability of 3-methyl-3-amino-2-oxindole to act as a catalyst (Table 8-1) and the increase in activity on increasing the size of the aromatic system. Thus, 3-amino-α-naphthoxindole and 3-amino-6, 7-benzo-α-naphthoxindole are more active than the simple 3-amino-2-oxindole, and the phenanthrene derivative is the most active oxindole

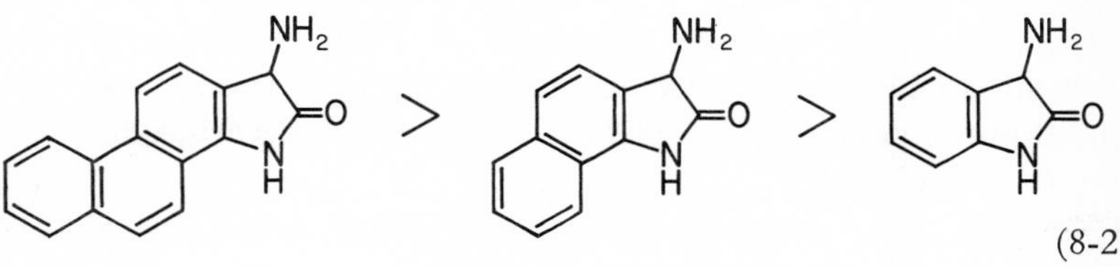

(8-29)

known. Similar resonance stabilization, by a planar conjugated system, of the transition states for pyridoxal catalyzed racemization and decarboxylation of amino acids is important.

The kinetics of 3-amino-2-oxindole catalysis of the decarboxylation of phenylglyoxylic acid have been studied in some detail.[17] The course of the reaction may be predicted from scheme (8-30). As previously mentioned, the introduction of the catalyst (ca. 10^{-3} M) to a solution of the

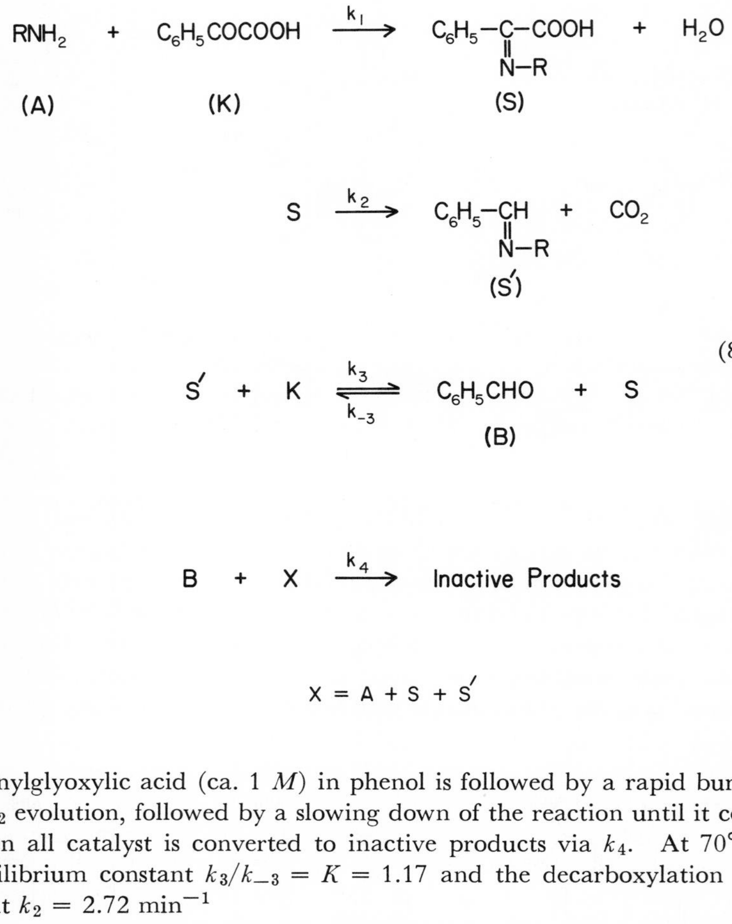

$$RNH_2 \;+\; C_6H_5COCOOH \xrightarrow{k_1} C_6H_5\!-\!\underset{\underset{N\!-\!R}{\|}}{C}\!-\!COOH \;+\; H_2O$$

$$(A) \qquad\qquad (K) \qquad\qquad\qquad (S)$$

$$S \xrightarrow{k_2} C_6H_5\!-\!\underset{\underset{N\!-\!R}{\|}}{CH} \;+\; CO_2$$

$$(S')$$

$$(8\text{-}30)$$

$$S' \;+\; K \underset{k_{-3}}{\overset{k_3}{\rightleftharpoons}} C_6H_5CHO \;+\; S$$

$$(B)$$

$$B \;+\; X \xrightarrow{k_4} \text{Inactive Products}$$

$$X = A + S + S'$$

phenylglyoxylic acid (ca. 1 M) in phenol is followed by a rapid burst of CO_2 evolution, followed by a slowing down of the reaction until it ceases when all catalyst is converted to inactive products via k_4. At 70° the equilibrium constant $k_3/k_{-3} = K = 1.17$ and the decarboxylation constant $k_2 = 2.72$ min^{-1}

2. AMINE CATALYZED ACYLOIN CONDENSATIONS INVOLVING PYRUVATE Acyloins also are formed under the Langenbeck conditions. For example, pyruvate yields both acetaldehyde and acetoin. It should be recalled that this is an important reaction catalyzed by thiamine diphosphate-requiring enzymes. For the amine catalysis the reaction most likely proceeds according to (8-31).

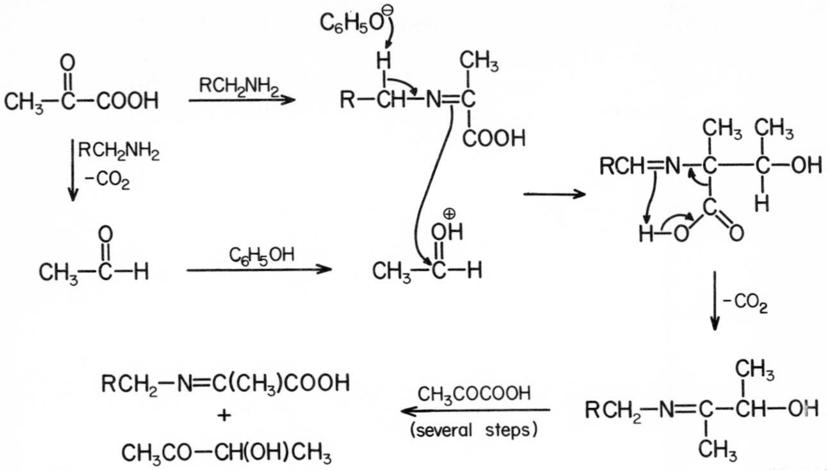

$$C_6H_5O^\ominus$$

$$CH_3-\overset{O}{\overset{\|}{C}}-COOH \xrightarrow{RCH_2NH_2} R-\overset{H}{\underset{}{CH}}-N=\overset{CH_3}{\underset{COOH}{C}}$$

$$\Big\downarrow \begin{array}{l} RCH_2NH_2 \\ -CO_2 \end{array}$$

$$CH_3-\overset{O}{\overset{\|}{C}}-H \xrightarrow{C_6H_5OH} CH_3-\overset{\overset{\oplus}{OH}}{\overset{\|}{C}}-H$$

$$RCH=N-\overset{CH_3}{\underset{H-O}{\overset{|}{C}}}\overset{CH_3}{\underset{\overset{|}{C}}{-}}\overset{}{\underset{O}{C}}-OH$$

$$\Big\downarrow -CO_2$$

$$\begin{array}{c} RCH_2-N=C(CH_3)COOH \\ + \\ CH_3CO-CH(OH)CH_3 \end{array} \xleftarrow[\text{(several steps)}]{CH_3COCOOH} RCH_2-N=\overset{CH_3}{\underset{CH_3}{\overset{|}{C}}}-CH-OH$$

$$\text{(8-31)}$$

3. TRANSAMINATION ACCOMPANIED BY DECARBOXYLATION   If the reaction of an α-amino acid and an α-keto acid is carried out in aqueous solution (ca. pH 3.0) rather than in phenol, a decarboxylative transamination reaction generally occurs.[25]   Thus, for α-phenylglycine and pyruvic acid:

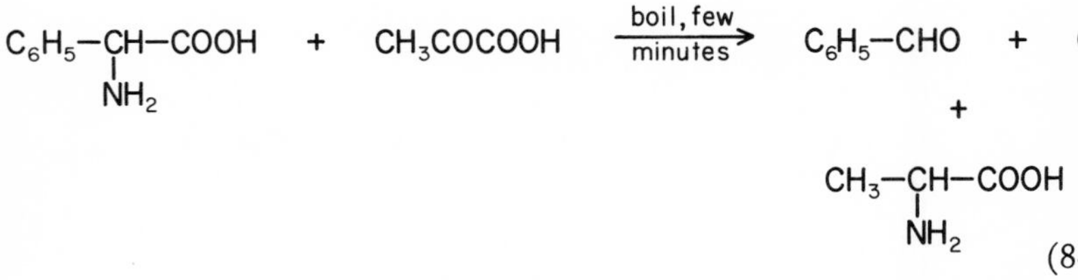

$$C_6H_5-\underset{NH_2}{\overset{|}{CH}}-COOH \quad + \quad CH_3COCOOH \xrightarrow[\text{minutes}]{\text{boil, few}} C_6H_5-CHO \quad + \quad CO_2$$

$$+$$

$$CH_3-\underset{NH_2}{\overset{|}{CH}}-COOH$$

$$\text{(8-32)}$$

The presence of alkali completely inhibits the reaction, and the addition of mineral acid causes an appreciable decrease in the rate of CO_2 evolution (a pH optimum).   The reaction leads to the formation of racemic products; the rates of CO_2 evolution and disappearance of optical activity are comparable.   From studies on an extended series of amino acids reacting with pyruvic acid [25–27] (Table 8-2) and the above, the following generalizations can be made: (1) a primary amine is essential, (2) a hydrogen in the α-position of an α-amino acid is not essential, (3) undissociated carboxyl groups are involved, and (4) two aldehydes are formed in some cases.

[25] R. M. Herbst and L. L. Engel, *J. Biol. Chem.* **107**, 505 (1934).
[26] R. M. Herbst, *J. Am. Chem. Soc.* **58**, 2239 (1936).
[27] R. M. Herbst, *Advan. Enzymol.* **4**, 76 (1944).

Table 8-2 *Reactions of amino acids with pyruvic acid*

Reactant plus $CH_3CO-COOH$	Products, plus alanine
NH_2CH_2COOH	CH_2O + $HCOCOOH$ + CO_2

$NH_2CH-COOH$
     $\mid$
     CH_3
	CH_3CHO + CO_2

CH_3 NH_2
    $CH-CH_2-C-COOH$
 CH_3 H
	CH_3
	    $CH-CH_2-CHO$ + CO_2
	 CH_3

NH_2 $\mid$ $C_6H_5-CH-COOH$	C_6H_5-CHO + CO_2

NH_2
        $\mid$
 $p-CH_3-C_6H_4-C-COOH$
           H
	$p-CH_3-C_6H_4-CHO$ + CH_3CHO
	 +
	 CO_2

NH_2 $\mid$ $C_6H_5-CH_2-CH-COOH$	$C_6H_5-CH_2CHO$ + CO_2
NH_2 $\mid$ $p-CH_3-C_6H_4-CH_2-CH-COOH$	$p-CH_3-C_6H_4-CH_2CHO$ + CH_3CHO + CO_2

CH_3
      $\mid$
 $CH_3-C-COOH$
      $\mid$
      NH_2
	CH_3CHO + CO_2 (no alanine)

NH_2
      $\mid$
 $C_6H_5-C-COOH$
      $\mid$
      CH_2
      $\mid$
      CH_3
	O
	        $\parallel$
	 $CH_3CH_2-C-C_6H_5$ + CH_3CHO
	 +
	 CO_2

CH_3-NH
 $C_6H_5-C-COOH$
      $\mid$
      H
	No Reaction

Reactant plus Phenyl Pyruvic Acid	Products

NH_2
      $\mid$
 $C_6H_5-C-COOH$
      $\mid$
      H
	C_6H_5CHO + CO_2
	 +
	          NH_2
	         $\mid$
	 $C_6H_5-CH_2-C-COOH$
	           H

NH_2
         $\mid$
 $p-CH_3-C_6H_4-C-COOH$
           H
	C_6H_5CHO + $p-CH_3-C_6H_4-CHO$
	 +
	 Mixed amino acids

When the reaction of α-aminophenylacetic acid and pyruvic acid is carried out in D_2O-H_2O solutions, the α- and β-positions on the resultant alanine are found to have deuterium while the aldehyde hydrogen of the resultant benzaldehyde has not exchanged with the solvent. Consistently, when α-deutero-α-aminophenylacetic acid and pyruvic acid were allowed to react in water, the deuterium remained with the resultant

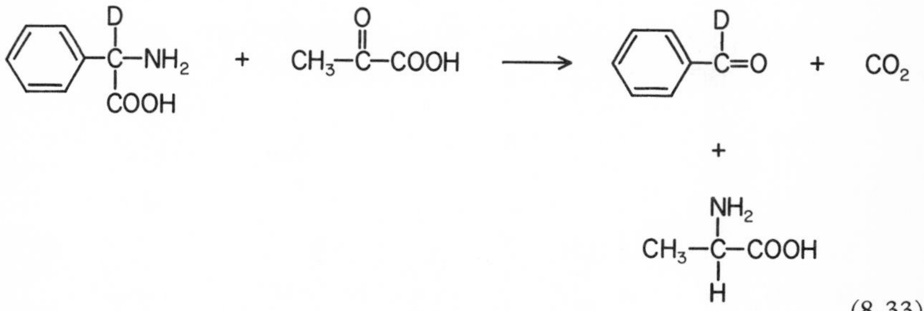

$$(8\text{-}33)$$

aldehyde [28] (8-33). This is best explained by a lack of a prototropic shift following aldimine formation in the case of α-aminophenylacetic acid

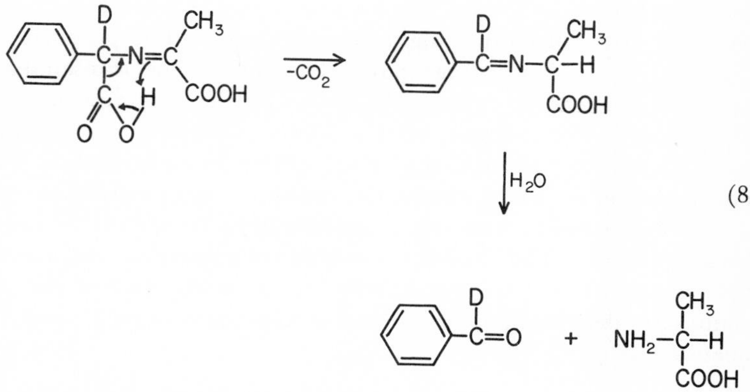

$$(8\text{-}34)$$

(8-34). For those reactions leading to the formation of two aldehydes, a prototropic shift is probably involved (8-35).

4. TRANSAMINATION WITHOUT DECARBOXYLATION Transamination without decarboxylation [29] has been reported to occur in the reaction of glyoxylic acid (but not α-ketoglutaric or pyruvic acid) with amino acids in

[28] R. M. Herbst and D. Rittenberg, *J. Org. Chem.* **8**, 380 (1943).
[29] H. I. Nakada and S. Weinhouse, *J. Biol. Chem.* **204**, 831 (1953).

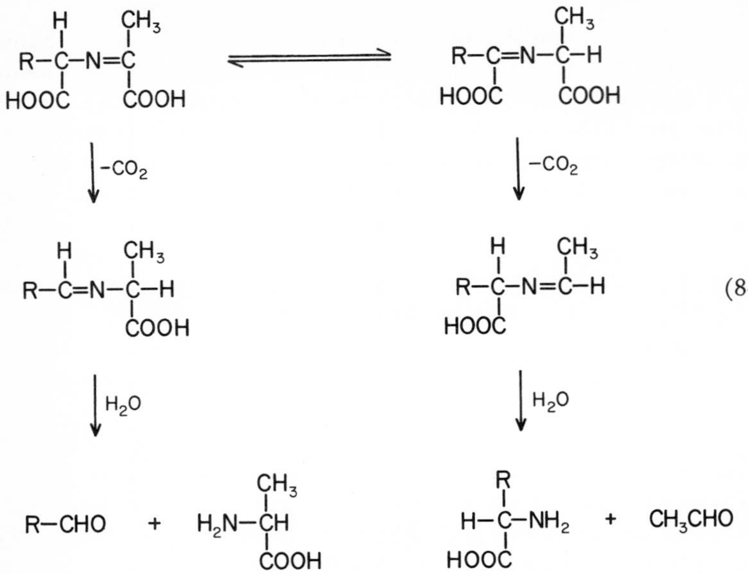

$$
\begin{array}{ccc}
\underset{\underset{HOOC}{|}}{R-\overset{\overset{H}{|}}{C}-N=\overset{\overset{CH_3}{|}}{C}-COOH}
& \rightleftharpoons &
\underset{\underset{HOOC}{|}}{R-\overset{\overset{CH_3}{|}}{C}=N-\overset{|}{C}-COOH}
\end{array}
$$

(8-35)

aqueous solutions.   The reactions were carried out at 25° at pH 7.4 in phosphate buffer 0.005 M in both glyoxylic acid and amino acid.   Unlike the reactions studied by Herbst, this transamination reaction is accelerated by base and does not require higher temperatures.   The products were identified by paper chromatography.   The rate of the transamination reaction was found to be strongly dependent on the nature of the amino acid employed.   For example, after a 2-hour reaction period, glutamic acid and glutamine had yielded glycine.   After an additional 22 hours, alanine, arginine, aspartate, asparagine, ornithine, and phenylalanine had reacted.   For the amino acids histidine and tryptophan a 48-hour reaction time was required.   The amides asparagine and glutamine were reported to be more reactive than the corresponding acids, but in the most optimum case the reaction was estimated to proceed to only about 10% completion.

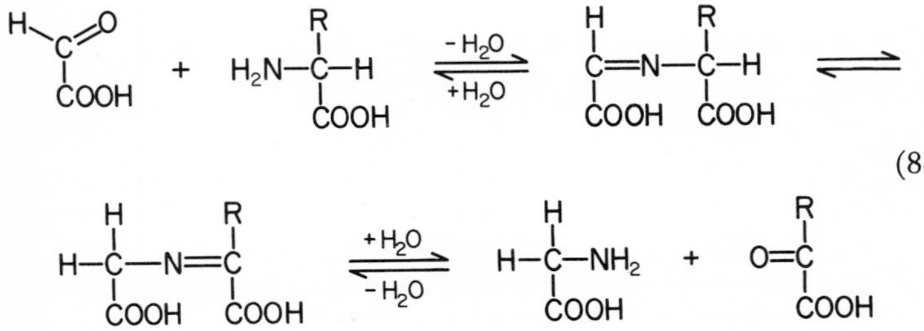

(8-36)

The ability of glyoxylic acid to undergo transamination at ambient temperatures may be related to the higher reactivity of the glyoxylic acid aldehyde carbonyl as compared to the keto function of an ordinary α-keto acid. Bruice and Butler [30] attempted a careful kinetic investigation of the transamination of α-aminophenylacetic acid by glyoxylic acid in water (pH 6–8) at 30°. Pseudo-first-order conditions were employed (glyoxylic acid ≫ α-aminophenylacetic acid), and the conversion of the amino acid to phenylglyoxylic acid was followed spectrophotometrically. Under these conditions the reaction was found to proceed to at least 90% completion and to be catalyzed by imidazole. However, good pseudo-first-order kinetics were not obtained and the appearance of phenylglyoxylic acid exhibited a pronounced and unreproducible lag phase.

The transamination of glyoxylic acid (pH 4–10.0 at 100°) is metal-ion catalyzed [31] particularly by Al(III) but not by Mg(II). The "rates" of reaction of amino acids with glyoxalate were estimated from the time dependence for the appearance of the corresponding keto acid 2,4-dinitrophenyl hydrazone on a paper chromatogram. As in the case of the non-metal-ion mediated reaction, glutamic acid reacted very rapidly. The order of reactivity obtained was glutamic > alanine = α-aminobutyric = leucine > tyrosine > isoleucine > valine > methionine. The reaction as catalyzed by metal ions (8-37) was more efficient than the non-metal-ion mediated reaction and could be employed preparatively. The transamination reactions of Section I-B 3 and 4 may be viewed as primitive models for pyridoxal catalyzed reactions.

$$
\underset{\text{HCCOONa}}{\overset{\overset{\displaystyle O}{\parallel}}{}} \; + \; \underset{\underset{\displaystyle CH_2-COOH}{|}}{H_2N-CH-COOH} \; \xrightarrow[\substack{100°,\, KAl(SO_4)_2 \\ 27\%\ \text{yield}}]{\text{pH } 5.0,\, 10\ \text{min.,}} \; \underset{\underset{\displaystyle CH_2-COOH}{|}}{O=C-COOH}
$$

+

$$H_2N-CH_2COOH$$

(8-37)

C. The Reaction of Cyanide with α-Dicarbonyl Compounds

Cyanide ion like thiamine possesses unique catalytic properties for the condensation of aldehydes to acyloins.[32] The essential features of the

[30] T. C. Bruice and A. R. Butler, unpublished experiments.
[31] D. E. Metzler, J. Olivard, and E. E. Snell, *J. Am. Chem. Soc.* **76,** 644 (1954).
[32] W. S. Ide and J. S. Buck, *Org. Reactions* **4,** 269 (1948).

reaction mechanism are those proposed at an early date by Lapworth.[33]

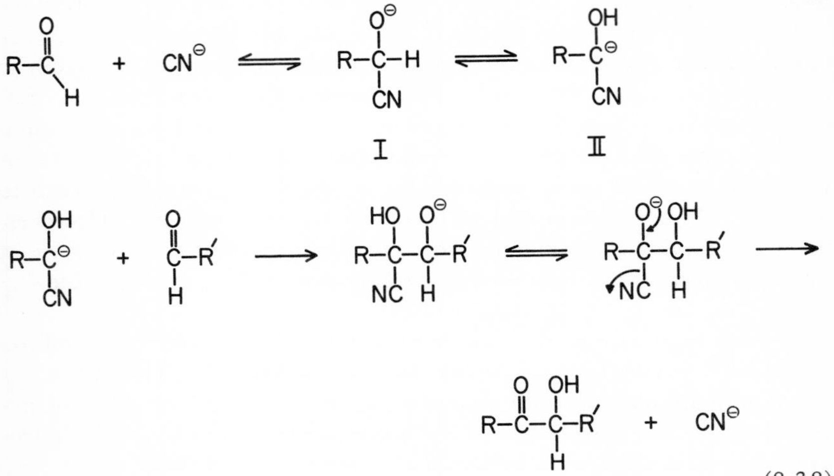

$$\tag{8-38}$$

Very few other anions are capable of acting as catalysts for the benzoin condensation. The essential properties possessed by $CN^{\ominus}$ that favor its function as a catalyst for this reaction are: (1) it is an effective nucleophile toward the aldehyde carbonyl group,[34] (2) the $C \rightarrow O$ proton shift (i.e., $I \rightarrow II$ in 8-38) is probably favored by the large electronegativity of the nitrile group, thus making the $C^{\oplus\delta}$, and (3) the negative charge in II is stabilized by the nitrile group.

Cyanide ion also is a particularly effective nucleophile toward α-diketones, the reaction resulting in C—C bond scission. In alcoholic solutions, $CN^{\ominus}$ catalyzes the formation of aldehyde and ester from α-diketones [35, 36]:

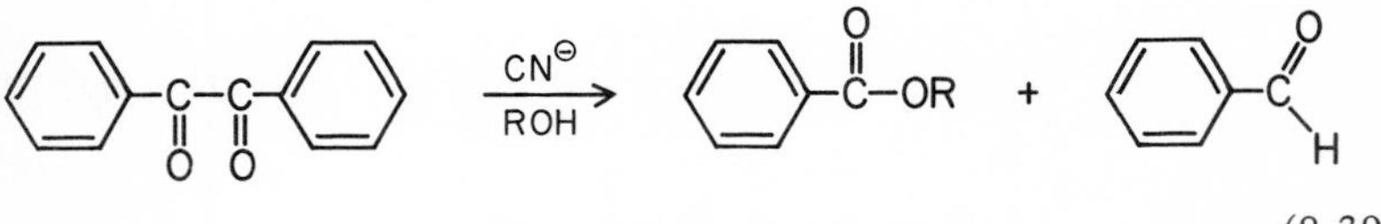

$$\tag{8-39}$$

[33] A. Lapworth, *J. Chem. Soc.* **83**, 995 (1903); **85**, 1206 (1904).

[34] Though not unusually effective toward the ester carbonyl group, see T. C. Bruice and R. Lapinski, *J. Am. Chem. Soc.* **80**, 2265 (1958).

[35] F. Jourdan, *Ber.* **16**, 658 (1883).

[36] H. Kwart and M. M. Baevsky, *J. Am. Chem. Soc.* **80**, 580 (1958) and earlier references therein.

The kinetics of the reaction have been studied [36] and are in substantial agreement with the mechanism of (8-40).

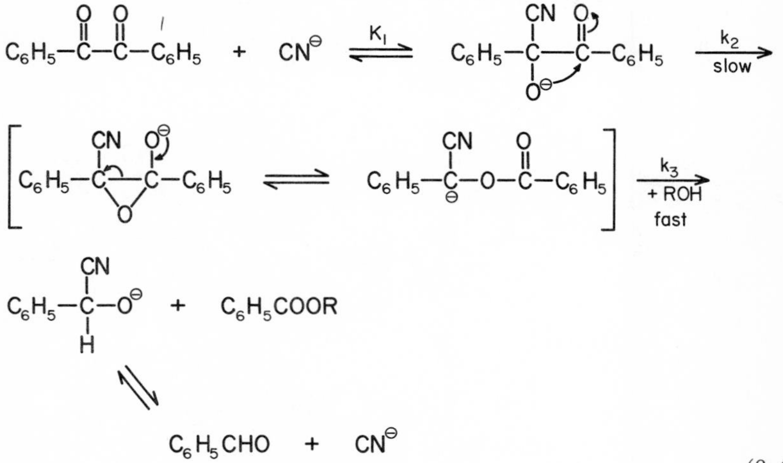

$$(8\text{-}40)$$

In aqueous solutions at 30°, $CN^{\ominus}$ reacts with triketohydrindane hydrate (ninhydrin) with a probable second-order constant [37] of about 10^7 liter mole^{-1} min^{-1} to yield hydrindantin (II) and phthalonic acid (III). The mechanism of the reaction is in accord with (8-42). As is the case

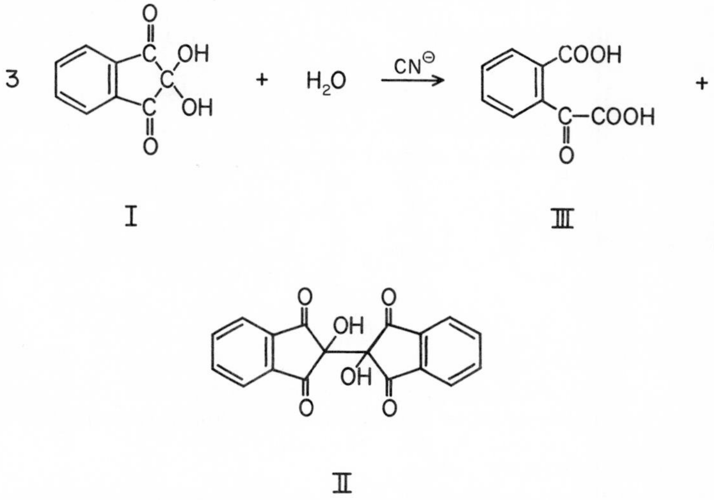

I   III

$$(8\text{-}41)$$

II

[37] T. C. Bruice and F. M. Richards, *J. Org. Chem.* **23,** 145 (1958).

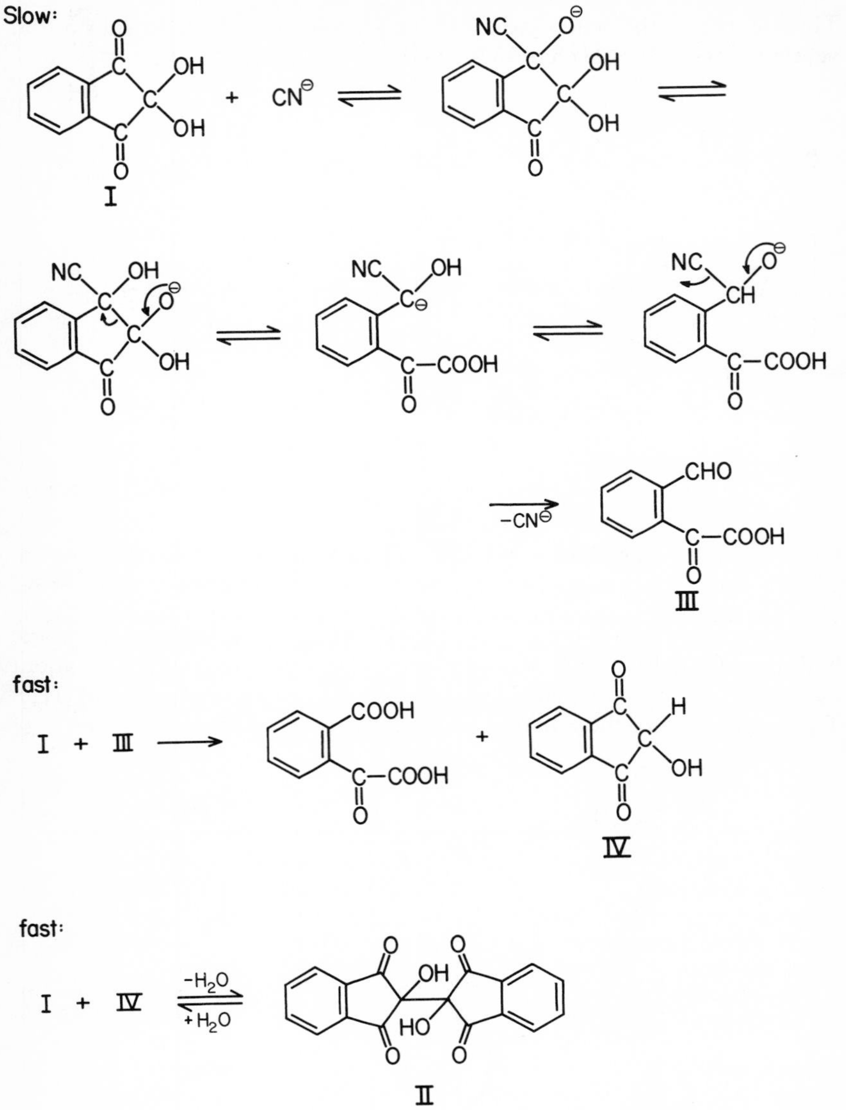

Slow:

I

+ CN⊖ ⇌

⇌

⇌

I

NC—C(OH)

C—COOH

⇌

NC—CH

C—COOH

$\xrightarrow{-CN^\ominus}$

CHO

C—COOH

III

fast:

I + III ⟶

COOH

C—COOH

+

IV

fast:

I + IV $\underset{+H_2O}{\overset{-H_2O}{\rightleftharpoons}}$

II

(8-42)

for (8-39), the facility of (8-42) is undoubtedly related to the stability of the
$-\overset{\ominus}{C}(OH)CN$ carbanion.

Franzen has shown that if the α-keto group of a dicarbonyl compound
happens to be that of an α-keto acid, then both decarboxylation and

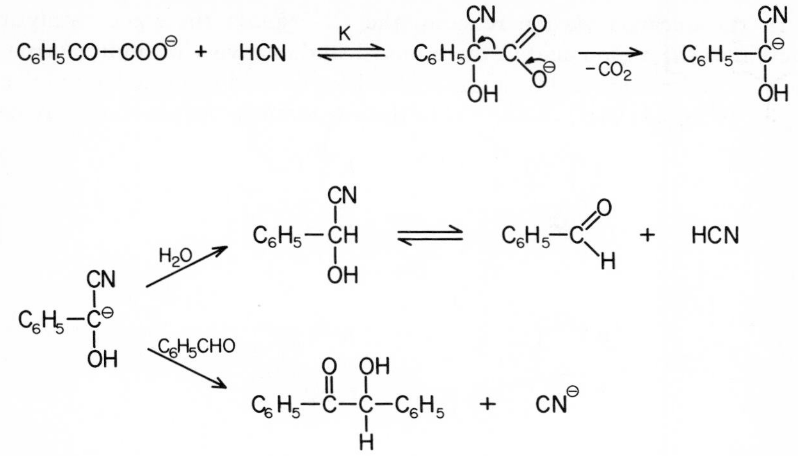

$$(8\text{-}43)$$

benzoin condensation occur (8-43).[38] The reactions were carried out at 90° with the sodium salts of the α-keto acids. The relative rates of CO_2 evolution and the formation constants for the cyanohydrin intermediates were found to be similarly dependent on the nature of the phenylglyoxylic acid employed (Table 8-3). When the reaction of sodium pyruvate with $CN^\ominus$ was carried out in aqueous dioxane solutions of dimedone, acetaldehyde was trapped as a derivative.

Table 8-3 * *Reaction of $CN^\ominus$ with α-keto acids*

α-Keto acid	K [a]	Relative rate of CO_2 evolution	Product
p-Bromophenyl glyoxylate	2.2	18	p,p'-Dibromobenzoin
Phenyl glyoxylate	0.84	8	Benzoin
p-Methylphenyl glyoxylate	0.30	0.8	p,p'-Dimethylbenzoin
p-Methoxyphenyl glyoxylate	0.12	1	Anisoin
α-Ketogluconic acid	—	—	Arabinose
			Acetaldehyde
Pyruvic acid	—	—	(as dimedone deriv.)

* Ref. 38.

[a] $K = \dfrac{[R{-}C(OH)CNCOO^\ominus]}{[RCOCOO^\ominus][HCN]}$.

[38] V. Franzen and L. Fikentscher, *Chem.* **613,** 1 (1958).

In the decarboxylation reaction the $CN^\ominus$ plays the same catalytic function as the amino acid in those model studies involving imine formation (i.e., to provide a β-unsaturated carboxylic acid intermediate which readily decarboxylates) (8-44).　The driving force for the reaction may be

OR

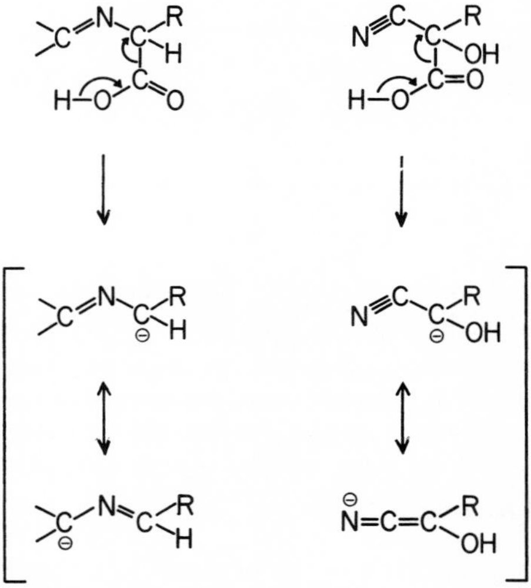

(8-44)

the cyclic mechanism or a carbanion mechanism in which the carbanion is resonance-stabilized.

II.　THE MECHANISMS OF THIAMINE CATALYSIS

A. *The Pseudo-Base Concept*

Ukai [39] first demonstrated the ability of thiamine to catalyze an acyloin condensation in the absence of enzyme, finding that in mildly basic solutions thiamine and other quaternary thiazole derivatives catalyzed the condensation of furfural to furoin.　Mizuhara [40] repeated Ukai's experiments, employing 50% aqueous ethanol solvent.　These workers also found that, in aqueous solution, acetoin and CO_2 were formed from

[39] T. Ukai, S. Tanaka, and S. Dokawa, *Yakugaku Zasshi* **63**, 296 (1943).

[40] S. Mizuhara, Reports from the Commission for Vitamin B Research, Japan, **27**, (1949).

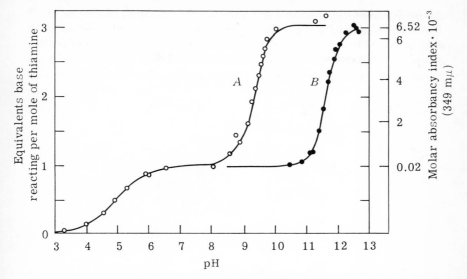

Fig. 8-1   *Titration curves for thiamine chloride hydrochloride.   Curve A was obtained by electrometric titration.   Equilibrium is attained slowly in the high pH limb.   Curve B was obtained by spectrophotometric measurement, the molar absorbancy indices being shown on the right-hand scale.   Curve B is an "instantaneous" titration curve representing the conversion of the unstable yellow thiol form to the yellow form III of (8-46).   The open and shaded circles represent experimental points.   The lines are theoretical curves based on the dissociation constant relationships described in Ref. 40a.*

pyruvic acid and acetaldehyde in the presence of thiamine hydrochloride

$$\begin{array}{c}\text{(furan)}\text{—CHO} \xrightarrow{\text{Thiamine}} \text{(furan)}\text{—}\underset{\underset{H}{|}}{\overset{\overset{HO}{|}}{C}}\text{—}\overset{\overset{O}{\|}}{C}\text{—}\text{(furan)}\end{array} \qquad (8\text{-}45)$$

when 2 equivalents of alkali were added to 1 molecule of thiamine hydrochloride, but not if more alkali were added.[41]   They interpreted their findings to suggest the involvement of the pseudo-base of thiamine as the catalyst.

The titration curve of thiamine, first described by Williams,[42] possesses two titration steps (Fig. 8-1).   The first titratable acidic group is that of

[40a] D. E. Metzler in P. D. Boyer, H. Lardy, and K. Myrbäck (eds.), "The Enzymes," Academic Press, New York, 1960, Vol. 2, p. 302.

[41] S. Mizuhara, R. Tamura, and H. Arata, *Proc. Japan Acad.* **27,** 302 (1951).

[42] R. R. Williams and A. E. Ruehle, *J. Am. Chem. Soc.* **57,** 1856 (1935).

the pyrimidine ring, probably at position 1,[43] with a pK'_a of 4.85 at 25° [44] The second step in the titration curve corresponds to the uptake of 2 equivalents of base, and is a slow and reversible reaction (anaerobically) affording, through the psuedo-base, a thiolate ion which arises from opening of the thiazole ring.[45-47] Because the midpoint of the second

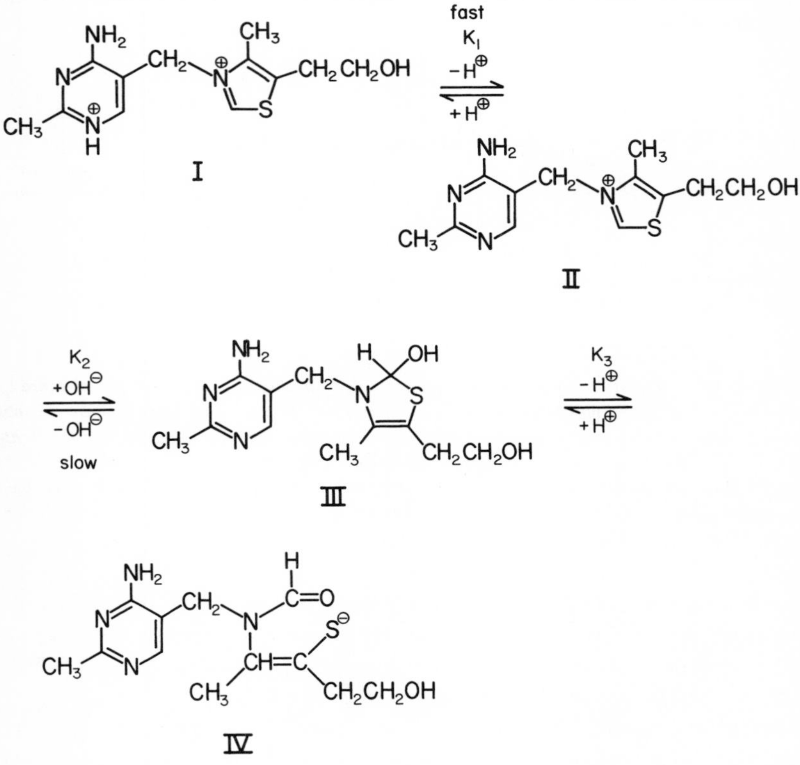

(8-46)

titration (at pH 9.2–9.3) involves 2 equivalents of base (i.e., $K_2 = [OH^\ominus]$ [III]/[II] and $K_3 = a_H[IV]/[III]$), it should be equal to $(pK_2 + pK_3)/2$.[48] The very narrow width of the second titration step indicates that $K_3 \gg K_2$, and that no appreciable amounts of III or undissociated IV are

[43] D. J. Brown, E. Hoerger, and S. F. Mason, *J. Chem. Soc.* **211**, 4035 (1955).
[44] A. Watanabe and Y. Asahi, *Yakugaku Zasshi* **75**, 1046 (1955).
[45] H. T. Clarke and S. Gurin, *J. Am. Chem. Soc.* **57**, 1876 (1935).
[46] S. Mizuhara and H. Arata, *Proc. Japan Acad.* **27**, 700 (1951).
[47] A. Watanabe and Y. Asahi, *Yakugaku Zasshi* **75**, 1050 (1955).
[48] R. G. Yount and D. E. Metzler, *J. Biol. Chem.* **234**, 738 (1959).

present at equilibrium. The mechanism proposed by Mizuhara [41] involved the pseudo-base form of thiamine, in accord with the observation that the optimum rates of catalysis were obtained when 2 equivalents of base were added. In opposition to this mechanism is the evidence that little pseudo-base is ever present in solution (*loc. cit.*). In the pseudo-base mechanism the acyl anion moiety was proposed to be stabilized via ylid formation (8-47).

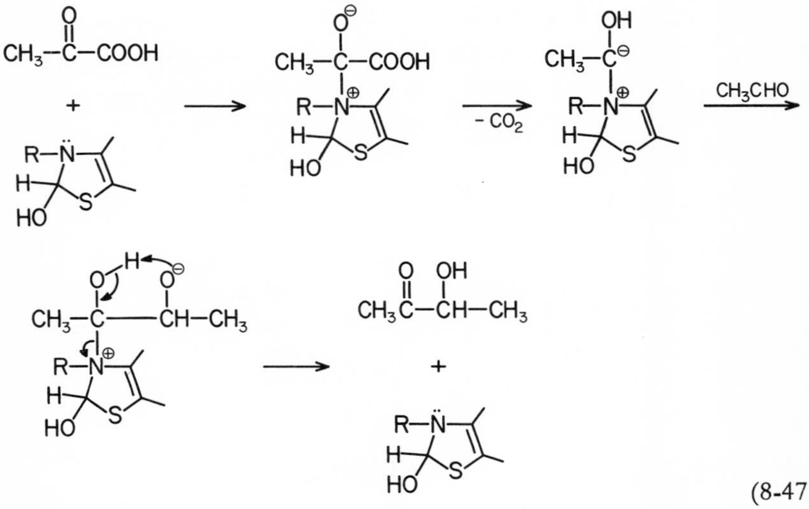

(8-47)

Thiamine and thiazoles are not of themselves impressive catalysts in model systems. Thus, Mizuhara [41] employed reaction times of 5–10 hr at 37° obtaining small yields optimal at pH 8.4.

Mizuhara found that thiamine also would catalyze the so-called diacetyl mutase reaction.[49] Again the largest yield of acetic acid was obtained when 2 equivalents of alkali were added ($T = 37°$; reaction

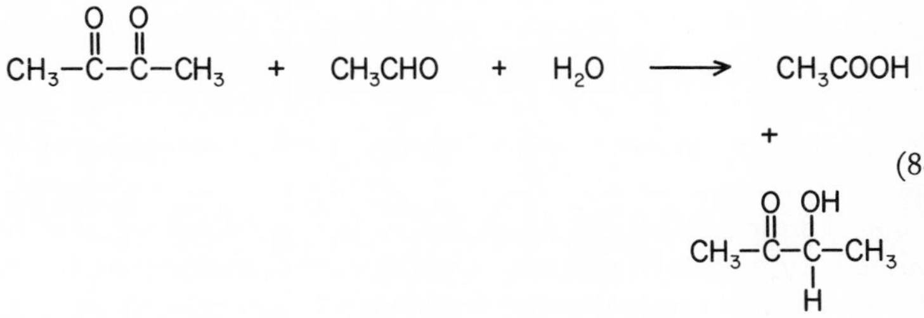

(8-48)

[49] S. Mizuhara and K. Oono, *Proc. Japan Acad.* **27**, 705 (1951).

time 10 hr) and a mechanism involving the same pseudo-base and intermediate ylid was suggested.

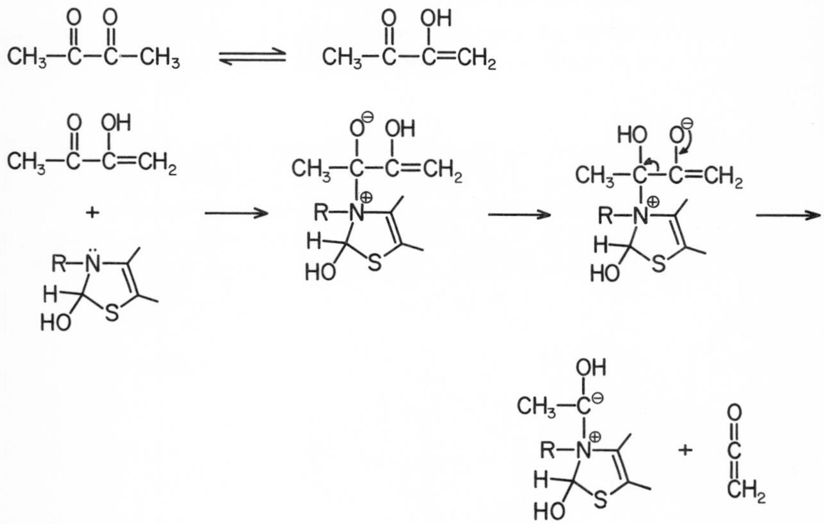

Then:

$$CH_2{=}C{=}O \ + \ H_2O \ \longrightarrow \ CH_3COOH$$

and

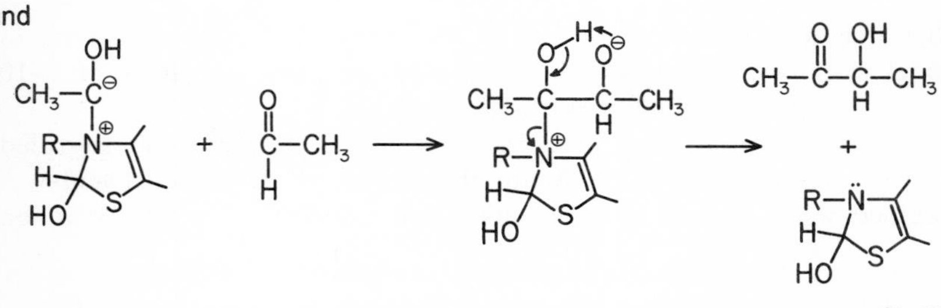

(8-49)

   Mechanism (8-49) left much to be desired, for the production of a
ketene is most improbable. That the reaction producing acetic acid
does not represent a simple oxidation of the acetaldehyde was firmly
established by studies [50] utilizing acetaldehyde-1,2-C^{14}, with the latter
being incorporated intact into the acetoin:

[50] S. Mizuhara and P. Handler, *J. Am. Chem. Soc.* **76,** 571 (1954).

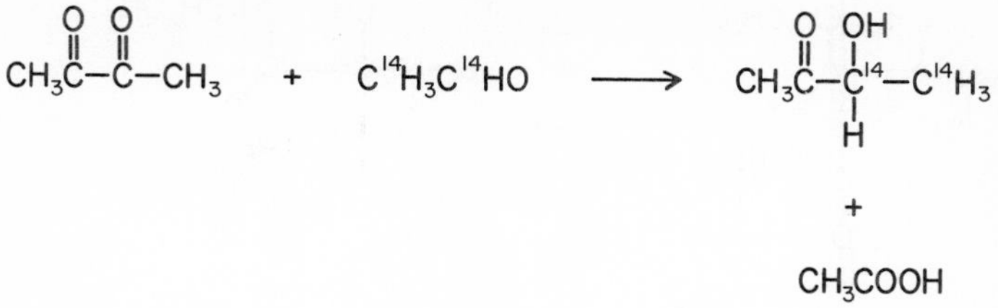

$$CH_3\overset{O}{\overset{\|}{C}}-\overset{O}{\overset{\|}{C}}-CH_3 \;+\; C^{14}H_3C^{14}HO \longrightarrow CH_3\overset{O}{\overset{\|}{C}}-\overset{OH}{\underset{H}{\overset{|}{C}}^{14}}-C^{14}H_3 \qquad (8\text{-}50)$$

$$+$$

$$CH_3COOH$$

During the course of this investigation it was discovered that at alkali concentrations of greater than 2 equivalents the thiamine was destroyed. In strongly basic solutions thiamine undergoes an intramolecular addition reaction analogous to the pseudo-base formation generating a thiolate ion.[51-54] This finding led to the suggestion by Karrer [55, 56] that the first

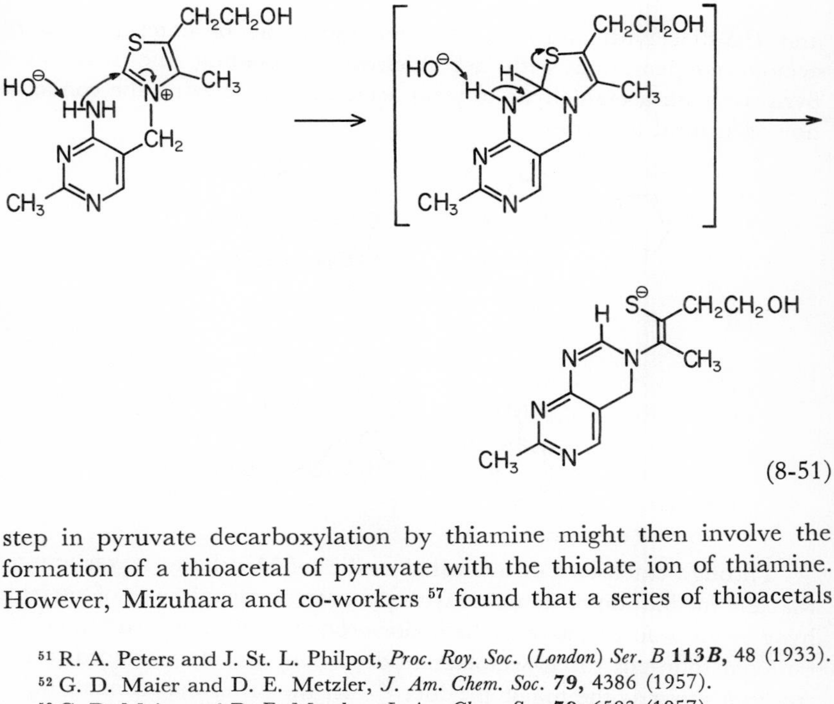

$$(8\text{-}51)$$

step in pyruvate decarboxylation by thiamine might then involve the formation of a thioacetal of pyruvate with the thiolate ion of thiamine. However, Mizuhara and co-workers [57] found that a series of thioacetals

[51] R. A. Peters and J. St. L. Philpot, *Proc. Roy. Soc. (London) Ser. B* **113 B**, 48 (1933).

[52] G. D. Maier and D. E. Metzler, *J. Am. Chem. Soc.* **79**, 4386 (1957).

[53] G. D. Maier and D. E. Metzler, *J. Am. Chem. Soc.* **79**, 6583 (1957).

[54] O. Zima and R. R. Williams, *Ber.* **73**, 941 (1940).

[55] P. Karrer, *Bull. Soc. Chim. France* **149**, 141 (1947).

[56] P. Karrer and M. Viscontini, *Helv. Chim. Acta* **29**, 711 (1946).

[57] Y. Takeuchi, K. Okuda, S. Hayakawa, and S. Mizuhara, *J. Biochem. Tokyo* **42**, 93 (1955).

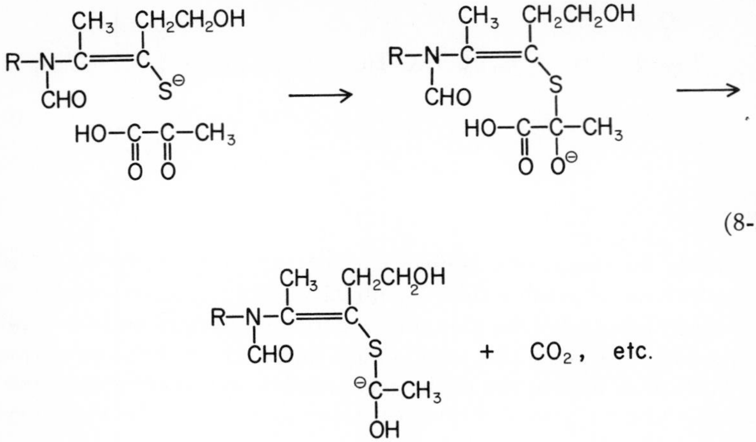

(8-52)

+ CO_2, etc.

and *O,S*-diacetylthiamine (8-53) were incapable of entering into the acetoin condensation with acetaldehyde, promoting the reaction of pyruvate with acetaldehyde to yield acetoin, or catalyzing the condensation of furfural to furoin.

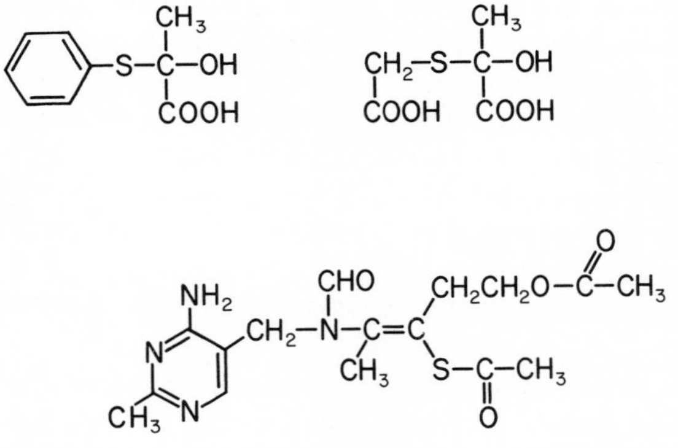

(8-53)

Through extensions of the initial studies of Mizuhara, it was found [58] that the incubation of thiamine with pyruvate in the absence of acetaldehyde yields α-acetolactate as the major product, and that if run in borate-buffered solutions the α-acetolactate decarboxylates as produced to give rise to acetoin as the major product.[59] In the latter experiments 0.2 *M* pyruvate was incubated with 0.02 *M* thiamine at pH 8.9–9.0 at 40°. In

[58] H. Koffler and L. O. Krampitz, *Bacteriol. Proc. (Soc. Am. Bacteriologists)* 113 (1955).
[59] E. Yatco-Manzo, F. Roddy, R. G. Yount, and D. E. Metzler, *J. Biol. Chem.* **234,** 733 (1959).

$$CH_3-\overset{\overset{O}{\|}}{C}-COO^{\ominus} \quad + \quad Thiamine \quad \longrightarrow \quad (\,Intermediate\,)$$

CH₃COCOOH / CH₃CHO

$-CO_2$

$$CH_3-\overset{\overset{O}{\|}}{C}-\overset{\overset{OH}{|}}{\underset{\underset{COO^{\ominus}}{|}}{C}}-CH_3 \quad \xrightarrow[-CO_2]{+\,H^{\oplus}} \quad CH_3-\overset{\overset{O}{\|}}{C}-\overset{\overset{OH}{|}}{\underset{\underset{H}{|}}{C}}-CH_3$$

(8-54)

one experiment after 40 hr, 22% of the pyruvic acid had been converted to acetoin and 68% to other nonidentified products. The thiamine (all reactions under anaerobic conditions) also undergoes decomposition (24% in 40 hr at 40°). By choosing carefully controlled conditions it was possible to establish that thiamine actually performed its role as a catalyst, turning over on the average three pyruvate molecules per mole of thiamine. In addition, the existence of an intermediate formed from thiamine and pyruvate was demonstrated by isolation of a substance formed from the incubation of thiamine and pyruvate at 40° for 30 min. This substance reacts rapidly with acetaldehyde to give acetoin. Various metal ions [Ca(II), Mg(II), Co(II), Fe(II), Mn(II), Al(III), and Cd(II)] have no effect on the rate of acetoin production. The pH-rate profile (acetoin plus α-acetolactate produced in 2 hr at 40°) affords a bell-shaped curve with a maximum at pH 8.9, which is in substantial agreement with the pH optimum (8.4) reported by Mizuhara.[41]

B. Postulated Mechanisms Involving the Amino Group of Thiamine

From the pioneering experiments of Langenbeck and others [11–19] on the catalysis of the decarboxylation of pyruvate by amines, it was inevitable that the amino function at position 4' of thiamine would be postulated as the catalytic center (8-55).[60] Similarly ingenious mechanisms were postulated to account for the other transformations catalyzed by thiamine diphosphate in combination with enzyme. However, Stern and Melnick [61] found that thiamine had no catalytic properties under the Langenbeck conditions. There is little wonder that this is the case, since the amino group in position 4' is an exceedingly weak base, as exemplified by the difficulty encountered in its diazotization.

[60] K. Wiesner and Z. Valenta, *Experientia* **12,** 190 (1956).
[61] K. G. Stern and J. L. Melnick, *J. Biol. Chem.* **131,** 597 (1939).

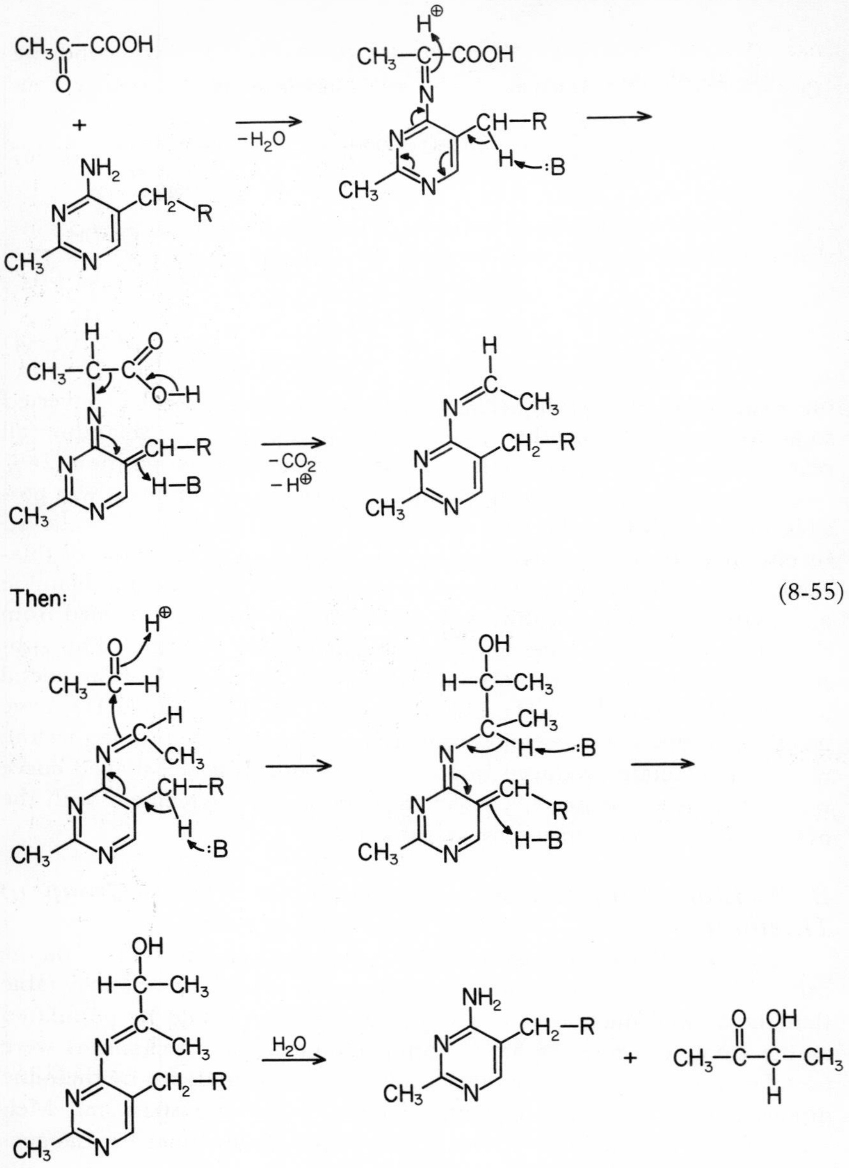

Then:

(8-55)

C. Postulated Mechanisms Involving the Methylene Group of Thiamine

The next position that received attention as the catalytic center of thiamine was the methylene group bridging the thiazole and pyrimidine rings. On the basis that certain pyridinium compounds [62] will condense readily with aldehydes (8-56) Ukai [39] attempted to realize such a con-

$$R-CH_2-\overset{\oplus}{N}\diagup\!\!\diagdown \quad + \quad R'CHO \quad \longrightarrow \quad \underset{R-CHOH}{R-CH-\overset{\oplus}{N}\diagup\!\!\diagdown} \qquad (8\text{-}56)$$

densation with thiazolium compounds.   However, in place of the adduct, he found that thiazolium salts catalyze the benzoin condensation (8-57).

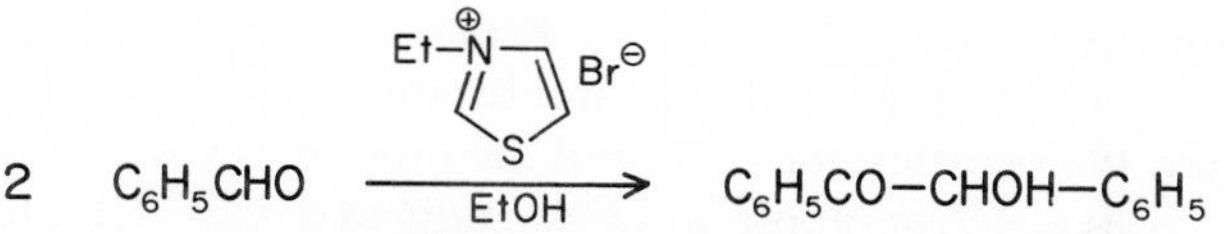

$$2 \quad C_6H_5CHO \quad \xrightarrow[\text{EtOH}]{\text{Et}-\overset{\oplus}{N}\diagup\!\!\diagdown\ \text{Br}^{\ominus}} \quad C_6H_5CO-CHOH-C_6H_5 \qquad (8\text{-}57)$$

On the basis that the pyridinium salt condensations must occur via ylids of the type (8-58), Breslow [63] proposed that the carbanion, stabilized as

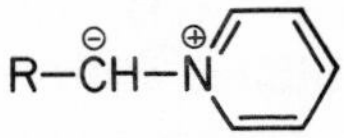

$$R-\overset{\ominus}{C}H-\overset{\oplus}{N}\diagup\!\!\diagdown \qquad (8\text{-}58)$$

the ylid, might be an intermediate in the catalytic process (8-59). But,

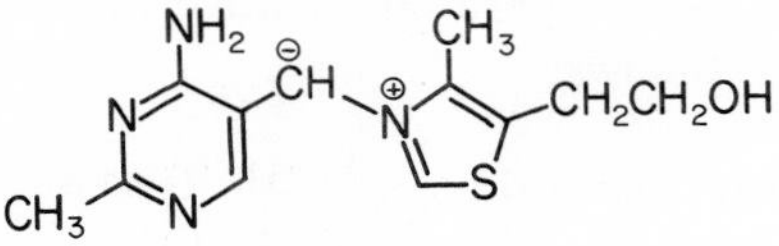

(8-59)

Ingraham, De Tar, Fry, Westheimer [64, 65] and Rose [66] showed that in the decarboxylation of pyruvate, in D_2O or tritiated H_2O with either thiamine or thiamine diphosphate in the presence of yeast carboxylase,

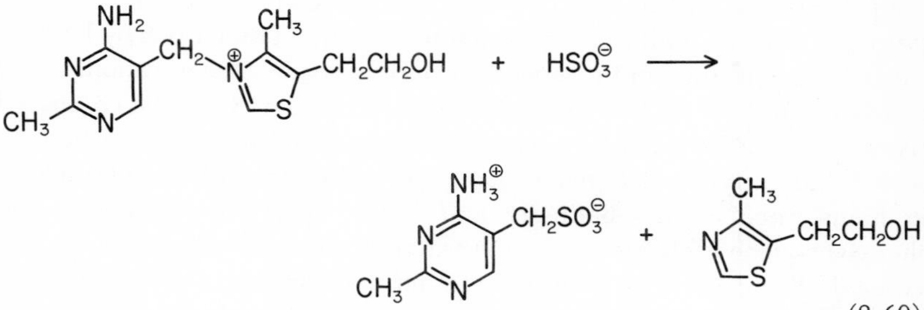

(8-60)

[62] F. Krohnke, *Angew. Chem.* **65,** 605 (1953).

[63] R. Breslow, *Chem. Ind. (London)* 28R (1956).

[64] K. Fry, L. L. Ingraham, and F. H. Westheimer, *J. Am. Chem. Soc.* **79,** 5225 (1957).

[65] D. F. De Tar and F. H. Westheimer, *J. Am. Chem. Soc.* **81,** 175 (1959).

[66] I. Rose, unpublished experiments.

no tritium or deuterium exchanged for the protons on the methylene carbon of thiamine or thiamine diphosphate. The technique employed was to treat the thiamine compound with bisulfite ion after the method of Williams (8-60).[67] The resultant pyrimidylmethane sulfonic acid was shown to possess no excess deuterium or tritium.

D. The 2-position of Thiamine as the Catalytic Center

The last position of thiamine examined as a possible catalytic site was the 2-position of the thiazolium ring. Breslow,[68] in an important study, found that when 3,4-dimethylthiazolium bromide was allowed to stand in D_2O at room temperature for 20 hr and the product recovered, dried, and pyrolyzed, mass spectrographic analysis indicated that 1.1 atoms of D had been incorporated. Similarily 3-benzyl-4-methylthiazoline bromide was found to gain 1.2 atoms of D, whereas thiamine chloride hydrochloride incorporated 5.2 atoms of D (including hydroxyl and amino groups). All the products exhibited a strong C-D stretch in the infrared at 4.5μ. The rate of proton exchange was determined by n.m.r. spectroscopy at 7050 gauss field with a probe of 30 megacycles/sec. Four bands were observed, whose positions relative to the hydrogens on benzene were assigned as follows:

$$\text{(8-61)}$$

The band of -108 cps disappeared in D_2O solution (28°) with a half-life of approximately 20 min. The rate of exchange was not dependent on the presence of added acid or base, and therefore establishes the C-2 hydrogen to be an active carbon-bond hydrogen. Later work by Breslow showed the exchange to be dependent on hydroxide concentration. The acidity of the H at C-2 was overestimated by Breslow when he compared his data to the fallacious results of Reyerson and Yuster,[69] who had reported that acetylene does not exchange its hydrogens with D_2O even after 36 hours' incubation. Ballinger and Long report that acetylene and phenylacetylene exchange tritium in water at about the same rate.[70] For tritiated phenylacetylene it has been found that the rate of exchange is not catalyzed by acid or water but is catalyzed by hydroxide ion, the second-

[67] R. R. Williams, R. E. Waterman, J. C. Keresztesy, and E. R. Buchman, *J. Am. Chem. Soc.* **57**, 536 (1935).

[68] R. Breslow, *J. Am. Chem. Soc.* **79**, 1762 (1957).

[69] L. H. Reyerson and S. Yuster, *J. Am. Chem. Soc.* **56**, 1426 (1934).

[70] P. Ballinger and F. A. Long, *J. Am. Chem. Soc.* **81**, 3148 (1959).

order rate constant [71] being 2.7×10^2 liter mole^{-1} sec^{-1}. From the approximate half-life for exchange of hydrogen at C-2 of the 3,4-dimethylthiazolium salt, the rate of exchange would be about 6×10^{-4} sec^{-1}. If one assumes that the pD of the solution employed was about 7.0, a second-order rate constant for exchange may be calculated as ca. 6×10^3 liter mole^{-1} sec^{-1}. This would indicate that the hydrogen in the 2-position of 3,4-dimethylthiazolium salt exchanges about 20 times faster than tritiated acetylene. With the consideration that a C—T bond should break about 8 times slower than a C—D bond, one concludes that acetylene and thiazolium salts should exchange hydrogen at about the same rate. The pseudo-acid character of the C-2 hydrogen of a thiazolium salt is probably related to the greater s-character of the double-bonded carbon as compared to a normal alkane, to the large inductive effect of the positive nitrogen in an adjacent position, as well as to possible ylid-type stabilization of the negative charge of the carbanion. Yet since 3-methylthiazolium iodide exchanges hydrogen only at the 2-position, the sp^2 character and the neighboring positive nitrogen are not sufficient criteria for rationalization of the C-2 hydrogen acidity. The conjugation of the 2-position to the nitrogen and the presence of the neighboring sulfur are important factors. The influence of the conjugation of the carbanion to the positive nitrogen is readily seen in the fact that 1,3,4-trimethylimidazole and 1,3-dimethylbenzimidazole catalyze the benzoin condensation and rapidly exchange deuterium.[72, 73] Other examples, illustrating the influence of a quaternary nitrogen on increasing the acidity or stabilization of a car-

$$(8\text{-}62)$$

banion at a neighboring carbon, are found in the facile decarboxylation of 1-methylpicolinic acid [74] and lability of the hydrogen at the 2-position of diphosphopyridine nucleotide [75] and at the 2- and 6-positions of

$$(8\text{-}63)$$

[71] E. A. Halevi and F. A. Long, J. Am. Chem. Soc. 83, 2809 (1961).

[72] T. Ukai, T. Dokawa, and S. Tsubokawa, Yakugaku Zasshi 64, 7A, 3 (1944).

[73] R. Breslow, J. Am. Chem. Soc. 80, 3719 (1958).

[74] B. Brown and D. Hammick, J. Chem. Soc. 659 (1949).

[75] A. San Pietro, J. Biol. Chem. 217, 589 (1955).

N-methylnicotinamide.[76]   The importance of the *s*-character of the carbon undergoing exchange in the above reactions is shown by the resistance

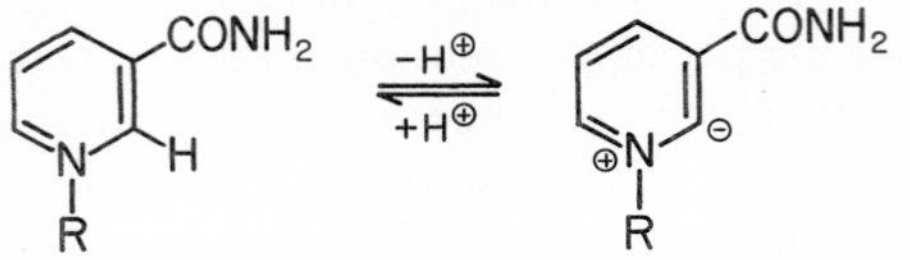

$$(8\text{-}64)$$

of tetramethylammonium iodide to exchange.   The latter requires 10

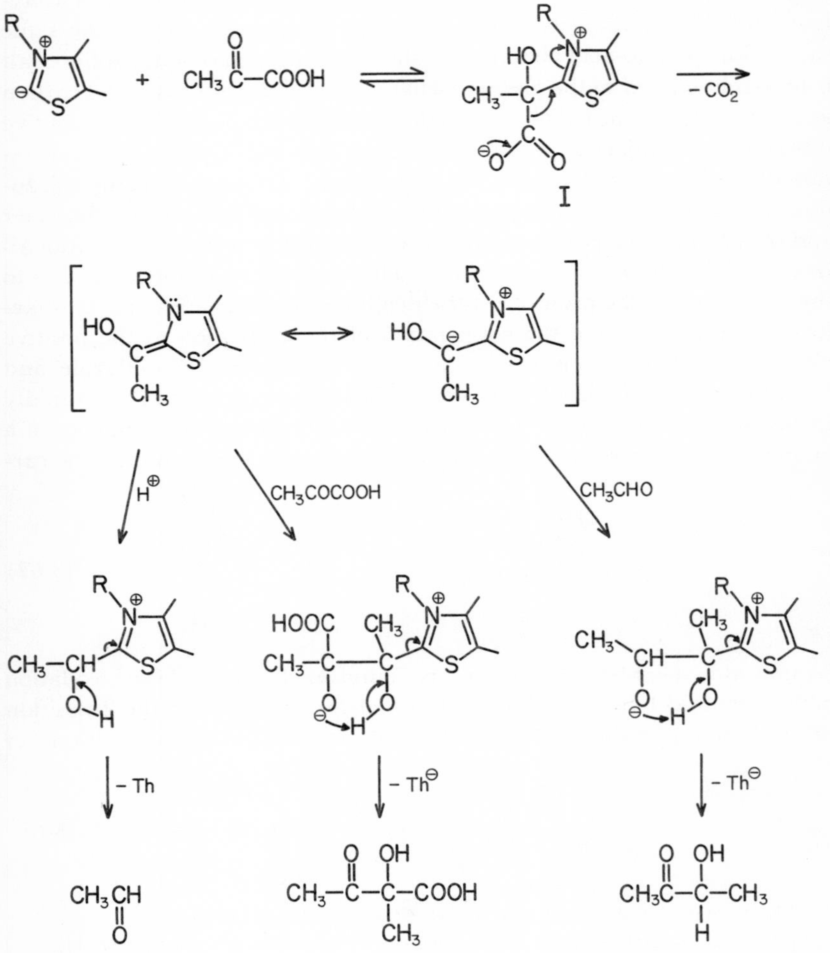

$$(8\text{-}65)$$

[76] H. E. Dubb, M. Saunders, and J. H. Wang, *J. Am. Chem. Soc.* **80,** 1767 (1958).

days of refluxing in 0.27 *N* base to exchange only 0.1% of each hydrogen.[77]

The mechanism, proposed by Breslow [78] for thiamine and thiazolium-ion catalysis of the decarboxylation and acetoin condensation of pyruvic acid, is provided in (8-65). In the case of the benzoin condensation catalyzed by 3,4-dimethylthiazolium iodide, the intermediate could not be isolated, suggesting it to be at a low steady state.

The similarity of the intermediate undergoing decarboxylation in this mechanism to the intermediate of the amine and cyanide catalyzed processes is obvious. Many model thiazolium compounds were studied by

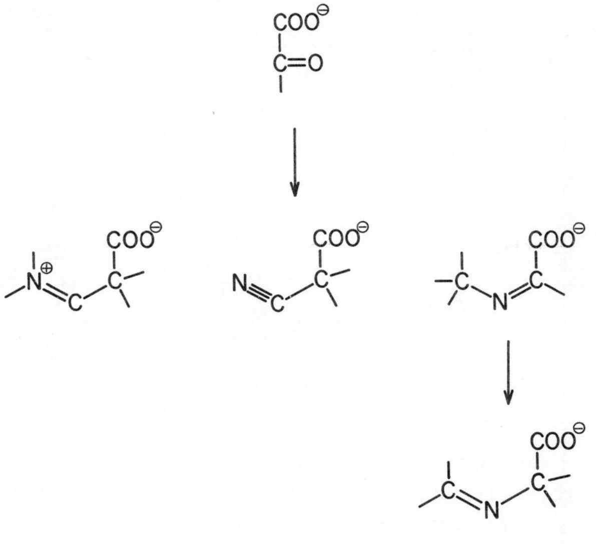

(8-66)

Thiazolium ion catalysis | Cyanide ion catalysis | Amine catalysis via a prototropic shift

Ukai and co-workers [39] and by Breslow [73] in the catalyzed acetoin condensation, among which the following are particularly pertinent:

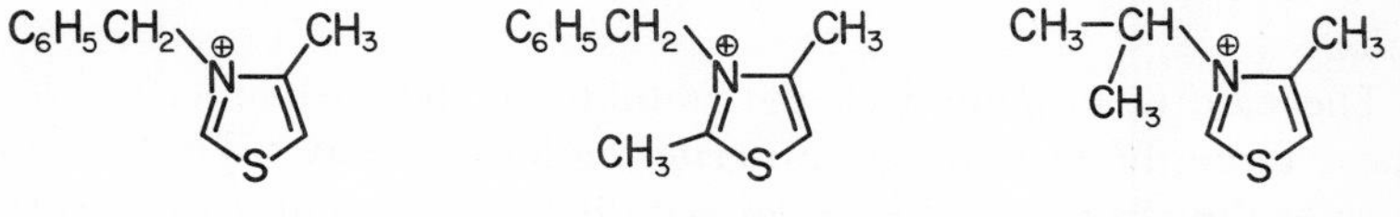

I active | II inactive | III inactive (8-67)

[77] W. E. von Doering and A. K. Hoffmann, *J. Am. Chem. Soc.* **77**, 521 (1955).
[78] R. Breslow, *Chem. Ind.* (*London*) 893 (1957).

Blocking of the 2-position either by a bulky neighboring substituent (8-67 III), or by substitution of a methyl group at this position (8-67 II), destroys the catalytic abilities of the thiazolium salt. These results with the model system conform to the earlier finding that a methyl group in the 2-position of thiamine destroyed its nutritional value.[78a]

The synthesis of the proposed type of intermediate in the mechanism of (8-65) [2-(1'-hydroxyethyl)-3,4-dimethylthiazolium salt], and proof of the position of the hydroxyethyl side chain of the product, were accomplished by Breslow and McNelis [79] via the route shown in (8-68). By

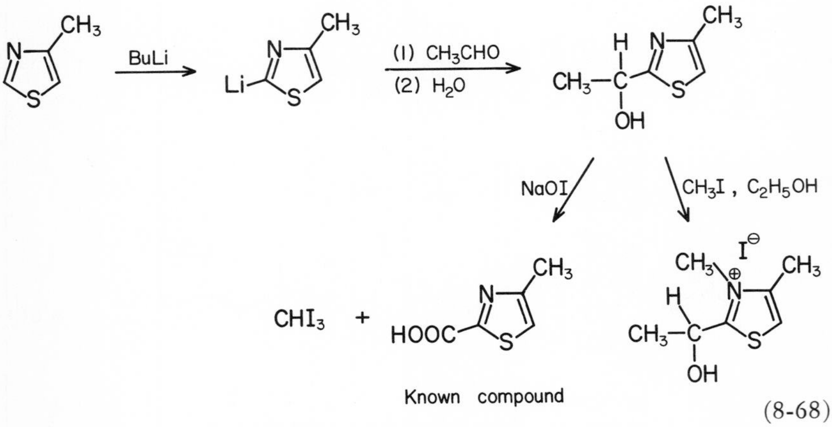

(8-68)

an analogous procedure the 3-benzyl analog was also prepared. The 2-(1'-hydroxyethyl) derivatives were compared to their parent thiazolium salts as catalysts in the acetoin condensation (Table 8-4).

The greater efficiency of the N-benzyl analogs as compared to their corresponding N-methyl analogs led Breslow to suggest that the benzyl group, through an inductive effect, increased the reactivity. A similar role was postulated to account for the greater reactivity of thiamine (i.e., inductive effect of the pyrimidine ring). However, Metzler [59, 80] has found that the p-nitrobenzyl analog is less effective than the benzyl analog.

The ease of formation or the stability of the carbanion would not appear to be the most important criterion for catalysis. Thus, although the rate of hydrogen exchange for 3,4-dimethyloxazolium iodide greatly

[78a] R. J. Williams, R. E. Eakin, E. Beerstecher, Jr., and W. Shive, "The Biochemistry of B Vitamins," Reinhold, New York, 1950, pp. 684–702.

[79] R. Breslow and E. McNelis, J. Am. Chem. Soc. 81, 3080 (1959).

[80] D. Metzler, private communication.

Table 8-4 *

Compound	Σ(Acetoin + α—Acetolactic Acid) micrograms
Thiamine	375 ± 18
$C_6H_5-CH_2-\overset{\oplus}{N}$, $CH_3-\overset{\|}{C}H$, OH (thiazolium with CH3)	239 ± 19
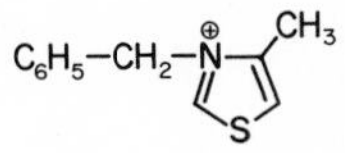 $C_6H_5-CH_2-\overset{\oplus}{N}$ (thiazolium with CH3)	79 ± 22
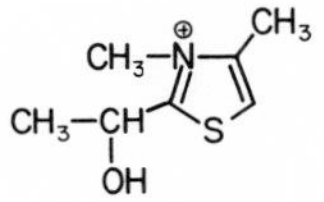 $CH_3-\overset{\oplus}{N}$, CH_3-CH, OH (thiazolium with CH3)	34 ± 9
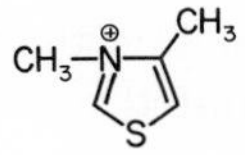 $CH_3-\overset{\oplus}{N}$ (thiazolium with CH3)	17 ± 7
No catalyst	15 ± 4

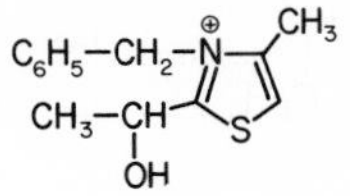

* Ref. 79.

exceeds that for the corresponding thiazolium salt,[81] the oxazolium salt does not catalyze the benzoin condensation or interact in a spectrophotometrically detectable manner with benzaldehyde. The observation that oxazolium salts exchange hydrogens at the 2-position more readily than thiazolium salts is in disagreement with the LCAO-MO calculations of Pullman and Spanjaard,[82] which predict that oxazolium salts are not catalytic because they form pseudo-bases instead of a carbanion. The labilizing influence of sulfur on adjacent methylene hydrogens in both acyclic and cyclic systems has been investigated. In acyclic systems, sulfur, due to $3d$ orbital overlap, has been found to be more acid strengthening than oxygen.[82a] Moreover, N,N'-diphenylimidazolium iodide was found to exchange the proton at the 2-position at approxi-

[81] W. Hafferl, R. Lundin, and L. L. Ingraham, *Biochemistry* 2, 1298 (1963).
[82] B. Pullman and C. Spanjaard, *Biochim. Biophys. Acta* 46, 576 (1961).
[82a] S. Oae, W. Tagaki, and A. Ohno, *Tetrahedron* 20, 417, 427, 437, 443 (1964).

mately the same rate as thiazolium ion.[81]   Wanzlick [83] found, however, that the N,N'-diphenylimidazolium anion was a poor catalyst.   The main product with benzaldehyde was the ketone (8-69 II).   This product is postulated to arise [81] because of the large amount of enol character

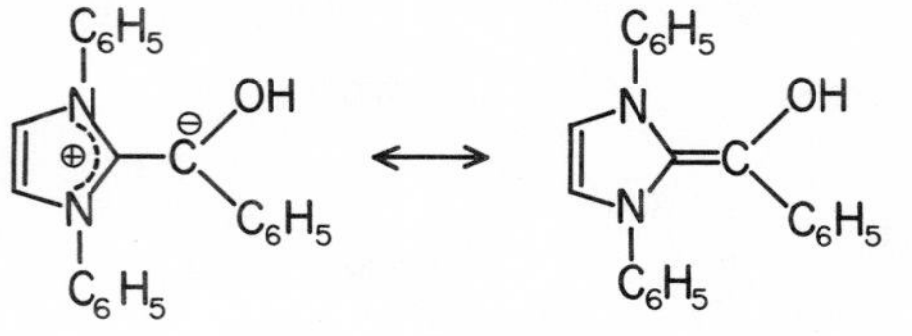

I

(8-69)

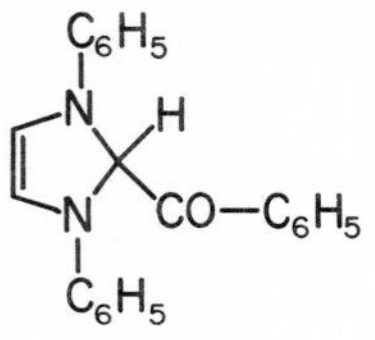

II

in the carbanion (8-69 I).   The absence of this type of product in the reaction of thiazolium salts, then, was attributed to a lessened enol character in the carbanion because of the partial aromatic character of the thiazolium ring.   The latter property is attributed to the sulfur which acts as a partial double bond.[84]   Alternatively, it should be noted that in the aforementioned cases, one is comparing a thermodynamic parameter (the exchange equilibrium) with a kinetically controlled parameter (the rate of catalysis of the benzoin condensation).   A rigid correlation is not required.   The carbanion of N,N'-diphenylimidazolium ion also behaves as a nucleophilic carbene, adding to the strongly electron-deficient tetra-cyanoethylene to form a cyclopropane derivative.[83]   The unique properties of the thiazolium carbanions may then arise from carbene-zwitterion resonance and possibly from pseudoaromatic character.

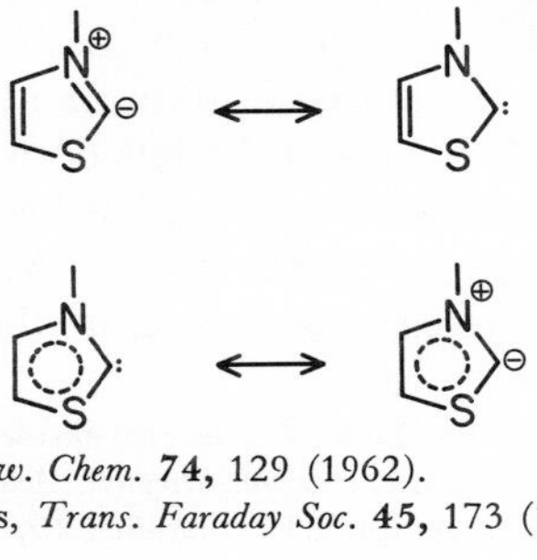

(8-70)

[83] H. W. Wanzlick, *Angew. Chem.* **74,** 129 (1962).
[84] H. C. Longuet-Higgins, *Trans. Faraday Soc.* **45,** 173 (1949).

Under oxidative decarboxylating conditions (α-keto acid oxidases) pyruvic acid is enzymically converted to acetic acid. $NAD^{\oplus}$ or an ex-

$$CH_3-\overset{\overset{O}{\|}}{C}-\overset{\overset{O}{\|}}{C}-O^{\ominus} \ + \ 2\ Fe(CN)_6^{3\ominus} \ + \ H_2O \ \longrightarrow \ CH_3COO^{\ominus} \ +$$

$$CO_2 \ + \ 2\ Fe(CN)_6^{4\ominus} \ + \ 2\ H^{\oplus}$$

$$(8\text{-}71)$$

traneous inorganic or organic oxidizing agent serves equally well in this reaction. The possible intermediate may be a 2-acyl thiamine, generated nonenzymically in (8-72). It has been shown [85] that 2-benzoyl-3-methylthiazolium salts readily undergo solvolysis in methanol to give

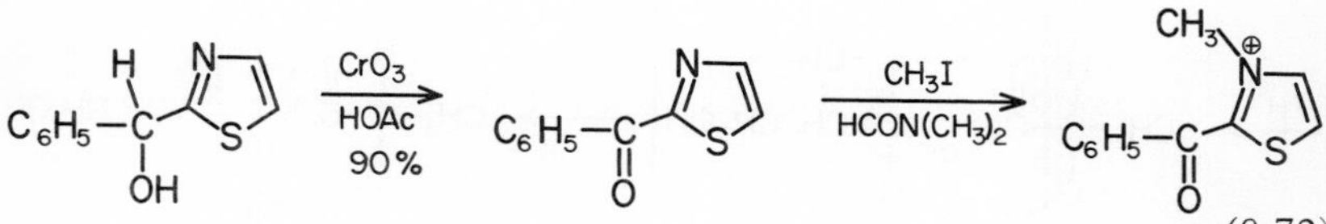

$$(8\text{-}72)$$

a 68% yield of methyl benzoate. This establishes that the 2-acetyl-thiamine possesses the kinetic lability required of an intermediate in the enzymic reaction and may arise as in (8-73):

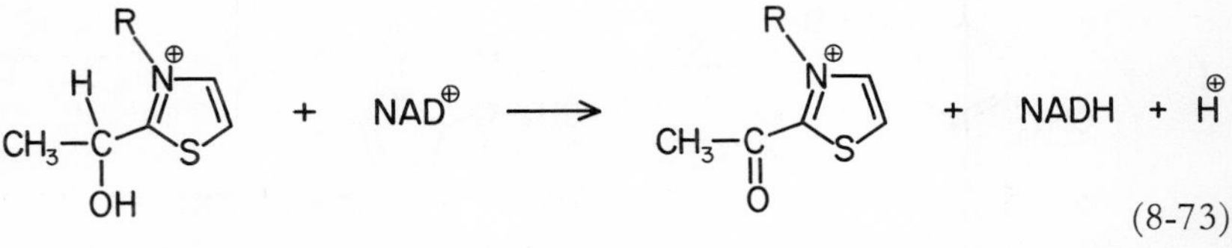

$$(8\text{-}73)$$

In addition, 2-acetyl-3,4-dimethylthiazolium bromide has been found to undergo nucleophilic attack by water to give acetic acid, by hydroxylamine to yield acethydroxamic acid, and by mercaptide ions to form thiolacetates.[86]

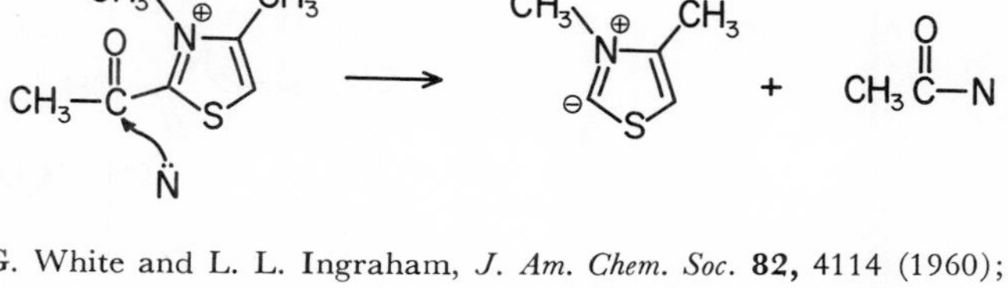

$$(8\text{-}74)$$

[85] F. G. White and L. L. Ingraham, *J. Am. Chem. Soc.* **82**, 4114 (1960); **84**, 3109 (1962).

[86] K. Daigo and L. J. Reed, *J. Am. Chem. Soc.* **84**, 659 (1962).

The important point of establishing whether an authentic sample of
2-(1'-hydroxyethyl)thiamine could serve as an intermediate in the
enzymic reaction was made through the biochemical endeavors of
Krampitz and Greull, and the organic chemical labors of Miller, Bicking,

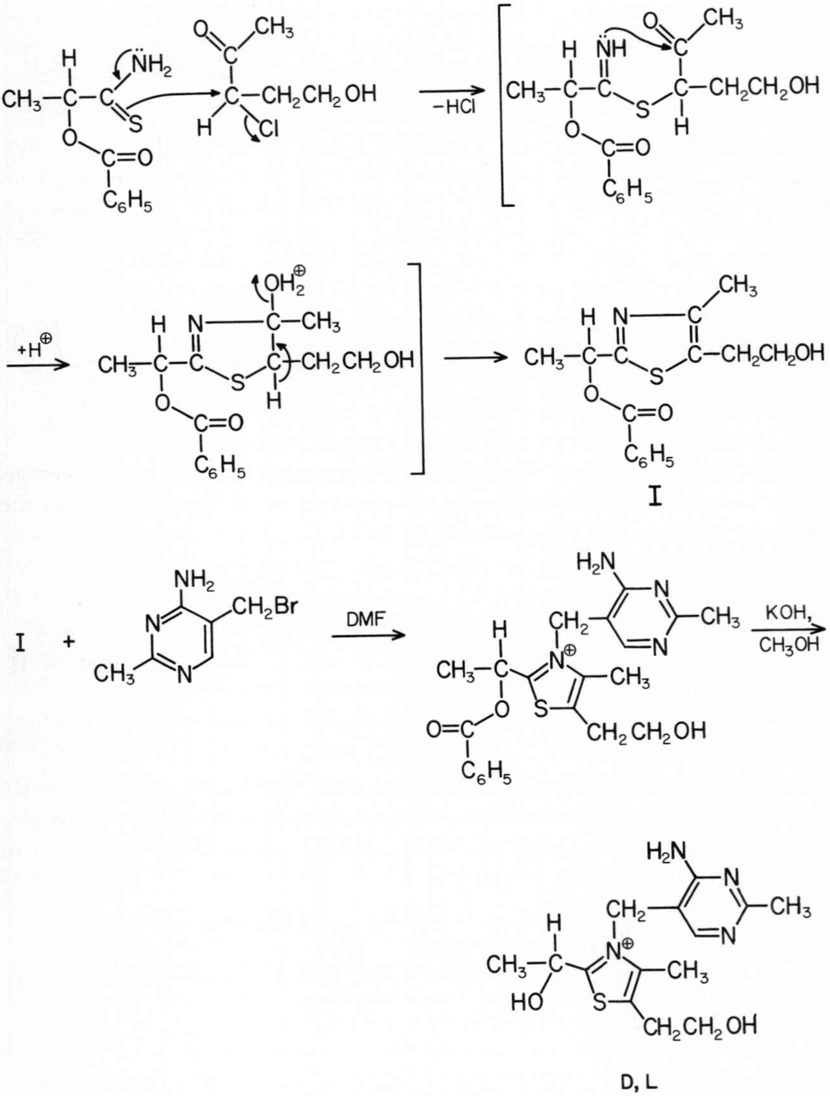

(8-75)

Skeggs, and Sprague.[87] The organic synthesis of this compound is represented in (8-75). The biological approach evolved from observations that yeast cells washed by alkali become deficient in thiamine diphosphate and. are no longer capable of decarboxylating pyruvate. Activity may be restored by adding thiamine and the ATP (phosphorylating agent) generating phosphoenol pyruvate and AMP. The synthetic hydroxyethylthiamine could substitute for thiamine in this system with equal activity. By employing a soluble yeast carboxylase preparation possessing thiamine kinase, acetaldehyde was reported to be liberated from hydroxyethylthiamine. Furthermore,[88] 2-methylthiamine is found to inhibit both thiamine and hydroxyethylthiamine. In nonenzymic systems,[88] 2-(1'-hydroxyethyl)thiamine at pH 8.8, with no other additions, produces no acetoin but, with the addition of acetaldehyde, substantial quantities of acetoin are formed. Under the same conditions thiamine and acetaldehyde give rise to only small quantities of acetoin. The hydroxyethylthiamine has been isolated [89] from *Escherichia coli* and found to be identical to the synthetic product of Sprague and co-workers.[87]

2-(1'-Hydroxyethyl)thiamine diphosphate has also been prepared and shown to be an actual intermediate in the enzymic acyloin condensation. The synthetic procedure employed was based on previous experience with "model" systems. 2-(1'-Hydroxyethyl)thiamine diphosphate was isolated [90] via paper chromatography from solutions of thiamine diphosphate and acetaldehyde-1,2-C[14] which had been incubated at pH 8.8. The compound also has been obtained from reaction mixtures of pyruvate with pyruvic decarboxylase [91, 92] and pyruvic oxidase,[93] respectively. Proof that the synthetic material was the desired product was obtained by treating the material with prostatic phosphatase and comparing the products with authentic 2-(1'-hydroxyethyl)thiamine. The acetoin complex of both thiamine and thiamine diphosphate also could be isolated when both thiazoles were incubated with acetaldehyde at pH 8.8, thereby substantiating their intermediacy. The acetoin-thiamine (8-76) and the acetoin-thiamine diphosphate compounds are more labile than hydroxyethylthiamine. The synthesis of the related dihydroxyethylthiamine diphosphate was carried out at pH 8.8 by incubating C[14]-formaldehyde

[87] L. O. Krampitz, G. Greull, C. S. Miller, J. B. Bicking, H. R. Skeggs, and J. M. Sprague, *J. Am. Chem. Soc.* **80**, 5893 (1958).

[88] L. O. Krampitz, G. Greull, and I. Suzuki, *Federation Proc.* **18**, 266 (1959).

[89] G. M. Brown, *J. Cellular Comp. Physiol.* **54**, Suppl. 1, 101 (1959); G. L. Carlson and G. M. Brown, *J. Biol. Chem.* **236**, 2099 (1961).

[90] L. O. Krampitz, I. Suzuki, and G. Greull, *Federation Proc.* **20**, 971 (1961).

[91] H. Holzer and K. Beaucamp, *Angew. Chem.* **71**, 776 (1959).

[92] H. Holzer and K. Beaucamp, *Biochim. Biophys. Acta* **46**, 225 (1961).

[93] P. Scriba and H. Holzer, *Biochem. Z.* **334**, 473 (1961).

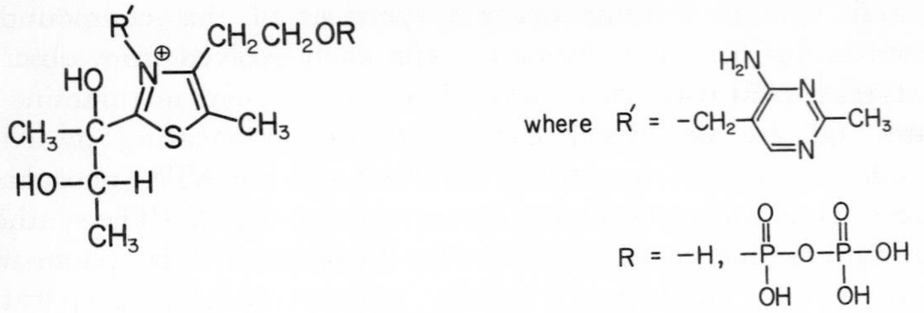

$$(8\text{-}76)$$

where $R' = -CH_2-$ (pyrimidine structure) $-CH_3$

$R = -H, -\overset{O}{\underset{OH}{P}}-O-\overset{O}{\underset{OH}{P}}-OH$

with thiamine diphosphate, suggesting the following condensation reaction to occur [90]:

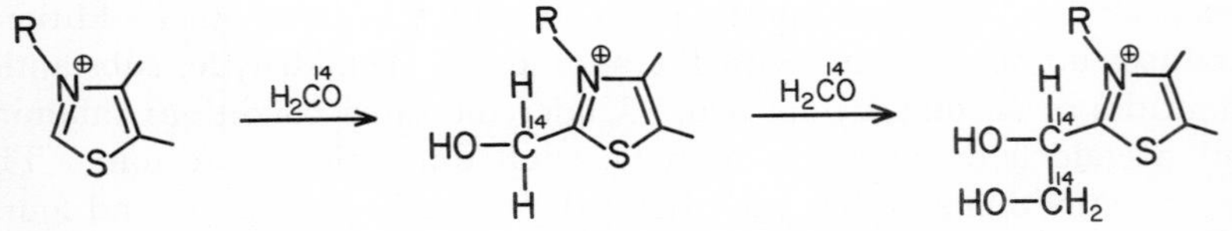

$$(8\text{-}77)$$

Krampitz,[90] employing high concentrations of wheat germ pyruvic carboxylase (resolved of thiamine diphosphate) with C^{14}-hydroxyethyl-thiamine diphosphate as substrate, found a rapid initial release of C^{14}-acetaldehyde followed by a slow continual formation of C^{14}-acetaldehyde. These results were interpreted as an initial saturation of the enzyme with hydroxyethylthiamine diphosphate, followed by a slow reaction whose rate-determining step is the release of thiamine diphosphate. Holzer and Kohlhaw [94] employed pyruvic oxidase from pig heart muscle and, as substrates, unlabeled pyruvate and hydroxyethylthiamine diphosphate labeled with C^{14} in the α-hydroxyethyl group.[93] α-Acetolactic acid was identified as the product by ion-exchange chromatography, high voltage

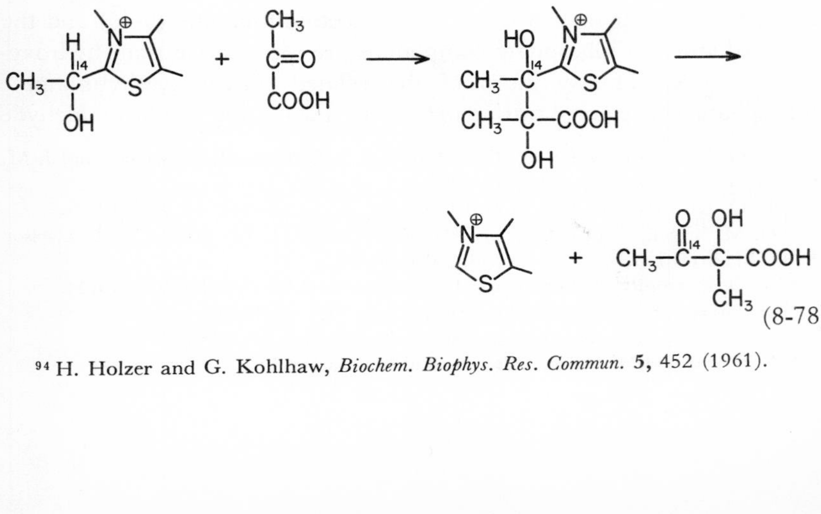

$$(8\text{-}78)$$

[94] H. Holzer and G. Kohlhaw, *Biochem. Biophys. Res. Commun.* 5, 452 (1961).

electrophoresis, and decarboxylation of the product and conversion of the resultant acetoin with ferric chloride to diacetyl, which was converted in turn to its bis-2,4-dinitrophenylhydrazone.

Similarly, C^{14}-hydroxyethylthiamine diphosphate was found to react with acetaldehyde in the presence of an *Aerobacter aerogenes* preparation to yield acetoin.[90] Degradation of the acetoin established the C^{14} to be exclusively in the acetyl group. Hydroxyethylthiamine diphosphate can

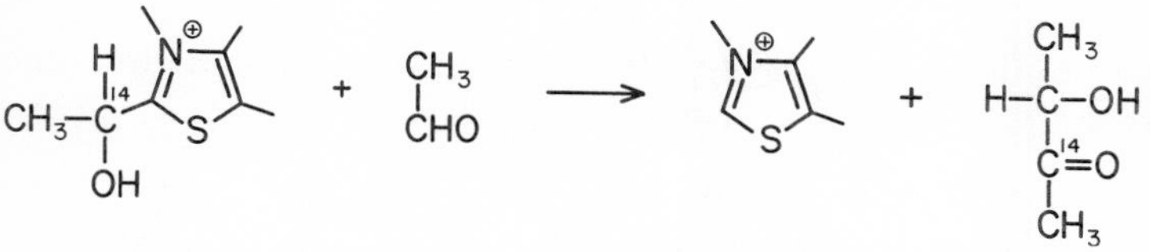

$$(8-79)$$

be isolated as an intermediate from a mixture of this enzyme, thiamine diphosphate, and pyruvate. The acetoin-forming system corresponds to the pyruvate oxidase system minus the essential cofactors lipoic acid, $NAD^{\oplus}$, and coenzyme A. In the presence of a suitable oxidizing agent this system will form acetate. For example, ferricyanide and inorganic phosphate lead to the formation of acetyl phosphate, trapped as the acethydroxamic acid, from hydroxyethylthiamine diphosphate. In the absence of enzyme the oxidation of the hydroxyethylthiamine diphosphate was negligible.[90]

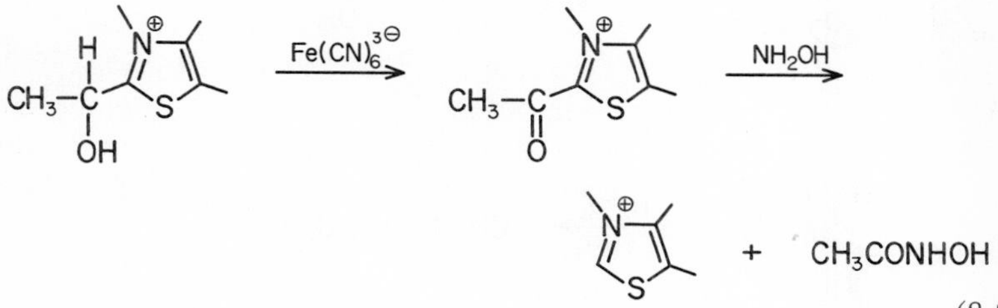

$$(8-80)$$

C^{14}-Labeled hydroxyethylthiamine diphosphate also has been shown to give rise to C^{14}-acetyl-CoA in the complete pyruvate oxidase system from yeast mitochondria.[95] Thus, after incubation with the pyruvic oxidase system plus arylamine acetylase from liver, *p*-nitroaniline, and $NAD^{\oplus}$, radioactive *N*-acetyl-*p*-nitroaniline could be isolated by paper chromatography.

The intermediacy of 2-substituted thiamine diphosphate in enzymic reactions is therefore now well established. In addition to the examples

[95] H. W. Goedde, H. Inouye, and H. Holzer, *Biochim. Biophys. Acta* **50**, 41 (1961).

provided above, 2-(1,2-dihydroxyethyl)thiamine diphosphate has been shown to be an intermediate in the transketolase reaction.[90, 96, 97]   Breslow [98] has suggested (8-81) and (8-82) as the mechanisms for the transketolase and phosphoketolase reactions.

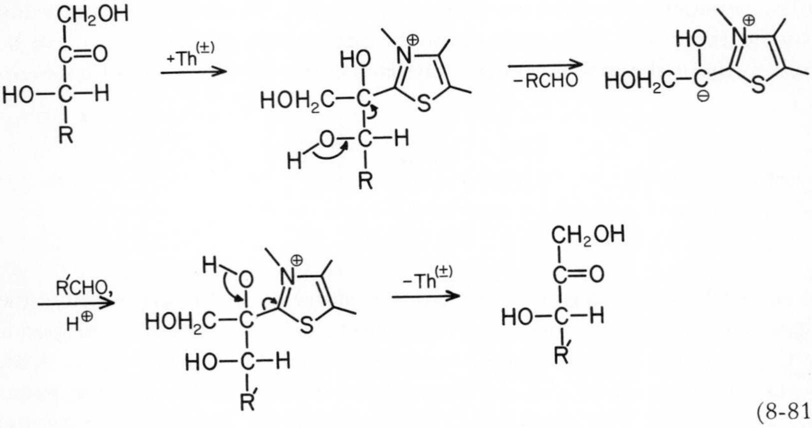

$$(8-81)$$

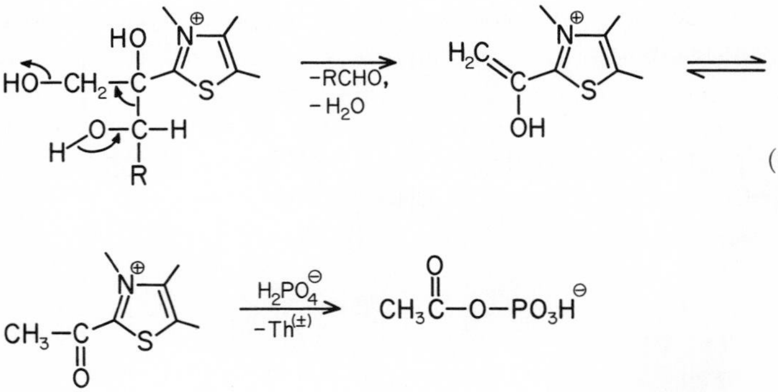

$$(8-82)$$

III. THE MECHANISMS OF PYRIDOXAL CATALYSIS

The two key steps in the transamination reaction are the formation of imines and their subsequent isomerization and hydrolysis. We will

[96] K. W. Bock, L. Jaenicke, and H. Holzer, *Biochem. Biophys. Res. Commun.* **9**, 472 (1962); F. da Fonseca-Wollheim, K. W. Bock, and H. Holzer, *Biochem. Biophys. Res. Commun.* **9**, 466 (1962).

[97] N. N. Prochoroff, R. Kattermann, and H. Holzer, *Biochem. Biophys. Res. Commun.* **9**, 477 (1962).

[98] R. Breslow, *J. Cellular Comp. Physiol.* **54**, Suppl. 1, 100 (1959).

consider first these topics, followed by a discussion of "model" systems involving 3-hydroxypyridine-4-aldehyde.

A. The Mechanism of Imine Formation

1. NITROGEN DERIVATIVE FORMATION WITH NONSPECIFIC KETONES AND ALDEHYDES   The very early work on acid and base catalysis of oxime formation by Acree and Johnson [99] and Barrett and Lapworth [100] included a discussion of intermediates of the type $>C(OH)\overset{\oplus}{N}H_2OH$ (carbinol-amine). Acree and Johnson discovered that oxime formation was catalyzed by acids, while Barrett and Lapworth, working on the formation of acetone and acetaldehyde oximes, found an optimum concentration of acid, above and below which the velocity of formation decreases sharply. Considerations by all subsequent workers have dealt with the factors uncovered by these early investigations (i.e., the rationale of the acidity optimum, catalysis by acids, and formation of intermediates), which are crucial to the understanding of the mechanism of imine formation. Barrett and Lapworth also clearly demonstrated catalysis of acetoxime formation by $OH^{\ominus}$ Due to a lack of modern instrumentation both the detection of intermediates and measurement of the activity of hydrogen ion in aqueous solutions proved difficult in these early studies.

Bodforss [101] was the first to provide definite experimental evidence for a carbinolamine intermediate in phenylhydrazone formation. He showed that the first-order rate of disappearance of phenylhydrazine is much faster than the appearance of product, hence the addition compound must have been formed rapidly and in relatively high concentration. In a later quantitative study of acetoxime formation, in which pH was accurately measured with the hydrogen electrode, Ölander [102] concluded from kinetic evidence alone that carbinolamine $[(CH_3)_2C(OH)NHOH]$ is an intermediate. Ölander also described maxima in pH-rate profiles for oxime formation and oxime cleavage.

In a related, quantitative study of semicarbazone formation, Conant and Bartlett [103] likewise encountered similar sharp maxima in the pH-rate profiles at slightly acidic pH. In addition they measured both the overall equilibrium constants and rate constants for semicarbazone formation and hydrolysis with a variety of aldehydes and ketones, and importantly established that the formation of semicarbazone is subject to general-acid

[99] S. F. Acree and J. M. Johnson, *Am. Chem. J.* **38,** 308 (1907).
[100] E. Barrett and A. Lapworth, *J. Chem. Soc.* **93,** 85 (1908).
[101] S. Bodforss, *Z. Physik. Chem. (Leipzig)* **109,** 223 (1924).
[102] A. Ölander, *Z. Physik. Chem. (Leipzig)* **129,** 1 (1927).
[103] J. B. Conant and P. D. Bartlett, *J. Am. Chem. Soc.* **54,** 2881 (1932).

catalysis. The maxima in the pH-rate profiles were rationalized by assuming that the increase in the acidity of the buffer acids employed is accompanied by an increase in their catalytic coefficients, as expressed by the Brönsted relationship. This in turn is being counteracted by conversion of the reactive species of the nitrogen base to its unreactive conjugate acid, i.e.:

$$NH_2CONHNH_2 \underset{-H^{\oplus}}{\overset{+H^{\oplus}}{\rightleftharpoons}} NH_2CONHNH_3^{\oplus}$$

Furthermore, Conant and Bartlett proposed that the acid catalysis probably occurs after formation of some complex between the carbonyl compound and semicarbazide. Unlike oxime formation, no specific-base catalysis could be established (only a 5-fold rate enhancement over the range 0.1 N to 1.0 N NaOH), but the kinetic study of Conant and Bartlett suffered in that both pH and buffer concentration were varied simultaneously rather than separately, making it impossible to separate specific- and general-acid catalyzed processes.

Jencks [104] found that the addition at pH's near neutrality of H_2NOH, H_2NOCH_3, and $H_2NHNCONH_2$ to furfural, pyruvate, and benzaldehyde brought about a rapid initial decrease in the carbonyl absorption, which was proportional to the concentration of nitrogen base employed. The initial decrease in absorbance was ascribed to the formation of carbinolamine. Equilibrium constants for carbinolamine formation were obtained by measuring the change in carbonyl absorption with time after addition of nitrogen base, followed by extrapolation back to zero time in order to obtain the initial drop in absorbance. Experiments in which the disappearance of the carbonyl band in deuterium oxide solutions was measured by infrared spectroscopy gave similar results. In the neutral pH range the rate of dehydration of addition compound to form oxime or semicarbazone was found to be linearly related to the product of the concentration of carbinolamine and the hydrogen ion activity where k_{dehy} is of the order of magnitude of 10^6–10^8 liter mole^{-1} min^{-1}. Also, in the neutral pH range the dehydration of the addition compound was found to

$$v = k_{\text{dehy}} \left[\overset{\displaystyle \overset{OH}{|}}{>C-NH-R} \right] [H_3O^{\oplus}] \qquad (8\text{-}83)$$

be general-acid catalyzed by phosphate ($H_2PO_4^{\ominus}$). With a lowering of pH, a change in the rate-limiting step from acid catalyzed dehydration of carbinolamine to formation of carbinolamine occurs. At these lower pH

[104] W. P. Jencks, *J. Am. Chem. Soc.* **81**, 475 (1959).

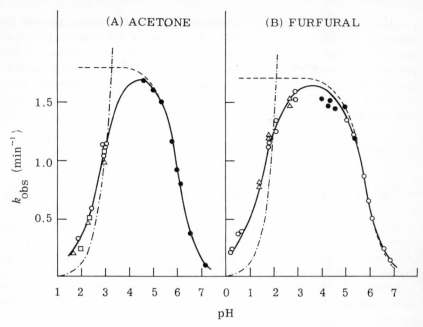

Fig. 8-2   *Rates of reaction of hydroxylamine with acetone and furfural as a function of pH:*
- - -, calculated for rate-limiting acid-catalyzed dehydration of addition complex; -·-·-, calcu-
lated for rate-limiting addition of free hydroxylamine to the carbonyl group.   (A) Acetone-
hydroxylamine: total hydroxylamine 0.0167 M, acetone 0.0005 M, ionic strength maintained
at 0.32 with NaCl, measured at 220 mμ; calculated curves from $k_{obs} = (1.08 \times 10^8) a_H$
(fraction as complex) and from $k_{obs} = 6.8 \times 10^4 [NH_2OH]$; concentration of addition compound
calculated from the equilibrium constant and the concentration of free hydroxylamine.   (B)
Furfural-hydroxylamine: total hydroxylamine 0.134 M, furfural 0.000055 M, ionic strength
maintained at 0.67 with NaCl, measured at 260 mμ; calculated curves from $k_{obs} = 2.2 \times 10^6 a_H$
(fraction as addition compound) and from $k_{obs} = 9 \times 10^4 [NH_2OH]$.   (Ref. 104.)

values, general-acid catalysis of derivative formation and carbinolamine
formation is not observable.   At very low pH values the rate of derivative
formation becomes independent of pH, which may be ascribed to a
hydronium-ion catalyzed addition of free hydroxylamine or semicarbazide.
It should be noted that the reaction is also subject to specific-base catalysis,[100] which has been suggested [104] to be due to base catalyzed dehydration of carbinolamine intermediate.   The bell-shaped pH-rate profiles
(Fig. 8-2) obtained for derivative formation consequently were suggested
by Jencks [104] to be the result of limiting free amine on the acid side, and
limiting hydrogen ion concentration on the base side.   This is most likely
the correct view.

In a reinvestigation of semicarbazone formation, which assessed the effect of structure on this reaction,[105] ρ values of 1.81 and -1.74 were obtained for the equilibrium constants for the formation of semicarbazide addition compounds and the rate of acid catalyzed dehydration of addition compound, respectively. The overall rates of semicarbazone formation exhibit a $\rho = 0.07$, reflecting the summation of both intermediate formation and dehydration and are consistent with mechanism (8-84). Further

$$R\!-\!NH_3^{\oplus} \overset{K_a'}{\rightleftharpoons} R\!-\!NH_2 + H^{\oplus}$$

$$R\!-\!NH_2 + R'\!-\!CHO \overset{K_e}{\rightleftharpoons} R\!-\!\overset{OH}{\underset{H}{\overset{|}{N}\!-\!CH}}\!-\!R' \xrightarrow{k_r(H^{\oplus})} R\!-\!N\!=\!CH\!-\!R'$$

$$(8\text{-}84)$$

evidence was provided by the dependence of the second-order rate constants for semicarbazone formation $(k_r[H_2NNHCONH_2][>C\!=\!O])$ on pH (Fig. 8-3).[106] The plot indicates that, at neutral pH, acid catalyzed dehydration of the carbinolamine intermediate is rate-determining and, at more acidic pH, the attack of semicarbazide becomes the acid catalyzed rate-determining step. At intermediate pH, a plateau is obtained indicating solvent catalyzed attack of semicarbazide. The second-order rate constants plotted in Fig. 8-3 have been corrected for general-acid catalysis by the conjugate acid of semicarbazide.

The ρ^+ values for the general-acid and hydronium-ion catalyzed formation of intermediate carbinolamines, formed from semicarbazide and substituted benzaldehydes, both fall between 0.77 and 0.84, suggesting that the hydrated proton is acting as a general acid. This hypothesis is supported by the findings that (1) the rate constant for hydronium-ion catalysis of the attack of semicarbazide on p-chlorobenzaldehyde exhibits a negative deviation from a Brönsted plot (slope $= 0.25$) for general-acid catalysts, which is no greater than that for other general acids, and (2) the calculated bimolecular rate constant for specific-acid catalysis of the attack of semicarbazide on p-nitrobenzaldehyde exceeds that for a diffusion-controlled process (1.6×10^{14} liter mole^{-1} min^{-1}). The deuterium solvent isotope effect on the catalytic constant for attack of semicarbazide on p-chlorobenzaldehyde for the hydrated proton is $k^{H_2O}/k^{D_2O} = 1.2$, and that for acetic acid is 1.6. The deuterium solvent kinetic effects must be considered mechanistically rather inconclusive.

[105] B. M. Anderson and W. P. Jencks, *J. Am. Chem. Soc.* **82,** 1773 (1960).
[106] E. H. Cordes and W. P. Jencks, *J. Am. Chem. Soc.* **84,** 4319 (1962).

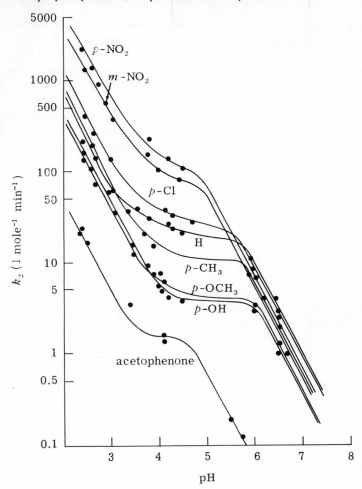

Fig. 8-3   *Logarithm of second-order rate constants, based on the concentration of the free base of semicarbazide, for semicarbazone formation from a series of substituted benzaldehydes and acetophenone at 25°.   All rate constants have been extrapolated to zero buffer concentration; ionic strength = 0.50 (for acetophenone experiments ionic strength = 1.0).   (Ref. 106.)*

The catalytic coefficients for the conjugate acids of the secondary amines, imidazole, morpholine, and N-methylaniline are close to those predicted from the Brönsted plot obtained for carboxylic acids.[107]   However, the catalytic constants for a series of substituted anilines were found to lie 1–3 orders of magnitude above the line in the Brönsted plot.   Substi-

[107] E. H. Cordes and W. P. Jencks, *J. Am. Chem. Soc.* **84,** 826 (1962).

tuted *N*-benzylideneanilines in dilute solutions of semicarbazide partition to aldehyde and semicarbazone, the fraction of semicarbazone formed being dependent on the concentration of semicarbazide. Cordes and Jencks [107] were able to show that the rate of Schiff base formation accounted quantitatively for the rate of aniline catalyzed semicarbazone formation and that, except in very dilute solutions, the rate of aniline catalyzed semicarbazone formation is independent of semicarbazide concentration. In addition it was found that the rate of aniline catalyzed semicarbazone formation is the same as the rate of aniline catalyzed oxime formation. These results substantiate a mechanism of nucleophilic catalysis via a transimination reaction (8-85):

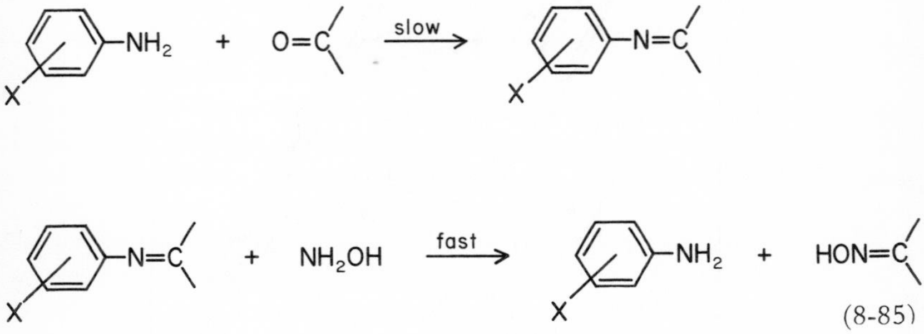

$$\text{(8-85)}$$

The rate of aniline-catalyzed *p*-chlorobenzaldehyde semicarbazone formation was reported to increase more rapidly than the first power of the anilinium ion concentration, suggesting that the catalyzed reaction is itself subject to general-acid catalysis.

The studies of oxime, semicarbazone, and hydrazone formation formed the basis for the technically more difficult investigations of imine formation. Since the formation equilibrium constants for imines in aqueous solution are much less favorable than for semicarbazones, oximes, and hydrazones, quantitative studies on imines have more often been concerned with hydrolysis.

Initial reports of isolation of carbinolamines [108] as intermediates in imine synthesis have been criticized,[109] and further progress on the mechanism of imine formation has come chiefly in recent years. Zuman [110] measured polarographically the equilibrium constants for imine formation with a variety of carbonyl compounds and amines including amino

[108] A. Hantzch and F. Kraft, *Ber.* **24,** 3521 (1891).
[109] O. Dimroth and R. Zoeppritz, *Ber.* **35,** 984 (1902).
[110] P. Zuman, *Collection Czech. Chem. Commun.* **15,** 839 (1951).

acids.   However, Willi and Robertson [111] were the first to undertake a detailed kinetic investigation of imine formation and hydrolysis.   From their careful measurements of the rates of hydrolysis of substituted benzylideneanilines in 50% aqueous methanol, these authors could calculate the rate constants for the specific-acid and general-acid catalyzed reactions in buffered solutions near neutrality.   By taking advantage of the fact that imine and aldehyde concentrations may be measured independently and simultaneously by polarographic methods, Kastening, Holleck, and Melkonian [112] were able to establish the presence of an intermediate during the course of hydrolysis of benzylideneaniline.   They also observed base catalyzed hydrolysis above pH 12.   At the same time Willi [113] independently deduced the presence of a carbinolamine on a kinetic basis, explained the anomalies reported previously, extended his pH-rate profile to acidic and basic solutions, and set forth the general kinetic equations for imine hydrolysis.   The rate-limiting step in neutral and alkaline solutions was found to be a combination of the uncatalyzed addition of water to imine to form carbinolamine ($\rho = -1.45$) or, as postulated by Willi, attack of $OH^{\ominus}$ on the conjugate acid of the imine and the acid catalyzed addition of water to imine.   The Hammett $\rho\sigma$ treatment for the latter reaction provided a nonlinear plot.   Crowell and co-workers [114] noted that, in the reaction of n-butylamine with benzaldehyde, the uncatalyzed rate constant also provided a maximum in the Hammett plot near the point corresponding to benzaldehyde (solvent methanol).   The latter workers also found general-acid catalysis.   The phenomenon of a maximum in the sigma-rho plot had previously been noted in imine formation by Oddo and Tognacchini [115] and in semicarbazone formation by Noyce and co-workers,[116] suggesting a multiple step mechanism with a balance of opposing substituent effects.

Evidence obtained by Willi suggested that in the hydrolysis reaction the addition of water to form the carbinolamine intermediate is rate-determining.   On the other hand, Kastening and co-workers [112] concluded from their polarographic measurements that the decomposition of the carbinolamine is rate-determining.   Cordes and Jencks,[117] employing semicarbazide as a trap, have measured both the rate of formation of p-chlorobenzylideneaniline and rate of hydrolysis as a function of pH in

[111] A. V. Willi and R. E. Robertson, *Can. J. Chem.* **31,** 361 (1953).

[112] B. Kastening, L. Holleck, and G. A. Melkonian, *Z. Elektrochem.* **60,** 130 (1956).

[113] A. V. Willi, *Helv. Chim. Acta* **39,** 1193 (1956).

[114] G. M. Santerre, C. J. Hansrote, and T. I. Crowell, *J. Am. Chem. Soc.* **80,** 1254 (1958).

[115] B. Oddo and F. Tognacchini, *Gazz. Chim. Ital.* **52,** II, 347 (1922).

[116] D. S. Noyce, A. T. Bottini, and S. G. Smith, *J. Org. Chem.* **23,** 752 (1958).

[117] E. H. Cordes and W. P. Jencks, *J. Am. Chem. Soc.* **84,** 832 (1962).

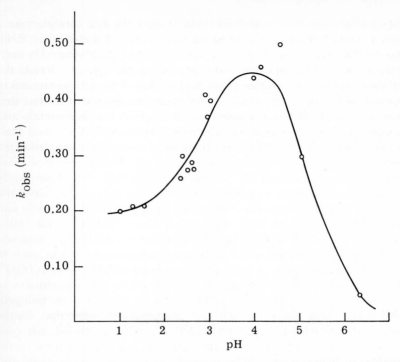

Fig. 8-4   *The rate of formation of N-p-chlorobenzylideneaniline as a function of pH at 25°: p-chlorobenzaldehyde 3.3 × 10⁻⁵ M, total aniline 0.004 M, total semicarbazide 0.0025 M, ionic strength 0.50.   (Ref. 117.)*

aqueous solutions.   They were able to show that the pH-rate maximum in imine formation represents, as in the case of oxime and semicarbazide formation, [104,106] transition from rate-limiting dehydration of carbino-lamine in neutral and alkaline solutions to rate-limiting attack of free nitrogen base on the carbonyl compound to form carbinolamine at acidic pH.   The carbinolamine intermediate was found to accumulate rapidly at neutral pH, with a concomitant decrease in absorbance in the ultraviolet, and with its dehydration being facilitated by general-acid and hydronium-ion catalysis.   In Fig. 8-4 there is plotted the pseudo-first-order rate constants for the formation of *N-p*-chlorobenzylideneaniline (25°) *vs.* pH.   All points on the pH-rate profile have been extrapolated to zero buffer concentration.   The rate equation providing the ascending portion of the curve of (Fig. 8-4) is

$$v = k_1[RNH_2][R'CHO] + k_2[RNH_2][R'CHO]a_H \qquad (8\text{-}86)$$

Employing a series of carboxylic acids as general-acid catalysts, the Brönsted coefficient was found to be ca. 0.25 on the acid side of the pH optima. The susceptibility of imine formation to general-acid catalysis was found to be different on the two sides of the pH optima. Thus, at pH 2.5 the catalytic constant for acetic acid was found to be approximately 10-fold greater than at pH 5.10. The detection of general-acid catalysis on both sides of the pH optima would tend to establish both carbinolamine formation and dehydration to be subject to general-acid catalysts in the forward direction and therefore, on the basis of microscopic reversibility,

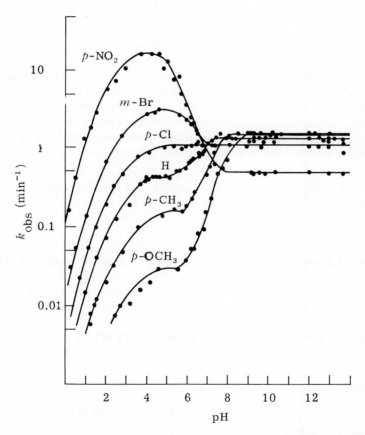

Fig. 8-5   *Logarithm of the first-order rate constants for the hydrolysis of substituted benzylidene-1,1-dimethylethylamines as a function of pH at 25°; 0.02 M chloroacetate, acetate, phosphate, borate, and carbonate buffers employed in the appropriate pH ranges. Ionic strength maintained at 0.50 by the addition of KCl.   (Ref. 118.)*

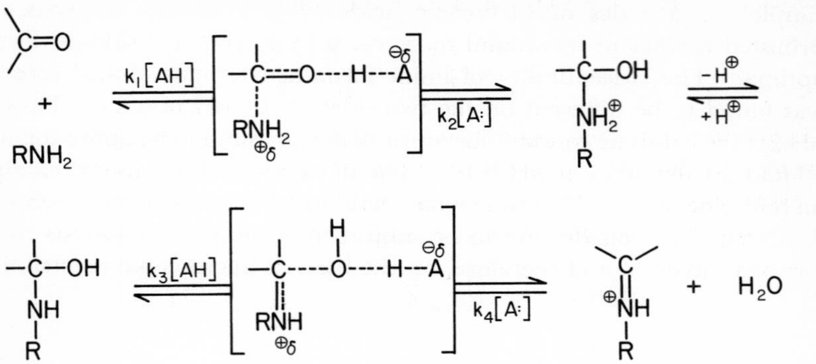

$$(8\text{-}87)$$

general-base catalysis in the reverse direction. The catalysis is of greater importance, the weaker the base strength of the amine (or imine).

A comprehensive study of the hydrolysis of m- and p-substituted benzylidene-1,1-dimethylethylamines has been carried out by Cordes and Jencks (see Fig. 8-5).[118] The pH-rate profiles suggest a mechanism whereby carbinolamine decomposition occurs via the neutral or kinetically equivalent dipolar forms (identical to the mechanism suggested by Willi). Assuming steady state in carbinolamine, the pseudo-first-order rate con-

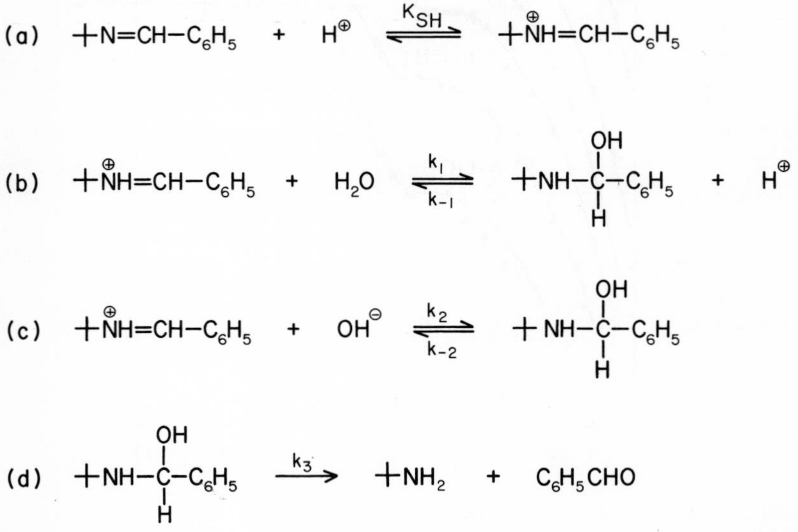

$$(8\text{-}88)$$

[118] E. H. Cordes and W. P. Jencks, *J. Am. Chem. Soc.* **85**, 2843 (1963).

stant at any constant pH would have the value:

$$k_{\text{obs}} = \frac{k_1 k_3 a_{\text{H}} + K_{\text{w}} k_2 k_3}{[a_{\text{H}} + K_{\text{SH}}][k_{-1} a_{\text{H}} + k_{-2} + k_3]} \tag{8-89}$$

The various rate and equilibrium constants may be evaluated as provided here for the p-nitrobenzylidene-1,1-dimethylethylamine. At pH 7.0 one may assume the reaction of $OH^{\ominus}$ with protonated carbinolamine (8-88c) to be negligible, $K_{\text{SH}} \gg a_{\text{H}}$ and $k_3 \gg k_{-1} a_{\text{H}}$:

$$k_{\text{obs pH 7.0}} = \frac{k_1 a_{\text{H}}}{K_{\text{SH}}}$$

$$k_1 = 4.2 \times 10^6 K_{\text{SH}} \tag{8-90}$$

At pH 1.0, one may again assume no contribution from $OH^{\ominus}$ reacting with protonated carbinolamine, $a_{\text{H}} \gg K_{\text{SH}}$ and $k_{-1} a_{\text{H}} \gg k_3$, therefore:

$$k_{\text{obs pH 1.0}} = \left(\frac{k_1}{k_{-1}}\right) \frac{k_3}{a_{\text{H}}}$$

$$\left(\frac{k_1}{k_{-1}}\right) k_3 = 0.10 \tag{8-91}$$

At those acidities where the reaction of protonated imine with hydroxide ion may be ignored, substitution of (8-90) and (8-91) into (8-89) yields

$$k_{\text{obs}} = \frac{4.2 \times 10^6 K_{\text{SH}} a_{\text{H}}}{[a_{\text{H}} + K_{\text{SH}}][1 + 4.2 \times 10^7 K_{\text{SH}} a_{\text{H}}]} \tag{8-92}$$

The value of K_{SH} may be determined from the k_{obs} constants at several pH values, ($pK_a' = 5.4$). Under alkaline conditions, pH > 8.0, $K_{\text{w}} k_2 k_3 \gg k_1 k_3 p K_{\text{SH}}$, $K_{\text{SH}} \gg a_{\text{H}}$, and, $k_{-2} + k_3 \gg k_{-1} a_{\text{H}}$, therefore:

$$k_{\text{obs}} = \frac{K_{\text{w}} k_2 k_3}{K_{\text{SH}}[k_{-2} + k_3]} = \frac{K_{\text{w}} k_2}{K_{\text{SH}}[k_{-2}/k_3 + 1]} \tag{8-93}$$

Realizing $k_{-2}/k_3 \ll 1$, then

$$k_{\text{obs}} = \frac{K_{\text{w}}}{K_{\text{SH}}} k_2$$

and

$$k_2 = 1.9 \times 10^8$$

With the value of K_{SH}, equation (8-89) becomes

$$k_{\text{obs}} = \frac{16.8 a_{\text{H}} + 1.9 \times 10^6}{[a_{\text{H}} + 4.0 \times 10^{-6}][1.68 \times 10^2 a_{\text{H}} + 1]} \tag{8-94}$$

Table 8-5 *   *Rate constants for the hydrolysis of substituted benzylidene-1,1-dimethylethylamines and dissociation constants for the protonated Schiff bases (25° and ionic strength 0.5)*

Substituent	K_{SH} [a] (M^{-1})	k_1 [b] (min^{-1})	k_{calcd} [c] (liter mole^{-1} min^{-1})	k_{H_2O} [d] (min^{-1})	pH 1 k_{obs} (min^{-1})
p-Nitro-	3.98×10^{-6}	0.48	1.91×10^8	16	11
m-Bromo-	7.95×10^{-7}	—	—	3.1	0.12
p-Chloro-	3.16×10^{-7}	1.09	3.45×10^7	1.1	0.038
Unsubstituted	1.99×10^{-7}	1.34	3.00×10^7	0.41	0.014
p-Methyl-	3.98×10^{-8}	1.50	5.98×10^6	0.16	0.004
p-Methoxy-	1.98×10^{-8}	1.54	3.05×10^6	0.029	

  * Ref. 118.

  [a] Dissociation constants for the protonated benzylidene-1,1-dimethylethylamines.

  [b] Observed first-order rate constant for the pH-independent reaction above pH 9.

  [c] Calculated second-order rate constant for attack of hydroxide ion on the protonated Schiff bases.

  [d] Observed rate constants for the attack of water on the protonated Schiff bases, estimated from the rates of hydrolysis in the pH region 4–5.

In Fig. 8-5 the pH-rate profile for the hydrolysis of p-nitrobenzylidene-1,1-dimethylethylamine is a theoretical curve calculated from equation (8-94). The calculated and estimated values of the acid dissociation constants of imines and the rate constants are presented in Table 8-5.

The ρ^+ for the dissociation constants of the substituted benzylidene-1,1-dimethylethylamines was found to be +1.6. The pH-rate profiles may be divided into four areas for discussion (see Fig. 8-5):

pH 9–14: The rates are insensitive to both pH and substituents ($\rho^+ = -0.21$). The insensitivity to polar effects suggests the hydrolysis in this region to be dictated by attack of $OH^\ominus$ on protonated imine [in (8-88) steps (a + c) rate-controlling]. Calculation of the rate constants for attack of $OH^\ominus$ on the protonated imine allows the assessment of ρ^+ as +1.26 for this step. The magnitudes of the rate constants calculated for this reaction approach those of diffusion-controlled processes. Thus, for p-chlorobenzylideneaniline, mentioned previously, the second-order rate constant is calculated to be 1.25×10^9 liter mole^{-1} min^{-1}.

pH about 9–5: The pH dependence of imine base hydrolysis in this area may be ascribed to the reaction of water with the protonated imine [steps (a + b) in (8-88)]. Imines possessing an electron-withdrawing substituent exhibit no change or an increase in hydrolysis rate with increasing acidity, and imines possessing an electron-donating substituent exhibit decreased rates of hydrolysis with increasing acidity. Since the variations in the rates of hydrolysis parallel the conversion of the imine bases to their conjugate acids, as indicated by changes in the ultraviolet spectra of the substrates, the reaction of water with the protonated imine base must become the predominant pathway as the pH is lowered.

pH 4–5: All the imines exist predominantly as the conjugate acids, and the hydrolysis rate again becomes pH-independent (see plateau in profile for *p*-nitro imine at pH 3–4.5). The value of ρ^+ for reaction (b) of (8-88) is $+1.7$, which may be compared to a ρ of 2.0 found by Culbertson for the hydrolysis of fully protonated diphenyl ketimines.[119]

pH below 4: Below pH 4.0 all imine is protonated and the decrease in rate is due to reversal of (b) in (8-88), so that below pH 1.0 the rates of hydrolysis of all the imines except the *p*-methoxy compound are linear with respect to $OH^\ominus$ concentration ($\rho^+ = 2.17$).

Cordes and Jencks were able to establish general-base catalysis in step (8-88b) by acetate ion at three constant pH values between pH 4 and 5. As anticipated, the weaker the amine base the easier is its displacement from the imine by nucleophilic attack. Thus, the first-order rate constant for the attack of water on protonated *p*-chlorobenzylidene-1,1-dimethyl-ethylamine is 1.1 min^{-1}, while the corresponding value for *p*-chloro-benzylideneaniline [117] has been calculated to be $1.58 \times 10^4\ min^{-1}$. This is also shown of course by the provided ρ^+ constants.

2. NITROGEN DERIVATIVE FORMATION WITH ANALOGS OF PYRIDOXAL-5'-PHOSPHATE   Pyridoxal-5'-phosphate is bound to the protein moiety of several enzymes as an imine formed with the ε-amino group of a lysine residue.[120–122] In the initial formation of an imine from an amino acid substrate with the enzyme-bound cofactor, a transimination reaction is apparently involved.[123] The rate constant for the enzymic transimination

(8-95)

[119] J. B. Culbertson, *J. Am. Chem. Soc.* **73,** 4818 (1951).

[120] E. H. Fischer and E. G. Krebs, Abstr. 136th Natl. Meeting Am. Chem. Soc., 24C (1959).

[121] E. H. Fischer, A. B. Kent, and E. R. Snyder, E. G. Krebs, *J. Am. Chem. Soc.* **80,** 2906 (1958).

[122] C. Turano, P. Fasella, P. Vecchini, and A. Giartosio, *Atti. Accad. Nazl. Lincei Rend. Classe Sci. Fis. Mat. Nat.* **30,** 532 (1961).

[123] E. E. Snell and W. T. Jenkins, *J. Cellular Compt. Physiol.* **54,** Suppl. 1, 161 (1959).

reaction has been determined at the single pH of 8.0 to be ca. 10^7 liter mole^{-1} sec^{-1} for glutamic-aspartic transaminase.[124] Almost all "model" studies have been carried out with pyridoxal, pyridoxal-5'-phosphate, and more recently 3-hydroxypyridine-4-aldehyde. Our interests in this section are, therefore, in the mechanisms of imine and nitrogen derivative formation with o-hydroxy-substituted aromatic aldehydes and various analogs of the cofactor or its imines.

French and Bruice [125] have studied the equilibria and rates of imine formation from pyridine-4-aldehyde and a variety of amino acids. This study was designed to be preliminary to the determination of the influence of the 3-hydroxyl group on the equilibria and rates of imine formation through studies with 3-hydroxypyridine-4-aldehyde. The latter substance along with its imines should serve as the most meaningful "models" of the enzyme-bound cofactor.

The following reactions and equilibria were considered for the reaction of pyridine-4-aldehyde with various amino acids:

$$\overset{\oplus}{N}H_3{-}CHR{-}COO^{\ominus} \overset{K_a'}{\rightleftharpoons} NH_2{-}CHR{-}COO^{\ominus} + H_3O^{\oplus}$$
$$(AH) \hspace{4.5cm} (A)$$

$$AH + PCHO \overset{K_e K_a'}{\rightleftharpoons} PCH(OH)NH{-}CHR{-}COO^{\ominus} + H_3O^{\oplus}$$
$$(P) \hspace{4.5cm} (C)$$

$$\overset{1/K_a''}{\rightleftharpoons} PCH(OH)\overset{\oplus}{N}H_2{-}CHR{-}COO^{\ominus}$$
$$(CH^{\oplus})$$

$$\overset{k_1}{\underset{k_{-1}}{\rightleftharpoons}} PCH{=}N{-}CHR{-}COO^{\ominus} + H_3O^{\oplus}$$
$$(I)$$

$$A + PCHO \overset{K_e}{\rightleftharpoons} C \overset{k_2}{\underset{k_{-2}}{\rightleftharpoons}} I + H_2O \hspace{2cm} (8\text{-}96)$$

K_a' and K_a'' are dissociation constants for AH and $CH^{\oplus}$, respectively. The equilibrium constants for imine formation are

$$K_H = K_0 K_a' = K_e K_a' k_1 / k_{-1} K_a'' = [I][H_3O^{\oplus}]/[AH][PCHO] \hspace{1cm} (8\text{-}97)$$

$$K_0 = K_e k_2 / k_{-2} = [I]/[A][PCHO] \hspace{2cm} (8\text{-}98)$$

At low concentrations of A_T (total amino acid concentration) and P_0 (initial aldehyde concentration), where the concentrations of C and $CH^{\oplus}$ are in low steady-state, the second-order rate constants for imine forma-

[124] G. G. Hammes and P. Fasella, *J. Am. Chem. Soc.* **84**, 4644 (1962).
[125] T. C. French and T. C. Bruice, *Biochemistry* **3**, 1589 (1964).

Table 8-6 *

Equilibrium and rate constants for imine formation[a]

Amino acid	Side chain	K_0 (M^{-1})	k_H' (M^{-1} min^{-1})	k_0 (M^{-1} min^{-1})	K_e (M^{-1})	k_1/K_a'' (M^{-1} min^{-1} × 10^{-10})	k_2 (min^{-1})	k_{-1} (M^{-1} min^{-1} × 10^{-7})	k_{-2} (min^{-1})
Leucine	$CH_2CH(CH_3)_2$	531 ± 9	5.82	17.9	1.1	2.0	16	4.1	0.034
Valine	$CH(CH_3)_2$	459 ± 5	3.06	14.4	0.7	1.4	21	2.0	0.031
Arginine·HCl	$(CH_2)_3NHC{=}NH$ $Cl^\ominus NH_3$	403 ± 8	7.08	9.5	2.2	0.44	4	2.4	0.023
Glycine	H	377 ± 8	9.18	28.4	3.8	0.84	7	8.4	0.072
Phenylalanine	$CH_2C_6H_5$	376 ± 17	8.28	9.9	2.7	0.66	4	4.7	0.026
Serine	CH_2OH	319 ± 4	4.86	16.0	0.87	0.5	19	1.5	0.050
Aspartate	$CH_2COO^\ominus$	306 ± 3	5.10	8.6	0.3	5.0	30	4.8	0.03
Glutamate	$CH_2CH_2COO^\ominus$	306 ± 21	6.30	12.2	0.56	2.5	28	4.6	0.040
Asparagine	CH_2CONH_2	300 ± 5	11.1	2.3	0.37	1.4	7	1.8	0.008
Alanine	CH_3	280 ± 14	2.94	19.7	0.86	1.5	23	4.6	0.072
Phenylglycine	C_6H_5	177 ± 18	5.76	4.4	—	—	—	—	—

* Ref. 125.

[a] H_2O, $T = 30°$, $\mu = 1.0$.

tion by the two pathways are given by

$$k'_H = k_1 K'_a K_e / K''_a \quad \text{(i.e., } d[I]/dt = k'_H[AH][PCHO]) \quad (8\text{-}99)$$

$$k_0 = k_2 K_e \quad \text{(i.e., } d[I]/dt = k_0[A][PCHO]) \quad (8\text{-}100)$$

Under these conditions the total second-order rate constant for imine formation is

$$k_f = k'_H \left[\frac{a_H}{K'_a + a_H} \right] + k_0 \left[\frac{K'_a}{K'_a + a_H} \right] \quad \text{(i.e., } d[I]/dt = k_f[A_T][PCHO])$$

$$(8\text{-}101)$$

and the total first-order-rate constant for the reverse direction, hydrolysis of imine, is

$$k_r = k_{-1} a_H + k_{-2} \quad (8\text{-}102)$$

Equilibrium constants for imine formation with pyridine-4-aldehyde and eleven amino acids are listed in Table 8-6. The pH dependence of

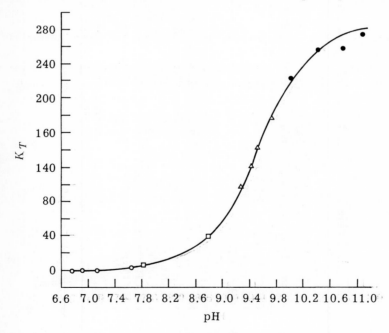

Fig. 8-6 *Apparent equilibrium constants, K_T (M^{-1}), for the formation of PCH=NCH$_2$-COO$^\ominus$ versus pH at 30° and $\mu = 1$. The solid line is a titration curve with its point of inflection at the pK'_a value observed for glycine. Buffers: —O—, potassium phosphate, 0.017 M; —□—, N-ethylmorpholine hydrochloride, 0.05 M; —△—, potassium borate, 0.05 M; —●—, triethylammonium acetate, 0.02 M. (Ref. 125.)*

the apparent equilibrium constant determined at constant pH on the basis of the total concentration of glycine is presented in Fig. 8-6. Inspection of Fig. 8-6 reveals that the plot has the form of a titration curve for the amino group of glycine as anticipated from the relationship $K_0/K_H = 1/K_a'$. The maximum variation of K_0 (leucine, 513; phenylglycine, 177 M^{-1}) is seen to be only 3-fold, showing that the relative thermodynamic stability of α-amino acid imines of pyridine-4-aldehyde is rather insensitive to the bulk of the substituent on the α-carbon.

If it is assumed that no detectable carbinolamine intermediate is present, equation (8-96) may be simplified and expressed as

$$\text{P} + \text{A}_\text{T} \underset{k_r'}{\overset{k_t'}{\rightleftharpoons}} \text{I} \tag{8-103}$$

Under the pseudo-first-order conditions of $[\text{A}_\text{T}] \gg [\text{P}_0]$, it can be shown that the observed pseudo-first-order rate constant and the apparent second-order rate constant of imine formation are related as in (8-104):

$$k_f' = \text{f}(k_{\text{obs}}/[\text{A}_\text{T}]) \tag{8-104}$$

where f is the mole fraction of completion of imine formation at equilibrium.

In Fig. 8-7, k_f' for glycine is plotted against the total concentration of glycine. The various plots represent apparent second-order rate con-

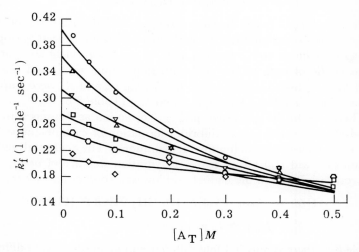

Fig. 8-7 *Plot of apparent second-order rate constants for the formation of 4-pyridylidene-carboxymethylamine* ($PCH\!=\!NCH_2COO^{\ominus}$) *at 30° versus total glycine concentration. The six curves (reading from top to bottom): pH 10.07–10.24; pH 9.67–9.73; pH 9.49–9.56; pH 9.30–9.41; pH 9.15–9.21; pH 8.91–8.98.* (Ref. 125.)

stants obtained at varying pH. The fan of curves that is obtained indicates k'_f to be dependent on both the pH and the concentration of glycine. At high glycine concentration the k'_f values obtained at varying pH become almost pH-independent. The fact that the plots are dependent on $[A_T]$ indicates that scheme (8-103) inadequately describes the experimental data. This suggests that intermediate carbinolamine is present in detectable concentrations at high glycine concentration, and that the expression of (8-103) is true only at infinite dilution in glycine. Extrapolation of the curves of Fig. 8-7 to zero glycine concentration provides k_f, the corrected apparent second-order rate constant at constant pH. In turn, it is apparent that k_f is composed of acid catalyzed and uncatalyzed rate constants due to k'_f's pH dependence. From (8-105) which includes the carbinolamine intermediate, equation (8-106) for the observed pseudo-first-order rate constants may be derived:

$$P + A_T \underset{}{\overset{K_e'}{\rightleftarrows}} C_T \underset{k'_{-3}}{\overset{k_3'}{\rightleftarrows}} I \qquad (8\text{-}105)$$

where $k_{obs} = \bar{K}/f$, and

$$\bar{K} = \frac{k_3' K_e' [A_T]}{1 + K_e' [A_T]} \qquad (8\text{-}106)$$

It follows from (8-104) and (8-106) that:

$$1/k'_f = 1/k_f + (K_e'/k_f)[A_T] \qquad (8\text{-}107)$$

where $k_f = k_3' K_e'$. It can be shown that (8-107) describes the observed kinetics. Moreover intermediate carbinolamine could be seen by stopped-flow spectrophotometry. Plots of $k_f(K_a' + a_H)$ vs. a_H yield straight lines characteristic of each amino acid with slope equal to k'_H and intercept equal to $k_0 K_a'$ (8-101). Values of K_0, K_e, k'_H, k_0, and K_a' were employed in the calculation of k_1/K_a'', k_2, k_{-1} and k_{-2} (Table 8-6).

Therefore, in the pH range $pK_a' \pm 0.6$, amino acid reacts with pyridine-4-aldehyde with pre-equilibrium formation of carbinolamine intermediate, followed by rate-limiting dehydration. The acid catalyzed (k'_H) and uncatalyzed (k_0) terms in the dehydration step are of nearly equal importance. Between the highest and lowest second-order rate constants

$$d[I]/dt = (k_H a_H + k_0)[NH_2\text{---}CH_2\text{---}COO^{\ominus}][PCHO]$$

$$k'_H = k_H a_H \cong k_0 \text{ at } pK_a' \pm 0.6 \qquad (8\text{-}108)$$

(Table 8-6) there is only a 4-fold difference in k'_H and a 12-fold difference in k_0. For most amino acids, $1 < k_0/k'_H < 3$. Phenylalanine closely approaches the conditions for complete insensitivity of k_f to pH, since $k'_H \cong k_0$. Asparagine and phenylglycine are the only amino acids for which $k'_H/k_0 < 1$.   Acid catalyzed imine formation from carbinolamine is equivalent to the acid catalyzed addition of water to imine in the reverse direction, and uncatalyzed imine formation corresponds to the "uncatalyzed" step in imine hydrolysis (8-109).[113]   The pH range investigated in these studies was too high to observe the change to rate-limiting amine

$$C \underset{-H^{\oplus}}{\overset{+H^{\oplus}}{\rightleftharpoons}} CH^{\oplus} \underset{k_{-a}(+H_2O)}{\overset{k_a(-H_2O)}{\rightleftharpoons}} IH^{\oplus} \overset{K_I}{\rightleftharpoons} I + H^{\oplus} \quad \text{(acid catalyzed)}$$

$$C \underset{k_{-b}(+OH^{\ominus})}{\overset{k_b(-OH^{\ominus})}{\rightleftharpoons}} IH^{\oplus} \rightleftharpoons I + H^{\oplus} \quad \text{(uncatalyzed)} \quad (8\text{-}109)$$

attack that generally occurs in slightly acid solution,[117, 118] and too low to observe base-catalyzed dehydration.[112]   No general-acid or general-base catalysis of carbinolamine dehydration by amino acid was detected at the relatively high concentrations of these species that were used in the glycine studies.   The rate of hydrolysis of p-nitrobenzylideneethylamine investigated by Cordes and Jencks [118] (8-110) most closely resembles kinetically pyridylidenecarboxymethylamine, investigated by French and Bruice [125] (8-111), since the electronic effects of the substituent groups, 4-pyridyl and p-nitrophenyl, are similar.[125a]

$$k_{\text{obs}} = 2 \times 10^7 a_H + 0.28 \ (25°) \qquad (8\text{-}110)$$

$$k_{\text{obs}} = 8.4 \times 10^7 a_H + 0.072 \ (30°) \qquad (8\text{-}111)$$

Velick and Vavra [126] have shown that the maximal velocity of glutamic-aspartic transaminase is independent of pH over the range 6–9. The first step in the enzymic reaction is postulated to involve the formation of an imine from free amino acid $[RCH(NH_2)COO^{\ominus}]$ and enzyme-bound cofactor.   Hammes and Fasella [127] have suggested that the same imine may be formed from protonated amino acid $[RCH(NH_3^{\oplus})COO^{\ominus}]$ by way of a rapid intramolecular proton transfer that occurs before imine formation.   If the rate of imine formation depended on free amine alone, the maximal velocity would increase markedly from pH 6 to 9.   This observed pH insensitivity of velocity of enzymic transamination under mildly alkaline conditions may indicate the presence of acid catalyzed and uncatalyzed pathways for enzymic imine formation that are of nearly equal importance.   The observations of the pyridine-4-aldehyde model study are in accord with this suggestion.   Also the fact that the acid catalyzed

[125a] H. S. Mosher, in P. C. Elderfield (ed.) "Heterocyclic Compounds," Wiley, New York, 1950, Vol. I, pp. 408–409.

[126] S. F. Velick and J. Vavra, *J. Biol. Chem.* **237,** 2109 (1962).

[127] G. G. Hammes and P. Fasella, *J. Am. Chem. Soc.* **85,** 3929 (1963).

rates of dehydration (k_1/K_a'') of carbinolamine $(0.4–5 \times 10^{10}\ M^{-1}\ min^{-1})$ are faster than the apparent overall enzymic rate for imine formation with glutamate $(2 \times 10^9\ M^{-1}\ min^{-1})$ [127] suggests that transaminases might dehydrate carbinolamine intermediates by acid catalysis.

Although no general-acid term was observed for carbinolamine dehydration in the presence of high concentrations of AH, intramolecular general-acid catalysis might be favored over intermolecular specific-acid catalysis. The rate constant for acid catalyzed dehydration of carbinolamine is represented formally as k_1/K_a'', where K_a'' is presumed to be the acid dissociation constant for protonated carbinolamine [CH$^\oplus$]. If the maximum rate for protonation of carbinolamine [128] is approximately $2 \times 10^{12}\ M^{-1}\ min^{-1}$, then the maximum velocity for the dehydration of protonated carbinolamine would be ca. 2000 min^{-1} at pH 9.0, assuming the protonation rate-limiting. The apparent pK_a'' for carbinolamine formed from the amino acids studied would then be 6.5–7.5, a value that is much higher than expected for an alcohol (pK_a' = ca. -2),[129] but that is reasonable for the pK_a' of the nitrogen function of a carbinolamine. This suggests that dehydration proceeds by an intramolecular general-acid catalyzed reaction (8-112):

$$(8\text{-}112)$$

The influence of an o-hydroxyl group on the rates and equilibria of imine formation with aromatic aldehydes is of fundamental importance in the understanding of the structural-functional relationship of pyridoxal-5'-phosphate. In studies of the reaction of a variety of nitrogen bases (semicarbazide, hydroxylamine, phenylhydrazine, and p-toluidine) with o- and p-substituted benzaldehydes, the ratios of the overall rate constants (o-/p-) have been found to be greater than one.[130–133] Knorre and Emanuel [131] have suggested that the rate-accelerating effect of the o-CH$_3$O- and o-HO-

$$(8\text{-}113)$$

[128] M. T. Emerson, E. Grunwald, and R. A. Kromhout, *J. Chem. Phys.* **33**, 547 (1960).

[129] E. M. Arnett and J. N. Anderson, *J. Am. Chem. Soc.* **85**, 1542 (1963).

[130] G. Vavon and P. Montheard, *Bull. Soc. Chim. France* **7**, 551 (1940).

[131] D. G. Knorre and N. M. Emanuel, *Dokl. Akad. Nauk SSSR* **91**, 1163 (1953).

[132] O. Bloch-Chaudé, *Compt. Rend.* **239**, 804 (1954).

[133] R. Wolfenden and W. P. Jencks, *J. Am. Chem. Soc.* **83**, 2763 (1961).

substituents is due to hydrogen bonding between the aldehyde hydrogen and the oxygen atom of the substituent. This hypothesis does not explain the greater rate of semicarbazone formation for o-CH$_3$ as compared to p-methylbenzaldehyde (rate ratio is close to unity, however).[133] Wolfenden and Jencks have suggested that the lessened reactivity of p- relative to o-substituted benzaldehyde for electron-donating substituents is due to a greater resonance stabilization of the p-isomer.[133] The influence of electronic effects on the rates of carbinolamine formation and dehydration have already been discussed, although it will be shown subsequently that such effects alone do not explain the function of an o-HO group in imine formation.

One of the first studies of pyridoxal imine formation was that of Folkers and co-workers,[134] who reacted some twenty amino acids as their potassium salts in alcoholic solution with pyridoxal. From the bright yellow solutions of the imines obtained, only potassium N-pyridoxylidene-DL-alanine was sufficiently insoluble for isolation. However, all but two of the other amino acids were shown to be present as their imines by reduction over Pd or Pt to the corresponding pyridoxylamino acids. In contrast, L-cysteine reacted with pyridoxal to give a 4-thiazolidinecarboxylic acid derivative. In this case only a fleeting yellow color of imine was obtained. The study

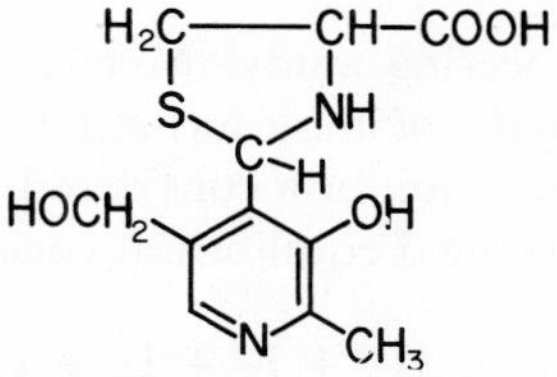

(8-114)

of this reaction has been extended to various vicinal amino thiols.[135, 136] The reaction of DL-histidine with pyridoxal was also found to be abnormal, yielding a white crystalline product which resisted hydrogenation and was assigned a structure [134] corresponding to the reaction product of histidine with formaldehyde.[137]

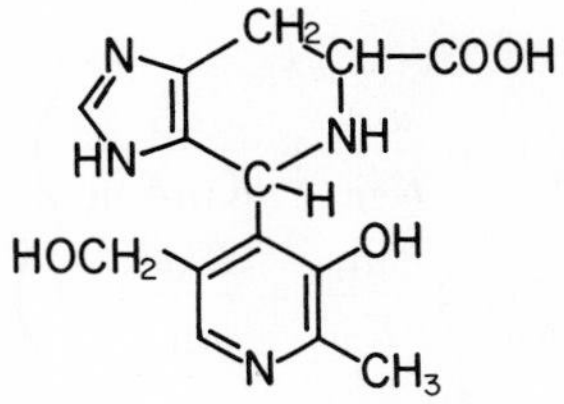

(8-115)

[134] D. Heyl, S. A. Harris, and K. Folkers, *J. Am. Chem. Soc.* **70,** 3429 (1948).

[135] M. V. Buell and R. E. Hansen, *J. Am. Chem. Soc.* **82,** 6042 (1960).

[136] D. Mackay, *Biochim. Biophys. Acta* **73,** 445 (1963); *Arch. Biochem. Biophys.* **99,** 93 (1962).

[137] J. Wellisch, *Biochem. Z.* **49,** 173 (1913).

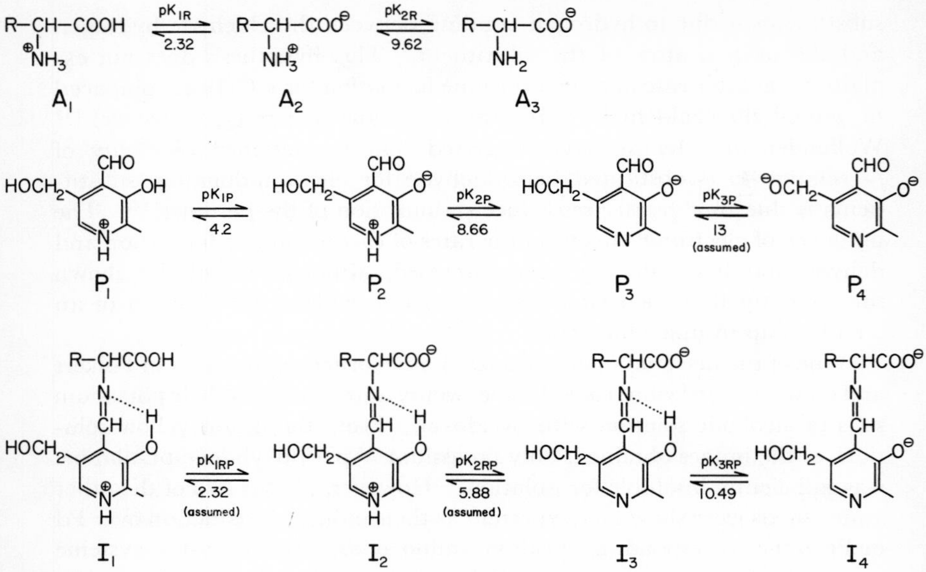

$$A_1 \quad \xrightarrow[2.32]{pK_{1R}} \quad A_2 \quad \xrightarrow[9.62]{pK_{2R}} \quad A_3$$

(R–CH(NH$_3^+$)–COOH)   (R–CH(NH$_3^+$)–COO$^-$)   (R–CH(NH$_2$)–COO$^-$)

$$P_1 \quad \xrightarrow[4.2]{pK_{1P}} \quad P_2 \quad \xrightarrow[8.66]{pK_{2P}} \quad P_3 \quad \xrightarrow[\substack{13 \\ (assumed)}]{pK_{3P}} \quad P_4$$

$$I_1 \quad \xrightarrow[\substack{2.32 \\ (assumed)}]{pK_{1RP}} \quad I_2 \quad \xrightarrow[\substack{5.88 \\ (assumed)}]{pK_{2RP}} \quad I_3 \quad \xrightarrow[10.49]{pK_{3RP}} \quad I_4$$

Fig. 8-8

In an important pioneering study, Metzler [138] provided a detailed analysis of the pH dependence of imine formation for pyridoxal with valine and glycine. The various equilibria considered are provided in Fig. 8-8. Defining K_{pH} as the determined equilibrium constant at any pH,

$$K_{pH} = \frac{[I_1 + I_2 + I_3 + I_4]}{[P_1 + P_2 + P_3 + P_4][A_1 + A_2 + A_3]} \tag{8-116}$$

and defining

$$K = \frac{I_4}{P_3 \cdot A_3} \tag{8-117}$$

it can be shown that

$$\log K_{pH} = \log K - \log \left(1 + \frac{a_H}{K_{2R}} + \frac{a_H^2}{K_{1R}K_{2R}} \right)$$
$$- \log \left(\frac{a_H^2}{K_{1P}K_{2P}} + \frac{a_H}{K_{2P}} + \frac{K_{3P}}{a_H} + 1 \right)$$
$$+ \log \left(\frac{a_H^3}{K_{1RP}K_{2RP}K_{3RP}} + \frac{a_H^2}{K_{2RP}K_{3RP}} + \frac{a_H}{K_{3RP}} + 1 \right) \tag{8-118}$$

[138] D. E. Metzler, *J. Am. Chem. Soc.* **79,** 485 (1957).

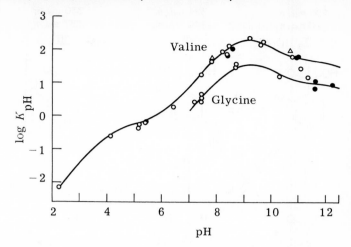

Fig. 8-9   *Variation of the logarithm of the equilibrium constant for imine formation with pH. Upper curve, valine + pyridoxal; lower curve, glycine + pyridoxal. Solid lines are theoretical curves (see text):* ○, *0.1 ionic strength (neglecting dipolar ions);* ●, *higher ionic strength;* △, *sodium ion-free solutions.* (*Ref. 138.*)

In Fig. 8-9 there is plotted the log K_{pH}-pH profiles for imine formation for pyridoxal with glycine and valine. The plot for valine was constructed assuming $K = 1.65$. The values of the various equilibrium constants may then be calculated from K with a knowledge of the different acid dissociation constants (8-117). In Fig. 8-8 it should be noted that the phenolic hydroxyl group is postulated to hydrogen bond with the azomethine nitrogen, although an exact assessment of its influence is complicated by the presence of the *o*-hydroxymethylene substituent.

For model enzyme studies, then, the most informative analog of pyridoxal is probably 3-hydroxypyridine-4-aldehyde. The latter compound possesses the essential phenolic hydroxyl and aldehyde groups but cannot form an internal hemiacetal, as can pyridoxal, and is devoid of the extra ionizations of the phosphate ester group of pyridoxal-5'-phosphate. The spectra and acid dissociation constants of 3-hydroxypyridine-4-aldehyde and its hydrated forms,[139] including also the spectra of several imine derivatives in nonaqueous solutions,[140] have been thoroughly investigated by Martell and co-workers. The water solution equilibrium and absorption maxima of 3-hydroxypyridine-4-aldehyde are provided in Fig. 8-10.

[139] K. Nakamoto and A. E. Martell, *J. Am. Chem. Soc.* **81,** 5863 (1959).
[140] D. Heinert and A. E. Martell, *J. Am. Chem. Soc.* **85,** 183, 188 (1963).

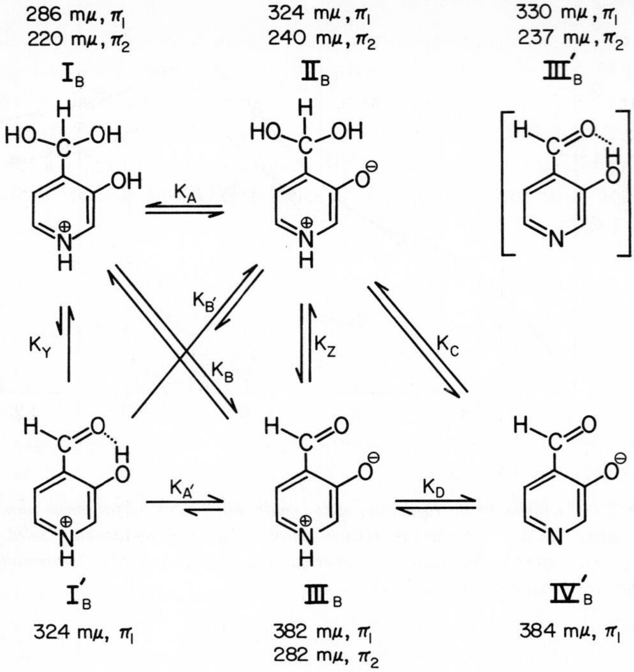

Fig. 8-10   *The solution equilibrium of 3-hydroxypyridine-4-aldehyde.*   *(Ref. 139.)*

It has been suggested by Martell [141] that the imine absorption occurring at ca. 410–425 $m\mu$ for 3-hydroxypyridine-4-aldehyde is due to the presence of keto-enimine in equilibrium with imine (8-119). This proposal is backed

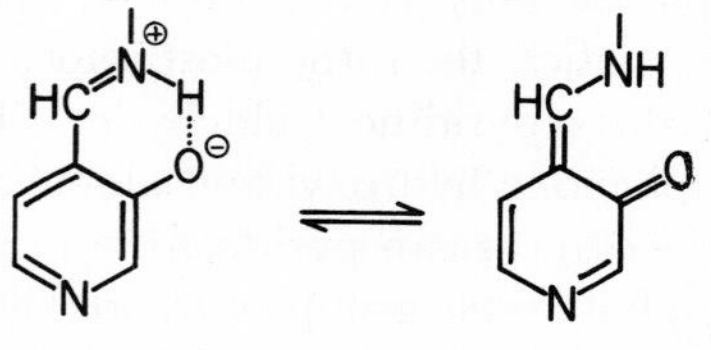

$$(8\text{-}119)$$

by other experimental evidence, including the facts that salicylaldimines also absorb at 410 $m\mu$ and methylation of the phenolic group abolishes the band. [142]   The position of equilibrium of (8-119) appears to be a function

---

[141] A. E. Martell, in E. E. Snell, P. M. Fasella, A. Braunstein, and A. Rossi Fanelli (eds.) "Chemical and Biological Aspects of Pyridoxal Catalysis," Pergamon, New York, 1963, p. 13.

[142] L. N. Ferguson and I. Kelly, *J. Am. Chem. Soc.* **73**, 3707 (1951).

of the pK_a' of the amino group of the parent amine.[143]   More conclusively, Dudek and Holm [144] through the employment of n.m.r. spectroscopy have shown that, in both aliphatic and aromatic systems, imines of *vicinal* hydroxy ketones exist predominantly in the keto-enimine form.   The stability of the keto-enimine form, with its chelated hydrogen-bonded ring, is sufficient to interrupt the aromatic structure of one of the naphthalene rings in (8-120).

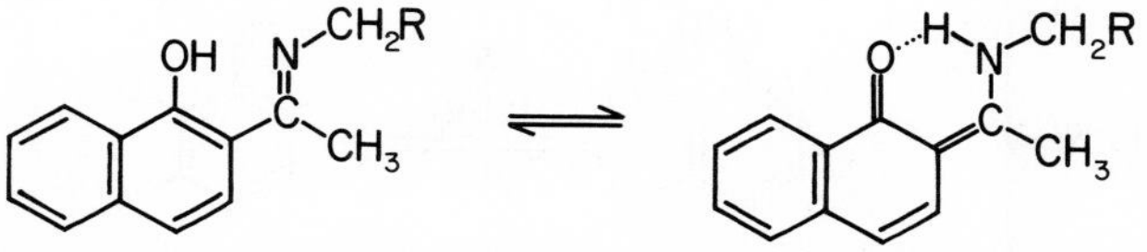

$$(8\text{-}120)$$

French, Auld, and Bruice have determined with 3-hydroxypyridine-4-aldehyde and the three amino acids, glycine, valine, and glutamic acid, the pH profiles for the aldehyde-imine equilibria and rate constants for imine formation and hydrolysis.[145]   The mathematical treatment of the experimental data for the equilibria of imine formation was similar to the general procedures employed by Metzler for pyridoxal.   A comparison of pK_a' and imine formation constants for pyridoxal and 3-hydroxypyridine-4-aldehyde with valine is provided in Fig. 8-11A.

Metzler [138] has attributed the increase in the pK_a' and stability of imines of pyridoxal, with respect to pyridine aldehyde, to hydrogen bonding between the phenolic hydroxyl and azomethine nitrogen.   This effect is more pronounced in the case of 3-hydroxypyridine-4-aldehyde.   For valine the value of K' is 360–850 times greater than K (Fig. 8-11A) because the values of pK_S are 2.6–2.9 units greater than pK_{PCHO}.   Similarly, K'' is 10–28 times greater than K' because $pK_{S\oplus}$ is 1.5 units greater than $pK_{PCHO\oplus}$.

$$K' = K(K_{PCHO}/K_S)$$
$$K'' = K'(K_{PCHO\oplus}/K_{S\oplus})$$

$$(8\text{-}121)$$

The neighboring hydroxyl groups, therefore, may play a role of possible biochemical significance in the stabilization of imine at neutral and slightly acidic pH values.   This can be made more evident by comparing the equilibrium constants for imine formation with pyridine-4-aldehyde (Table 8-6) to those with 3-hydroxypyridine-4-aldehyde (Fig. 8-11A).   In slightly acidic solution no detectable imine is formed with pyridine-4-aldehyde, whereas a significant amount of imine may be formed from 3-hydroxypyridine-4-aldehyde, even below pH 5.   For 3-hydroxypyridine-4-

[143] W. P. Jencks, private communication.
[144] G. O. Dudek and R. H. Holm, *J. Am. Chem. Soc.* **83,** 2099, 3914 (1961).
[145] T. C. French, D. S. Auld, and T. C. Bruice, *Biochemistry* **4,** 77 (1965).

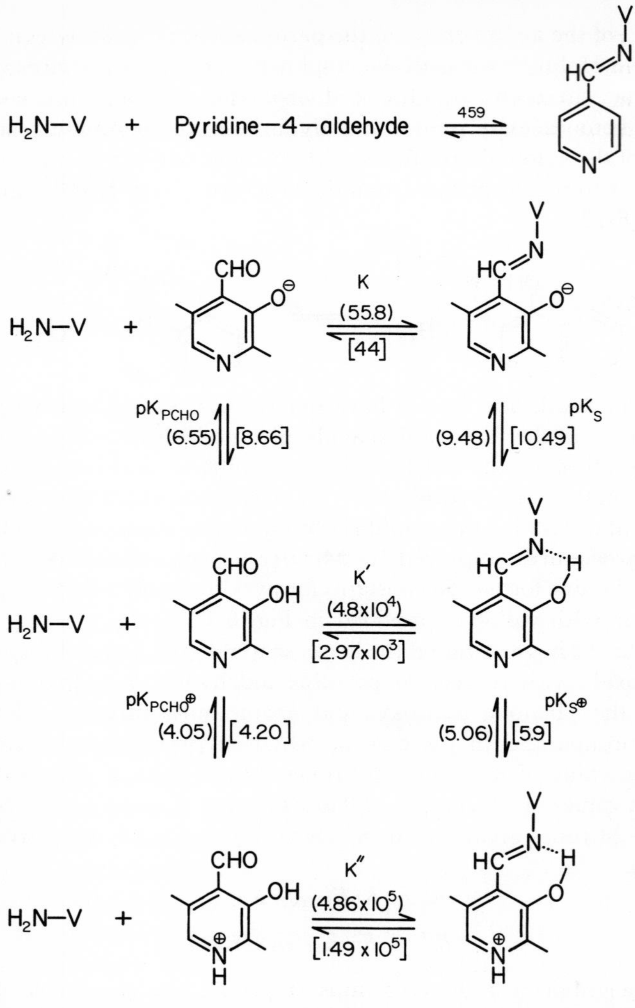

Fig. 8-11A   *Comparison of equilibrium constants for 3-hydroxypyridine-4-aldehyde and pyridoxal* $(H_2N—V = (CH_3)_2CH—CH(NH_2)COO^{\ominus})$. *Values in parentheses refer to 3-hydroxypyridine-4-aldehyde, values in brackets to pyridoxal (data calculated from refs. 145 and 138). Values recorded are pKa's and formation equilibrium constants.*

aldehyde the values of the apparent equilibrium constant rise rapidly with increasing pH in the range 5.5–7.5, where K_{PCHO} is the controlling parameter, and are nearly constant from pH 7.5 to 8.5.   The reason for this plateau behavior is most easily appreciated by inspection of equation (8-122), in which no proton is released on imine formation.   In comparison, over the same pH range a proton must be released when imine is formed from pyridine-4-aldehyde (8-123) and, therefore, the apparent equilibrium constant for pyridine-4-aldehyde increases with increasing pH. This is another manifestation of the influence of the hydrogen bonding.

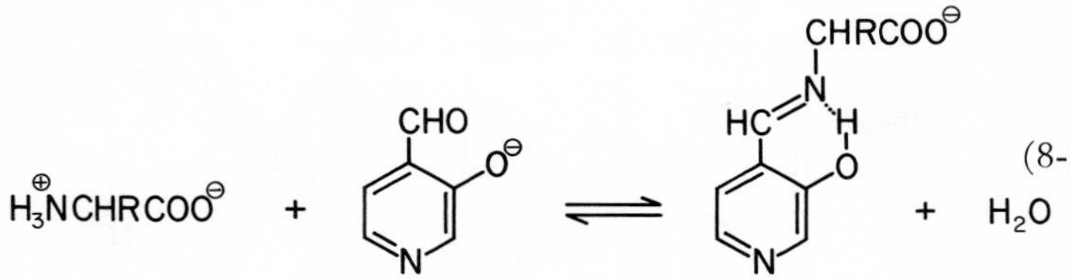

$$(8\text{-}122)$$

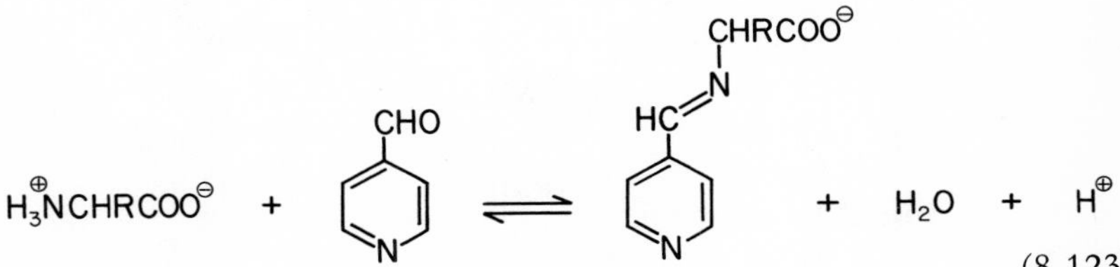

$$(8\text{-}123)$$

For the reaction of 3-hydroxypyridine-4-aldehyde with glycine, valine, and glutamic acid, the second-order rate constant (k_f) for imine formation could be determined from the observed pseudo-first-order rate constant (k_{obs}), the mole fraction of completion of reaction (f), and the total amino acid concentration (A_T) via (8-104).[145] This suggests that there is no kinetically detectable carbinolamine formed and, indeed, k_f is independent of amino acid concentration at the pH's investigated. Moreover if one assumes the existence of a carbinolamine intermediate whose dehydration is rate-limiting, it can be shown that the calculated first-order rate constants for attack of free amine on aldehyde are unreasonably large. Thus, the rate expression for imine formation assumes as a reasonable model the reaction of amino acid as the uncharged amine with the anionic, zwitter-ionic, and cationic forms of aldehyde (as in Fig. 8-11B). The rate constants for imine hydrolysis (k_r) at the same pH as the forward rates can

$$k_f = \left[\frac{K_{AH}}{K_{AH} + a_H}\right]\left[\frac{k_{f,0}K_{PCHO}K_{PCHO\oplus} + k_{f,1}a_H K_{PCHO\oplus} + k_{f,2}a_H^2}{K_{PCHO}K_{PCHO\oplus} + a_H K_{PCHO\oplus} + a_H^2}\right]$$

$$(8\text{-}124)$$

be calculated from (8-125):

$$k_r = \frac{k_f}{K_{pH}}$$

$$(8\text{-}125)$$

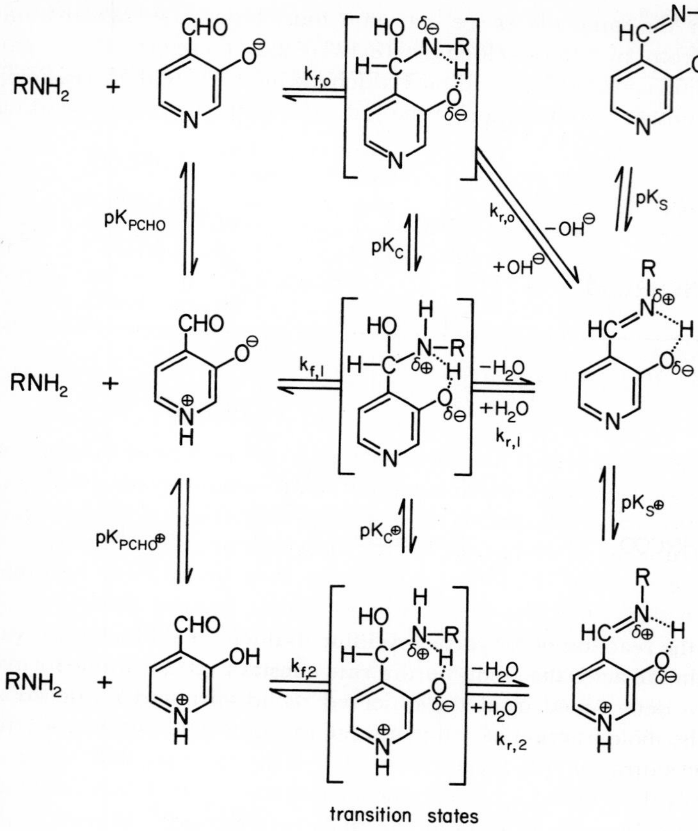

transition states

Fig. 8-11B

The rate expression for the simplest model of imine hydrolysis assumes attack of hydroxide ion on imine, S, and attack of water on imines, S, and $S^{\oplus}$ (8-126);

$$\frac{-d[S_T]}{dt} = k_r[S_T] = k_{r,0}[OH^{\ominus}][S] + k_{r,1}[S] + k_{r,2}[S^{\oplus}]$$

$$k_r = \frac{1.479 \times 10^{-4} k_{r,0} K_S^{\oplus} + k_{r,1} a_H K_S^{\oplus} + k_{r,2} a_H^2}{K_S K_S^{\oplus} + a_H K_S^{\oplus} + a_H^2} \qquad (8-126)$$

Values of k_r and k_f are presented in Table 8-7. Of the terms in equation (8-126), only the first is kinetically ambiguous, being kinetically indistinguishable from attack of water on $S^{\ominus}$. However, the attack by hydroxide ion on S is favored in view of the findings of Jencks and Cordes.[118]   The

Table 8-7 *   *Rate constants for imine formation and hydrolysis with 3-hydroxypyridine-4-aldehyde* [a]

Amino acid	$k_{f,0}$ (liter mole^{-1} min^{-1})	$k_{f,1}$ $\times10^{-4}$ (liter mole^{-1} min^{-1})	$k_{f,2}$ $\times10^{-6}$ (liter mole^{-1} min^{-1})	$k_{r,0}$ $\times10^{-5}$ (liter mole^{-1} min^{-1})	$k_{r,1}$ (min^{-1})	$k_{r,2}$ (min^{-1})
Glycine	200	1.40	5.70	2.75	1.46	19.4
Valine	244	1.56	2.25	1.01	0.310	5.25
Glutamic	80.2	1.12	2.30	1.16	0.805	15.0

* Ref. 145.
[a] H_2O, 30°, $\mu = 1.0$.

most interesting result, already apparent from the kinetic solution, is that the phenolic hydroxyl group intramolecularly catalyzes the dehydration of carbinolamine.   This fact is visualized by comparison of the rate constants for dehydration of the carbinolamine derived from glycine and pyridine-4-aldehyde (7 min^{-1}) to that calculated as a lower limit necessary for experimental detection of the carbinolamine formed from glycine and 3-hydroxypyridine-4-aldehyde (≤ 1800 min^{-1}).   Of the several possible mechanisms for participation of the *o*-hydroxyl group in carbinolamine dehydration, those of (8-127) involving intramolecular general-base catalysis, or ring transmitted expulsion of the hydroxide ion, are worthy of mention.[145a]

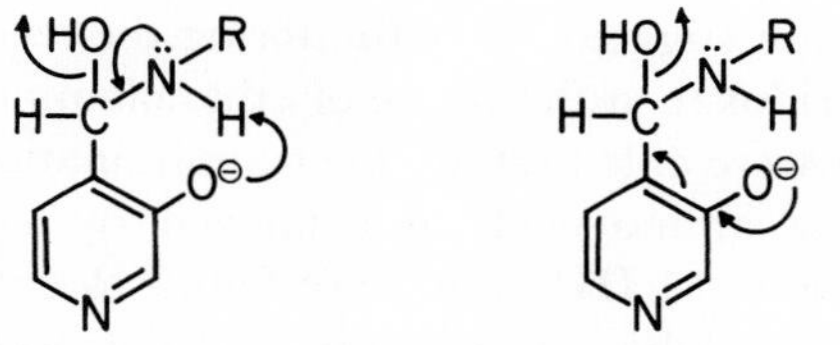

(8-127)

B. Transamination

1. METAL ION CATALYSIS   *a. Pyridoxal and pyridoxal-5′-phosphate* The transamination reaction noted by Braunstein [146] and Cohen [147] to be mediated in enzymic reactions by pyridoxal was first reproduced in a pyridoxal model system by Snell.[148]   Employing both chemical assay and bioassay of products, Snell was able to show that when pyridoxal and

[145a] R. L. Reeves [*J. Org. Chem.* **30**, 3129 (1965)] has recently corroborated the finding that the *o*-hydroxyl group catalyzes imine formation.
[146] A. E. Braunstein, *Enzymologia* **7**, 25 (1939).
[147] P. P. Cohen, *Biochem. J.* **33**, 1478 (1939).
[148] E. E. Snell, *J. Am. Chem. Soc.* **67**, 194 (1945).

glutamic acid or, alternatively, pyridoxamine and α-ketoglutaric acid were autoclaved together a transamination reaction occurred. A large excess of amino acid or keto acid was necessary to drive the reaction to completion (8-128).

$$\begin{array}{c}
\text{H}_2\text{N}-\text{CH}-\text{COOH} \\
| \\
\text{CH}_2-\text{CH}_2\text{COOH}
\end{array}
\quad + \quad
\text{HOH}_2\text{C} \underset{\text{N}}{\overset{\text{CHO}}{\bigcirc}} \overset{\text{OH}}{\underset{\text{CH}_3}{}}
\quad \rightleftharpoons$$

(8-128)

$$\begin{array}{c}
\text{O}=\text{C}-\text{COOH} \\
| \\
\text{CH}_2-\text{CH}_2\,\text{COOH}
\end{array}
\quad + \quad
\text{HOH}_2\text{C} \underset{\text{N}}{\overset{\text{CH}_2\text{NH}_2}{\bigcirc}} \overset{\text{OH}}{\underset{\text{CH}_3}{}}$$

The transamination of pyridoxal was then extended to a number of amino acids and shown to be general. Whereas glutamic acid and lysine reacted readily, methionine, phenylalanine, valine, cysteine, and glycine were less reactive, while proline, hydroxyproline, serine, and β-alanine were inactive. This order is similar to that previously noted for the transamination of glyoxylic acid. Also, as in the case of transamination with glyoxylic acid, the reaction was found to be reversible and did not occur with concomitant decarboxylation.

Since the addition of chelating agents such as citrate and EDTA slowed down the reaction, the influence of metal ions on the transamination reaction was investigated.[149] Monitoring the reaction by converting the remaining pyridoxal to the imine of ethanolamine ($\lambda_{\max} \sim 365$ mμ), Snell and Metzler were able to study the transamination of pyridoxal with a large number of amino acids as catalyzed by metal ions. At 100° Cu(II), Fe(III), and Al(III) salts were found to catalyze the reaction. Substitution in the β-carbon of the amino acid decreased the rate of transamination, in the order $\text{CH}_3 \approx \text{OH} > \text{C}_6\text{H}_5$. In the case of glutamic acid plus pyridoxal or α-ketoglutaric acid plus pyridoxamine, the same equilibrium value was approached with various concentrations of metal ion, carbonyl compound, and pyridoxamine.

The reversible [150] transamination of the phosphorylated cofactor pyridoxal phosphate by glutamic acid [151] was found to be catalyzed by

[149] D. E. Metzler and E. E. Snell, *J. Am. Chem. Soc.* **74,** 979 (1952).

[150] W. W. Umbreit, D. J. O'Kane, and I. C. Gunsalus, *J. Biol. Chem.* **176,** 629 (1948).

[151] J. C. Rabinowitz and E. E. Snell, *J. Biol. Chem.* **169,** 643 (1947).

Table 8-8 * *The comparative activities of metal ions in catalysis of transamination between pyridoxamine and α-ketoglutaric acid*

Metal ion	pH optimum	Relative rate (100°)
Ga(II)	4.3	114
Cu(II)	4.8	100
Al(III)	4.8	85
Fe(II)	4.8	61
Fe(III)	4.8	53
Zn(II)	7.0	50
In(III)	4.3	41
Ni(II)	8.0	38
Co(II)	7.0	26
Sc(III)	6.0	20
(none)	5.0	3

* Ref. 154.

Cu(II) (other metals forming insoluble precipitates) with the equilibrium [149] lying farther toward the side of pyridoxamine phosphate than in the case of pyridoxal. The ability of pyridoxal [152, 153] but not pyridoxal phosphate to form an internal hemiacetal may account for the apparent greater thermodynamic stability of pyridoxal as compared to pyridoxal phosphate in the transamination reaction.

The effect of various metal ions on the rate of the reaction (8-129):

Pyridoxamine + α-ketoglutaric acid → pyridoxal + glutamic acid

(8-129)

has been investigated. [154] At low metal ion concentrations (100°) the rate was found to be proportional to the metal ion concentration. At higher concentrations the rate increases but not proportionately to metal ion concentration, and at still higher concentrations may decrease. In the range where the rate is proportional to metal ion concentration, the relative rates (based on Cu(II) at 100°) and pH optima shown in Table 8-8 were obtained.

[152] D. Heyl, E. Luz, S. A. Harris, and K. Folkers, *J. Am. Chem. Soc.* **73,** 3430 (1951).
[153] E. T. Stiller, J. C. Keresztesy, and J. R. Stevens, *J. Am. Chem. Soc.* **61,** 1237 (1939).
[154] J. B. Longenecker and E. E. Snell, *J. Am. Chem. Soc.* **79,** 142 (1957).

On the basis of the above studies, Snell and Metzler propose the mechanism of the transamination reaction involving pyridoxal cofactors to be as in (8-130).[155, 156] The metal ion was suggested to function by (a) stabilizing the intermediate imine, (b) providing a planar conjugated system, and (c) increasing the inductive effect away from the α-carbon and thereby increasing the acidity of this carbon. The main driving force for the reaction would be expected to be the stabilization of the transition state for carbanion formation via charge delocalization through a conjugated system. It is interesting to note that, in the enzymic pyridoxal-catalyzed transamination between alanine and α-ketoglutaric acid, exchange of protons for $D^{\oplus}$ of solvent D_2O occurs in the β-position of the amino acid as well as in the α-position.[157] Exchange of the proton in the α-position is expected in II $\rightarrow$ III of (8-130), and loss of a β-proton from III would be

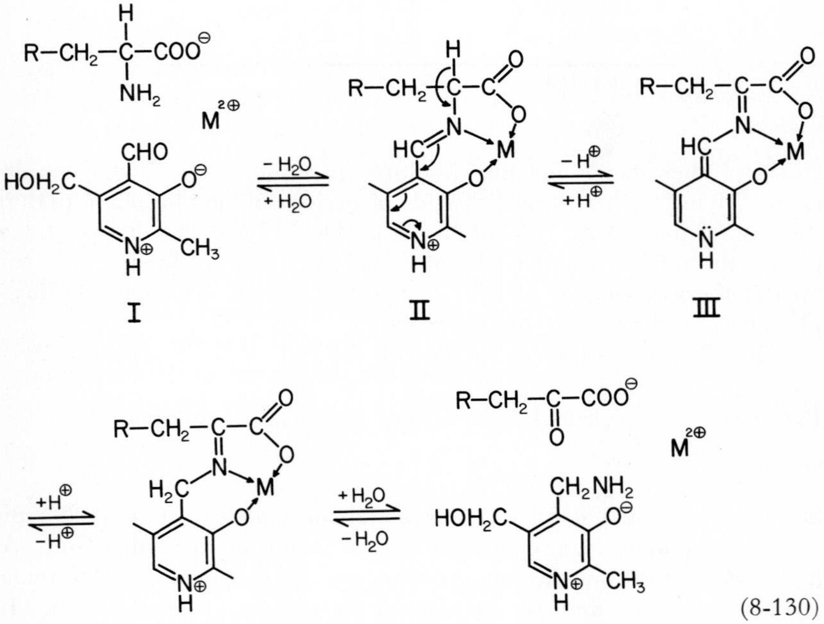

$$(8\text{-}130)$$

favored since the resultant intermediate carbanion would form the terminal end of a conjugated system. No evidence exists for the formation of III as a discrete chemical species in model reactions. The slowly forming 505-mμ absorbing species, obtained from the initial ES complex of D-alanine and serine transhydroxymethylase by loss of a proton, has been

[155] D. E. Metzler, M. Ikawa and E. E. Snell, *J. Am. Chem. Soc.*, **76**, 648 (1954).
[156] See also A. E. Braunstein, *Advan. Protein Chem.*, **3**, 1 (1947).
[157] T. Oshima and N. Tamiya, *Biochem. J.*, **78**, 116 (1961).

suggested to have the structure of III (in which a proton replaces the metal ion).[157a]

Solid chelate salts of ethylenediamine and pyridoxal, similar to those formed from salicylaldehyde with Cu(II), Ni(II), and Mg(II), were isolated by Baddiley,[158] who also reported the isolation of a solid tyrosine-Cu(II)-pyridoxal complex. Baddiley assigned a structure to the tyrosine complex similar to that formed from ethylenediamine and pyridoxal, and proposed that the transamination reaction occurred via the mechanism (8-131). Eichhorn and Dawes,[159] utilizing the pyruvic acid, Ni(II), and

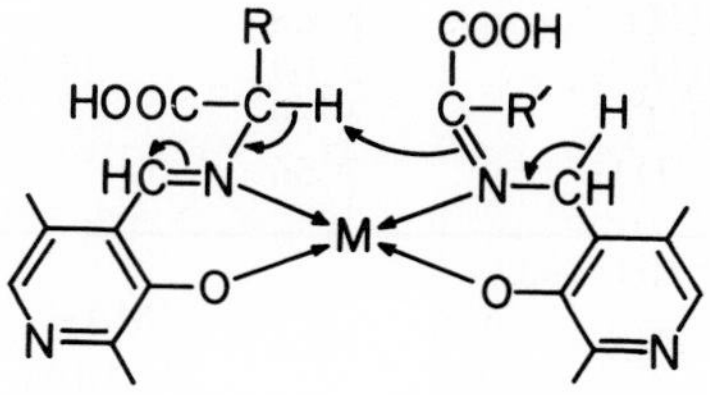

(8-131)

pyridoxamine system showed that its solution spectral characteristics changed upon standing to that of the complex Ni(II), alanine, and pyridoxal. The transamination presumably occurred through a 2:2:1 Ni(II)-imine complex (ratio of amino acid:pyridoxal:metal ion).

The contribution of the imine nitrogen as a ligand group to the formation of chelates has been investigated by Eichhorn and Bailar.[160, 161] The complex of Cu(II) with bis(thiophenal)ethylenediamine (8-132) formed instantly. As might have been anticipated on the basis of the positive nature of Cu(II), the resultant complex hydrolyzed with comparative ease. These results suggest that the formation of the pyridoxylidene metal complex may also serve to increase the rate of Schiff base hydrolysis as well as formation.

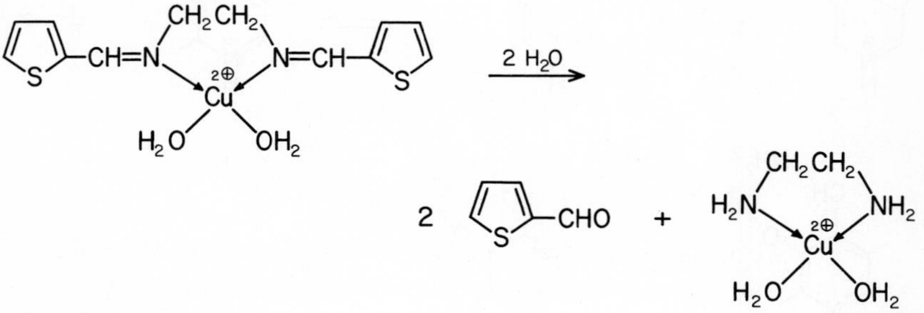

(8-132)

[157a] L. V. Schirch and W. T. Jenkins, J. Biol. Chem., 239, 3801 (1964).
[158] J. Baddiley, Nature 170, 711 (1952).
[159] G. L. Eichhorn and J. W. Dawes, J. Am. Chem. Soc. 76, 5663 (1954).
[160] G. L. Eichhorn and J. C. Bailar, J. Am. Chem. Soc. 75, 2905 (1953).
[161] G. L. Eichhorn and I. M. Trachtenberg, J. Am. Chem. Soc. 76, 5183 (1954).

Table 8-9 *   *First and second formation*
constants for pyridoxa-
mine chelates [a]

Metal ion	log K_{MA}	log K_{MA_2}
Fe(III)	>15	—
Fe(II)	—	—
Cu(II)	10.20	5.77
Ni(II)	6.00	4.92
Zn(II)	5.68	—
Co(II)	5.09	4.51
Cd(II)	4.59	—
Mn(II)	3.56	—

* Ref. 162.

[a] $K_{MA} = \dfrac{[MA]}{[M][A]}; \; K_{MA_2} = \dfrac{[MA_2]}{[MA][A]}.$

It is also of interest to note that chelate formation occurs with pyridox-amine alone and various metal ions. Gustafson and Martell [162] have measured the first and second formation constants (K_{MA} and K_{MA_2}) for various such chelates, and the values are listed in Table 8-9. From their titration data the sequence (8-133) of dissociations was suggested for pyridoxamine in the presence of Cu(II). It follows that there is a reversal of the acid dissociation steps for pyridoxamine when a stable chelate compound can be formed. Martell [162] points out that although the formation

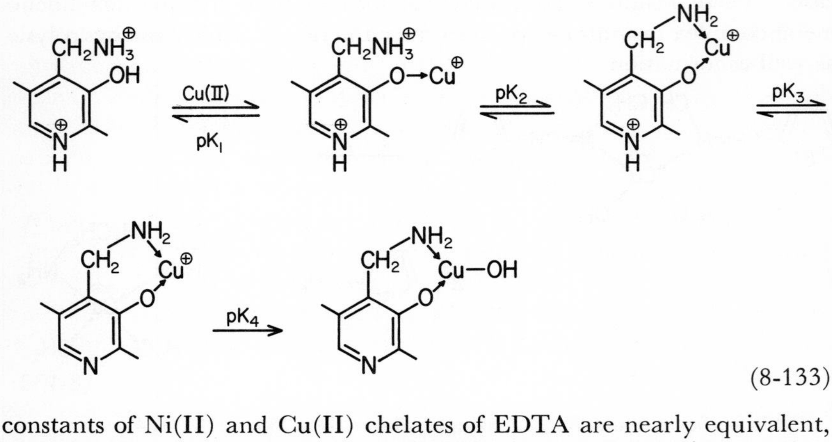

$$(8\text{-}133)$$

constants of Ni(II) and Cu(II) chelates of EDTA are nearly equivalent, pyridoxamine is highly selective for Cu(II) by a factor of 10^4.

[162] R. L. Gustafson and A. E. Martell, *Arch. Biochem. Biophys.* **68**, 485 (1957).

Recent investigations of the imine chelates have revealed much about their properties and stoichiometry. Christensen,[163] in studying the Fe(III)-(pyr-val)$_2$ complex in aqueous solution, found a short but measurable time interval needed for the exchange of the Fe(III) in the complex with Fe^{59}(III) of the structurally similar ornithine complex. In contrast, the Mn(II) and Cu(II) pyridoxylidenevaline chelates exchanged their metal ions with radioactive metal ion pools too rapidly for feasible study. Titration of the Fe(III) and Cu(II) chelates indicated that the pK_a' of the pyridoxal nitrogen was shifted downward by 3 pH units or more, presumably because of linkage of the metal to the phenolic oxygen. No shift in pK_a' was observed for Mn(II) and Ni(II) chelates, indicating the absence of extensive linkage between the metal ion and phenolic oxygen. This interpretation, however, is refuted by the X-ray studies on pyridoxylidenevaline-Mn(II) by Hoard et al.,[164] which establish strong complexing between metal ion and phenolic oxygen in a planar chelate structure. In both investigations 2:2:1 complexes were employed.

Metzler and co-workers [165] continued the examination of the solution chemistry of the pyridoxal-valine complexes by employing the specific λ_{max} values for the various species in solution. The three species have separate absorption maximum, i.e., 315 mμ for pyridoxal, 380 mμ for chelates, and 420 mμ for imines. The investigation was carried out under conditions of low free pyridoxylidenevaline and high metal ion concentration in order to study the formation of the 1:1:1 species only. For Zn(II) the log of the formation constant (K), calculated for the conversion of Zn(II) and pyridoxylidenevaline imine to 1:1:1 chelate in all ionic forms, when plotted vs. pH, gave a linear plot of slope $\sim$1 below pH 6 and of slope zero above pH 7.0. This indicates that a single proton is taken up by the chelate (pK_a' = 6.5) below pH 6 and that the form of chelate above pH 7.0 is neutral. The 2:2:1 complex of Christensen, when dissolved in water, was found to quickly break down to give the equilibrium distribution of free pyridoxal and 1:1:1 chelate. Thus Metzler [165] concluded that the chelates of the 2:2:1 type are of low stability compared to that of the 1:1:1 complexes. Furthermore, the 2:2:1 complexes would not exist except at high concentrations of ligand. Interestingly, the pK_a' values of the ring nitrogen of the 1:1:1 chelates ($\sim$5.5–6.5) are close to those for the hydrogen-bonded forms of the imines ($\sim$5.9). However, in the 2:2:1 chelates this pK_a' may be as high [165] as 8 or as low [164] as 4.

[163] H. N. Christensen, J. Am. Chem. Soc. **79,** 4073 (1957).

[164] E. Willstadter, T. A. Hamor, and J. L. Hoard, J. Am. Chem. Soc. **85,** 1205 (1963).

[165] L. Davis, F. Roddy, and D. E. Metzler, J. Am. Chem. Soc. **83,** 127 (1961).

The absolute structures of the metal imine complexes are of special interest, particularly the determination of the structure of the catalytically important specie(s) in transamination. However, the methods usually employed to ascertain the composition of a metal complex in solution by continuous variation [166] leave much to be desired. A particular objection is that the catalytically important species may not be the dominant one in solution and therefore not observable by the continuous variation method. The isolation of a particular chelate salt merely indicates that it has a low solubility, and not that it is the predominant form in solution or that it is catalytically important. Employing the techniques of paper chromatography, paper electrophoresis, and continuous variation to separate intermediates and to establish the structure of complexes in solution, Fasella et al.[167] found direct proof for the interconversion of imines as the mechanism of the transamination reaction involving Al(III), pyridoxal,

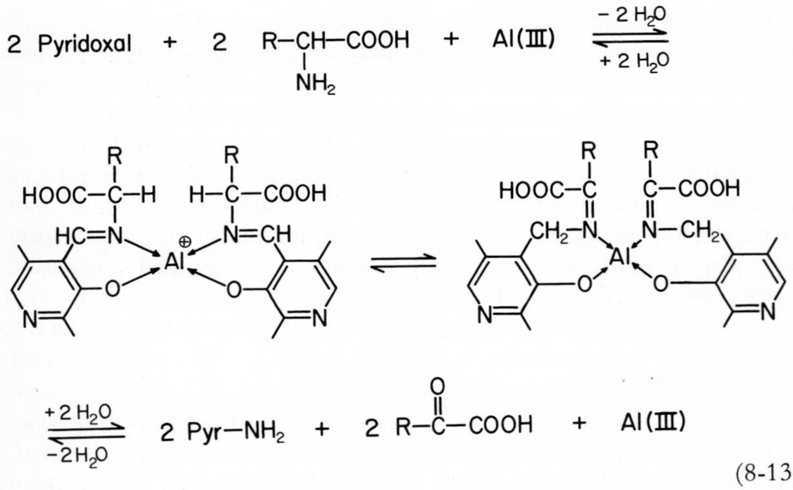

$$(8\text{-}134)$$

and glycine (8-134). The complexes C_1 and C_2 could be separated. The following evidence was offered to support the proposed structures and their intermediacy in the reaction: (1) formation of either C_1 or C_2 requires the presence of the three indicated reactants; (2) C_1 and C_2 are devoid of CHO or NH_2 groups; (3) C_1 is formed first when the initial reaction mixture contains pyridoxal, amino acid, and Al(III); C_2 is formed first when the initial reaction mixture contains Al(III), pyruvate, and pyridoxamine;

[166] P. Job, *Compt. Rend.* **180**, 928 (1925).

[167] P. Fasella, H. Lis, N. Siliprandi, and C. Baglioni, *Biochim. Biophys. Acta* **23**, 417 (1957).

Table 8-10 *   *Optical specificity of transamination between alanine and α-ketoglutaric acid*

Alanine isomer	$T°$	mM	α	$[\alpha]_D^{30}$	L-Glutamate (%)	D-Glutamate (%)
D	100	4.1	−0.026	−1.3	47.7	52.3
L	100	4.5	0.20	+1.0	51.6	48.4
DL	100	4:0	0.00	0.0	50.0	50.0
D	37	6.6	−0.037	−2.0	46.7	53.3
L	37	6.2	+0.027	+1.4	52.3	47.7

* Ref. 168.

(4) the structures of C_1 and C_2 can be inferred from continuous variation studies; and (5) in the initial phase of the reaction the transamination rate was found to be proportional to the concentration of C_1. Continuous variation studies by these workers also indicated that the Al(III)-glycine complex (unlike the alanine complex) to be of the 1:1:1 type, although the same objections to continuous variation studies mentioned above are pertinent.

An interesting consequence of chelation is the phenomenon of stereo-chemical induction in the metal-ion mediated transamination reaction of optically active amino acid.[168] For this purpose D- or L-alanine and α-ketoglutaric acid were allowed to react with pyridoxal and Cu(II) in sterile solutions at 100°. The glutamic acid formed was isolated by absorption on a sulfonated polystyrene resin (Dowex 50). The recovered glutamic acid was assayed by the ninhydrin method and the optical rotation measured with a Rudolph polarimeter. The results are recorded in Table 8-10. Approximately the same results were obtained in the trans-amination reaction with phenylalanine. Although the observed rotations are quite small they apparently exceed the recorded duplications of the readings (0.002°). The observation of an asymmetric induction supports the presence of an asymmetric center in the intermediate chelated imine. This necessity would be met by either the structures suggested by Baddiley[158] or Fasella[167] or a complex containing imine, metal, and amino acid in a 1:1:1 ratio. The imine complex possessing two centers of asymmetry could exist as diastereoisomers. Apparently that of structure LL is favored over the one of structure DL(8-135).

[168] J. B. Longenecker and E. E. Snell, *Proc. Natl. Acad. Sci. U.S.* **42,** 221 (1956).

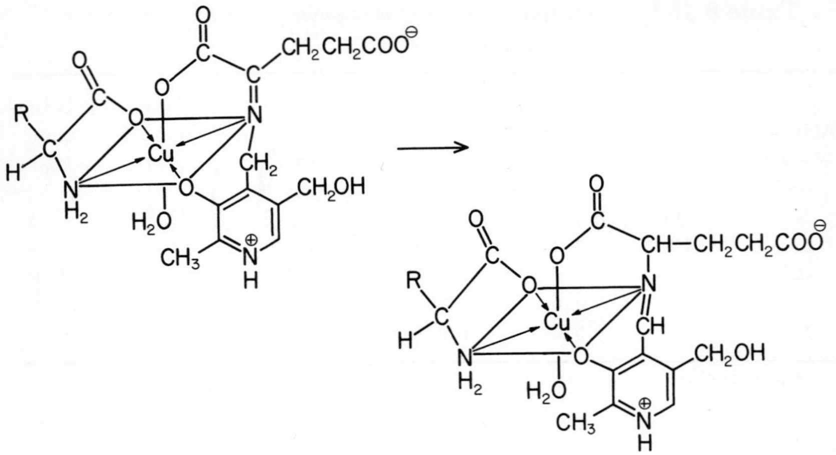

(8-135)

Precedents for stereochemical control of reaction rates through formation of asymmetric chelates exist in the literature. An interesting example is recorded by Richtmyer and Hudson [169] in the Fehling reaction of aldoses. Employing alkaline Cu(II) tartrate solutions, d-altrose was oxidized by d-tartrate reagent only 61.8% as fast as l-altrose. Conversely, using the Cu(II) reagent prepared from l-tartaric acid, the l-altrose had only 61.0% the rate of oxidation as its d-isomer. Thus, the d-sugar with the d-reagent showed the same reactivity as the l-sugar with the l-reagent. Similar results were obtained with the arabinoses. For both the altroses and the arabinoses, oxidation with reagent containing racemic tartaric acid gave values between those found for the d-reagent and those for the l-reagent. No difference in the rates of oxidation of d- and l-altrose or d- and l-arabinose was noted with the symmetrical noncomplexed ferricyanide ion. Shibata and co-workers [170] record that the l-form of chloro-ammino-bis-ethylenediamine cobaltic bromide oxidizes L-3,4-dihydroxy-phenylalanine faster than the D-isomer. Similarly the D-form of the chelate oxidizes the D-form of the amino acid more rapidly than it does the L-form. (Other examples of stereochemical induction may be found in Chapter 4.)

[169] N. K. Richtmyer and C. S. Hudson, *J. Am. Chem. Soc.* **58**, 2540 (1936).

[170] Y. Shibata and R. Tsuchida, *Bull. Chem. Soc. Japan* **4**, 142 (1929); Y. Shibata, Y. Tanaka, and S. Goda, *Bull. Chem. Soc. Japan* **6**, 210 (1931); Y. Shibata and K. Sakai, *J. Chem. Soc. Japan* **55**, 841 (1934); Y. Shibata and K. Shibata, "Katalytische Wirkungen der Metallokomplexverbindungen," Tokyo Tsukiji Type Foundry Ltd., Tokyo, 1936.

b. Salicylaldehyde and related compounds Shortly after elucidation of the structure of pyridoxal,[171–173] its synthesis,[174–176] and suggestions as to its mechanism of action, Pfeiffer, Offermann, and Werner [177] studied reactions of substituted bis(salicylaldimine) chelates of Cu(II) and Ni(II) as model systems. It was found impossible to prepare optically active Cu(II) chelates from imines of optically active amino acid esters with salicylaldehyde. In each case rapid racemization of the optically active carbon was observed. Also, both Cu(II) and Ni(II) chelates, when

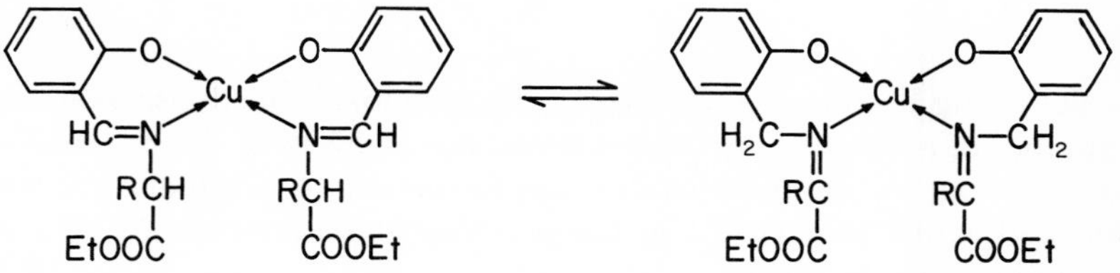

(8-136)

allowed to remain in solution in the presence of air, gave rise to the corresponding bis(salicylaldimino) complexes (8-137). Since air was required, an oxidative deamination reaction was postulated. Similarly the elimina-

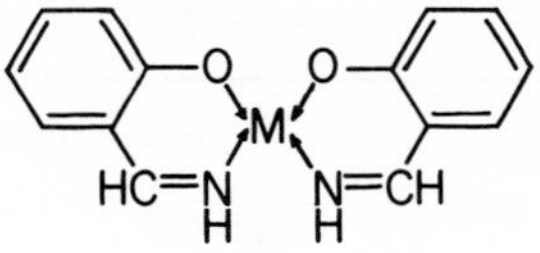

(8-137)

tion of hydrogen sulfide from cysteine under alkaline conditions in the presence of lead oxide was found by Clarke and Inouye [178] to be enhanced by aldehyde and in particular by salicylaldehyde. (Model reactions with pyridoxal derivatives involving this type of elimination will be considered in a later portion of this chapter.)

[171] R. Kuhn and G. Wendt, *Ber.* **71**, 1534 (1938).

[172] R. Kuhn, H. Andersag, K. Westphal, and G. Wendt, *Ber.* **72**, 309 (1939).

[173] R. Kuhn and G. Wendt, *Ber.* **72**, 305, 311 (1939).

[174] S. A. Harris and K. Folkers, *Science* **89**, 347 (1939); *J. Am. Chem. Soc.* **61**, 1245 (1939).

[175] R. Kuhn, K. Westphal, G. Wendt, and O. Westphal, *Naturwissenschaften* **27**, 469 (1939).

[176] S. Morii and K. Makino, *Enzymologia* **7**, 385 (1939).

[177] P. Pfeiffer, W. Offermann, and H. Werner, *J. Prakt. Chem.* **159**, 313 (1942).

[178] H. T. Clarke and J. M. Inouye, *J. Biol. Chem.* **89**, 399 (1930).

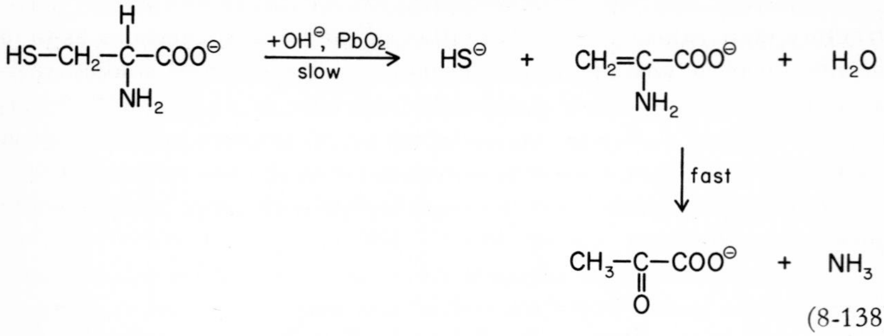

$$\underset{\substack{|\\ NH_2}}{\overset{\substack{H\\|}}{HS-CH_2-C-COO^{\ominus}}} \xrightarrow[\text{slow}]{+OH^{\ominus},\ PbO_2} HS^{\ominus} + \underset{\substack{|\\NH_2}}{CH_2=C-COO^{\ominus}} + H_2O$$

$$\downarrow \text{fast}$$

$$\underset{\substack{\|\\O}}{CH_3-C-COO^{\ominus}} + NH_3 \tag{8-138}$$

Following his initial model work with pyridoxal, Snell also examined a number of aromatic o-hydroxyaldehydes as catalysts of the transamination reaction.[179] In these studies the formation of α-ketoglutaric acid from L-glutamic acid (100°) in the presence and absence of Al(III) was determined (Table 8-11).

From the results of Table 8-11 it was postulated that the 4-nitro group, in either the absence or presence of metal ions, could play the same role as the pyridine nitrogen of pyridoxal by acting as an electron sink. The reaction of serine and cysteine with 4-nitrosalicylaldehyde was found to proceed analogously to pyridoxal, in that both pyruvic acid and NH_3

Table 8-11 *

| | α-Ketoglutarate formation | | | |
| | pH 4–5 | | pH 11.7–12.3 | |
Aldehyde	With Al(III)	Without Al(III)	With Al(III)	Without Al(III)
Salicylaldehyde		$--$	$--$	$--$
4-NO$_2$-salicylaldehyde	$++++$	$++$	$++++$	$++++$
6-NO$_2$-salicylaldehyde	$++++$		$-$	$-$
5-NO$_2$-salicylaldehyde	$-$		$-$	$-$
3,5-di-NO$_2$-salicylaldehyde	$-$		$-$	$-$
4-Cl-salicylaldehyde	$-$		$-$	$-$
4-COOH-salicylaldehyde	$-$		$-$	$-$
4-OH-salicylaldehyde	$-$		$-$	$-$
2-OH-naphthaldehyde	$-$		$-$	$-$
4-NO$_2$-benzaldehyde	$+$	$+$		

* Ref. 179.

---

[179] M. Ikawa and E. E. Snell, *J. Am. Chem. Soc.* **76,** 653 (1954).

were liberated from the former and H_2S was formed from the latter. However, the reaction of 4-nitrosalicylaldehyde with glutamic acid is actually not a transamination reaction, but an oxidative deamination reaction in which the nitro group acts as an oxidizing agent. The nitro group is reduced during the course of the reaction and therefore 4-nitro-salicylaldehyde does not serve as a reasonable model for pyridoxal in the transamination reaction, and the experiments with other aldehydes are equally inconclusive.

2. GENERAL-ACID AND GENERAL-BASE CATALYSIS OF TRANSAMINATION
The metal-ion promotion of the transamination of pyridoxal by α-amino acids may or may not be of biochemical significance. It would appear that a number of highly or partially purified pyridoxal phosphate-requiring enzymes do not need addition of metal ions for full activity,[180–183] and in at least one instance a highly purified, fully active transaminase has been shown to be devoid of metal ions.[184]

In alcohol solutions, where imine formation is greatly favored, metal ions are not required for the model transamination reactions of pyridoxal.[185] The yellow color of the imine of pyridoxamine and α-ketoglutaric acid develops almost instantaneously [185] in ethanol. In light of the fact that pyridoxal-glutamate aldimine is destroyed rapidly in water,[186] Matsuo was able to quench the ethanol reaction and thereby follow its progress. When aliquots of an ethanol solution of pyridoxamine-α-ketoglutarate ketimine were assayed with time (by quenching in water at alkaline pH and assaying pyridoxal at 390 mμ), the prototropic shift to form the aldimine was established to occur in the absence of metal ion. Furthermore, when an α-keto acid in absolute ethanol was incubated with pyridoxamine, an amino acid corresponding to the keto acid employed was detected by paper chromatography. In other experiments the transamination of α-ketoglutaric acid by alanine under the influence of pyridoxal was established. All these reactions were carried out at room temperature in a solvent classically known to favor imine formation and in the absence of metal ions.

In an aqueous medium, the slow step in the transamination reaction must involve the interconversion of aldimine and ketimine. As a pseudo-

---

[180] W. T. Jenkins and I. W. Sizer, *J. Am. Chem. Soc.* **79**, 2655 (1957); *J. Biol. Chem.* **234**, 1179 (1959); *J. Biol. Chem.* **235**, 620 (1960); W. T. Jenkins, D. A. Yphantis, and I. W. Sizer, *J. Biol. Chem.* **234**, 51 (1959).

[181] Y. Matsuo and D. M. Greenberg, *J. Biol. Chem.* **230**, 545, 561 (1958).

[182] N. Alexander and D. M. Greenberg, *J. Biol. Chem.* **220**, 775 (1956).

[183] M. A. Karasek and D. M. Greenberg, *J. Biol. Chem.* **227**, 191 (1957).

[184] P. Fasella, G. G. Hammes, and B. Vallee, *Biochim. Biophys. Acta* **65**, 142 (1962).

[185] Y. Matsuo, *J. Am. Chem. Soc.* **79**, 2016 (1957).

[186] H. Brandenberger and P. P. Cohen, *Helv. Chim. Acta* **36**, 549 (1953).

acid, the ionization of the proton on the α-carbon would be anticipated to be a slow process requiring enzymic catalysis. Three mechanisms may be written for the catalysis of the interconversion of simple imines (8-139, 8-140, 8-141). Mechanism (8-139) involves the abstraction of a proton

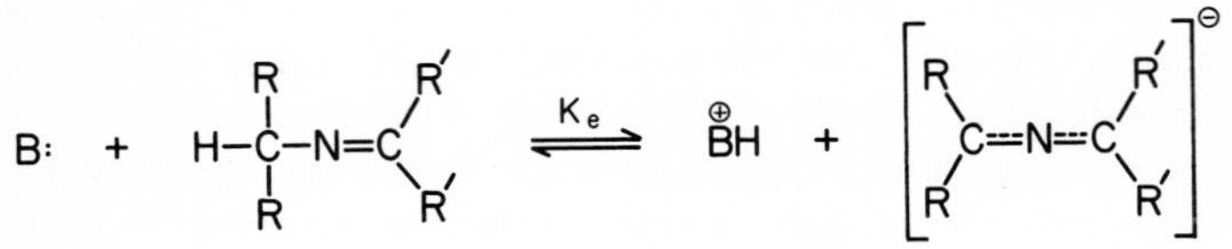

$$\text{B:} + \overset{R}{\underset{R}{\text{H--C--N=C}}}\overset{R'}{\underset{R'}{\Big\langle}} \underset{}{\overset{K_e}{\rightleftharpoons}} \overset{\oplus}{\text{BH}} + \left[\overset{R}{\underset{R}{\text{C==N==C}}}\overset{R'}{\underset{R'}{\Big\langle}}\right]^{\ominus}$$

I

$$\left[\overset{R}{\underset{R}{\text{C==N==C}}}\overset{R'}{\underset{R'}{\Big\langle}}\right]^{\ominus} + \overset{\oplus}{\text{BH}} \overset{K_f}{\rightleftharpoons} \overset{R}{\underset{R}{\text{C=N--C--H}}}\overset{R'}{\underset{R'}{}} + \text{B:}$$

II

$$(8\text{-}139)$$

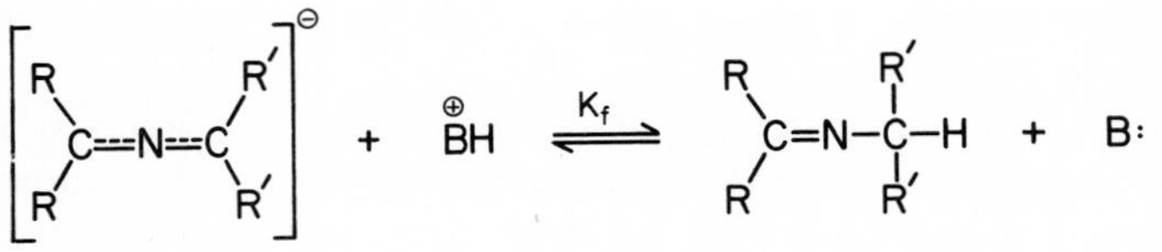

$$\overset{R}{\underset{R}{\text{H--C--N=C}}}\overset{R'}{\underset{R'}{\Big\langle}} + \overset{\oplus}{\text{H}_3\text{O}} \overset{K_a}{\rightleftharpoons} \overset{R}{\underset{R}{\text{H--C--NH=C}}}\overset{R'}{\underset{R'}{\Big\langle}} + \text{H}_2\text{O}$$

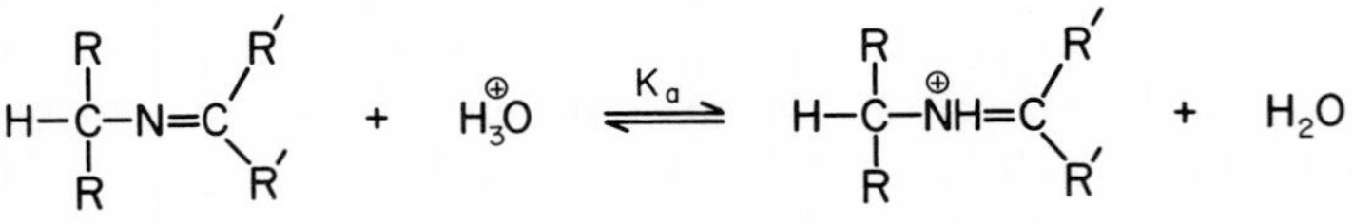

I

$$(8\text{-}140)$$

$$\text{B:} + \overset{R}{\underset{R}{\text{H--C--NH=C}}}\overset{R'}{\underset{R'}{\Big\langle}} \underset{k_{-r}}{\overset{k_r}{\rightleftharpoons}} \overset{\oplus}{\text{BH}} + \overset{R}{\underset{R}{\text{C=N--C--H}}}\overset{R'}{\underset{R'}{}}$$

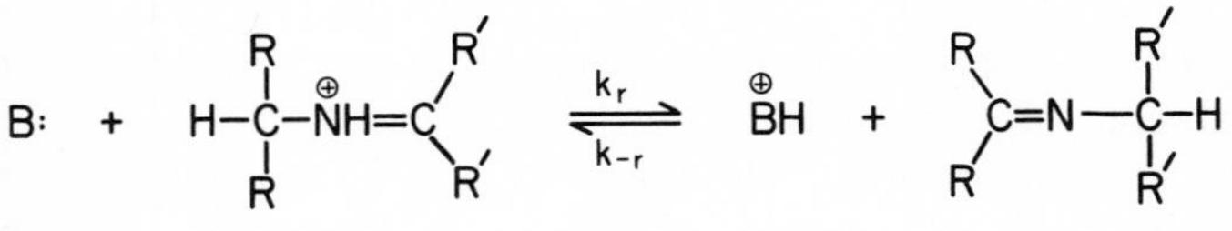

II

from imine to yield a resonance-stabilized anion, which could then be protonated to yield an equilibrium mixture of imines I and II. This mechanism may be ruled out for enzymic catalysis on the basis that the pK'_a of the C—H bond is so great that the concentration of the intermediate anion would be controlled only by the pH of the medium and not by the

$$\text{B:} \;+\; \underset{I}{H-\overset{\overset{\displaystyle R}{|}}{\underset{\underset{\displaystyle R}{|}}{C}}-N=\overset{\displaystyle R'}{\underset{\displaystyle R'}{C}} \;+\; \overset{\oplus}{HB} \;\longrightarrow\; \left[\overset{\oplus\delta}{B}\text{----}H\text{----}\overset{\overset{\displaystyle R}{|}}{\underset{\underset{\displaystyle R}{|}}{C}}=\!=\!=N=\!=\!=\overset{\overset{\displaystyle R'}{|}}{\underset{\underset{\displaystyle R'}{|}}{C}}\text{----}H\text{----}\overset{\oplus\delta}{B} \right]$$

$$\longrightarrow\; \overset{\oplus}{BH} \;+\; \underset{II}{\overset{\displaystyle R}{\underset{\displaystyle R}{C}}=N-\overset{\overset{\displaystyle R'}{|}}{\underset{\underset{\displaystyle R'}{|}}{C}}-H} \;+\; \text{:B}$$

$$(8\text{-}141)$$

concentration of feebly basic species present at the enzyme active site. Mechanism (8-139) was originally favored by Ingold [187] but was discarded on the basis that the rate of racemization of an optically active imine was found to be identical with the rate of isomerization as measured by other means. These studies were carried out in methanol, employing $CH_3O^{\ominus}$ as base catalyst.[187, 188a] Recently, Cram and Guthrie[188b] have shown that a number of imines isomerize via (8-139) (*t*-butoxide base in *t*-butanol solvent). Mechanisms (8-140) and (8-141) do not involve the formation of an intermediate anionic species. Mechanism (8-140) refers to a specific-acid general-base catalysis, and mechanism (8-141) to a concerted general-acid general-base catalysis. The latter two processes are those anticipated to be of importance in the enzymic reactions. In the studies of Ingold and Cram, strongly basic species (alkoxide ion) and very weak acid species (alcohol) were employed, so that mechanisms such as (8-140) and (8-141) would not be anticipated. Blake et al.[189] determined that L-protioalanine transaminates with pyridoxal 2.4 times faster than L-deuterioalanine. This result is of course in accord with the abstraction of the α-hydrogen in the rate-determining step. For the one transaminase that has been kinetically investigated the rate-determining step would also appear to be a prototropic shift, leading to the interconversion of imines. Hammes and Fasella, employing the temperature-jump method, found six relaxation times for glutamic-aspartic transaminase.[124] In (8-142) E_L is the aldehyde form of the enzyme, E_M the amino form,

[187] C. K. Ingold, C. W. Shoppee, and J. F. Thorpe, *J. Chem. Soc.* 1477 (1926).

[188a] S. K. Hsü, C. K. Ingold, and C. L. Wilson, *J. Chem. Soc.* 1778 (1935).

[188b] D. J. Cram and R. D. Guthrie, *J. Am. Chem. Soc.* **87**, 397 (1965).

[189] M. I. Blake, F. P. Siegel, J. J. Katz, and M. Kilpatrick, Jr., *J. Am. Chem. Soc.* **85**, 294 (1963).

$$E_L + As \underset{>5\times10^3 \text{ sec}^{-1}}{\overset{>10^7 \; M^{-1}\text{sec}^{-1}}{\rightleftharpoons}} X_1 \underset{26 \text{ sec}^{-1}}{\overset{80 \text{ sec}^{-1}}{\rightleftharpoons}} X_2 \underset{1.4\times10^2 \text{ sec}^{-1}}{\overset{7\times10^7 \; M^{-1}\text{sec}^{-1}}{\rightleftharpoons}} Oa + E_M$$

$$Kg + E_M \underset{70 \text{ sec}^{-1}}{\overset{2\times10^7 \; M^{-1}\text{sec}^{-1}}{\rightleftharpoons}} Y_2 \underset{61 \text{ sec}^{-1}}{\overset{30 \text{ sec}^{-1}}{\rightleftharpoons}} Y_1 \underset{3.3\times10^7 \; M^{-1}\text{sec}^{-1}}{\overset{2.8\times10^3 \text{ sec}^{-1}}{\rightleftharpoons}} Gm + E_L$$

$$(8\text{-}142)$$

Oa is oxaloacetate, As is aspartate, Kg is ketoglutarate, Gm is glutamate, and the X's and Y's are reaction intermediates. Inspection of the rate constants of (8-142) reveals that the rate-determining steps involve the interconversion of intermediates, which were suggested as imines on the basis of their absorption spectra. The magnitude of the rate constants suggests a diffusion-controlled formation of imine. However, the rate constants for the interconversion of intermediate imines are of magnitudes encountered in acid-base catalysis.[190] Thus it might appear that the enzymic reaction has been shown to occur via imine interconversion. But it has been found that buffers interact with the enzyme and thus could be responsible for the relaxation times observed. These buffer interactions have precluded determinations of relaxation times at pH values other than 8.0.[191] One must therefore question the values for the rate constants obtained at the single pH reported. Nevertheless the abstraction of the proton and concomitant isomerization of imines must be the primary role of the protein. In the model experiments considered so far, the role of the metal ion must be to facilitate the proton abstraction by stabilization of the transition state via electron withdrawal.

Studies of general-base and general-acid catalysis of the kinetically important prototropic shift in the transamination reaction were initiated independently by Banks, Diamantis, and Vernon [192] and by Bruice and Topping.[193] The investigations of these two groups marked the first instances of attempts to apply kinetic methods to model transamination reactions. Unlike the investigations of metal-ion promotion of the transamination reaction, which were carried out at 100°, these investigations were made at ambient temperatures.

Banks, Diamantis, and Vernon examined the reaction between pyridoxamine and pyruvic acid in water at 25° over the pH range 7–10 The reverse reaction was also investigated but in less detail. Initial rates were followed spectrophotometrically to only ca. 6% completion of reaction. It was established that imine formation proceeded in a pre-equilibrium step followed by the rate-limiting prototropic shift. On the basis of

[190] M. Eigen and G. G. Hammes, *Advan. Enzymol.* **25**, 1 (1963).

[191] G. G. Hammes and P. Fasella, private communication.

[192] B. E. C. Banks, A. A. Diamantis, and C. A. Vernon, *J. Chem. Soc.* 4235 (1961).

[193] T. C. Bruice and R. M. Topping, *J. Am. Chem. Soc.* **85**, 1480, 1488, 1493 (1963).

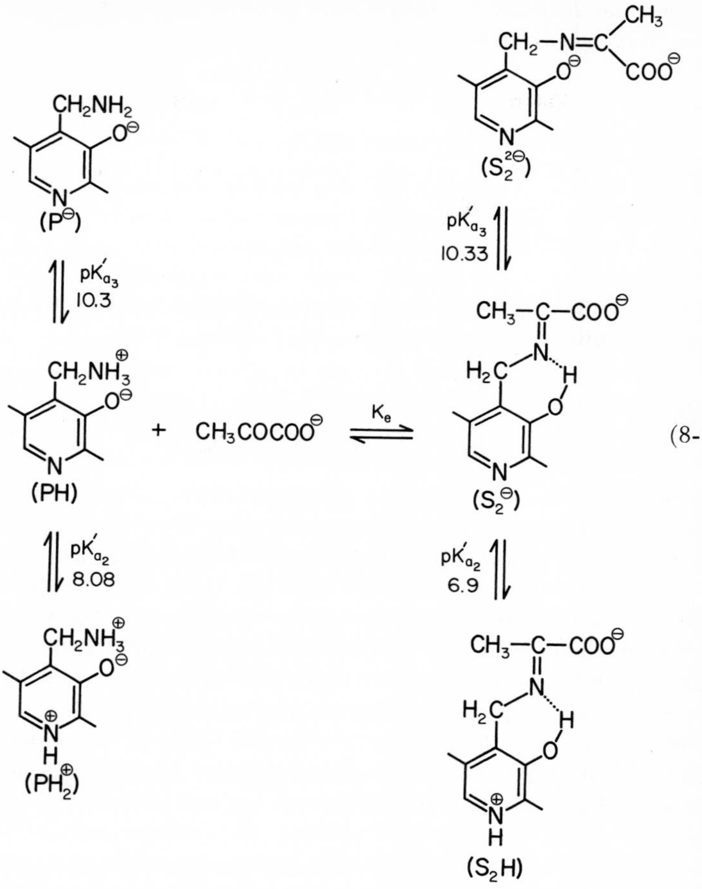

$$\text{(8-143)}$$

determined dissociation constants and spectral data, the scheme (8-143) was proposed to represent the predominant forms of keto acid, pyridoxamine, and imine.

For the general reaction (8-144) it can be shown that the reciprocal of

$$\text{Pyridoxamine} + \text{pyruvic acid} \overset{K_e}{\rightleftarrows} \text{S} \overset{k_2}{\rightarrow} \text{products} \qquad \text{(8-144)}$$

the initial reaction rate is related to the first-order constant k_2 and the initial concentrations $(P_0 + K_0)$ of the substrates by

$$\frac{1}{v} = \frac{1}{[K_0]} \left[\frac{1}{K_e k_2 [P_0]} + \frac{1}{k_2} \right] + \frac{1}{k_2 [P_0]} \qquad \text{(8-145)}$$

It follows that K_e is related to the slope (S) and intercept (I) of a plot of $1/v$ vs. $(K_0)^{-1}$ at constant P_0 by

$$K_e = [(S/I) - [P_0]]^{-1} \tag{8-146}$$

Analysis of the results by equations (8-145) and (8-146) provided the same values of K_e but different values of k_2, at constant pH but varying buffer concentration. Expressing k_2 as

$$k_2 = k_2^0 + k_2'[B] \tag{8-147}$$

where k_2^0 is the rate constant in the absence of buffer and k_2' is the catalytic constant for buffer of concentration [B], it follows that

$$v = \alpha(k_2^0 + k_2'[B]) \tag{8-148}$$

Therefore,

$$(v_0/v)_{K_0} = k_2^0/(k_2^0 + k_2'[B]) \tag{8-149}$$

where v and v_0 are the velocities at buffer concentrations [B] and zero buffer, respectively, and pyruvate concentration $[K_0]$. By employing the equations provided above the kinetic results for each pH were analyzed and are tabulated in Table 8-12. On the basis that k_2' increases in approximately the same proportion as the conjugate acid of the N,N-di-methylglycine buffer, it was proposed that general-acid catalysis of the prototropic shift was involved. At pH 10.0 product analysis indicated that the reaction of pyridoxal and alanine produces pyridoxamine and pyruvic acid in the molar ratio 2:1, rather than in the equal molar amounts required of a transamination reaction. No explanation of this result was offered, tending to weaken the above analysis, especially the assigning of values to k_2'.

Bruice and Topping [193] studied the transamination reaction between pyridoxal and α-aminophenylacetic acid, which proceeded in two phases (8-150). The amino acid choice was based on the anticipated stabilization

Table 8-12 *

pH	Buffer	K_0	$10^2\, k_2^0$ (sec^{-1})	$10^4\, k_2'$ (liter mole^{-1} sec^{-1})
6.85	Phosphate	1.0	71.0	—
8.0	Triethanolamine	8.2	0.95	0.18
9.0	N,N-Dimethylglycine	9.8	0.95	1.98
9.8	Carbonate-bicarbonate	9.9	—	—
10.0	N,N-Dimethylglycine	8.9	0.59	0.92

* Ref. 192.

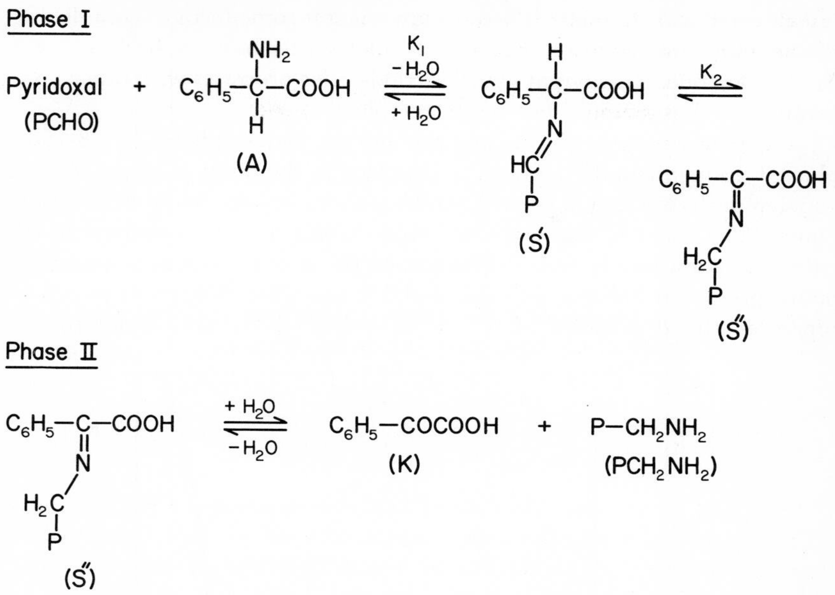

Phase I

Pyridoxal + $C_6H_5-\underset{\underset{H}{|}}{\overset{\overset{NH_2}{|}}{C}}-COOH$ $\underset{+H_2O}{\overset{\substack{K_1 \\ -H_2O}}{\rightleftharpoons}}$ (A) $C_6H_5-\underset{\underset{N}{|}}{\overset{\overset{H}{|}}{C}}-COOH$ $\overset{K_2}{\rightleftharpoons}$ (S′)

Phase II

$C_6H_5-\underset{\underset{N}{||}}{C}-COOH$ $\underset{-H_2O}{\overset{+H_2O}{\rightleftharpoons}}$ $C_6H_5-COCOOH$ (K) $+$ $P-CH_2NH_2$ (PCH$_2$NH$_2$)

(S″)

where P = substituted pyridine ring of pyridoxal in its various ionic forms.

(8-150)

of the transition state for proton abstraction from the α-position of S′ by electron delocalization to the benzene ring, and the expectancy that the conjugation of the benzene ring to the imine double bond of S″ should increase the latter's stability and allow its spectrophotometric detection. Reactions were followed at 30° in water at constant ionic strength both spectrophotometrically (PCHO at 395 mμ and S″ at 245 mμ) and by conversion of S″ plus K to 2-hydroxy-3-phenylquinoxaline (8-151). In the

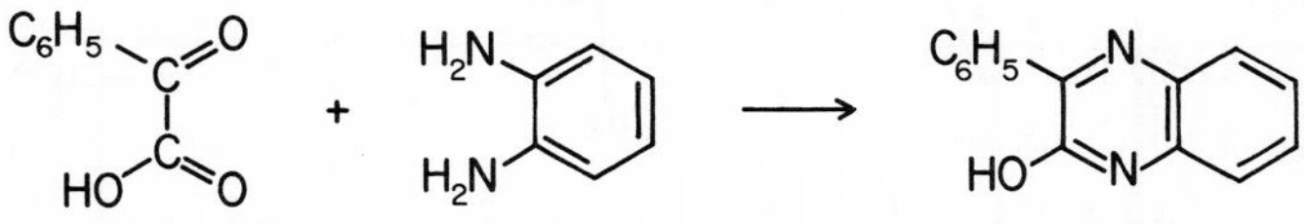

(8-151)

spectrophotometric studies, reactants were at $10^{-4}\ M$. The reaction at these concentrations proceeded in imidazole buffer but not in the presence of morpholine, carbonate, or borate buffers or in the absence of buffer (pH 8.2). In the quinoxaline experiments, reactants were present at much higher concentration and imidazole, morpholine, and carbonate buffer acted as catalysts.   These results suggest some form of complexing of the imidazole to reactants, which allows this base to perform as a catalyst at concentrations at which second-order processes with other non-complexing bases would not be detectable.

The reactions were shown to occur in two distinct phases (see 8-150), phase I going virtually to equilibrium prior to the onset of phase II.   It was demonstrated that in phase I, which is characterized by three isosbestic points (282 mμ, 307 mμ, and 348 mμ), PCHO + A is converted to S$''$ with S$'$ at a low steady state.   The second phase of the reaction (isosbestic points present at 260 mμ, 310 mμ, and 350 mμ) (Fig. 8-12) was shown to represent the conversion of S$''$ to K + PCH$_2$NH$_2$ and simultaneous

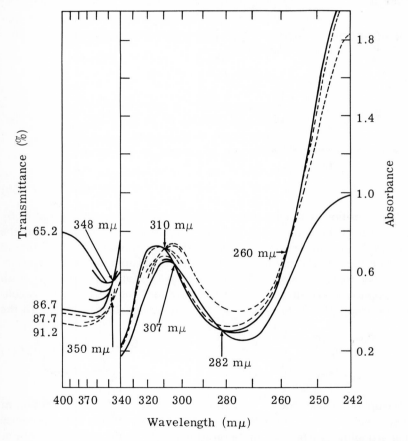

Fig. 8-12   *Spectral–time study for the reaction of pyridoxal (10^{-4} M) with α-amino-phenylacetic acid (2×10^{-4} M) in the presence of imidazole (1.8 M) in water at pH 8.61 and 30°.   The tracing shows the shape of the absorbance curves and isosbestic points for the first (———) and second (------) phases of the reaction.   (Ref. 193.)*

attainment of equilibrium between all components [i.e., PCHO + A $\rightleftarrows$ S′(steady state) $\rightleftarrows$ K + PCH₂NH₂]. At the end of phase I, the reaction had proceeded to only 55% completion. The rate constants for disappearance of PCHO and appearance of S″ plus K, determined spectrophotometrically and also by conversion of S″ plus K to the quinoxaline derivative, were identical. In addition the disappearance of 1 mole of PCHO was accompanied by the appearance of 1 mole of S″, except at very low buffer concentration where PCHO disappeared faster than the appearance of S″.

Because phase I contains the rate-limiting prototropic shift this initial portion of the reaction received major consideration. The approach to equilibrium in phase I was found to follow apparent first-order kinetics at all pH's, the first-order rate constant being a function of the buffer concentration (Fig. 8-13A and B). The adherence to first-order kinetics provides evidence for (8-152):

$$\text{PCHO} + \text{A} \underset{k_{-1}}{\overset{k_1}{\rightleftarrows}} \text{S}' \underset{k_{-2}}{\overset{k_2}{\rightleftarrows}} \text{S}'' \tag{8-152}$$

For (8-152) the rate of appearance of S″ is given by (8-153), where at t_0, PCHO = a, A = b; and at any time (t), S″ = x, PCHO = $a - x$, and A = $b - x$, since S″ is at low steady state [K_1 and K_2 are the equilibrium

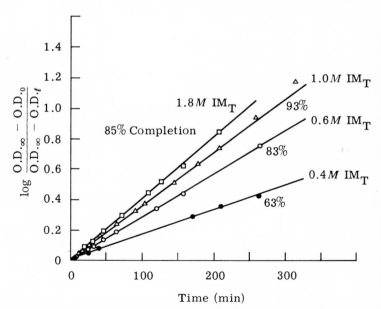

Fig. 8-13A   *First-order plots for the appearance of S″ (as determined at 246 mμ) in the presence of varying concentrations of imidazole.   (Pyridoxal and α-aminophenylacetic acid initially at 10⁻⁴ M; pH 8.61; μ = 0.05; 30°.)   (Ref. 193.)*

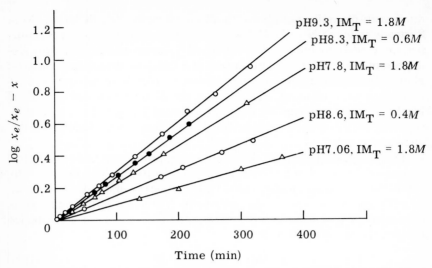

Fig. 8-13B   *First-order plots for the appearance of S" at various pH values.*   (*Pyridoxal and α-aminophenylacetic acid initially at 10^{-4} M; 30°.*)   (*Ref. 193.*)

constants provided in (8-150)]:

$$\frac{dS''}{dt} = \frac{dx}{dt} = k_2[S'] - k_{-2}[S'']$$

$$S' = K_1[\text{PCHO}][A]$$

$$\frac{dx}{dt} = k_2 K_1[\text{PCHO}][A] - k_{-2}[S'']$$

$$\frac{dx}{dt} = k_2 K_1 \left[(a - x)(b - x) - \frac{(x)}{K_1 K_2} \right] \qquad (8\text{-}153)$$

Integration of (8-153) provides (8-154).

$$k_2 K_1 t = \frac{1}{2c} \ln\left(\frac{c - \mu}{c + \mu}\right) + B$$

where $$c = \left[\frac{a^2 + b^2 + 2\left(\dfrac{(a + b)}{K_1 K_2} - ab\right) + \dfrac{1}{(K_1 K_2)^2}}{4} \right]^{1/2} \qquad (8\text{-}154)$$

$$\mu = x - \left[\frac{a + b + 1/(K_1 K_2)}{2} \right]$$

$$B = \frac{-1}{2c} \ln\left(\frac{c - \mu + x}{c + \mu - x}\right)$$

In (8-154), $(c - \mu)$ changes by only $\sim 20\%$ while $(c + \mu)$ goes to zero at t_∞, so that the term $\ln[(c - \mu)/(c + \mu)]$ approaches very closely the general form $\ln(ya - x)/(a - x)$ where $ya \gg x$, resulting in a close approximation to first-order kinetics. The observed first-order rate constant for attainment of equilibrium is then

$$k_{\text{obs}} \cong \frac{k_2 K_1 2c}{2.303} = \frac{1}{t}\log\left(\frac{c - \mu}{c + \mu}\right) + B \tag{8-155}$$

and the second-order rate constant (k_{II}) for the reaction of PCHO and A to equilibrium in S'' is

$$k_{\text{II}} \cong k_2 K_1 = \frac{1.15}{ct}\log\left(\frac{c - \mu}{c + \mu}\right) + B \tag{8-156}$$

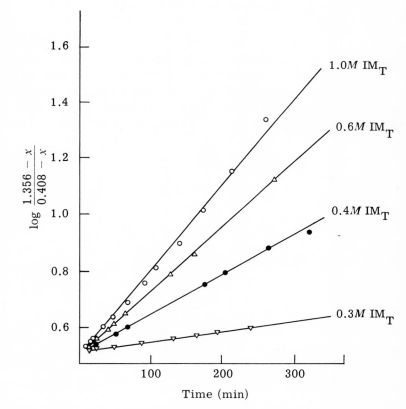

Fig. 8-14   *Plots of the experimentally determined rates of formation of S'' (determined at 246 mµ) employing the derived theoretical rate expression for approach to equilibrium in phase 1. (Ref. 193.)*

The value of k_{II} is then obtained from plots of $\log[(c - \mu)/(c + \mu)]$ vs. t (Fig. 8-14). Inspection of Fig. 8-14 reveals that the derived equation is as satisfactory in correlating the experimental data as is the conventional first-order rate equation (Fig. 8-13A). The value of k_{II} is found to be independent of the values of $PCHO_0$ and A_0, as anticipated from (8-154).

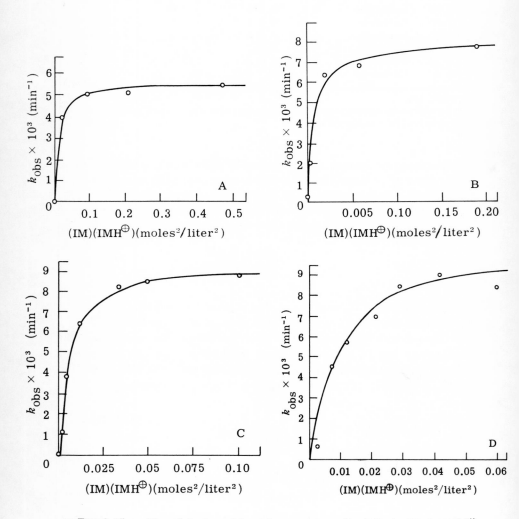

Fig. 8-15 *Plots of the observed first-order rate constants (k_{obs}) for the appearance of S″ vs. the product of the concentrations of imidazole and imidazolium ion. The points are experimental and the curves are those obtained from equation 8-157 employing the constants provided in Table 8-13.* (Ref. 193.)

Table 8-13 *   *Values of K_m and V_m calculated from equation (8-157)
and the final equilibrium concentration of S'' at t_∞ for
the imidazole catalysis of phase 1* [a]

pH	Buffer	IM IMH$^\oplus$ (mole fraction)	$V_m \, 10^3$ (min^{-1})	K_m (mole^2 liter^{-2})
7.06	Imidazole	0.466 0.534	2.46	—
7.80	Imidazole	0.827 0.173	5.5	7.15×10^{-3}
8.30	Imidazole	0.938 0.062	8.0	7.0×10^{-3}
8.60	Imidazole	0.968 0.032	9.5	6.2×10^{-3}
9.30	Carbonate	0.993 0.0066	10.5	8.5×10^{-3}
10.20	Carbonate		>11	—

* Ref. 193.
[a] Initial concentration of pyridoxal and amino acid was $10^{-4} \, M$, temperature 30°,
ionic strength 1.0, and solvent water.

Furthermore, the position of equilibrium of phase I at t_∞ was found to be
independent of imidazole buffer concentration (and pH), establishing the
buffer to be a true catalyst.   The dependence of the apparent first-order
rate constant on imidazole (**IM**) and imidazolium ion (**IMH**$^\oplus$) concentrations at constant pH (Fig. 8-15) was found to follow (8-157):

$$k_{\mathrm{obs}} = \frac{V_m[\mathrm{IM}][\mathrm{IMH}^\oplus]}{K_m + [\mathrm{IM}][\mathrm{IMH}^\oplus]} \qquad (8\text{-}157)$$

The dependence of V_m and K_m on pH is provided in Table 8-13.
    The constancy of K_m with pH when calculated on the basis of (8-157)
is in accord with the involvement of an imidazole base species and an
imidazolium ion as catalysts.   Three mechanisms may be invoked to
explain the Michaelis-Menten type kinetics, but only the first, as will be
shown, is tenable.   The first mechanism requires saturation of S' by an

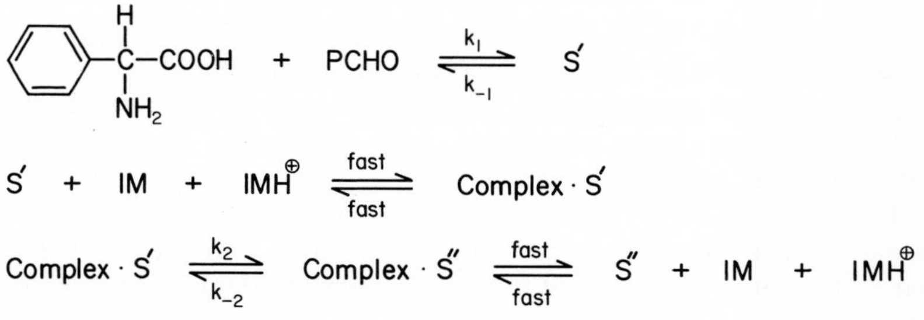

$$(8\text{-}158)$$

$$\text{PCHO} \quad + \quad \underset{\substack{|\\ \text{NH}_2}}{\overset{\substack{\text{H}\\ |}}{\text{C}}}\text{-COOH} \quad \underset{k_{-1}(\text{IM} + \text{IMH}^\oplus)}{\overset{k_1(\text{IM} + \text{IMH}^\oplus)}{\rightleftharpoons}}$$

$$\tag{8-159}$$

$$S' \quad \underset{k_{-2}}{\overset{k_2}{\rightleftharpoons}} \quad S''$$

imidazole molecule and an imidazolium ion followed by a rate-determining intracomplex general-base and/or general-acid conversion of S' to S'', as depicted in (8-158). The second mechanism (8-159) involves the catalysis of a rate-determining formation of S' by the two imidazole species. At high imidazole buffer concentrations this step would no longer be rate-controlling. The third mechanism (8-160) involves a rate-controlling complex formation between PCHO and the two imidazole species, which at high imidazole buffer concentrations becomes zero-order in imidazole as a result of saturation of the PCHO:

$$\text{PCHO} \quad + \quad \text{IM} \quad + \quad \text{IMH}^\oplus \quad \underset{\text{slow}}{\overset{\text{slow}}{\rightleftharpoons}} \quad \text{Complex}$$

$$\text{Complex} \quad + \quad \underset{\substack{|\\ \text{NH}_2}}{\overset{\substack{\text{H}\\ |}}{\text{C}}}\text{-COOH} \quad \underset{}{\overset{\text{fast}}{\rightleftharpoons}} \quad \text{aldimine} \quad \underset{}{\overset{\text{fast}}{\rightleftharpoons}}$$

$$\text{ketimine}$$

$$\tag{8-160}$$

Thus, imidazole buffer is acting as a catalyst for the prototropic shift in (8-158) and for the formation of Schiff base in (8-159) and (8-160). Although these mechanisms explain the observed rate dependence on imidazole buffer concentration equally well, compelling evidence points to mechanism (8-158) as being the correct one. Thus, if mechanism (8-160) were operative then the observed overall rate should be independent of amino acid concentration. The observed rate, however, is found to show exactly the same dependence upon amino acid concentration as it does upon PCHO concentration.

Furthermore, all previous work on this reaction suggests that imine formation is much more rapid than prototropy. Convincing evidence that (8-159) does not represent the reaction path is obtained from experiments in which the morpholine imine (S) of PCHO is used in place of PCHO. The catalytic rate constants for the imidazole catalyzed forma-

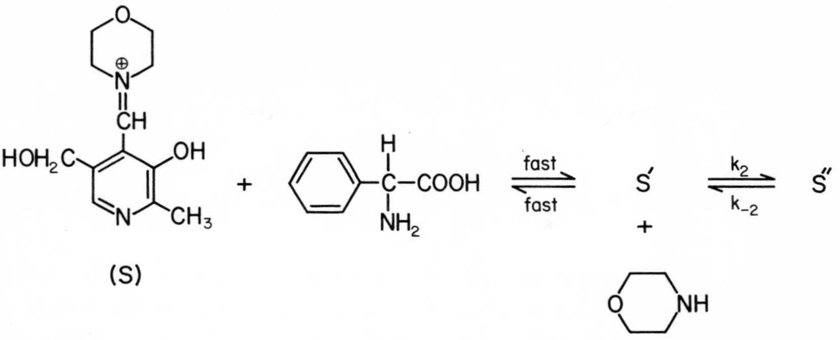

$$(8\text{-}161)$$

tion of ketimine [S" from S' (8-161)] are similar to those for the reaction involving PCHO. This result would not be predicted on the basis of (8-160), since it is well established that imines react at a greater rate with general reagents of type R—NH_2 than do the corresponding aldehydes or ketones.[194–198] Cordes and Jencks have shown that S reacts with semi-carbazide at a greater rate than does PCHO.[199]

Inspection of Table 8-13 shows that V_m increases with increasing pH. The values of V_m were shown to follow (8-162). The kinetically apparent

$$V_m = \frac{V_{m_1} a_H + V_{m_2} K_{app}}{K_{app} + a_H}$$

$$V_{m_1} = 0.9 \times 10^{-3} \text{ min}^{-1}$$

$$V_{m_2} = 10.2 \times 10^{-3} \text{ min}^{-1}$$

$$pK'_{app} = 7.78 \qquad (8\text{-}162)$$

dissocation constant (pK'_{app}) is close to the value of 8.6 for the phenolic hydroxyl of pyridoxal, and the dependence of V_m on pH would be in accord with a proportional increase in concentration of S'. The mechanism of Fig. 8-16 was proposed.

Studies of the kinetics of the imidazole catalysis of the transamination reaction were extended to the reaction of glutamic acid with 3-hydroxy-pyridine-4-aldehyde by Thanassi, Butler, and Bruice.[200a] The choice of

[194] Bruzau, *Ann. chim.* (*Paris*) **1**, 332 (1934).

[195] A. Brodhag and C. R. Hauser, *J. Am. Chem. Soc.* **77**, 3024 (1955).

[196] C. R. Hauser and D. S. Hoffenberg, *J. Am. Chem. Soc.* **77**, 4885 (1955).

[197] T. I. Crowell and F. A. Ramirez, *J. Am. Chem. Soc.* **73**, 2268 (1951).

[198] T. I. Crowell and D. W. Peck, *J. Am. Chem. Soc.* **75**, 1075 (1953).

[199] E. H. Cordes and W. P. Jencks, *Biochemistry* **1**, 773 (1962).

[200a] J. W. Thanassi, A. R. Butler, and T. C. Bruice, *Biochemistry* **4**, 1463 (1965).

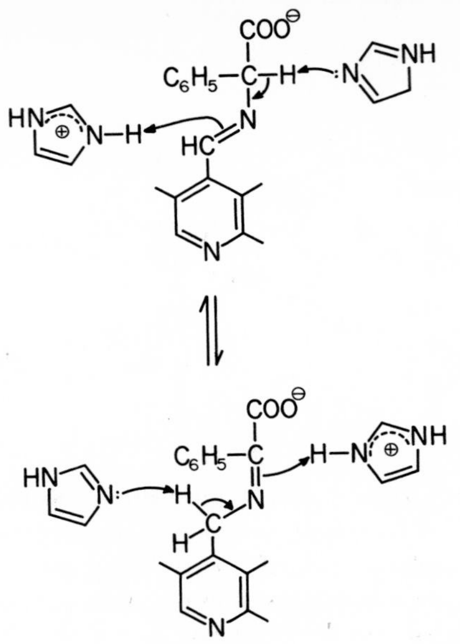

Fig. 8-16   *Proposed mechanism for the imidazole catalysis of the transamination of pyridoxal by α-aminophenylacetic acid.*   *(Ref. 193.)*

the aldehyde was to obviate the complexities of internal hemiacetal formation occurring with pyridoxal. Reactions were carried out at 30° in aqueous solution between pH 4.5 and pH 7.5 at a constant ionic strength of 0.5. The employment of the amino acid at concentrations greatly exceeding that of aldehyde simplified the form of the kinetics from that of

$$A + B \underset{}{\overset{K}{\rightleftarrows}} C \underset{k_{-r}}{\overset{k_r}{\rightleftarrows}} D$$

to

$$E \xrightarrow{k_{obs}} D \qquad\qquad (8\text{-}163)$$

where E represents the equilibrium mixture of 3-hydroxypyridine-4-aldehyde and its aldimine with L-glutamic acid. In this study no kinetic evidence was obtained for the accumulation of the intermediate ketimine of 3-hydroxy-4-aminomethylpyridine and α-ketoglutaric acid. This result is anticipated from the lack of extra resonance stabilizing factors, as found for the ketimine of phenylglyoxylic acid and pyridoxamine.

From the known pK_a' values of reactants and from the separately determined pH dependence of the apparent equilibrium constant for formation of aldimine, the concentration of the various species of imine in acid-base

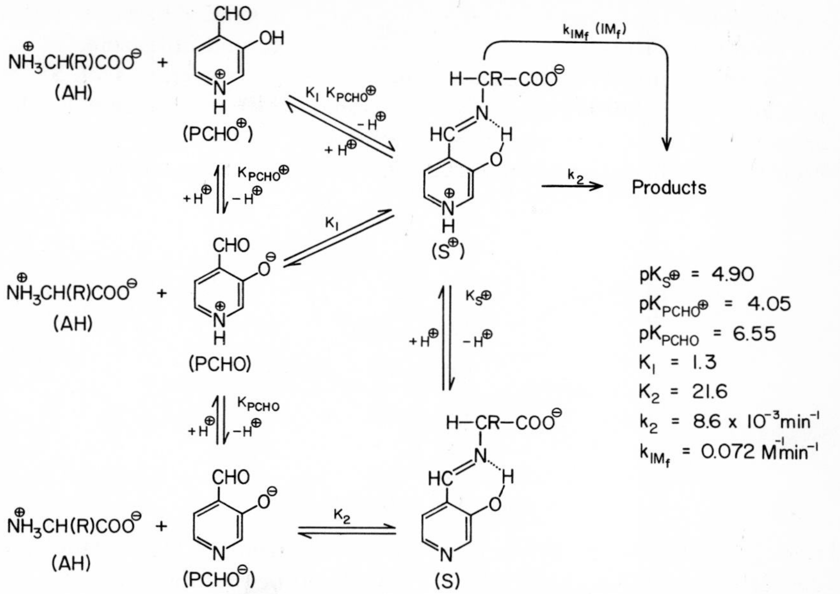

The scheme shows reaction paths with:

$$pK_{S^\oplus} = 4.90$$
$$pK_{PCHO^\oplus} = 4.05$$
$$pK_{PCHO} = 6.55$$
$$K_1 = 1.3$$
$$K_2 = 21.6$$
$$k_2 = 8.6 \times 10^{-3}\,min^{-1}$$
$$k_{IM_f} = 0.072\ M^{-1}min^{-1}$$

where $R = -CH_2CH_2COO^\ominus$

$$k_{obs} = k_2 \left[\frac{K_1 a_H + K_2 K_{PCHO}}{K_{PCHO} + a_H + a_H^2/K_{PCHO^\oplus}} \right] \left[\frac{a_H}{a_H + K_{S^\oplus}} \right] [AH]$$

Fig. 8-17. *Reaction paths and constants for the transamination of glutamic acid by 3-hydroxypridine-4-aldehyde. Ref. 200a.*

equilibrium at any pH was determined. A combination of these equilibria with the kinetic results led to the scheme of Fig. 8-17, where $S^\oplus$ undergoes spontaneous or imidazole general-base catalyzed conversion to products. Alternatively, the kinetically equivalent conversion of S to products via hydronium-ion or imidazolium-ion catalysis may be postulated. It should be noted that whereas in the pH range investigated the concentration of aldimine species increases with increasing pH, the pseudo-first-order rate constant for product appearance increases with decreasing pH. Product analysis via isotope dilution experiments indicates that, although only a portion of products arising from $S^\oplus$ via the spontaneous reaction is α-ketoglutaric acid, all the product arising by imidazole catalysis is α-ketoglutaric acid. Thus, imidazole acts as a specific catalyst of the transamination reaction. Experiments in which alanine replaces glutamic acid provide evidence for general base catalysis of the prototropic shift by amino acid, acetate anion, and imidazole.[200b]

In the spontaneous and imidazole catalyzed conversions of $S^\oplus$ to products, the 3-hydroxyl group was suggested to act as an intramolecular general-acid catalyst and water or imidazole as the proton acceptor. Both the 3-hydroxyl and carboxyl groups in (8-164) are required for reac-

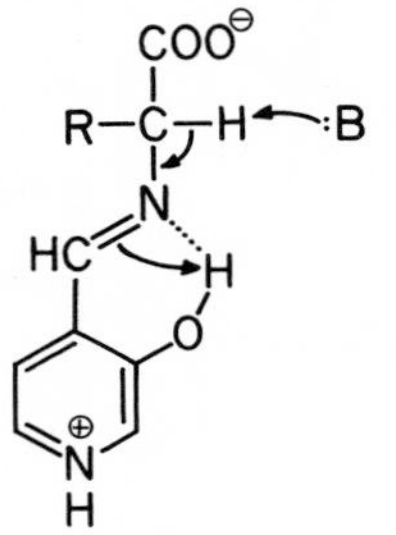

(8-164)

where B = H_2O, imidazole

tion.   Kinetically (8-164) is indistinguishable from (8-165).   However, the rate constant associated with (8-165) would be prohibitively large due to the low concentration of this imine species.   In Fig. 8-16 the imidazolium ion replaces the phenolic hydroxyl group (8-164) as a general-acid catalyst.   This would be reasonable on the basis that within the complex

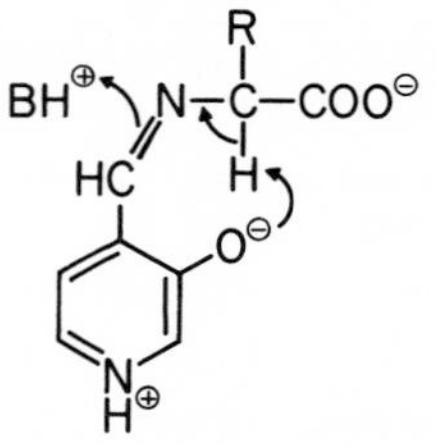

(8-165)

of imine, imidazole, and imidazolium ion, the imidazolium ion could compete as an intracomplex participant with the phenolic hydroxyl group. In addition the lower pK_a' of imidazole would make it a better general-acid catalyst than the phenolic hydroxyl group.

From consideration of the work of French, Auld, and Bruice as well as of Thanassi, Butler, and Bruice, the phenolic hydroxyl group would appear to play an essential role as a general acid-base catalyst in both imine formation (dehydration of carbinolamine) and in prototropy.   As already noted, due to the change of pK_a' of the phenolic hydroxyl group on imine formation, the hydroxyl group lends important thermodynamic

[200b] D. S. Auld and T. C. Bruice, unpublished results.

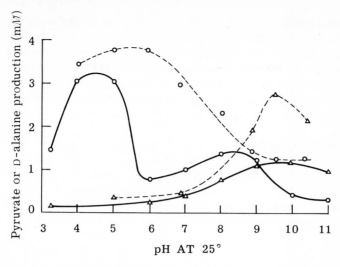

Fig. 8-18   *The effect of pH on the copper or aluminum catalyzed transamination and racemization of amino acids by pyridoxal.   The reaction mixtures contained 0.01 M L-alanine, 0.01 M pyridoxal, 0.001 M AlNH$_4$(SO$_4$)$_2$ or CuSO$_4$, and buffers as follows: pH 3.2, 0.05 M phthalate; pH 4–5, 0.1 M acetate; pH 5.9–8, 0.1 M phosphate; pH 8.9–11, 0.02 M borate. Reaction time, 10 min at 100°.   ○, transamination; △, racemization; ———, alum; -----, copper.   (Ref. 201.)*

stability to aldimine at neutral and acidic pH values, thus increasing the concentration of this intermediate species.

C. Racemization

The racemization of α-amino acids by pyridoxal has been studied by Olivard, Metzler, and Snell.[201]   The reaction was enhanced by the metal ions Fe(III), Cu(II), and Al(III) with the order of reactivity of the amino acids being Phe = Met > Ala > Ileu.   A comparison was made with L-alanine of the pH-rate profile for racemization and transamination. From Fig. 8-18 it may be observed that racemization predominates at pH 9.6 while transamination is the major reaction at pH 5.   The decrease in rate for transamination with Al(III) at pH ∼ 6.0 occurs at a point where aluminum oxide begins to precipitate.   The pH maximum for transamination corresponds to the pK_a' of the pyridine nitrogen, whereas the racemization reaction possesses a pH optimum at a pH at which the pyridine nitrogen is not protonated.   A detailed analysis of the pH dependence curves is made difficult by complexities due not only to the

[201] J. Olivard, D. E. Metzler and E. E. Snell, *J. Biol. Chem.* **199**, 669 (1952).

ionizable groups on the imine portion of the chelate, but to the hydrolytic equilibria of the metal ions involved in chelation and in solution. It would appear that the relative electron densities on the aldimine at the carbons derived from the α-position of the amino acid and the aldehyde of pyridoxal are strongly influenced by the ionic form of the aldimine. Thus, return of the proton to either the α-position or aldehyde carbon produces racemization or transamination, respectively.

D. Decarboxylation

1. NONOXIDATIVE ENZYMIC DECARBOXYLATION   The enzymic decarboxylation of amino acids by pyridoxal phosphate-requiring enzymes, if carried out in D_2O solvent, results in the introduction of only one deuterium atom into the generated amine.[202]   This observation is in accord with the expected mechanisms of (8-166).

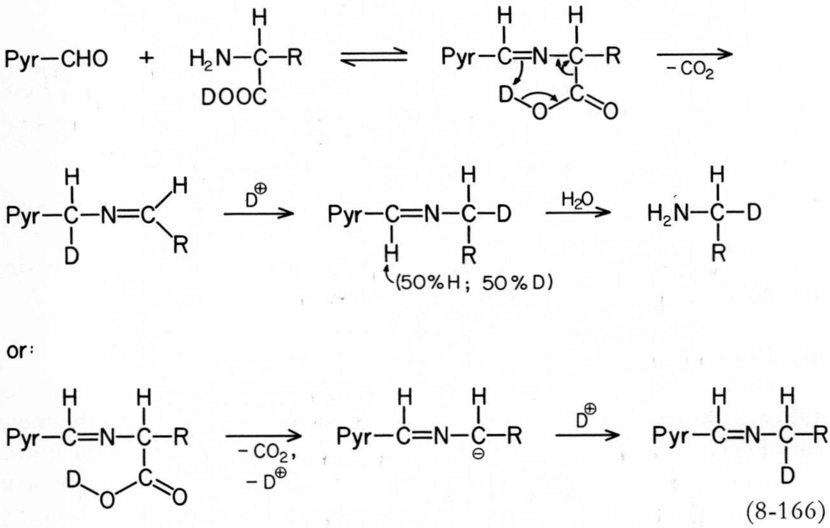

$$
\text{Pyr—CHO} + \underset{\text{DOOC}}{\text{H}_2\text{N—}\overset{\text{H}}{\underset{|}{\text{C}}}\text{—R}} \;\rightleftharpoons\; \text{Pyr—}\overset{\text{H}}{\text{C}}=\text{N}\!-\!\overset{\text{H}}{\text{C}}\text{—R} \xrightarrow{-\,CO_2}
$$

$$
\text{Pyr—}\overset{\text{H}}{\underset{\text{D}}{\text{C}}}\text{—N}=\text{C}\overset{\text{H}}{\underset{\text{R}}{}} \xrightarrow{\;D^{\oplus}\;} \text{Pyr—C}=\text{N—}\overset{\text{H}}{\underset{\text{R}}{\text{C}}}\text{—D} \;\; \underset{(50\%\text{H};\;50\%\text{D})}{} \xrightarrow{\;H_2O\;} \text{H}_2\text{N—}\overset{\text{H}}{\underset{\text{R}}{\text{C}}}\text{—D}
$$

or:

$$
\text{Pyr—}\overset{\text{H}}{\text{C}}=\text{N—}\overset{\text{H}}{\text{C}}\text{—R} \xrightarrow[-\,D^{\oplus}]{-\,CO_2,} \text{Pyr—}\overset{\text{H}}{\text{C}}=\text{N—}\overset{\text{H}}{\underset{\ominus}{\text{C}}}\text{—R} \xrightarrow{\;D^{\oplus}\;} \text{Pyr—}\overset{\text{H}}{\text{C}}=\text{N—}\overset{\text{H}}{\underset{\text{D}}{\text{C}}}\text{—R}
$$

$$(8\text{-}166)$$

Belleau and Burba,[203] in an elegant study, have shown that the amine obtained from tyrosine in the above reaction is asymmetrically labeled with D.   The configurations of both R- and S-α-tyramine were established by synthesis of each enantiomorph and identification by their relative rates of oxidation by monoamine oxidase.[204]   The synthetic procedure employed (for the R isomer) is presented in (8-167) and (8-168).

[202] S. Mandeles, R. Koppelman, and M. E. Hanke, *J. Biol. Chem.* **209**, 327 (1954).
[203] B. Belleau and J. Burba, *J. Am. Chem. Soc.* **82**, 5751 (1960).
[204] B. Belleau, M. Fang, J. Burba, and J. Moran, *J. Am. Chem. Soc.* **82**, 5752 (1960).

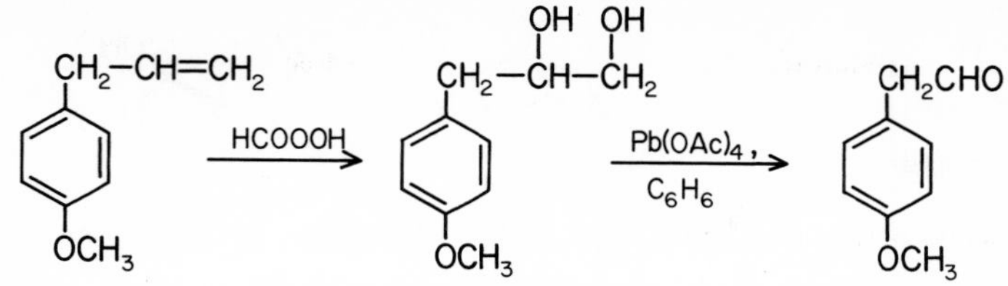

(8-167)

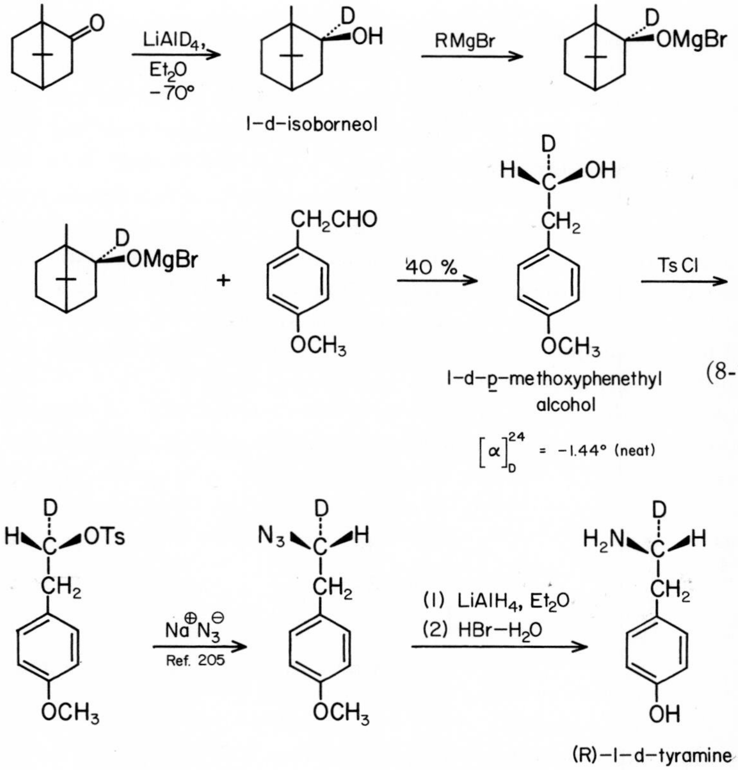

1-d-isoborneol

1-d-p-methoxyphenethyl   (8-168)
alcohol

$[\alpha]_D^{24} = -1.44°$ (neat)

(R)-1-d-tyramine

The crucial step in the synthetic sequence for the R antipode (the asymmetric reduction of the aldehyde to yield 1-d-*p*-methoxyphenethyl alcohol) was based on the studies of Streitwieser and co-workers [206] on the assumption that, as Streitwieser suggests, these reductions are nearly 100% asymmetric. In the formulas shown the symbols L and S pertain to the most bulky (L) and smallest (S) groups attached to the asymmetric center (8-169). The most suitable cyclic transition state would be one in

[205] A reaction previously shown to go by complete inversion; see A. Streitwieser and W. D. Schaeffer, *J. Am. Chem. Soc.* **78,** 5597 (1956).

[206] A. Streitwieser, J. R. Wolfe, and W. D. Schaeffer, *Tetrahedron* **6,** 339 (1959).

(+)-camphor

which the steric repulsions of L and R are minimized (8-170).   (For other

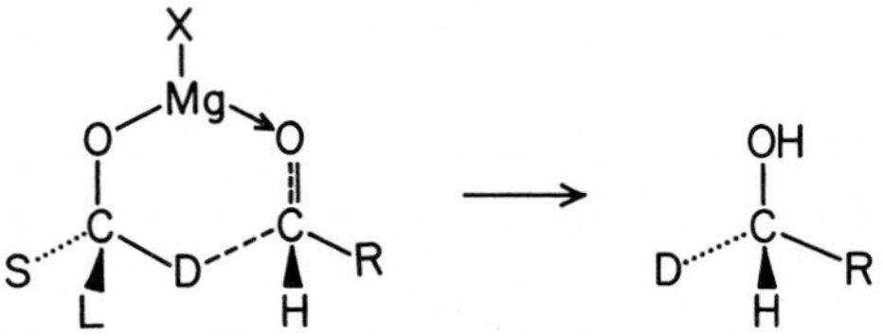

examples of asymmetric induction, see Chapter 4.)

These results would tend to discredit an imine in which the α-carbon is sp^2 hybridized as an intermediate unless the enzyme were to direct the addition of the $D^{\oplus}$.   This is quite probable since the imine can be considered to possess a meso carbon (see Chapter 4).   In this light it is interesting to note that the action of L-amino acid decarboxylase can be established to be reversible, minute amounts of the L-amino acid being formed at equilibrium from the amines and bicarbonate.[202]   It is also quite possible that the imine could undergo decarboxylation to produce an asymmetrically solvated carbanion which retained its configuration on protonation (8-171).   Thus, $(-)$-2-cyano-2-phenylbutanoic acid, as its

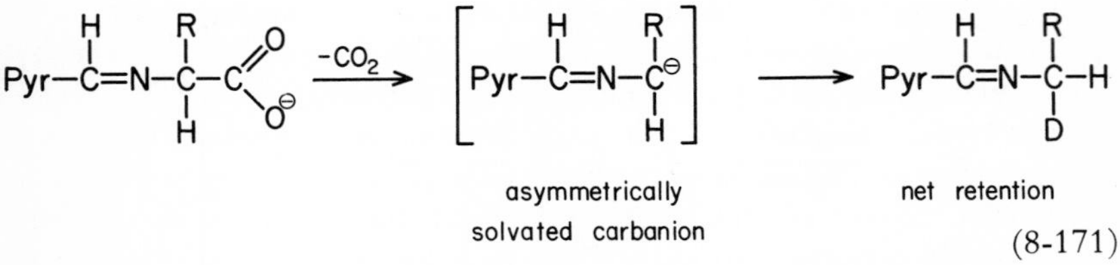

ammonium salt, undergoes decarboxylation at 100° in t-butanol or phenol with partial (10–16%) retention of configuration [22] (8-23).

The possibility exists that decarboxylases requiring pyridoxal phosphate may also act as rather nonspecific transaminases.   Meister and co-workers [207, 208] have shown that aspartate β-decarboxylase acts both as a relatively nonspecific L-amino acid transaminase and as an aspartate β-decarboxylase.   It would appear that the same active site participates in two reactions, one of which either destroys or regenerates the coenzyme necessary for the other (Fig. 8-19).   The intriguing possibility has been

[207] A. Novogrodsky, J. S. Nishimura, and A. Meister, J. Biol. Chem. 238, 1903PC (1963).
[208] A. Novogrodsky and A. Meister, J. Biol. Chem. 239, 879 (1964).

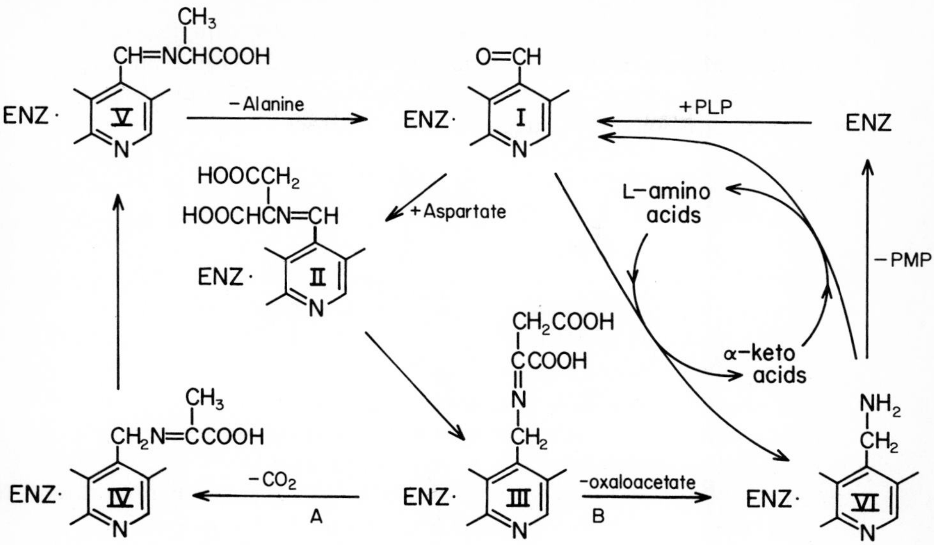

Fig. 8-19   *Scheme for β-decarboxylation and transamination of aspartate;* PLP, *pyridoxal-5′-phosphate;* PMP, *pyridoxamine-5′-phosphate;* ENZ, *enzyme.   (Ref. 207.)*

suggested [208] that the transamination reaction may serve as a control mechanism.

2. MODEL STUDIES OF NONOXIDATIVE DECARBOXYLATION   Until very recently the unconfirmed report of Werle and Koch, [209] that pyridoxal and pyridoxal phosphate catalyze the decarboxylation of histidine to histamine, provided the only possible example of a model system for cofactor catalyzed decarboxylation.   The inability to note decarboxylations of α-amino acids in the presence of pyridoxal would appear strange when one recalls that the simple imines of amino acid and α-keto acids undergo decarboxylation or transaminative decarboxylation with ease.

Thanassi and Fruton [210] have established that aminomalonic acid and α-methylaminomalonic acid undergo decarboxylation in the presence of pyridoxal or pyridoxal phosphate.   The initial rate of decarboxylation (pH 6.0, 25°, H_2O) diminishes with time due to side reactions, which for aminomalonic acid were shown to be partially due to a transamination reaction.[210, 211]

Kalyankar and Snell [212] found that, when α-aminoisobutyric acid, α-methylserine, or α-phenylglycine was heated with pyridoxal in dilute

[209] E. Werle and W. Koch, *Biochem. Z.* **319,** 305 (1949).
[210] J. Thanassi and J. S. Fruton, *Biochemistry* **1,** 975 (1962).
[211] J. Thanassi, Ph.D. Thesis, Yale University (1963).
[212] G. D. Kalyankar and E. E. Snell, *Biochemistry* **1,** 594 (1962).

aqueous solutions, decarboxylation probably occurred via the two mechanisms previously noted in the reaction of α-keto acids with amino acids.
From α-aminoisobutyric acid there was obtained CO_2, isopropylamine,
acetone, and pyridoxamine, suggesting the sequence (8-172).

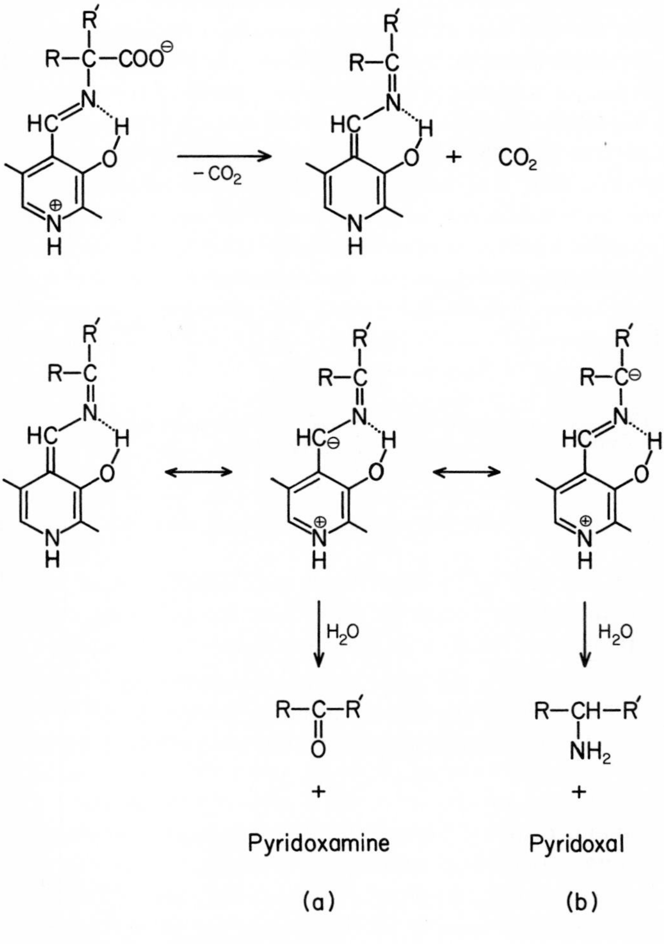

(8-172)

where R = $-CH_3$, $-H$, $-OH$, $-C_6H_5$

The optimum pH, as measured by formation of either CO_2 or acetone, was
3.5–6.0, but some reaction occurs from pH 2.0 to pH 9.0.   The decarboxylation reaction was found to be inhibited by metal ions.

With α-methylserine as the substrate, acetol and CO_2 were the products, the reaction proceeding as in (8-172 a).   Addition of metal pre-
vented the decarboxylation reaction and led to products anticipated of a

β-elimination of formaldehyde and transamination. Entirely similar results were obtained when α-hydroxy-methylserine was the amino acid. α-Phenylglycine yielded, with pyridoxal, products anticipated for the reactions (8-172 a and b).

The inhibition of the decarboxylation reactions by metal ions may be attributed to the fact that in the chelate structure the pair of electrons of the carboxyl anion is shared by the metal ion, and that the carboxyl group forms a portion of a chelate ring structure. Both of these factors would *a priori* be anticipated to greatly decrease the leaving tendency of the CO_2.

The enzymic decarboxylation of an aromatic carboxyl group, as in *p*-aminobenzoic acid and anthranilic acid,[213] can be duplicated in the nonenzymic decarboxylation of *o*- and *p*-aminobenzoic acids by pyridoxal in model reactions (reflux temperature, pH 7.2).[214] The decarboxylation of *p*-aminobenzoic acids cannot be formulated via the mechanism of Metzler, Ikawa, and Snell, [115] and the following transformation was suggested:

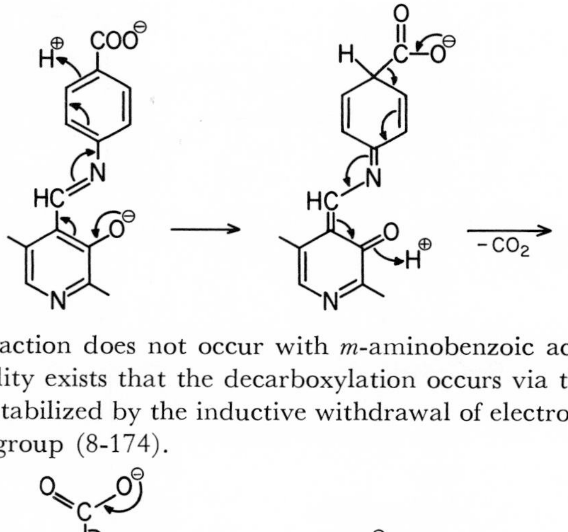

(8-173)

The reaction does not occur with *m*-aminobenzoic acid. However, the possibility exists that the decarboxylation occurs via the formation of an anion stabilized by the inductive withdrawal of electrons by a protonated imine group (8-174).

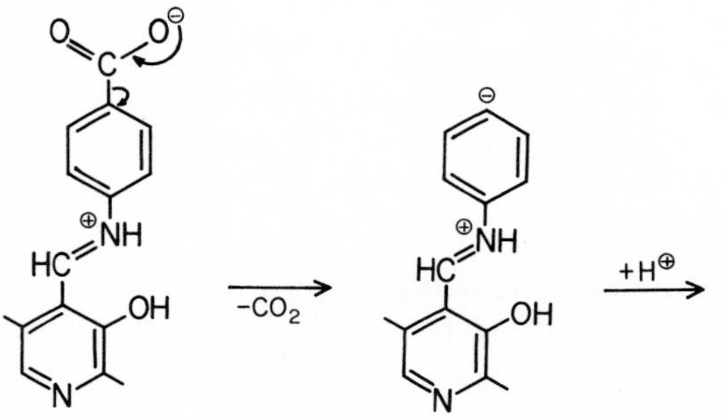

(8-174)

[213] W. G. McCullough, J. T. Piligian, and I. J. Daniel, *J. Am. Chem. Soc.* **79**, 628 (1957).

[214] L. Davis and C. Trotman, *Biochem. Biophys. Res. Commun.* **14**, 482 (1964).

3. ENZYMIC OXIDATIVE DECARBOXYLATION   The enzymic oxidative decarboxylation of methionine, methionine sulfoxide, serine, alanine, and phenylalanine by peroxidase in the presence of catalytic amounts of metal ion and pyridoxal phosphate has been reported by Mazelis.[215, 216]   Manganese was found to be at least 10 times more effective than other metals employed, and pyridoxal phosphate more effective than pyridoxal.   The 4-nitrosalicylaldehyde was ineffective.   The pH optimum of the reaction appeared to be dependent upon the buffer employed.   At concentrations of ca. 10^{-6} M, phenol or resorcinol was found to stimulate the reaction. The identification of 3-methylthiopropionamide as the product of oxidative decarboxylation of methonine led to the postulation of mechanism (8-175).

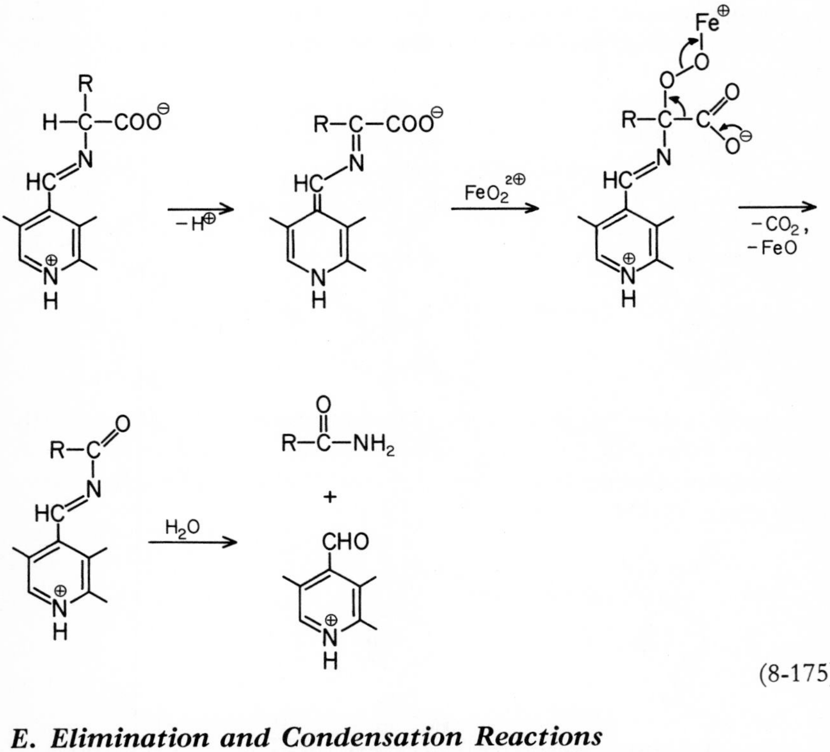

(8-175)

E. Elimination and Condensation Reactions

1. ELIMINATION   Pyridoxal and pyridoxal phosphate in the presence of metal ions bring about two types of elimination reactions and their

[215] M. Mazelis, *J. Biol. Chem.* **237,** 104 (1962).
[216] M. Mazelis and L. L. Ingraham, *J. Biol. Chem.* **237,** 109 (1962).

retrogression with β-substituted amino acids. The products produced are consistent with mechanisms (8-176) and (8-177). In (8-176) keto acid is

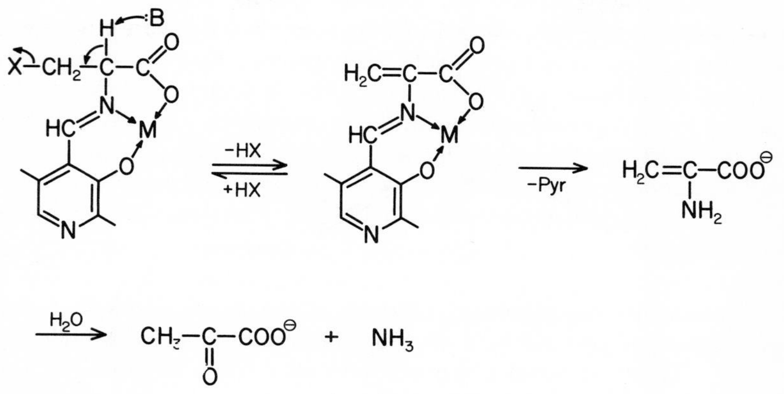

where X = 3–indolyl, –SH, –OH

(8-176)

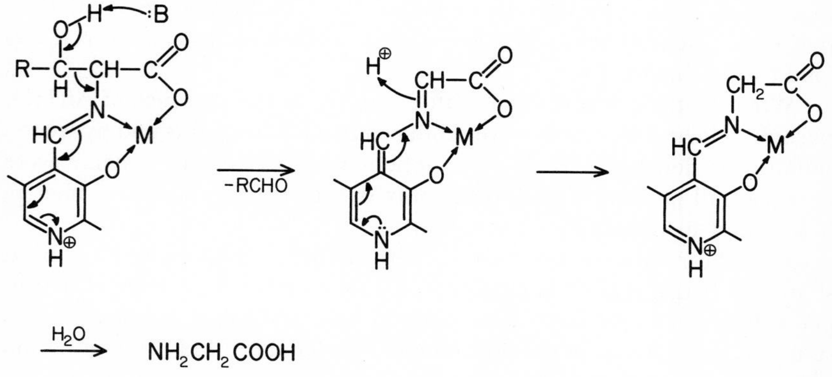

etc.

(8-177)

the product while in (8-177) amino acid is the product. In neither reaction is pyridoxal consumed. Snell and co-workers [217] have recently isolated a crystalline enzyme from *E. coli* capable of catalyzing the β-eliminations of cysteine, serine, and tryptophan. The interconversion of the

[217] W. A. Newton and E. E. Snell, *Proc. Natl. Acad. Sci. U.S.* **51**, 382 (1964); W. A. Newton, Y. Morino, and E. E. Snell, *J. Biol. Chem.* **240**, 1211 (1965).

various amino acids establishes a common intermediate (8-178) as postulated in (8-176).

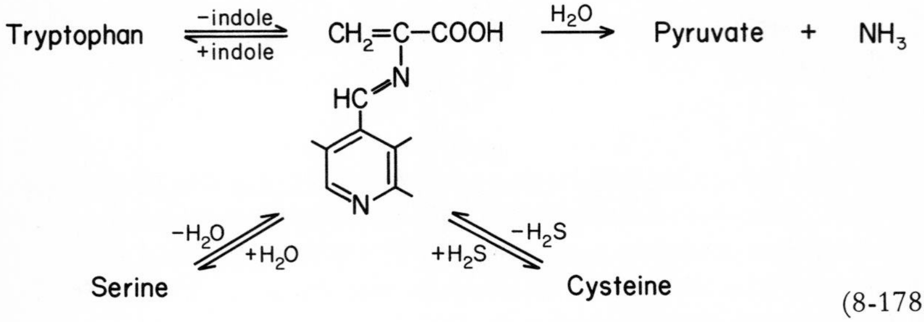

$$\text{Tryptophan} \; \underset{+\text{indole}}{\overset{-\text{indole}}{\rightleftharpoons}} \; CH_2=C-COOH \; \xrightarrow{H_2O} \; \text{Pyruvate} \; + \; NH_3$$

(8-178)

The nonenzymic pyridoxal catalysis of the decomposition of serine and cysteine to pyruvic acid (8-176) was established by Metzler and Snell.[218]   The same metal ions noted to be effective in the transamination reaction were active in the formation of pyruvic acid from serine, i.e., Al(III), Cu(II), Fe(II), and Fe(III).   Inactive were Co(II), Mg(II), Mn(II), Ni(II), and Zn(II).   The reaction does not occur through a transamination reaction, since the keto acid produced far exceeded the pyridoxal lost and no hydroxypyruvic acid was formed.   Pyridoxal phosphate and 5-deoxypyridoxal are better catalysts for the reaction than pyridoxal (internal hemiacetal formation), while 3-methoxypyridoxal was found to be ineffective.

When cysteine was reacted with pyridoxal in the presence of Al(III), pyruvic acid and ammonia were produced in equal amounts and hydrogen sulfide was detected.   Both the reactions with serine and cysteine were noted to fall off with time, presumably due to the formation of inactive imines and to thiazolidine formation.

Vanadium salts in combination with pyridoxal phosphate have been shown by Bergel et al.[219] to catalyze a highly specific elimination of hydrogen sulfide from cysteine.   The reaction was established to occur in two stages: (1) ring fission of the thiazolidine intermediate, and (2) elimination of hydrogen sulfide (8-179).   The specificity of vanadium appears to have no simple rationale, since Hg(II) and Ag(I) which have an affinity for sulfur are far less effective.

The formation of tryptophan in low yield from serine and indole in a model system, due to trapping of the α,β-unsaturated intermediate by indole, has been realized.[156]   Thus, when a solution 0.05 M in serine, 0.05 M in indole, 0.02 M in pyridoxal, and 0.002 M in alum was heated

[218] D. E. Metzler and E. E. Snell, J. Biol. Chem. 198, 353 (1952).
[219] F. Bergel, K. H. Harrap, and A. M. Scott, J. Chem. Soc. 1101 (1962).

$$(8-179)$$

at 100° for 30 min at pH 5.0 there was obtained 0.3–0.4 mM tryptophan, 0.6–0.8% yield (by microbiological assay). The chief competing reaction was the irreversible deamination of serine. When pyridoxal was left out of the reaction mixture no tryptophan was formed. This result lends further support to mechanism (8-176).

The reactions of phosphoserine and phosphothreonine with pyridoxal have been studied by Longenecker and Snell.[220] Neither reaction pro-

$$\text{Serine-P} + H_2O \rightarrow \text{pyruvic acid} + H_3PO_4 + NH_3$$

$$\text{Threonine-P} + H_2O \rightarrow \alpha\text{-ketobutyric acid} + H_3PO_4 + NH_3$$

$$(8-180)$$

ceeds at a significant rate in the absence of pyridoxal and the reactions are relatively slow in the absence of metal ions. Transamination was not found to be an important side reaction. The presence of the phosphate ester grouping (8-180) increases the rate several hundredfold over that of the corresponding reactions for free serine and threonine. Just as deamination of serine is more facile than the deamination of threonine, the reaction with serine phosphate is significantly more rapid than that with threonine phosphate. The comparative effectiveness (with Cu(II) at 100° as the reference ion) of various metal ions has been determined in the deamination of threonine and serine phosphate [154] and found to vary somewhat from that for transamination.

Carbamyl serine and azaserine [220] also undergo deamination under the influence of pyridoxal and various M(II) ions (8-181). These carboxylic acid esters of serine are decomposed somewhat more rapidly than serine phosphate at room temperature. Pyridoxal is an essential catalyst and the reactions are greatly facilitated by metal salts.

The cleavage of cystathionine to homocysteine, pyruvic acid, and ammonia was investigated by Binkley and Boyd,[221] who reported that oxalic acid or other chelating agents were essential for the cleavage reaction (8-182). The rate of deamination in this case was comparable to that

[220] J. B. Longenecker and E. E. Snell, J. Biol. Chem. 225, 409 (1957).

[221] F. Binkley, J. Am. Chem. Soc. 77, 501 (1955); F. Binkley and M. J. Boyd, J. Biol. Chem. 217, 67 (1955).

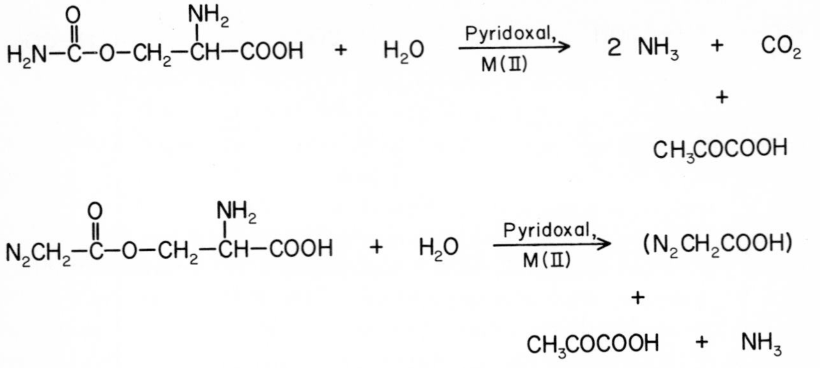

$$H_2N-\overset{\overset{\displaystyle O}{\|}}{C}-O-CH_2-\overset{\overset{\displaystyle NH_2}{|}}{CH}-COOH \;+\; H_2O \;\xrightarrow[M(\text{II})]{\text{Pyridoxal,}}\; 2\;NH_3 \;+\; CO_2$$

$$+$$

$$CH_3COCOOH$$

$$N_2CH_2-\overset{\overset{\displaystyle O}{\|}}{C}-O-CH_2-\overset{\overset{\displaystyle NH_2}{|}}{CH}-COOH \;+\; H_2O \;\xrightarrow[M(\text{II})]{\text{Pyridoxal,}}\; (N_2CH_2COOH)$$

$$+$$

$$CH_3COCOOH \;+\; NH_3$$

$$(8\text{-}181)$$

$$HOOC-\overset{\overset{\displaystyle |}{\underset{\underset{\displaystyle NH_2}{|}}{CH}}}{}-CH_2-S-(CH_2)_2-\overset{\underset{\underset{\displaystyle NH_2}{|}}{CH}}{}-COOH \;\xrightarrow{H_2O}\; CH_3\overset{\overset{\displaystyle O}{\|}}{C}COOH \;+\; NH_3$$

$$+$$

$$HS-(CH_2)_2-\overset{\underset{\underset{\displaystyle NH_2}{|}}{CH}}{}-COOH$$

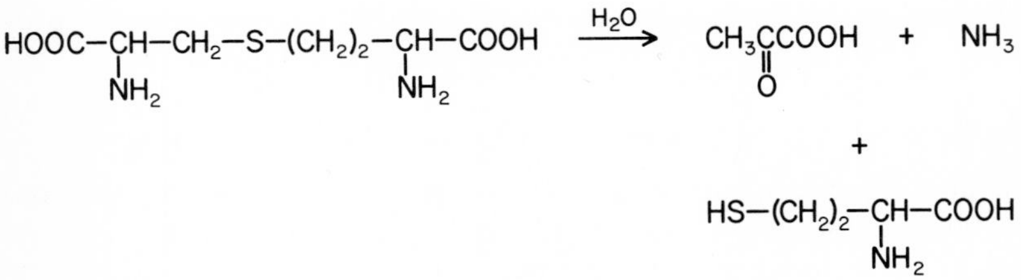

$$(8\text{-}182)$$

for serine phosphate. The reaction was subsequently reinvestigated by Longenecker and Snell [220] in systems containing oxalic acid, bicarbonate, Tris, and Fe(III) (see Table 8-14).

These results show that added buffer salts are not essential for the reaction, and that nonchelating bases as tris(hydroxymethyl)amino-methane are equally effective as chelating ligands such as oxalate. In any event the facilitation is not great and a similar effect of acetate and

Table 8-14 *   *Effect of buffer salts on cleavage of cystathionine to homocysteine and pyruvic acid*

Buffer salts	Product formed (mM) at pH 9.0 (in 60 min at 37°C)	
	Homocysteine	Pyruvic acid
(none)	0.80	0.84
Oxalic acid (0.05 M)	1.15	1.07
$HCO_3^{\ominus}$ (0.05 M)	0.97	1.44
Tris	1.46	—

* Ref. 220.

phosphate buffers on deamination of serine was obtained.[220]   These effects are probably too great to be rationalized as due to ionic strength effects, and may represent general-base catalysis of a proton abstraction from the α-carbon.   This possibility warrants further and careful study. It should be pointed out that all model studies discussed to this point represent eliminations proceeding predominantly through pathway (8-176) and occur most readily at alkaline pH values.

In α-amino acids γ-eliminations occur only in enzymically catalyzed reactions.   Flavin and Slaughter [222] have studied elimination of phosphate from O-phosphohomoserine to yield threonine (8-183), for which mecha-

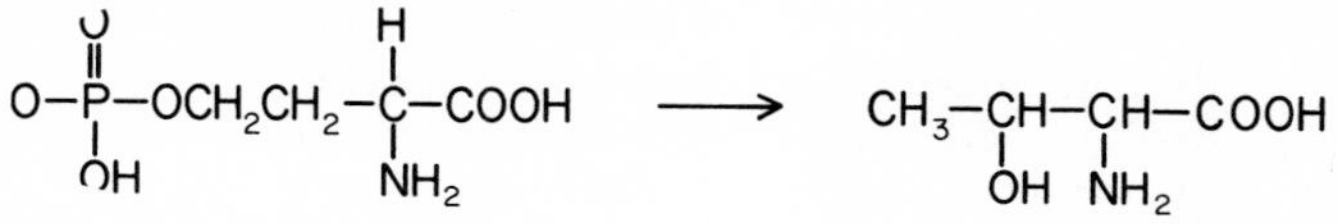

nism (8-184) was proposed.

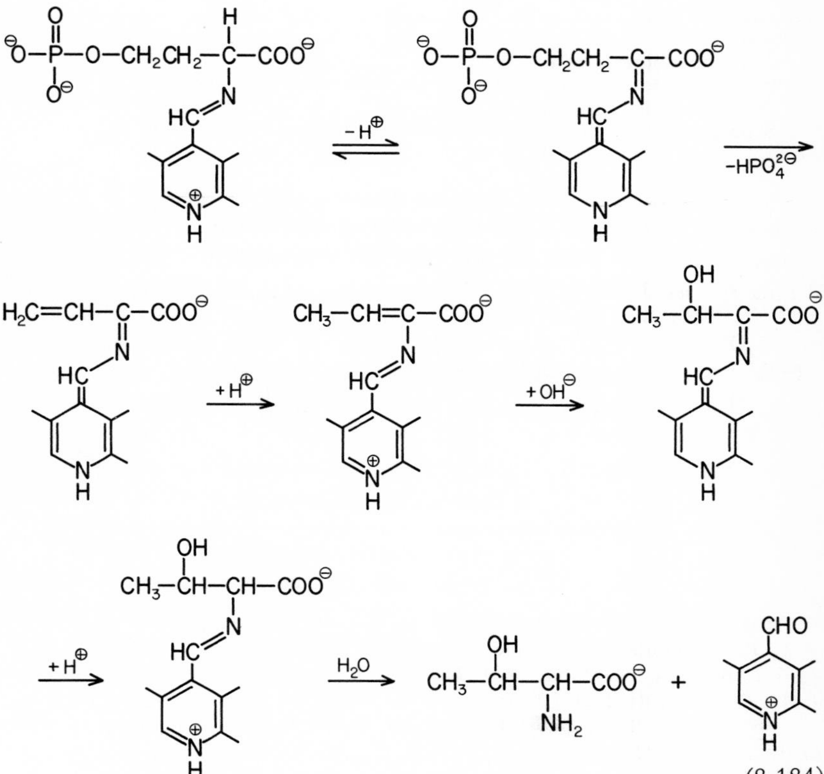

[222] M. Flavin and C. Slaughter, *J. Biol. Chem.* **235**, 1112 (1960).

Table 8-15 *   *β-Hydroxyamino acids prepared via condensation of an*
α-amino acid with a carbonyl compound

Precursor		Product	
α-Amino acid	Carbonyl component	(β-hydroxyamino acid)	Ref.
Glycine	Formaldehyde	Serine	226
Glycine	Formaldehyde	α-(Hydroxymethyl)serine	227
Alanine	Formaldehyde	α-Methylserine	227
Butyrine [a]	Formaldehyde	α-Ethylserine	227
Serine	Formaldehyde	α-(Hydroxymethyl)serine	227
Glycine	Acetaldehyde	Threonine-allothreonine	223
Glycine	Isobutyraldehyde	β-Hydroxyleucine [b]	[c]
Glycine	n-Butyraldehyde	β-Hydroxynorleucine [b]	[c]
Glycine	Glyoxylic acid	β-Hydroxyaspartic acid [b]	[c]
Glycine	p-Nitrobenzaldehyde	p-Nitrophenylserine [b]	[c]
Glycine	Pyruvic acid	β-Hydroxy-β-methylaspartic acid [d]	225

* Ref. 224.
[a] α-Amino-n-butyric acid.
[b] Presumably formed as a mixture of the diastereomeric racemates.
[c] Preparation described in Ref. 224.
[d] Separation of the diastereomeric racemates has been described.[225]

2. CONDENSATION   The α-amino-β-hydroxy acids may be synthesized by heating in aqueous solution, amino acid, and aldehyde in the presence of cupric ion.[223]   The reaction has been investigated by Otani and Winitz [224] (see Table 8-15).   The same type of condensation and its retro-

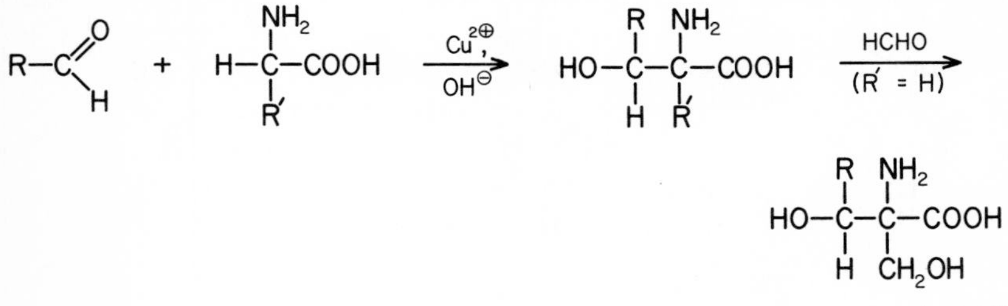

$$(8\text{-}185)$$

[223] M. Sato, K. Okawa, and S. Akabori, *Bull. Chem. Soc. Japan* **30,** 937 (1957).

[224] T. T. Otani and M. Winitz, *Arch. Biochem. Biophys.* **102,** 464 (1963).

[225] L. Benoiton, M. Winitz, R. F. Coleman, S. M. Birnbaum, and J. P. Greenstein, *J. Am. Chem. Soc.* **81,** 1726 (1959).

[226] S. Akabori, T. T. Otani, R. Marshall, M. Winitz, and J. P. Greenstein, *Arch. Biochem. Biophys.* **83,** 1 (1959).

[227] T. T. Otani and M. Winitz, *Arch. Biochem. Biophys.* **90,** 254 (1960).

gression catalyzed by pyridoxal and metal ions have been investigated by Metzler, Longenecker, and Snell.[228]   The cleavage of threonine to yield glycine and acetaldehyde occurred more rapidly than the dehydration of serine when the two reactions were carried on under similar conditions. The reaction was found to be readily reversible in the presence of Cu(II), Al(III) or Fe(III), and pyridoxal between pH 3 and 12.   Other aldehydes such as propionaldehyde, glyoxylic acid, and pyridoxal could be condensed with glycine under the same conditions to yield a variety of β-hydroxyamino acids.   Furthermore, in experiments at pH's near neutrality, where deamination is slow, the cleavage of serine to glycine and formaldehyde could be readily demonstrated.[229]   Pertinent experimental results are summarized in (8-186):

$$\left.\begin{array}{l} 0.02\ M\ \text{serine} \\ 0.01\ M\ \text{alum} \\ 0.01\ M\ \text{PCHO} \end{array}\right\} \xrightarrow[100°]{\text{pH 6.0}} \begin{array}{c} 5\%\ (\text{glycine} + CH_2O) \\ + \\ 40\%\ (\text{pyruvic acid}) \end{array}$$

$$\left.\begin{array}{l} 0.02\ M\ \text{glycine} \\ 0.02\ M\ CH_2O \\ 0.017\ M\ \text{alum} \end{array}\right\} \xrightarrow[100°]{\text{pH 6.0}} \begin{array}{c} 16\%\ (\text{pyruvic acid}) \\ + \\ 23\%\ (\text{serine}) \end{array}$$

(8-186)

A quantitative paper chromatographic study of the reaction of threonine with pyridoxal in the presence of Al(III) (pH 5.0, $t = 30$ min, $T = 100°$, 0.02 M threonine, 0.01 M pyridoxal, 0.002 M potassium alum) showed [229] that

$$\text{Threonine} \xrightarrow[64\%]{(a)} \text{glycine} + CH_3CHO$$

$$\xrightarrow[6\%]{(b)} NH_3 + \alpha\text{-ketobutyric acid}$$

(8-187)

$$\xrightarrow[8\%]{(c)} \beta\text{-pyridoxal serine}$$

Reductive transamination (b) was a minor reaction; cleavage (a) accounted for the major path.   Reaction (c) amounts to a retrogression of (a) in which pyridoxal in place of acetaldehyde condenses with glycine:

[228] D. E. Metzler, J. B. Longenecker, and E. E. Snell, *J. Am. Chem. Soc.* **75**, 2786 (1953).

[229] D. E. Metzler, J. B. Longenecker, and E. E. Snell, *J. Am. Chem. Soc.* **76**, 639 (1954).

$$Al(III) \quad + \quad PyrCHO \quad + \quad Glycine \quad \longrightarrow \quad Chelate \quad \longrightarrow$$

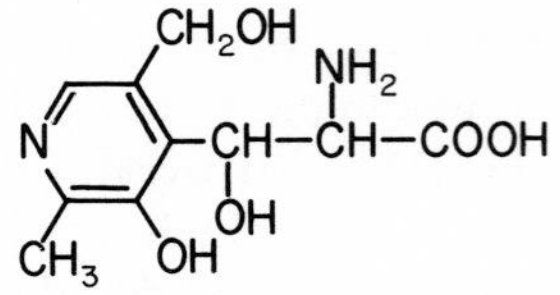

(8-188)

Unlike serine, neither threonine nor allothreonine was found to be deaminated rapidly at pH 10.0 in the presence of pyridoxal and Cu(II) salts. Interestingly, serylglycine peptides could be prepared from glycylglycine and acetaldehyde under the conditions employed to condense glycine with acetaldehyde. These latter studies therefore serve as examples for the retrogression pathway (8-177), which apparently is favored at pH values near neutrality although quite sensitive to the particular amino acid.

chapter
nine

Nicotinamide
Nucleotides

I. INTRODUCTION

The pyridine nucleotides, nicotinamide-adenine dinucleotide ($NAD^{\oplus}$) and its 2′-phosphoric acid derivative ($NADP^{\oplus}$), with their reduced forms (NADH, NADPH), are coenzymes in a very large number of enzymic oxidations and reductions. The structures of the oxidized forms are given in (9-1). Enzymes are known which will catalyze the conversion of $NAD^{\oplus}$ [1, 2] or NADH [1] to the corresponding NADP form in the presence of ATP. Included among the many biological oxidation-reduction

[1] A. Kornberg, *J. Biol. Chem.* **182,** 805 (1950).
[2] T. P. Wang and N. O. Kaplan, *J. Biol. Chem.* **206,** 311 (1954).

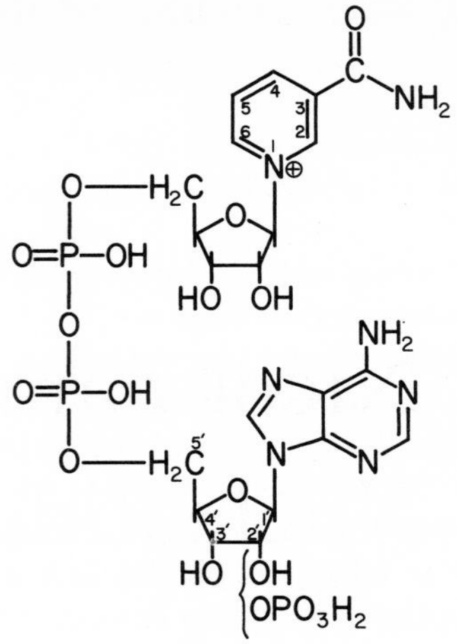

(9-1)

reactions requiring the pyridine nucleotides as coenzymes are the following examples (not including oxidized and reduced forms of coenzyme):

(1) L-Glutamate $\rightleftarrows$ α-ketoglutarate $+ NH_4^{\oplus}$ (liver L-glutamate dehydrogenase,[3] $NAD^{\oplus}$ or $NADP^{\oplus}$; yeast L-glutamate dehydrogenases,[3, 4] $NAD^{\oplus}$, $NADP^{\oplus}$; L-glutamate dehydrogenase[5] from pea seedlings, $NAD^{\oplus}$).

(2) R—CHO $\rightleftarrows$ R—CH$_2$OH (liver alcohol dehydrogenase,[6] $NAD^{\oplus}$; yeast alcohol dehydrogenase,[6] $NAD^{\oplus}$).

(3) L-α-Glycerophosphate $\rightleftarrows$ dihydroxyacetone phosphate (α-glycerophosphate dehydrogenase,[7] $NAD^{\oplus}$).

(4) Isocitrate $\rightleftarrows$ α-ketoglutarate $+ CO_2$ (isocitrate dehydrogenase from porcine heart,[8, 9] $NADP^{\oplus}$; yeast and heart muscle isocitrate dehydrogenase,[10, 11] $NAD^{\oplus}$).

[3] H. von Euler, E. Adler, G. Günther, and M. B. Das, *Z. Physiol. Chem.* **254,** 61 (1938).

[4] H. Holzer and S. Schneider, *Biochem. Z.* **329,** 361 (1957).

[5] M. Damodaran and K. R. Nair, *Biochem. J.* **32,** 1064 (1938).

[6] M. E. Pullman, S. P. Colowick, and N. O. Kaplan, *J. Biol. Chem.* **194,** 593 (1952).

[7] H. von Euler, E. Adler, G. Günther, and H. Hellström, *Z. Physiol. Chem.* **245,** 217 (1937).

[8] E. Adler, H. von Euler, G. Günther, and M. Plass, *Biochem. J.* **33,** 1028 (1939).

[9] G. Siebert, J. Dubuc, R. C. Warner, and G. W. E. Plaut, *J. Biol. Chem.* **226,** 965 (1957).

[10] A. Kornberg and W. E. Pricer, Jr., *J. Biol. Chem.* **189,** 123 (1951).

[11] G. W. E. Plaut and S. C. Sung, *J. Biol. Chem.* **207,** 305 (1954).

(5) Lactate $\rightleftarrows$ pyruvate (muscle lactic dehydrogenase,[12] $NAD^{\oplus}$).

(6) $RCHO + H_2O \rightleftarrows RCOOH + H^{\oplus}$ (aldehyde dehydrogenases,[13] $NAD^{\oplus}$ and $NADP^{\oplus}$).

(7) Glyceraldehyde-3-phosphate $+ HPO_4^{\ominus} \rightleftarrows$ 3-phosphoglycerol phosphate (rabbit muscle glyceraldehyde 3-phosphate dehydrogenase,[14, 15] $NAD^{\oplus}$).

(8) $NADH + 2$ ferricytochrome $c \rightarrow NAD^{\oplus} + H^{\oplus} + 2$ ferrocytochrome c (NADH-cytochrome c reductase [16]).

Other enzyme systems requiring $NAD^{\oplus}$ or $NADP^{\oplus}$ along with a detailed discussion of the above enzymic reactions may be found in Vol. VII of "The Enzymes," P. D. Boyer, H. Lardy, and K. Myrbäck (eds.), Academic Press, New York, 1963.

It is also pertinent to mention several analogs of $NAD^{\oplus}$: (1) the α-anomer of $NAD^{\oplus}$ [17] in which the glycosidic linkage of the nicotinamide riboside grouping is opposite from that in structure (9-1) [2] and is enzymically inactive, (2) $NAD^{\oplus}$ bearing other substitutents at the 3-position of the pyridine ring, 3-acetylpyridine $NAD^{\oplus}$, 3-nicotinic acid $NAD^{\oplus}$, and 3-pyridylaldehyde $NAD^{\oplus}$, which are particularly useful in enzymic studies, and (3) the quaternary pyridinium compounds such as 1-methylnicotinamide and 1-benzylnicotinamide, which eliminate the contribution of the adenine moiety to the absorption spectra and effectively serve as model compounds for the $NAD^{\oplus}$ and $NADP^{\oplus}$ reactions. Our discussion will be concerned mainly with the chemistry of these quaternary 3-substituted pyridinium compounds.

II. REDUCED ENZYMICALLY ACTIVE FORM

It is now firmly established that $NAD^{\oplus}$ and its analogs are all reduced during the enzyme reaction at the 4-position, yielding a 1,4-dihydropyridine derivative. The correct structure of the reduced pyridine nucleotide was first elucidated by Pullman, San Pietro, and Colowick [18] through a

[12] A. H. Mehler, A. Kornberg, S. Grisolia, and S. Ochoa, *J. Biol. Chem.* **174**, 961 (1948).

[13] W. B. Jakoby, in P. D. Boyer, H. Lardy, and K. Myrbäck (eds.) "The Enzymes," Academic Press, New York, 1963, Vol. VII, p. 203.

[14] J. F. Taylor, S. F. Velick, G. T. Cori, C. F. Cori, and M. W. Slein, *J. Biol. Chem.* **173**, 619 (1948).

[15] C. F. Cori, S. F. Velick, and G. T. Cori, *Biochim. Biophys. Acta* **4**, 160 (1950).

[16] E. E. Lockhart and V. R. Potter, *J. Biol. Chem.* **137**, 1 (1941).

[17] N. O. Kaplan, M. M. Ciotti, F. E. Stolzenbach, and N. R. Bachur, *J. Am. Chem. Soc.* **77**, 815 (1955).

[18] M. E. Pullman, A. San Pietro, and S. P. Colowick, *J. Biol. Chem.* **206**, 129 (1954).

reaction sequence commencing with deutero-reduced $NAD^{\oplus}$ prepared through reduction of $NAD^{\oplus}$ with sodium hydrosulfite in a medium of deuterium oxide.   Oxidation of this compound by yeast alcohol dehydrogenase and acetaldehyde followed by enzymic cleavage of the nicotinamide riboside linkage yields some free deutero-oxidized nicotinamide.   Methylation of the deuteronicotinamide with methyl iodide gives 1-methylnicotinamide iodide which, when oxidized by alkaline ferricyanide, forms approximately equal concentrations of the 2- and 6-pyridones [19] with *no* loss of deuterium.   Since reduction in the *meta* position is made unlikely by structural considerations, Pullman, San Pietro, and Colowick concluded that the dithionite reduction occurred at the 4-position and that the enzymically active coenzyme was a 1,4-dihydropyridine derivative (9-2).

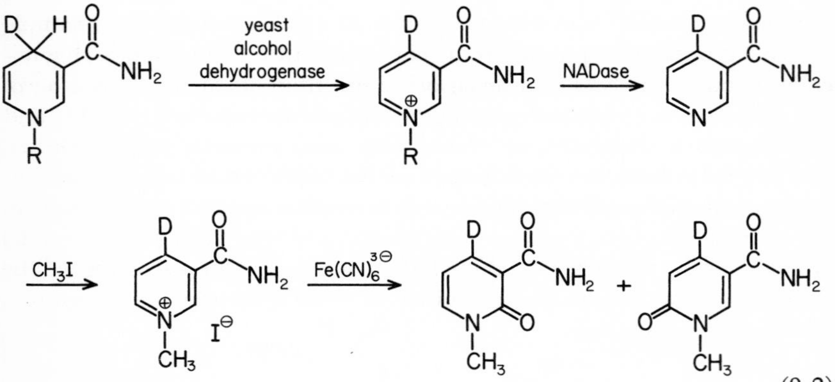

$$(9\text{-}2)$$

This assignment has since been confirmed by many other observations, notably that a 4-deutero-reduced NADH but not a 2- or 6-deutero derivative would transfer deuterium to pyruvic acid in the presence of lactic acid dehydrogenase.[20]   Direct proof for the presence of the deuterium in the 4-position, upon dithionite reduction of the 1-methylnicotinamide analog, has been obtained from n.m.r. studies.[21, 22]

The reduction of $NAD^{\oplus}$ by dithionite in a D_2O medium results in the formation of an asymmetric center.[19, 23]   The structure of the two isomers and their designations are given in (9-3).   The forms are defined on the basis of their reactions with specific enzymes; enzymes of class A (e.g.,

[19] M. E. Pullman and S. P. Colowick, *J. Biol. Chem.* **206**, 121 (1954).

[20] F. A. Loewus, B. Vennesland, and D. L. Harris, *J. Am. Chem. Soc.* **77**, 3391 (1955).

[21] H. E. Dubb, M. Saunders, and J. H. Wang, *J. Am. Chem. Soc.* **80**, 1767 (1958).

[22] R. F. Hutton and F. H. Westheimer, *Tetrahedron* **3**, 73 (1958).

[23] H. F. Fisher, E. E. Conn, B. Vennesland, and F. H. Westheimer, *J. Biol. Chem.* **202**, 687 (1953).

yeast alcohol dehydrogenase)[23] transfer D of form A to a substrate, while
those of Class B (e.g., β-hydroxysteroid dehydrogenase)[24] transfer D of form
B to a substrate. The two classes of enzymes are tabulated in a recent
review.[25] Cornforth and co-workers [26] have demonstrated which of the

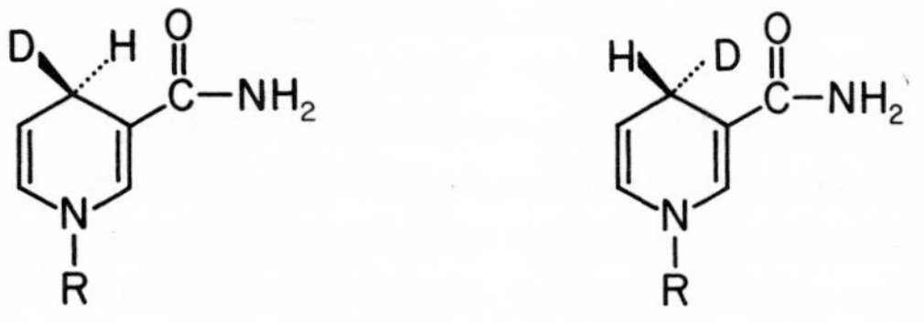

$$ \text{(9-3)} $$

A or α   B or β

hydrogen atoms at C-4 of NADH is involved in the two classes of enzyme
reactions. Starting with two specimens of 4-deutero-NADH prepared
through enzymic reactions which would yield form A and B, respectively,
the assignment was achieved through an oxidative degradation sequence.
The course of an identical procedure applied to 1-methyl-1,4-dihydro-
nicotinamide is illustrated in (9-4). The final product, succinic acid,
must originate from positions 3,4,5,6 of the nicotinamide ring, since no
other interpretation of the course of degradation appears tenable. For

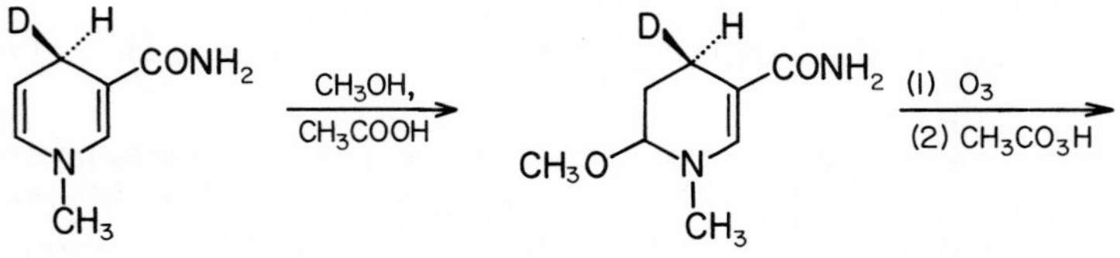

$$ \text{(9-4)} $$

the two specimens of 4-deutero-NADH, the corresponding 2-monodeu-
terosuccinic acids were isolated and compared with a 2-monodeutero-
succinic acid of known absolute configuration (9-5).

The optical rotatory dispersion curves of the 2-monodeuterosuccinic
acid obtained from the 4-deutero-NADH of form A and that of 2R-mono-
deuterosuccinic acid coincided, while the acid derived from form B

[24] A. San Pietro, N. O. Kaplan, and S. P. Colowick, *J. Biol. Chem.* **212,** 941 (1955).
[25] H. R. Levy, P. Talalay, and B. Vennesland, in P. B. D. de la Mare and W. Klyne
(eds.) "Progress in Stereochemistry," Butterworths, London, 1962, Vol. III, Chap 8.
[26] J. W. Cornforth, G. Ryback, G. Popjak, C. Donninger, and G. Schroepfer. Jr.,
Biochem. Biophys. Res. Commun. **9,** 371 (1962).

$$(9\text{-}5)$$

possessed an opposite rotation. The result is thus expressed in the following rule: when an enzyme of class A transfers hydrogen from a substrate to a pyridine nucleotide, the hydrogen is added to that side of the nicotinamide ring on which the ring atoms 1 to 6 appear in anticlockwise order (9-5). Fortuitously the absolute conformation originally and arbitrarily assigned to form A is correct.

The ability to classify the pyridine nucleotide dehydrogenase reactions implies a steric specificity of the hydrogen transfer. This was first demonstrated in the classical work of Vennesland and Westheimer,[23, 27–29] who at the same time showed that the added hydrogen in the reduced $NAD^{\oplus}$ is derived directly from the substrate molecule per se, rather than from the medium in which the reaction is carried out. Two procedures were utilized for demonstrating this direct transfer, and the results are illustrated for the alcohol dehydrogenase reaction in (9-6a,b). The possibility that the hydrogen may be transferred via an oxidation and reduction

$$CH_3CH_2OH + NAD^{\oplus} \underset{D_2O}{\rightleftarrows} CH_3CHO + NADH + H^{\oplus} \quad (9\text{-}6a)$$

$$CH_3CD_2OH + NAD^{\oplus} \underset{H_2O}{\rightleftarrows} CH_3CDO + NADD + H^{\oplus} \quad (9\text{-}6b)$$

of the protein was considered unlikely [30] and experimentally appeared to have been ruled out for yeast alcohol dehydrogenase.[31] It is also disfavored on the basis of present model studies. The observation that the amount of deuterium found in the isolated ethanol (carrying out (9-6a) in the reverse direction) is far below the one atom per molecule that would be required for reduction if the acetaldehyde were reduced as an enol, suggests that the keto compound is the active form in the enzymic reduction.[27, 32]

[27] P. Talalay, F. A. Loewus, and B. Vennesland, *J. Biol. Chem.* **212,** 801 (1955).

[28] F. A. Loewus, P. Ofner, H. F. Fisher, F. H. Westheimer, and B. Vennesland, *J. Biol. Chem.* **202,** 699 (1953).

[29] B. Vennesland, *J. Cellular Comp. Physiol.* **47,** Suppl. 1, 201 (1956).

[30] B. Vennesland and F. H. Westheimer, in W. D. McElroy and B. Glass (eds.) "The Mechanism of Enzyme Action," Johns Hopkins Press, Baltimore, 1954, pp. 357–379.

[31] N. O. Kaplan, S. P. Colowick, and E. F. Neufeld, *J. Biol. Chem.* **195,** 107 (1952).

[32] F. A. Loewus, T. T. Tchen, and B. Vennesland, *J. Biol. Chem.* **212,** 787 (1955).

Significant recent experiments by Schellenberg,[32a] however, have revealed that yeast alcohol dehydrogenase will incorporate tritium into the protein from ethanol-1-H^3 in the presence of NADP$^\oplus$. The amount of tritium found in the protein is sensitive to the isolation technique employed (precipitation by $HClO_4$ or heat at pH 9–11) and is readily reversible, thus explaining the apparent oversight of earlier experiments. Acid hydrolysis of the tritiated enzyme protein indicates that the radioactive carrier is an L-tryptophan with the tritium probably residing on the methylene group of the alanine side chain. It is suggested that tryptophan is reversibly dehydrogenated to an indolenine during enzyme catalysis (9-6c).

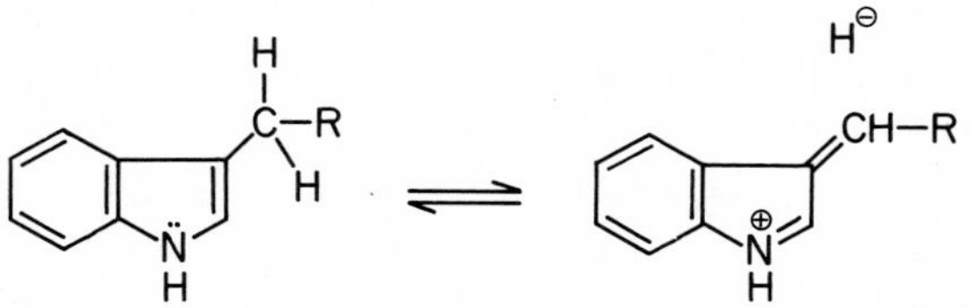

(9-6c)

Chemical models for the suggestions of Schellenberg arise from certain observations on 3-substituted indoles. Thus, Mannich bases of the gramine (9-6d) type [32b] or 3-cyanomethylindoles [32c] serve as alkylating agents forming, as an intermediate, 3-methylene-3H-pseudoindole·

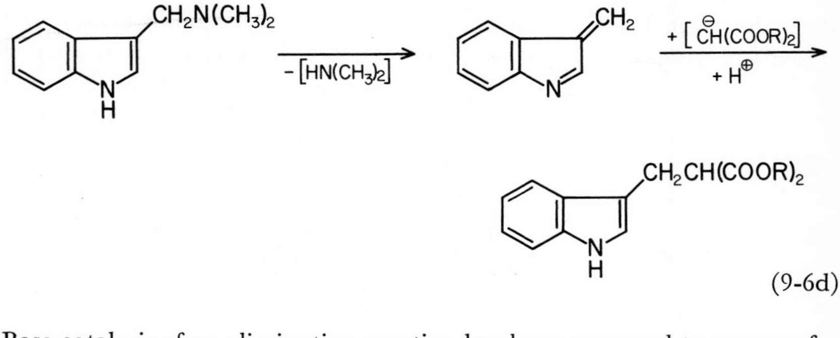

(9-6d)

Base catalysis of an elimination reaction has been proposed to account for the ready LiAlH$_4$ reduction of 3- as compared to 2-hydroxymethylindole (9-6e). It has been found that 3,5-dicarbethoxy-2,6-dimethyl-1,4-dihydropyridine reduces phenyl-α-methylindolidene-methanes in very facile

[32a] K. A. Schellenberg, J. Biol. Chem. 240, 1165 (1965).
[32b] J. D. Albright and H. R. Snyder, J. Am. Chem. Soc. 81, 2239 (1959).
[32c] P. N. James and H. R. Snyder, J. Am. Chem. Soc. 82, 589 (1960).

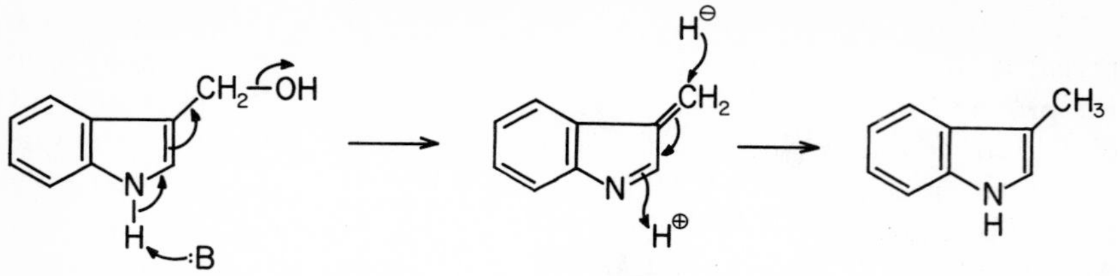

$$(9\text{-}6e)$$

reactions to yield the corresponding indoles in nearly quantitative yield.[32d] Also, it may be noted that compounds of type (9-6f) readily eliminate $X^{\ominus}$

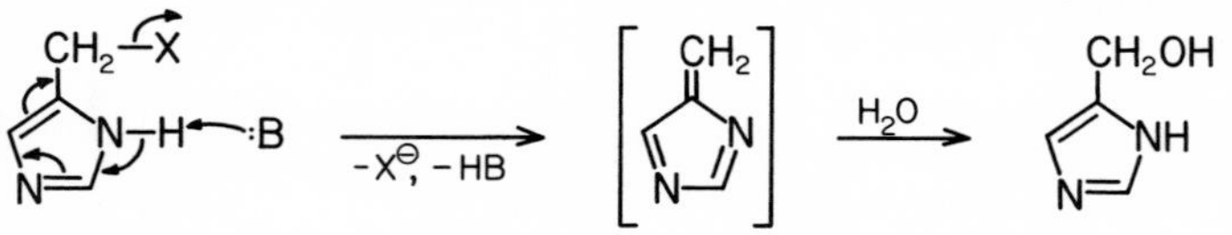

$$(9\text{-}6f)$$

by both general- and specific-base catalysis [32e,f] so that histidine might also be considered as a possible hydrogen transfer vehicle.

Yeast alcohol dehydrogenase is stereospecific not only for NADH but also for the alcohol or acetaldehyde substrate.[33] It was found that deuteroacetaldehyde, when reduced with NADH in the presence of yeast alcohol dehydrogenase, yields an α-monodeuteroethanol which proves to be the enantiomorph of the α-monodeuteroethanol formed by reducing unlabeled acetaldehyde with 4-deutero-NAD possessing form A. The reverse reaction gives labeled and unlabeled acetaldehyde, respectively. With the absolute configuration of $(-)$-ethanol-1-d having been ascertained, the geometry of the enzymic reduction leading to the reversible formation of the alcohol may be pictured [34] as in (9-7). Thus the same hydrogen is being transferred in both directions. At present, absolute

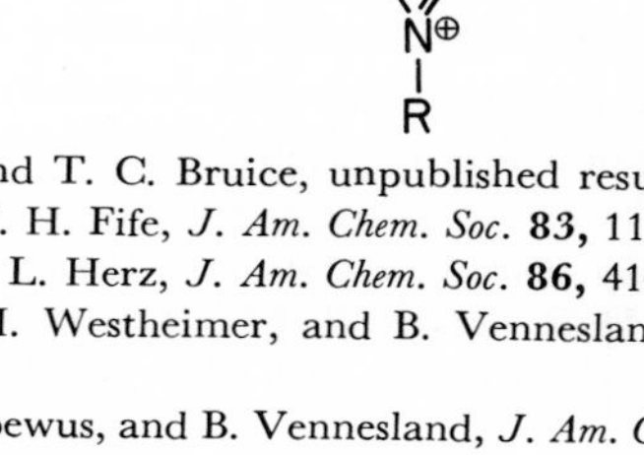

$$(9\text{-}7)$$

[32d] R. W. Huffman and T. C. Bruice, unpublished results.

[32e] T. C. Bruice and T. H. Fife, *J. Am. Chem. Soc.* **83**, 1124 (1961).

[32f] T. C. Bruice and J. L. Herz, *J. Am. Chem. Soc.* **86**, 4109 (1964).

[33] F. A. Loewus, F. H. Westheimer, and B. Vennesland, *J. Am. Chem. Soc.* **75**, 5018 (1953).

[34] H. R. Levy, F. A. Loewus, and B. Vennesland, *J. Am. Chem. Soc.* **79**, 2949 (1957).

stereoselectivity in reduction has been demonstrated only for the acetalde-hyde substrate.   Mosher and co-workers [35] have found that the reduction of a series of unnatural ketone substrates by fermenting yeast leads to stereoselective formation of the corresponding carbinols.   Stereoselectivity varies from values as high as 90% for *n*-propyl phenyl ketone to as low as 12% for ethyl *n*-propyl ketone.   Assuming that the yeast alcohol dehydrogenase system is responsible for these reductions, the authors conclude that the difference in steric requirements of the two groups attached to the carbonyl function is the important factor in determining the configuration of the predominant transition state, and not the absolute preference of one group or the other for a particular site on the enzyme surface.

It is of interest that in the reverse reaction, namely the oxidation of various carbinols with purified yeast alcohol dehydrogenase, van Eys and Kaplan [36] have observed that (+)-2-butanol is oxidized whereas the (−)-isomer does not react, demonstrating a stereoselectivity of 98–100%. However, fermenting yeast reduces methyl ethyl ketone to (+)-2-butanol of 64–67% optical purity.   This raises the yet unanswered question whether a completely different system is involved in the purified yeast oxidation and the fermenting yeast ketone reductions, or whether differences in experimental conditions are involved.

In addition to the concept of steric fit, it has been postulated that the orientation of acetaldehyde relative to the coenzyme is probably achieved by a combination of several bonding factors, including enzyme binding of the polar oxygen atom and hydrophobic-type binding of the methyl group.[29]   However, the stereospecificity of the hydrogen transfer reaction also may be viewed as an example of stereochemical control through a meso-carbon compound.   The reaction of compounds possessing a meso carbon may involve enantiomorphic ground states and diastereoisomeric transition states, leading to the preferred formation of one enantiomorph relative to the other (see Chapter 4).   Preferential binding of the NAD molecule at the $CONH_2$ and pyridine rings could explain the stereospecificity.   This amounts to a special means of stereochemical direction through a meso-carbon compound (as in the three-point attachment hypothesis for citric acid; see Chapter 4).   The binding of NADH, 3-acetyl-pyridine NADH, and thionicotinamide NADH to liver alcohol dehydrogenase has been shown by optical rotatory dispersion to be asymmetric, supporting this contention.[37]   Evidence for the presence of a hydrophobic region in yeast alcohol dehydrogenase which could influence

[35] R. MacLeod, H. Prosser, L. Fickentscher, J. Lanyi, and H. S. Mosher, *Biochemistry* **3**, 838 (1964).

[36] J. van Eys and N. O. Kaplan, *J. Am. Chem. Soc.* **79**, 2782 (1957).

[37] T. K. Li, D. D. Ulmer, and B. L. Vallee, *Biochemistry* **1**, 114 (1962).

the binding of pyridine nucleotides also has been obtained.   It was found
that 1-alkyl-nicotinamide chlorides can competitively inhibit reactions of
this enzyme; their effectiveness increases with increasing chain length of
the 1-alkyl substituent.[38]

It has been observed [39] with n.m.r. spectra that the two C-4 protons on
the dihydropyridine ring of 1-benzyl-1,4-dihydronicotinamide and with
less certainty of NADH are in equivalent environments.   Thus the
dihydropyridine ring is either planar or if boat-like is undergoing rapid
rotational enantiomeric interconversion, which disfavors but does not
rule out a structural conformation of the coenzyme as the reason for the
stereospecificity of the hydrogen transfer to and from the pyridine ring.
The enzyme may impose a structural constraint on the coenzyme but this
remains to be seen.[40]   With this introduction to the more salient characteristics of the enzymic dehydrogenase reactions, attention will be centered
on the properties of $NAD^{\oplus}$ and $NADP^{\oplus}$ analogs before further discussion
of the mechanistic aspects of the hydrogen transfer.

III. ABSORPTION SPECTRA

It is appropriate to begin with a consideration of the ultraviolet
spectra of $NAD^{\oplus}$, NADH, and their analogs which will be useful in char-
acterizing the products obtained in their chemical transformations.   The
spectra of $NAD^{\oplus}$ and NADH are shown in Fig. 9-1.   The peak absorption of $NAD^{\oplus}$ occurs at 259 mμ ($\epsilon = 17,000$) [41] and may be attributed to
absorption by both the adenine and nicotinamide portions of the mole-
cule.   The spectrum of $NAD^{\oplus}$, unlike pyridine, is not affected by a
change in pH over the range 2–10.   Enzymic or chemical reduction of
$NAD^{\oplus}$ results in the appearance of a new maximum at 340 mμ ($\epsilon = 6220$),[42, 43] which correlates with a decrease in absorption at 260 mμ.
The absorption maxima for a series of $NAD^{\oplus}$ and NADH analogs are
given in Tables 9-1 and 9-2.   (Additional spectra for various other analogs may be found especially in Refs. 44–48.)

[38] B. M. Anderson and C. D. Anderson, *Biochem. Biophys. Res. Commun.* **16,** 258 (1964).

[39] W. L. Meyer, H. R. Mahler, and R. H. Baker, Jr., *Biochim. Biophys. Acta* **64,** 353 (1962).

[40] F. A. Loewus, H. R. Levy, and B. Vennesland, *J. Biol. Chem.* **223,** 589 (1956).

[41] J. M. Siegel, G. A. Montgomery, and R. M. Bock, *Arch. Biochem. Biophys.* **82,** 288 (1959).

[42] B. L. Horecker and A. Kornberg, *J. Biol. Chem.* **175,** 385 (1948).

[43] N. O. Kaplan, in P. D. Boyer, H. Lardy, and K. Myrbäck (eds.) "The Enzymes," Academic Press, New York, 1960, Vol. III, pp. 105–169.

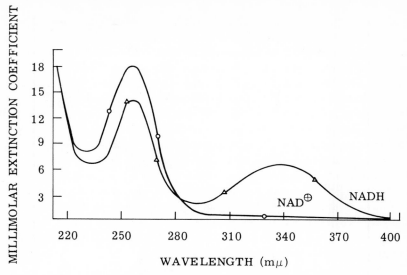

Fig. 9-1 *Absorption spectra of NAD$^{\oplus}$ and NADH.* (*Ref. 41.*)

Table 9-1 *Spectra of pyridinium ions*

No.	Pyridinium ion	λ_{max}	ϵ_{max}	Solvent	Ref.
(1)	1-(2,6-Dichlorobenzyl)-(Br$^{\ominus}$)	260 mμ	4680	CH$_3$OH	44
(2)	1-(2,6-Dichlorobenzyl)-3-carboxy-(Br$^{\ominus}$)	266 mμ	4130	H$_2$O	45
(3)	1-(2,6-Dichlorobenzyl)- 3-N,N'-dimethylcarbamido-(Br$^{\ominus}$)	268 mμ	4480	H$_2$O	45
(4)	1-(2,6-Dichlorobenzyl)- 3-carbomethoxy-(Br$^{\ominus}$)	267 mμ	4180	H$_2$O	45
(5)	1-(2,6-Dichlorobenzyl)- 3-carbamido-(Br$^{\ominus}$)	275 mμ	4000	H$_2$O	45
(6)	1-(2,6-Dichlorobenzyl)- 3-acetyl-(Br$^{\ominus}$)	268 mμ	4070	H$_2$O	45
(7)	1-(2,6-Dichlorobenzyl)-3-cyano-(Br$^{\ominus}$)	270 mμ	4070	H$_2$O	45
(8)	1-Methyl-3-carbamido-(I$^{\ominus}$)	260 mμ	—	H$_2$O	46
(9)	1-Methyl-3-carbamido-(ClO$_4^{\ominus}$)	265 mμ	4480	H$_2$O	47
		210 mμ			
(10)	1-Methyl-3-benzoyl-(I$^{\ominus}$)	226 mμ	—	H$_2$O	46
		268 mμ	—	H$_2$O	46
(11)	1-Ribose-(β)-3-carbamido-(I$^{\ominus}$)	265 mμ	—	H$_2$O	48
(12)	1-Ribose-5-phosphate-3-carbamido-(I$^{\ominus}$)	265 mμ	—	H$_2$O	48

Table 9-2 *Spectra of dihydropyridines*

No.		1,4-Dihydropyridine (Na$_2$S$_2$O$_4$)		1,6-Dihydropyridine (NaBH$_4$)		Solvent	Ref.
		λ_{max}	ϵ_{max}	λ_{max}	ϵ_{max}		
(1)	1-Methyl-3-cyano-	340 mμ	5600	2400 3490	5400 4950	H$_2$O	49
(2)	1-Methyl-3-carbamido-	360 mμ 355 mμ	—	—	—	H$_2$O 95% EtOH	48 22
(3)	1-(2,6-Dichlorobenzyl)-3-cyano-	335 mμ	6250	240 350	6100 6020	CH$_3$OH	44
(4)	1-(2,6-Dichlorobenzyl)-3-N,N'-dimethylcarbamido-	339 mμ	4820	265 351	7350 5950	CH$_3$OH	44
(5)	1-(2,6-Dichlorobenzyl)-3-carbamido-	350 mμ	7510	265 355	9840 7450	CH$_3$OH	44
(6)	1-(2,6-Dichlorobenzyl)-3-carbomethoxy-	352 mμ	7740	259 353	7650 7970	CH$_3$OH	44
(7)	1-(2,6-Dichlorobenzyl)-3-N-phenylcarbamido-	361 mμ	10810	280 363	21980 11670	CH$_3$OH	44
(8)	1-Glucose-β-3-carbamido-	332 mμ	—	—	—	H$_2$O	48
(9)	1-Ribose-β-3-carbamido-	332 mμ	—	—	—	H$_2$O	48
(10)	1-Benzyloxymethyl-3-carbamido-	355 mμ	6200	—	—	CH$_3$OH	50
(11)	Ribose-5-phosphate-	332 mμ	—	—	—	H$_2$O	48

The electronic transition in the 1,4-dihydropyridines (Table 9-2) with an electron-attracting 3-substituent corresponds to the charge rearrangement shown in equation (9-8).[44]   The transition energy for such a process is lowered by electron-attracting groups at position 3 capable of interacting

$$\underset{5\quad 6\quad 1\quad 2\quad 3}{\text{>C=C-N-C=C-X=Y}} \quad \xrightarrow{h\nu} \quad \text{>C=C-}\overset{\oplus}{\text{N}}\text{=C-C=X-Y}^{\ominus}$$

$$\text{II}$$

(9-8)

through resonance and inductive effects or by electron-donating groups at position 1, and resulting in a shift of the absorption maximum to longer wavelengths.   Comparison of compounds 8, 9, 10, 5, and 2 illustrates the effect of increased electron supply to the nitrogen atom.   Compounds 3, 4, 5, 6, and 7 reflect an increasing ability of the 3-substituent to conjugate with the dihydropyridine ring.   A similar trend is not as obvious in the pyridinium compounds, but the appearance of a second absorption maximum, for 10 as well as for the 1-methyl derivatives [46] of 3-isobutyrylpyridine, 3-pyridylacryloamide, and thionicotinamide, presumably arises due to the increased resonance of these compounds through the conjugating effect of the groups substituted at position 3 of the pyridine ring.[51]

The importance of the dipolar structure (II) in equation (9-8) has been assessed through dipole moment measurements and the effect of solvent on λ_{max}.   A lower transition energy or a shift to longer wavelengths is anticipated in more polar solvents.   Experimental measurements [52] of the solvent effect on λ_{max} for 1-benzyl-1,4-dihydronicotinamide reveal a moderate shift from 340 mμ in diethyl ether to 357 mμ in water.   As a comparison it may be noted that the λ_{max} of (9-9) is shifted 40 mμ toward longer wavelengths on passing from methanol to aqueous

$$(\text{CH}_3)_2\text{N-}\underset{\text{H}}{\text{C}}\text{=}\underset{\text{H}}{\text{C}}\text{-}\underset{\text{H}}{\text{C}}\text{=}\underset{\text{H}}{\text{C}}\text{-C}\overset{\text{O}}{\diagdown}_{\text{H}}$$

(9-9)

[44] K. Wallenfels and H. Schüly, *Ann.* **621**, 106 (1959).

[45] K. Wallenfels and H. Diekmann, *Ann.* **621**, 166 (1959).

[46] B. M. Anderson, C. J. Ciotti, and N. O. Kaplan, *J. Biol. Chem.* **234**, 1219 (1959).

[47] E. M. Kosower and S. W. Bauer, *J. Am. Chem. Soc.* **82**, 2191 (1960).

[48] A. Stock, E. Sann, and G. Pfleiderer, *Ann.* **647**, 188 (1961).

[49] K. Schenker and J. Druey, *Helv. Chim. Acta* **42**, 1960 (1959).

[50] K. Wallenfels, M. Gellrich, and F. Kubowitz, *Ann.* **621**, 137 (1959).

[51] M. L. Swain, A. Eisner, C. F. Woodward, and B. A. Brice, *J. Am. Chem. Soc.* **71**, 1341 (1949).

[52] G. Cilento, E. de Cavalho Filho, and A. C. Giora Albanese, *J. Am. Chem. Soc.* **80**, 4472 (1958).

solution.[53]   Determination of the dipole moment of 1-benzyl-1,4-dihydro-nicotinamide in dioxane solution gives a value of 3.89 D, between that of formamide (3.0 D) [54] and that of urea (4.56 D).[55]   Collectively these data suggest that it is not warranted to regard the dihydronicotinamides as existing predominantly in a dipolar ground state structure as previously thought.[56—58]

With certain enzymes, namely liver alcohol dehydrogenase and liver and heart lactic dehydrogenases, NADH forms complexes in which the ultraviolet absorption maximum has shifted to shorter wavelengths.[59, 60] The shape of the absorption curve and the magnitude of ϵ suggest that the electronic transition observed for the NADH-enzyme complex is the same as that for NADH.[61]   Possible rationales for this behavior are that (1) in view of the effect of solvent on λ_{max} the enzyme provides a nonpolar medium for the NADH molecule,[62] and (2) a positive charge exists in close proximity to the nitrogen of the dihydropyridine ring.[63,63a]   The former has been criticized on the grounds that it is unreasonable to expect the enzymic generation of pyridinium ion in a nonpolar medium without access to water for solvation.[61]   The latter proposition does enjoy experimental support based on a study of the absorption of an α,β-unsaturated ketone system (9-10).   The ketone with the positively charged nitrogen

$$(9\text{-}10)$$

absorbs at shorter wavelengths than the analog which has a methylene in place of the nitrogen.[63]   A similar observation has been made in a study to be discussed in the section on charge-transfer behavior.   Although a choice between the two is problematic, it may be concluded that the

[53] D. L. Peterson and W. T. Simpson, *J. Am. Chem. Soc.* **79,** 2375 (1957).

[54] G. D. Burdun and P. B. Kantor, *Dokl. Akad. Nauk SSSR* **67,** 985 (1949).

[55] W. D. Kumler and G. M. Fohlen, *J. Am. Chem. Soc.* **64,** 1944 (1942).

[56] N. O. Kaplan and M. M. Ciotti, *J. Biol. Chem.* **221,** 823 (1956).

[57] K. Wallenfels and H. Sund, *Biochem. Z.* **329,** 59 (1957).

[58] H. R. Mahler and J. Douglas, *J. Am. Chem. Soc.* **79,** 1159 (1957).

[59] J. van Eys, F. E. Stolzenbach, L. Sherwood, and N. O. Kaplan, *Biochim. Biophys. Acta* **27,** 63 (1958).

[60] H. Theorell and R. Bonnichsen, *Acta Chem. Scand.* **5,** 1105 (1951).

[61] E. M. Kosower, "Molecular Biochemistry," McGraw-Hill, New York, 1962, pp. 166–219.

[62] G. Weber, private communication, in S. Shifrin and N. O. Kaplan, *Advan. Enzymol.* **22,** 353 (1960).

[63] E. M. Kosower and D. C. Remy, *Tetrahedron* **5,** 281 (1959).

[63a] E. M. Kosower, *Biochim, Biophys. Acta* **56,** 474 (1962).

Zn(II) ions of liver alcohol dehydrogenase [64] probably are not located in the neighborhood of the amide group of NADH, for this should lead to a lowering of the transition energy required for excitation by light, placing the absorption maximum at longer wavelengths.

Inspection of Table 9-2 reveals the presence of two absorption bands for the 1,6-dihydropyridine derivatives. The appearance of a second band at 265–275 mμ arises from cross-conjugation of the vinyl-amine group and the vinylogous amide group.[49]

The third possible isomer, a 1,2-dihydropyridine, is expected to be characterized by an absorption maximum at abnormally long wavelengths. This should result from the extension of the conjugating π system by the incorporation of an additional double bond. Wallenfels and Schüly have reported a λ_{max} of 392 mμ for a dihydropyridine product obtained from the NaBH$_4$ reduction of 1-(2,6-dichlorobenzyl)-4,6-dimethylnicotinamide bromide, which they attribute to a 1,2-dihydropyridine structure.[65]

Elucidation of much of the chemistry of dihydropyridines and pyridinium salts is based on identification of various products by analogy to the ultraviolet absorption spectra of the reduced and oxidized forms discussed previously. Later discussions will center on additional spectral evidence which has been associated with charge-transfer behavior.

IV. REACTION AT THE PYRIDINE RING

A. Acid and Base Properties

1. PYRIDINIUM IONS   The oxidized forms of the coenzymes are stable in acid but are destroyed by alkali. In dilute alkali NAD$^{\oplus}$ undergoes cleavage at the nicotinamide riboside linkage, liberating nicotinamide and the adenosine nucleotide [66] which may undergo further hydrolysis.[67, 68] At pH 7 little inactivation of NAD$^{\oplus}$ is brought about by heating at 100° for 5 minutes.[69]

The action of strong alkali on NAD$^{\oplus}$ produces a material having an absorption maximum at 345 mμ which shifts to a maximum at 360 mμ

[64] B. L. Vallee, in P. D. Boyer, H. Lardy, and K. Myrbäck (eds.) "The Enzymes," Academic Press, New York, 1960, Vol. III, Chap. 15, pp. 225–276.

[65] K. Wallenfels and H. Schüly, Ann. **621**, 215 (1959).

[66] N. O. Kaplan, S. P. Colowick, and C. C. Barnes, J. Biol. Chem. **191**, 461 (1951).

[67] F. Schlenk, H. von Euler, H. Heiwinkel, W. Gleim, and H. Nyström, Z. Physiol. Chem. **247**, 23 (1937).

[68] R. Vestin, F. Schlenk, and H. von Euler, Ber. **70**, 1369 (1937).

[69] S. P. Colowick, N. O. Kaplan, and M. M. Ciotti, J. Biol. Chem. **191**, 447 (1951).

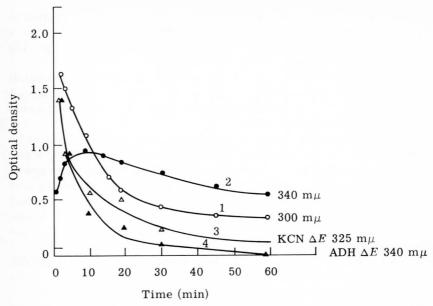

Fig. 9-2 *Time course of NAD$^\oplus$ reactions with alkali. NAD$^\oplus$ (2 × 10^{-3} M) was placed in 0.17 N KOH at 23°C. Aliquots were removed after the indicated time intervals and examined for light absorption at 300 mμ (curve 1) and 340 mμ (curve 2) for ability to react with 1 M KCN (curve 3), and for ability to be reduced by alcohol and yeast alcohol dehydrogenase (curve 4). (Ref. 70.)*

with time.[66] Re-examination of this reaction disclosed that the addition of 0.17 N KOH to NAD$^\oplus$ leads to the apparent instantaneous appearance of an absorption maximum at 290 mμ which decays with time, leading to the relatively slow development of the known maximum in the 340–360 mμ region.[70] The same temporal spectra relationships seem to exist for nicotinamide mononucleotide and nicotinamide riboside. Difference spectra for 1-methylnicotinamide iodide in 0.3 N KOH solution reveal the very rapid formation of an absorption maximum at 282 mμ and the subsequent absorption of light at 360 mμ.

The relationship between the chemical and enzymic reactivity and the spectral changes of NAD$^\oplus$ in an alkaline medium was examined by assessing the ability of NAD$^\oplus$ to react (1) with cyanide (see p. 199), and (2) with alcohol and yeast alcohol dehydrogenase. Both the cyanide and alcohol dehydrogenase activities are maximal immediately after alkali addition, but suffer a decrease with time that parallels the loss of absorption at 290 mμ (Fig. 9-2). Concurrent with the loss of chemical and

[70] R. M. Burton and N. O. Kaplan, *Arch. Biochem. Biophys.* **101,** 139 (1963).

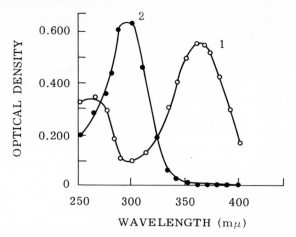

Fig. 9-3   *Spectra of 1-methylnicotinamide-alkali product and acid product.   1-Methyl-nicotinamide iodide was reacted with alkali, and the product was isolated.   Curve 1, spectrum of alkali product in water.   Curve 2, spectrum of alkali product after acid decomposition.   (Ref. 70.)*

enzymic activity are the appearance of the absorption at 340 mμ and an increase in the fluorescence of the solution.

Measurements of the initial rapid formation of the 280–290 mμ peak were extrapolated to zero time for 1-methylnicotinamide iodide, nicotinamide mononucleotide, and NAD$^{\oplus}$ at varying concentrations of the pyridinium derivatives.   The data indicate a linear dependence of the optical density (concentration of the 290-mμ species) on the initial concentration of the pyridinium ion.   Variation in the KOH concentration for 1-methylnicotinamide iodide reveals that the concentration of the 290-mμ absorbing product increases linearly with the one-half power of KOH activity.   All attempts to isolate the 290-mμ product of this derivative were unsuccessful; rapid neutralization of the alkaline medium resulted in its reconversion to starting material, and partitioning into a nonpolar solvent led only to trapping of the 360-mμ product.   Some hydrolysis of the amide group was detected.   Isolation of the 360-mμ product led to its postulated identification as 1-methyl-6-hydroxy-3-carbamido-1,6-dihydropyridine, whose spectrum along with that of the product resulting from its acid decomposition is given in Fig. 9-3.

It is a long-established experimental finding that the addition of hydroxide ions to heterocyclic bases, such as *N*-alkylquinolinium salts, gives rise to the corresponding pseudo-base.[71]   Furthermore, pyridinium

[71] W. J. Gensler, in R. C. Elderfield (ed.) "Heterocyclic Compounds," Wiley, New York, 1952, Vol. IV, Chap. 3.

salts easily undergo nucleophilic addition reactions, as later discussion will demonstrate. Related to the hydroxide ion addition, therefore, is the study by Hantzsch and Kalb, who have subjected 1-(2,4-dinitrophenyl)-pyridinium chloride to cold alkali, forming an intermediate which upon aqueous acid cleavage yields $\Delta^{2,3}$-pentene-1,5-dialdehyde and 2,4-dinitro-aniline (addition of hydroxide ion at the 1- and 6-positions).[72] Kosower [61] has reported that 1-methyl-2- and -4-cyanopyridinium ions hydrolyze in alkali to a mixture of 1-methyl-2- or -4-pyridone and 1-methyl-2- or -4-car-bamidopyridinium ion, whereas the 3-cyanopyridinium ion yields 1-methyl-3-carbamidopyridinium ion along with ring-opened products from addition of hydroxide ion at the 6-position.

In view of these findings, Burton and Kaplan [70] have suggested the sequence (9-11) for the alkali-acid transformation of 1-methyl-3-car-bamidopyridinium iodide. The proposition of a charge-transfer inter-

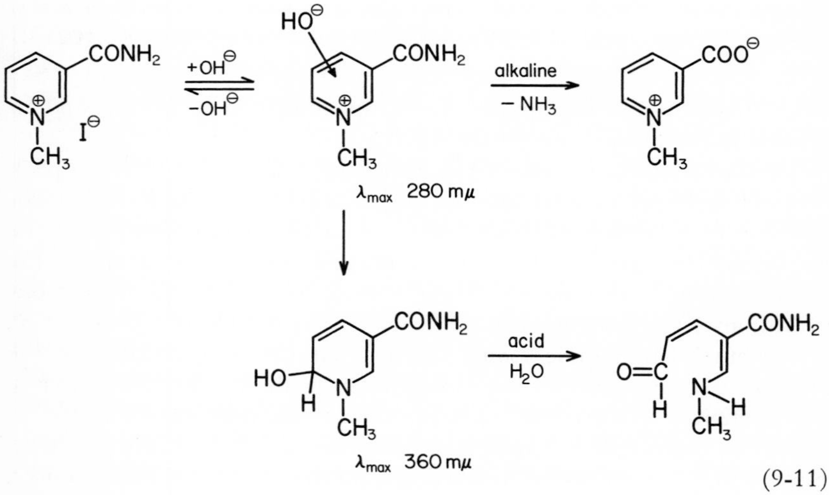

$$(9\text{-}11)$$

mediate for the 280-mμ absorbing product derives support from its rapid, reversible formation and nonfluorescence. In general the oxidized pyridine nucleotides and the model analogs do not fluoresce, whereas the reduced forms and most of the addition products exhibit strong fluo-rescence. The proposal of 6-hydroxy-1,6-dihydropyridine is consistent with synthetic routes. However, it is difficult to reconcile the above scheme with the observed half-order dependency on hydroxide ion activity.

[72] H. S. Mosher, in R. C. Elderfield (ed.) "Heterocyclic Compounds," Wiley, New York, 1950, Vol. I.

In view of the results of Anderson and Berkelhammer [73] and Dittmer and Kolyer,[74] the reaction may involve the formation of a dimolecular ether of a pseudo-base, which thus would explain the observed kinetic order, although an intermediate complex of some nature is still required to rationalize the initial 280-mμ absorbing product.   The treatment of 1-benzyl-3-carbamidopyridinium chloride with sodium hydroxide leads to the precipitation of the dimolecular ether formulated as a 1,4-dihydro structure [74] (9-12 I).   The assignment is based on the presence of only one ultraviolet absorption maximum at 330–335mμ in the nonpolar solvent, benzene or ether.   A dimolecular ether obtained by treatment of 1-benzyl-3-acetylpyridinium chloride with hydroxide ion also has been isolated [73] and assigned a 1,2-dihydro structure, although it is quite probable in the light of subsequent spectral data that this dimolecular ether also possesses the 1,4-dihydro structure.   The data of Fig. 9-3 (curve 1) can be explained without invoking a 1,6-dihydro structure by assuming that the dimolecular ether partially dissociates, leading to the 260-mμ absorption peak.   Evidence for this dissociation has been obtained by Dittmer and Kolyer through a solvent study of the ultraviolet spectrum of a series of dimolecular ethers.[74a]   It is of further interest to note that treatment of 1-benzyl-3-carbamidopyridinium chloride with sodium hydroxide in dilute ethanol results in the formation of a cyclic trimer, whose structure is based on extensive spectral studies, analysis, molecular weight, and chemical reactions (9-12 II).   The precursor may be the ylid (9-12 III).

Some uncertainty also is associated with the exact structure of the acidified product in (9-11), although the presence of a free carbonyl group is suggested by a test indicative of oxime formation.   The proposed saturation of the 4,5 double bond cannot be achieved through a simple mechanistic pathway without introduction of hydroxyl into one of these positions.   Moreover, if one commences with a 1,4-dihydro dimer structure, a pathway analogous to that stated in the following section may be

[73] A. G. Anderson, Jr., and G. Berkelhammer, *J. Org. Chem.* **23,** 1109 (1958).

[74] D. C. Dittmer and J. M. Kolyer, *J. Org. Chem.* **28,** 2288 (1963).

[74a] An alternate explanation for the behavior of 1-methyl-3-carbamidopyridinium iodide in alkali has been advanced recently by R. B. Martin and J. G. Hull, *J. Biol. Chem.* **239,** 1237 (1964).   The rapid spectral changes at 290 mμ in weakly alkaline solution (up to 2.0 *M* NaOH) are not attributed to a charge-transfer complex but rather to an equilibrium reaction between substrate and OH$^\ominus$, resulting in ionization of an amide hydrogen (this will also rationalize the half-order dependency on OH$^\ominus$). Moreover, at these OH$^\ominus$ concentrations, the slower reaction appears to be alkaline hydrolysis of the neutral amide group.   Above 2.0 *M* NaOH, Martin and Hull's results parallel those of Kaplan.   It remains of interest to establish the conditions under which dimer formation becomes important.

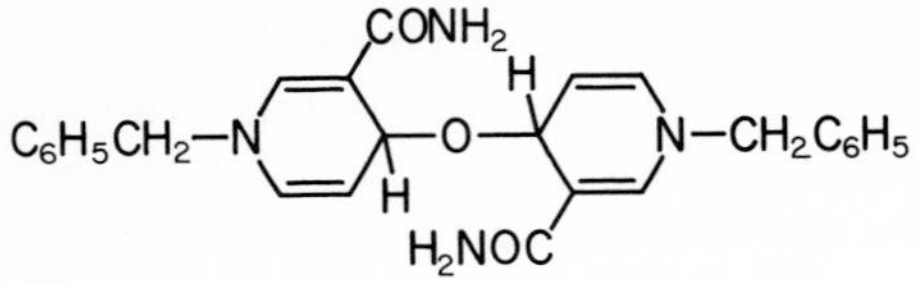

(9-12)

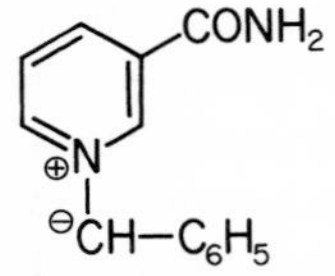

visualized, leading to the hydration of the 5,6 double bond with the loss of absorption in the 360-mμ region. The dimeric structure also may break down with the formation of a carbonyl function at the 4-position; however, further experimentation is required to clarify this and other possibilities.

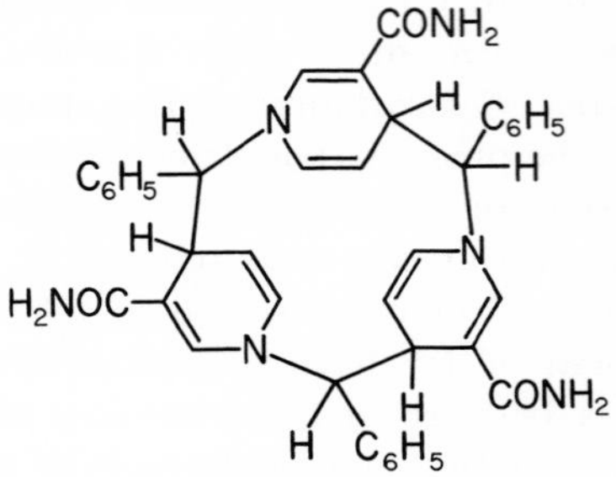

2. DIHYDROPYRIDINES   Both NADH and NADPH [75-77] as well as other 1-substituted 1,4- and 1,6-dihydronicotinamides are unstable in acid [45, 48, 78, 79] but relatively stable in basic solution.   NADH and other 1,4-dihydronicotinamide derivatives undergo a rapid alteration in acidic solutions, resulting in a shift of the characteristic ultraviolet absorption band in the 340–360 mμ region downward to around 290 mμ.   The primary acid-modification product undergoes a slower secondary reaction to form less strongly absorbing products.   From the acid decomposition of 1-benzyl-3-acetyl-1,4-dihydropyridine, Anderson and Berkelhammer [78] have isolated two crystalline products which have been identified as the 6-hydroxy adduct and its dimeric ether.   On the other hand, Segal and Stein [80] have proposed that the product is a 5-hydroxy adduct on the basis that (1) the 1-benzyl-1,4- and -1,6-dihydropyridines yield identical prod-

[75] O. Warburg and W. Christian, *Biochem. Z.* **274,** 112 (1934).

[76] P. Karrer, G. Schwarzenbach, F. Benz, and U. Solmssen, *Helv. Chim. Acta* **19,** 811 (1936).

[77] P. Karrer, B. H. Ringier, J. Buchi, H. Fritzsche, and U. Solmssen, *Helv. Chim. Acta* **20,** 55 (1937).

[78] A. G. Anderson, Jr., and G. Berkelhammer, *J. Am. Chem. Soc.* **80,** 992 (1958).

[79] K. Wallenfels and H. Schüly, *Biochem. Z.,* **329,** 75 (1957).

[80] R. Segal and G. Stein, *J. Chem. Soc.* 5254 (1960).

ucts, and (2) the different rate of disappearance of the two derivatives excludes a fast isomerization which might precede the addition of water. This interpretation of the rate data, however, ignores the fact that a reversible acid-catalyzed isomerization of the 1,6-dihydropyridine derivative to the 1,4 compound would alter the rate of disappearance of the former in direct proportion to the magnitude of the isomerization constant.

Metzler and co-workers have studied the acidic transformation of NADH and 1-propyl-1,4-dihydronicotinamide spectrophotometrically in the presence of a series of acids.[81]   Decay of 1-propyl-1,4-dihydronicotinamide (NPrNH) in 0.001 M HCl, in acetate buffer at pH 5, or in phosphate buffer at pH 7 leads to what is apparently the same compound, all solutions displaying identical ultraviolet absorption spectra, as in Fig. 9-4.   The observed spectral shift of NPrNH is completely reversible before the secondary reaction takes place, whereas that for NADH has been reported to be irreversible.[82]   The sharp isosbestic points of Fig. 9-4 do not reveal the existence of any intermediates between NPrNH and that of the primary acid-modification product.   Spectrophotometric titration of the primary acid product from NPrNH gives a titration curve which could be fitted to that resulting from a single ionizable group of $pK_a' = 2.3 \pm 0.1$, or, when applied to the primary acid product from NADH, indicates a $pK_a' = 0.6$.   The ionizing group may be the carbamide moiety whose pK_a' might be altered by possible hydrogen bonding to the dihydropyridine ring and the amino group of adenine (only for NADH).

The experimentally observed first-order rate constants for the conversion of NPrNH to the primary acid-modification product in general can be described by equation (9-13):

$$k = k_0 + k_H a_H + k_{HA}[HA] \tag{9-13}$$

where k_0, k_H, and k_{HA} are the catalytic constants associated with water, hydronium ion, and the buffer, respectively.   The values of k_0 and k_H were obtained by independent measurements in water and dilute HCl, with the latter value being corroborated by those obtained from buffered solutions at pH's where k_0 is negligible.   For several of the acids, namely the conjugate acids of pyridine, 2-picoline, and imidazole and the bisulfite anion, plots of $(k - k_0)/a_H$ versus [HA] were nonlinear, the conjugate acids of all but bisulfite anion exhibiting a saturation effect with increasing concentration, while the bisulfite data could be fitted by the inclusion of an additional term $k'[HSO_3^{\ominus}]^2$.   The full significance of the nonlinear behavior awaits further investigation.

[81] C. C. Johnston, J. L. Gardner, C. H. Suelter, and D. E. Metzler, *Biochemistry* **2**, 689 (1963).
[82] G. W. Rafter, S. Chaykin, and E. G. Krebs, *J. Biol. Chem.* **208**, 799 (1954).

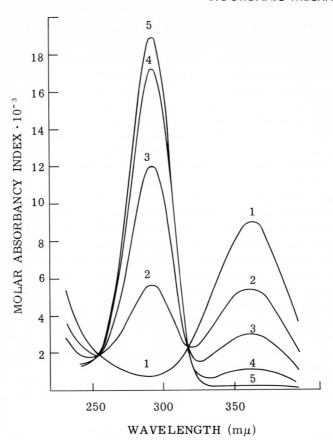

Fig. 9-4   *Absorption spectra of 1-propyl-1,4-dihydronicotinamide (NPrNH) and of its primary acid modification product.   Curve 1 is the spectrum of freshly recrystallized NPrNH in 0.5 M NaCl solution at pH 8.7.   Curves 2–5 were measured at various times after plunging an 0.1-ml aliquot of stock NPrNH solution into 3.0 ml phosphate buffer of pH 7.1 and ionic strength 0.5.   Curve 2 was obtained with a recording spectrophotometer with measurements starting at 400 mμ immediately after mixing (60 sec or less) at a scanning rate of 150 mμ/min.   Curve 3 was begun 6 min after mixing and curves 4 and 5 at 18 and 50 min respectively.   (Ref. 81.)*

The kinetic behavior of the secondary acid-modification reaction can be described by equation (9-14):

$$k = \frac{k_1 a_H}{K_a' + a_H} + \frac{k_2 K_a'}{K_a' + a_H} \qquad (9\text{-}14)$$

where K_a' is the apparent acid dissociation constant of the primary acid-modification product (in agreement with the spectrophotometric pK_a'), and k_1 and k_2 are the rate constants associated with the protonated and nonprotonated forms of the primary acid-modification product, respectively. Burton and Kaplan [83] in a related study have reported that the addition of bisulfite or hydroxylamine leads to the respective stabilization or acceleration of the disappearance of the primary acid product obtained from NADH. Furthermore, they have found that the primary acid product from NADH gives a positive Hinsburg test, which is interpreted as signifying dihydropyridine ring cleavage and fission of the ribose-nitrogen bond. Their spectral studies of model compounds lead to the generalization that the 290-mμ absorbing chromophore is NH_2—CH=CH—CO—.

In spite of the latter evidence the initial acid-modification reaction of 1,4-dihydropyridine derivatives may be viewed as a general-acid catalyzed hydration at the 5-6-position [81] or a kinetically indistinguishable pre-equilibrium protonation followed by a general-base catalyzed addition of water (9-15). A third possibility is a concerted catalysis in which HA

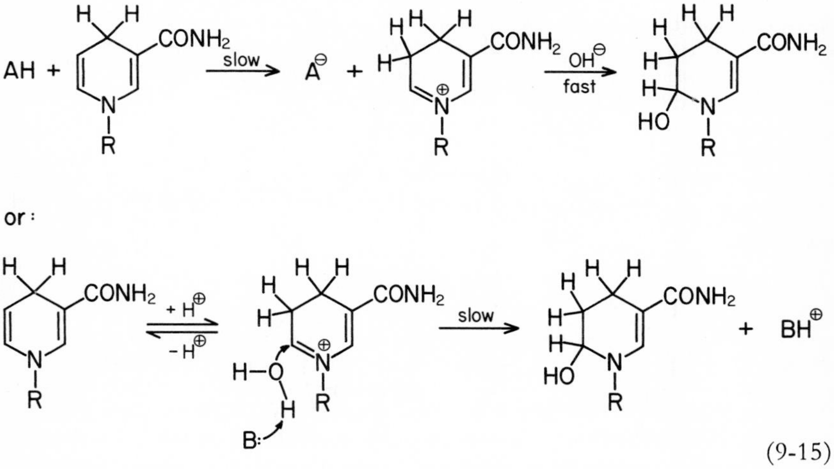

or:

$$(9\text{-}15)$$

serves as both a nucleophile and general-acid catalyst (9-16). There is no spectrophotometric evidence for the requisite intermediate, nor does the existence of a single Brönsted plot support this latter proposal (Fig. 9-5). On the other hand, Stock, Sann, and Pfleiderer [48] have interpreted their spectral study of the same systems as indicating an acetate-dihydro-pyridine adduct, on the basis of a small shift in the position of the isosbestic point with time. Consequently, a clear choice is not presently possible.

[83] R. M. Burton and N. O. Kaplan, *Arch. Biochem. Biophys.* **101**, 150 (1963).

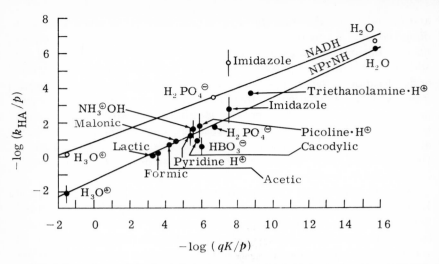

Fig. 9-5   *Brönsted plot for the hydration of 1-propyl-1, 4-dihydronicotinamide and NADH. The negative logarithm of the catalysis constant, k_{HA}, divided by p, the number of equivalent dissociable protons, is plotted against the negative logarithm of the acid dissociation constant K, multiplied by the statistical correction factor q/p, where q is the number of equivalent sites in the conjugate base available for protonation.   The solid lines represent the equations $k_{HA}/p = 23.2(qK/p)^{0.48}$ for NPrNH, and $k_{HA}/p = 0.12\ (qK/p)^{0.38}$ for NADH.   (Ref. 81.)*

The influence of electron-withdrawing substituents in the 1- and 3-positions acts to accelerate the overall rate, in accord with all three proposed pathways.

$$\text{(scheme)} \tag{9-16}$$

In contrast to the aforementioned mechanisms is one advocated by Burton and Kaplan,[83] who propose a ring-opened primary acid-modification product (9-17).   Protonation at the ring nitrogen followed by addi-

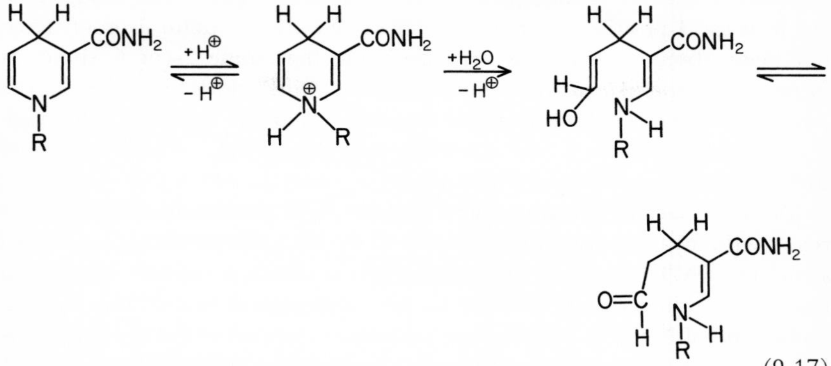

(9-17)

tion of water gives ring cleavage and formation of a carbonyl group at the 6-position. Their evidence, indicated for the aldehyde group, however, is not conclusive since (1) the basic conditions of the Hinsburg test may in themselves lead to ring opening, (2) the effect of added hydroxylamine may be only catalytic, and (3) the 290-mμ chromophore may be due to a tertiary as well as a secondary amine. The reaction with bisulfite probably represents a special case and will be discussed in a later section. Furthermore, Anderson and Berkelhammer appear to have definitely isolated the 6-hydroxy adduct.[78]

The nature of the secondary modification reaction is uncertain. The simplest explanation assumes ring opening to the corresponding aldehyde, which then may condense with the carbamido group. An alternative explanation is the addition of a second hydroxide ion at the 2-position, followed by ring cleavage yielding the dialdehyde.[48] In this connection the alkaline spectrum of the secondary modification product obtained from NADH has a maximum at 280 mμ, which has been assigned to an enolate anion. Moreover, the rate of transformation of the primary to the secondary product may require the carbamido group, since the 3-acetyl-dihydropyridine is only slowly converted to its secondary product.[83]

It should be obvious that many facets of the acid-base behavior of the pyridinium and dihydropyridine derivatives remain unresolved. The role that these reactions may play in biological systems is equally uncertain, but the addition of an anion to the 6-position may be pertinent to oxidative phosphorylation.[81]

B. Addition Reactions

1. PYRIDINIUM IONS   Recent years have seen the reporting of a profusion of nucleophilic addition reactions to the ring of 3-substituted

pyridinium salts. Although these reactions are generally thought to occur at the 4-position, in many instances definitive structural proofs have not been obtained and it is very probable that some 2- or 6-isomer is formed. Resonance structures favor nucleophilic addition at these three positions. The reactions of unsubstituted 1-alkoxypyridinium salts have recently been reviewed (the reader is referred to Ref. 84 and references therein for a discussion of pyridinium chemistry in general).

$NAD^\oplus$, $NADP^\oplus$, nicotinamide riboside, and nicotinamide nucleotide react with cyanide to form adducts with an absorption spectrum resembling NADH.[43, 85] A new absorption maximum appears at 327 mμ upon the addition of cyanide with the concomitant loss of the 260-mμ absorption of $NAD^\oplus$. The cyanide addition reaction of $NAD^\oplus$ is reversible, and upon dilution in water or at moderately acidic pH the adduct dissociates to $NAD^\oplus$ and cyanide ion.[69] Since $NAD^\oplus$ has been found to exchange only the hydrogens at the 4-position in the presence of cyanide and D_2O, San Pietro[86] proposed a 1,4-dihydropyridine adduct (9-18). Crystalline cyanide complexes of 1-methylnicotinamide[87] and 1-benzoyl-nicotinamide[88] have been isolated. The original assignment of the

$$(9\text{-}18)$$

structure of the adduct is strongly favored by the spectral similarities between the cyanide adduct of 1-(2,6-dichlorobenzyl)-3-carbamidopyridinium ion and the corresponding 1,4-dihydropyridine.[89]

Wallenfels and Diekmann have determined the position of the long wavelength absorption maximum and the equilibrium constants for the reaction of cyanide with a series of $NAD^\oplus$ analogs.[45] Substituents in the 3-position favor the addition of the anion in the order —$COCH_3$ > —$CONH_2$ > —$COOCH_3$ > —$CON(CH_3)_2$ > $COO^\ominus$, and electron-withdrawing substituents in the 1-position also act to facilitate the addition. This order is roughly that anticipated on electronic grounds, with the more effective substituents in the 3-position acting to lower the electron density in the pyridine ring through non-cross-conjugated resonance

[84] L. Bauer and L. A. Gardella, *J. Org. Chem.* **28,** 1320 (1963).

[85] O. Meyerhof, P. Ohlmeyer, and W. Mohle, *Biochem. Z.* **297,** 113 (1938).

[86] A. San Pietro, *J. Biol. Chem.* **217,** 579 (1955).

[87] M. Marti, M. Viscontini, and P. Karrer, *Helv. Chim. Acta* **39,** 1451 (1956).

[88] A. G. Anderson, Jr., and G. Berkelhammer, *J. Org. Chem.* **23,** 1109 (1958).

[89] K. Wallenfels and H. Schüly, *Ann.* **621,** 86 (1959).

and inductive effects. Of interest is the linear correlation observed between λ_{max} and the corresponding equilibrium constant for a given cyanopyridinium derivative.

Wallenfels and Diekmann [45] also showed that the ratio of the equilibrium constants for the cyanide adduct of the 3-acetylpyridine analog of $NAD^{\oplus}$ and $NAD^{\oplus}$ itself is in good agreement with the ratio of the equilibrium constants observed between the oxidized and reduced forms of these coenzymes in the presence of yeast alcohol dehydrogenase, ethanol, and acetaldehyde. This suggests that the cyanide adducts are thermodynamically similar to the reduced coenzyme form, but of course discloses nothing about the intervening pathway. Utilizing the known redox potential of the $NAD^{\oplus}$-NADH system,[90, 91] Wallenfels and Diekmann further assigned a numerical value to the anion affinity of the various pyridinium derivatives, placing the above substituent effects on a quantitative basis. Kaplan and co-workers also have shown that the ability of $NAD^{\oplus}$ analogs to add cyanide parallels their susceptibility to reduction by dithionite.[46, 56] Collectively, the above data substantiate the 1,4 structure of (9-18).

Other inorganic anions such as bisulfite, phosphate, thiocyanide, halides, and sulfoxylate (dithionite reduction) also appear to interact with 3-substituted pyridinium ions.[89, 92] Wallenfels and Schüly have postulated a dimeric 1,4 adduct for the addition of bisulfite to 1-(2,6-dichlorobenzyl)-3-carbamidopyridinium ion. An interesting observation in regard to the structure of the bisulfite adduct is the rapid formation of an NAD-bisulfite complex at pH 7.5, whereas at the same pH the nicotinylhydroxamic acid analog gives no detectable reaction. At pH 5.5 the analog reacts to the same extent as the coenzyme. Van Eys and Kaplan [93] attribute this phenomenon to interaction of the ionized hydroxamate group with the 4-position of the pyridine ring, inhibiting the bisulfite addition (this evidence does not eliminate possible attack at the 2-position). Further consideration of other inorganic anionic reactions leads to the strong possibility of charge-transfer complexing, and as such will be discussed under that heading.

Besides the cyanide and bisulfite reactions, 1,4 adducts have been postulated for the addition of thiols,[93] hydroxylamine,[94] enolate anions,[95–97]

[90] K. Burton and T. H. Wilson, *Biochem. J.* **54**, 86 (1953).

[91] F. L. Rodkey, *J. Biol. Chem.* **213**, 777 (1955).

[92] F. Ungar and S. G. A. Alivisatos, *Biochim. Biophys. Acta* **46**, 406 (1961).

[93] J. van Eys and N. O. Kaplan, *J. Biol. Chem.* **228**, 305 (1957).

[94] R. M. Burton and N. O. Kaplan, *J. Biol. Chem.* **211**, 447 (1954).

[95] R. M. Burton, A. San Pietro, and N. O. Kaplan, *Arch. Biochem. Biophys.* **70**, 87 (1957).

[96] R. M. Burton and N. O. Kaplan, *J. Biol. Chem.* **206**, 283 (1954).

[97] W. von E. Doering and W. E. McEwen, *J. Am. Chem. Soc.* **73**, 2104 (1951).

imidazole derivatives,[98] and p-aminobenzoic acid[99] to the 3-substituted pyridinium ions. The sulfhydryl adducts have been synthesized from the reaction of sodium sulfide and various mercaptans (e.g., cysteine; ethyl, propyl, and butyl mercaptan) with $NAD^{\oplus}$, 3-acetylpyridine $NAD^{\oplus}$, 1-(2,6-dichlorobenzyl)-3-carbamidopyridinium ion, and other analogs, but most have not been isolated and therefore their postulated structures rely primarily on spectral evidence drawn in analogy with 1,4-dihydropyridine derivatives. However, Wallenfels and Schüly [89] have crystallized the oxidized product of the reaction between sodium sulfide and 1-(2,6-dichlorobenzyl)-3-carbamidopyridinium bromide and have identified it as the dimeric 1,4-disulfide derivative (9-19) on the basis of spectral and analytical evidence. Dittmer and Kolyer [100] have isolated as crystalline solids the adducts of L-cysteine ethyl ester, ethyl thioglycolate, and n-propyl mercaptan with the same $NAD^{\oplus}$ analog. The structural assignment of the 1,4-dihydropyridine structure, however, was again made through spectral analogy.

(9-19)

Although it has been postulated that enzyme-bound $NAD^{\oplus}$ may interact with a free thiol group on the enzyme [101] glyceraldehyde-3-phosphate dehydrogenase, this proposal has been criticized by Kosower [61] on the grounds that the mercaptide-$NAD^{\oplus}$ adducts, when combined with enzyme, exhibit absorption maxima at a wavelength much shorter than that of the enzyme-bound $NAD^{\oplus}$. The question of enzymic mechanism will be considered in greater detail in the last section.

The addition of enolate anions to unsubstituted pyridinium derivatives is a long-established reaction [102] and one in which structural proofs of the adducts have been accomplished. The structure of the adduct obtained from the enolate anion of acetophenone and 1-benzoylpyridinium ion has been elaborated by McEwen and Doering,[97] who carried out the (9-20) sequence of reactions on the adduct, establishing its 1,4 identity.

[98] J. van Eys, J. Biol. Chem. 233, 1203 (1958).
[99] A. L. Guardiola, D. Paretsky, and W. McEwen, J. Am. Chem. Soc. 80, 418 (1958).
[100] D. C. Dittmer and J. M. Kolyer, J. Org. 28, 1720 (1963).
[101] E. Racker and I. Krimsky, J. Biol. Chem. 198, 731 (1952).
[102] L. Claisen and E. Haase, Ber. 36, 3674 (1903).

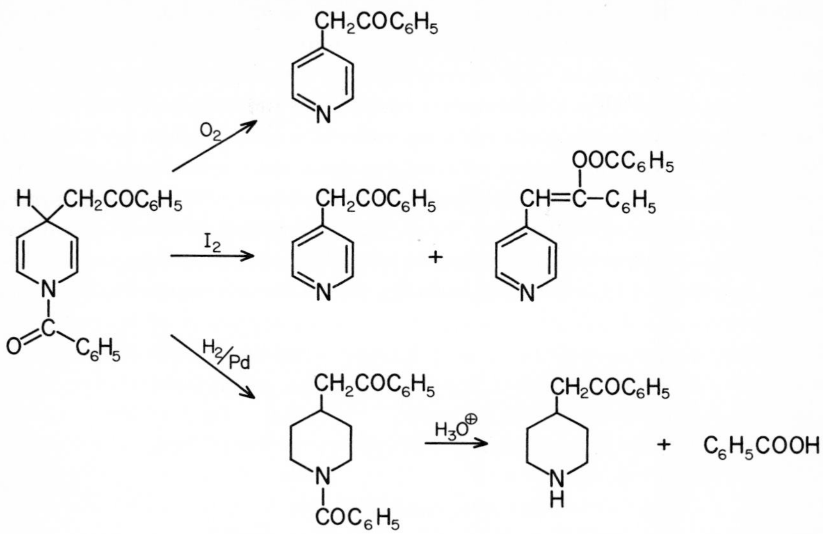

(9-20)

Burton and Kaplan [95, 96] have reported the alkaline condensation of *sym*-dichloroacetone, chloroacetone, α-chloroacetophenone, dihydroxy-acetone, and acetone with $NAD^{\oplus}$ (given in the order of decreasing reactivity).   On the basis of their ultraviolet spectra, 1,4-dihydronicotin-amide derivatives are proposed.   The acetone adduct of 1-methyl-nicotin-amide iodide,[103] $NAD^{\oplus}$, and $NADP^{\oplus}$ [104] exhibits strong fluorescence and is useful in determining the concentration of these pyridine derivatives.

A related condensation is that of certain C_{21} steroids [105] such as cortisol, 11-deoxycorticosterone, and 17α-hydroxy-11-deoxycorticoster-one, which react with $NAD^{\oplus}$ and several analogs to yield also a proposed 1,4-dihydropyridine adduct.   The reaction appears specific for steroids containing a 17-deoxyketol or 17-hydroxyketol side chain, which may be regarded as derivatives of dihydroxyacetone.   Unlike the reaction of dihydroxyacetone with $NAD^{\oplus}$, that of cortisol is readily reversible and no product can be isolated, thus precluding direct structural studies.   How-ever, the rate of formation of the condensation product is directly propor-tional to the hydroxyl ion and cortisol concentrations but independent of $NAD^{\oplus}$ concentration, consistent with a mechanism featuring a rate-deter-mining cortisol anion formation.   The fact that the reaction of cortisol

[103] J. W. Huff, *J. Biol. Chem.* **167,** 151 (1947).

[104] N. Levitas, J. Robinson, F. Rosen, J. W. Huff, and W. A. Perlzweig, *J. Biol. Chem.* **167,** 169 (1947).

[105] C. Monder, *Biochemistry* **2,** 684 (1963).

with 1-methyl-3-carbamidopyridinium perchlorate yields the adduct, whereas 1-methyl-4-carbamidopyridinium perchlorate gives no reaction, supports the structural assignment of a 1,4-dihydropyridine derivative.

Interest in the dihydroxyacetone adduct was recently revived with the finding that $NAD^{\oplus}$ carbonyl addition compounds form when commercial samples of $NAD^{\oplus}$ are stored in frozen weakly alkaline solutions,[106] and has led to a direct study of the carbonyl adduct. Employing n.m.r. spectra, Ludowieg, Bhacca, and Levy [107] proposed that the two crystalline compounds isolated from a solution of acetone and 1-n-propylnicotin-amide iodide (pH 11; yields less than 5%) have the structures (9-21 I) and

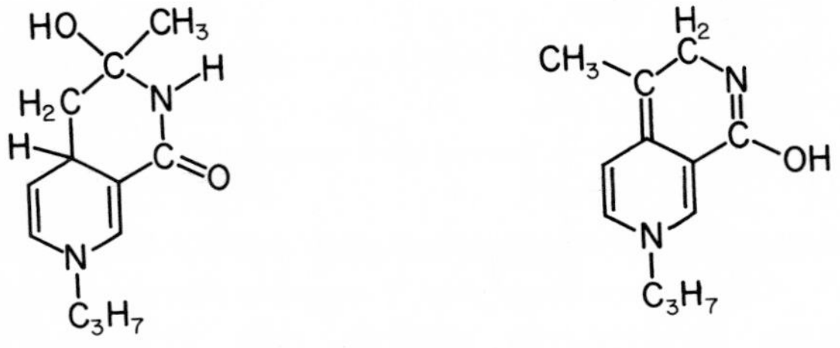

(9-21)

I   II

(9-21 II).   Structure (9-21 I) corresponds to a 1,4 adduct which has undergone cyclization through participation of the neighboring amide group.   Structure (9-21 II) is less readily rationalized but a possible pathway may involve nucleophilic attack by a pyridinium ylid.[107a]   The authors believe that other addition reactions of this form of pyridinium ylid to electrophilic centers should exist in view of the rapid exchange in weak base (Na_2CO_3) of the hydrogens at the 2- and 6-positions.[21]

A related reaction,[108-112] the o-acylation of β-keto esters by treatment of the ester with an acid chloride in pyridine solution, also involves a dihydropyridine adduct.   For example, the reaction of benzoyl chloride

[106] M. I. Dolin and K. B. Jacobson, *Biochem. Biophys. Res. Commun.* **11,** 102 (1963).

[107] J. Ludowieg, N. Bhacca, and A. Levy, *Biochem. Biophys. Res. Commun.* **14,** 431 (1964).

[107a] Carbonyl adducts involving acetone and $NAD^{\oplus}$ also form readily in ice.   The structure of the oxidized acetone-$NAD^{\oplus}$ adduct possesses the carbon-nitrogen skeleton of (9-21 I): M. I. Dolin and K. B. Jacobson, *J. Biol. Chem.* **239,** 3007 (1964).

[108] L. Claisen, *Ann.* **291,** 25 (1896).

[109] L. Claisen and E. Haase, *Ber.* **33,** 1242 (1900).

[110] W. Dieckmann and R. Stein, *Ber.* **37,** 3370 (1904).

[111] S. M. McElvain and D. Kundiger, *J. Am. Chem. Soc.* **64,** 254 (1942).

[112] P. E. Wright and W. E. McEwen, *J. Am. Chem. Soc.* **76,** 4540 (1954).

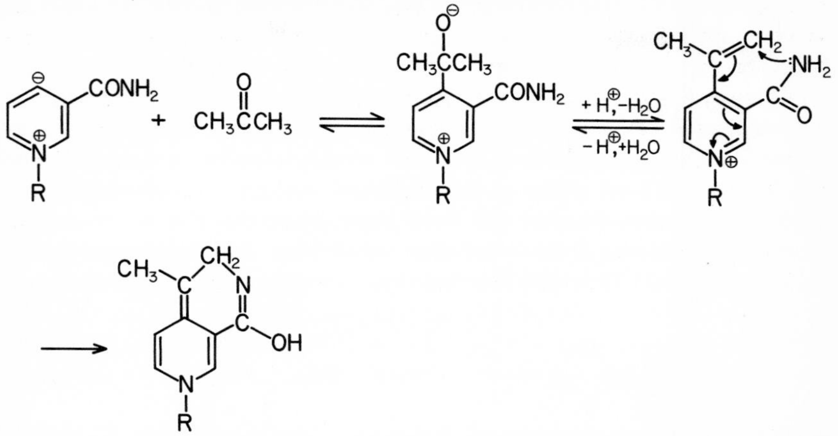

(9-22)

with ethyl benzoylacetate in pyridine gives ethyl β-benzoxycinnamate in 83% yield.[111] It has been suggested [97] that the reaction proceeds through an intermediate condensation product, ethyl benzoyl-(1-benzoyl-1,2-dihydro-2-pyridyl) acetate, which by way of a quasi-six-membered ring transition species yields the product (9-23). Evidence in support of this

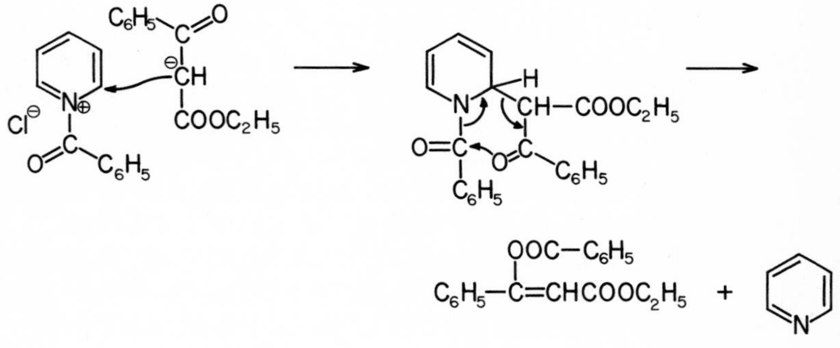

(9-23)

mechanism has been obtained by the isolation and identification of the corresponding 1,2-dihydroquinolyl derivative [113] and through kinetic studies.[114] A similar reaction is the acylation of phenols in pyridine solution which is thought to proceed through an analogous mechanism,[115, 116]

[113] R. L. Stutz, C. A. Reynolds, and W. E. McEwen, *J. Org. Chem.* **26,** 1684 (1961).
[114] W. R. Gilkerson, W. J. Argersinger, Jr., and W. E. McEwen, *J. Am. Chem. Soc.* **76,** 41 (1954).
[115] H. E. Baumgarten, *J. Am. Chem. Soc.* **75,** 1239 (1953).
[116] C. A. Reynolds, F. H. Walker, and E. Cochran, *Anal. Chem.* **32,** 983 (1960).

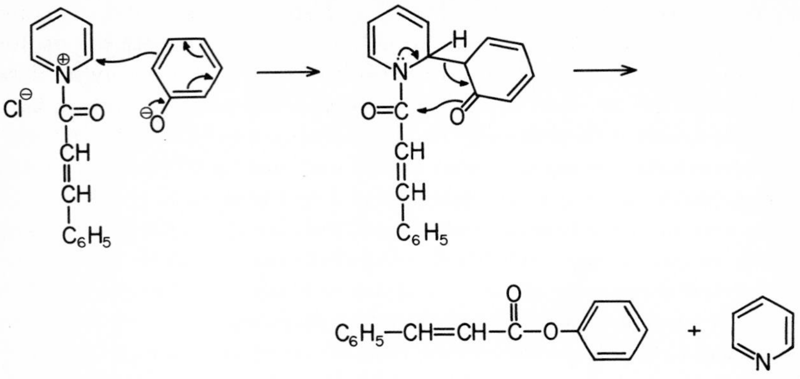

$$C_6H_5-CH=CH-\overset{\overset{O}{\|}}{C}-O-\langle\text{phenyl}\rangle \quad + \quad \langle\text{pyridine}\rangle$$

(9-24)

as illustrated for the reaction of cinnamoyl chloride with phenol (9-24), although in this case the intervention of such intermediates is not required. Moreover, direct attack on the carbonyl is greatly favored in acylpyridinium compounds.

In the above enolate condensations there is therefore direct evidence for both 2- and 4-condensation in the unsubstituted, and predominantly 4-condensation in the 3-substituted, pyridinium ion. There appears to be no completely satisfactory explanation for this behavior. Kosower [117] has proposed that, in general, 4-substitution occurs with reactants that might reasonably be expected to form charge-transfer complexes. Yet in the steroid condensations and thiol additions where the presence of such a complex was carefully sought, no charge-transfer bands appeared to exist in the ultraviolet spectrum. Other reactions of $NAD^\oplus$ analogs for which there is strong evidence of a charge-transfer complex—namely, the dithionite reduction [118] and the addition of iodide ion [89]—have been postulated as leading to addition at the 2- and 6-positions, respectively. An alternate proposal envisages a rapid equilibrium between 2- and 4-isomers with thermodynamic control of product formation. [97]

Amines also show abrupt changes as to the site of adduct formation in unsubstituted pyridinium ions. Whereas dimethylaniline and 1-benzoyl-pyridinium ion yield a 1,4-dihydropyridine adduct, [115, 119, 120] aniline and N-methylaniline add at the 2-position with eventual ring opening. [121] On the other hand, van Eys [98] has shown that besides imidazole a variety

[117] E. M. Kosower, J. Am. Chem. Soc. **78,** 3497 (1956).
[118] K. Wallenfels and H. Schüly, Ann. **621,** 178 (1959).
[119] E. Koenigs and E. Ruppelt, Ann. **509,** 142 (1934).
[120] W. E. McEwen, R. H. Terss, and I. W. Elliott, J. Am. Chem. Soc. **74,** 3605 (1952)
[121] T. Zincke, Ann. **330,** 361 (1904).

of 2-, 4-, or 5-substituted imidazoles, histidine, histamine, 2-methyl-imidazole, benzimidazole, and 2-methylbenzimidazole appear to form compounds only at the 4-position with $NAD^{\oplus}$. The 1-methylimidazole derivatives fail to react with $NAD^{\oplus}$, thus indicating a reaction at the nitrogen atom. A proposed 1-methyl-3-acetyl-4-(1-imidazolyl)pyridinium reineckate was isolated after ferricyanide oxidation, but the substitution at the 4-position is not based on a direct structural proof. In contrast, p-aminobenzoic acid [99] may react with $NAD^{\oplus}$ at the positions ortho to the amino group, since blockage of these sites by methyl substituents completely stops the reaction. Acetylation of the amino group retards but does not block the formation of the addition product. Since the cyanide adduct of $NAD^{\oplus}$ is unreactive, the reaction is formulated as a 1,4-addition involving a carbanion. Unfortunately a structural proof is again lacking.

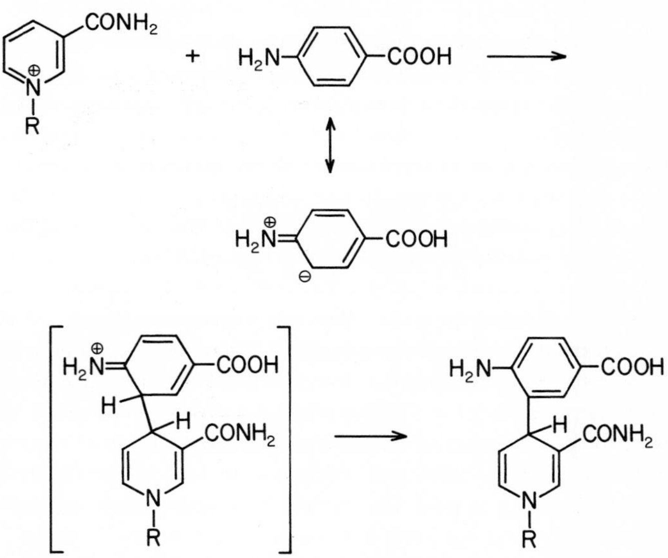

(9-25)

Lyle [121a] has tentatively offered the following generality to explain the above reaction of pyridinium ions with nucleophiles. The attack of the nucleophile at a position adjacent to the nitrogen will be favored kinetically, resulting in 1,2- or 1,6-dihydropyridine, unless attack at these positions is sterically hindered or the reaction is reversible. Under the latter conditions, the formation of 1,4-dihydropyridine is favored.

2. CHARGE-TRANSFER COMPLEXING The intriguing possibility that some adducts of pyridinium ions might exist in solution as charge-transfer complexes was first suggested by Kosower (for a more detailed treatment

[121a] R. E. Lyle, *Chem. Eng. News* **44,** 72 (1966).

of charge-transfer theory and its application to the pyridinium ions, see E. Kosower, "Molecular Biochemistry" [61] and references therein) and well documented by a detailed study of solutions of 1-alkylpyridinium iodides.   It has been proposed on the basis of light absorption in the near-ultraviolet region that the following equilibrium is present in these solutions:

$$(9\text{-}26)$$

The species on the right-hand side of equation (9-26) is a charge-transfer complex, which should be regarded, in this case, as an ion pair with the property of undergoing an observable charge-transfer transition.   Light absorption by the complex gives rise to the excited state of the complex. According to charge-transfer theory, stabilization of the ground state of the complex or the excited state is achieved by contributions of both forms (charge-transfer forces) and additional factors such as electrostatic attraction between proximate positive and negative charges.

$$(9\text{-}27)$$

The position of the charge-transfer light absorption band is empirically a linear function of the ionization potential of the donor.   The more easily a donor gives up an electron or the lower its ionization potential, the longer the wavelength of the charge-transfer band for a given acceptor. Moreover, the position of the charge-transfer band also is a sensitive measurement of the electron affinity of a given acceptor.   The higher the electron affinity for an acceptor, the longer the wavelength of the charge-transfer band.

The ultraviolet spectra for 1-ethyl-4-carbomethoxypyridinium iodide and perchlorate are given in Fig. 9-6.   The band in the vicinity of 2500 Å is the typical pyridinium ring absorption, whereas the lower-intensity and poorly defined bands at 3100 and 4508 for the iodide (completely absent for the perchlorate) are the two charge-transfer bands. The long wavelength charge-transfer band is the most intensively studied, but the second band also is explicable on the basis of the description of charge-transfer absorption.   From quantum mechanics the separation between the transition energies or the two charge-transfer bands should correspond to the two low-lying states of the iodine atom, the $^2P_{3/2}$ and $^2P_{1/2}$ states.   In fact the theoretically expected separation between the two bands is observed for potassium iodide in water and for 1-methyl-

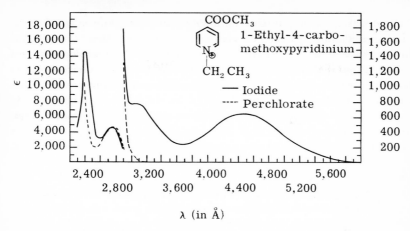

Fig. 9-6 *Complete absorption curves for 1-ethyl-4-carbomethoxypyridinium iodide and perchlorate in ethylene dichloride. (Ref. 61.)*

pyridinium iodide in chloroform, even though the longest wavelength band has changed in position from 2263 to 3737 Å. In contrast, certain other pyridinium iodides exhibit $^2P_{3/2}-^2P_{1/2}$ separations either smaller or larger than theoretically anticipated; thus, only a qualitative conformity can be expected. The change of the position of the charge-transfer absorption band with a change in the polarity of the solvent is quite pronounced and serves as a diagnostic tool for the detection of such complexes (Fig. 9-7). Deviation from Beer's law when both reactants are varied simultaneously serves as a second experimental method of detection.

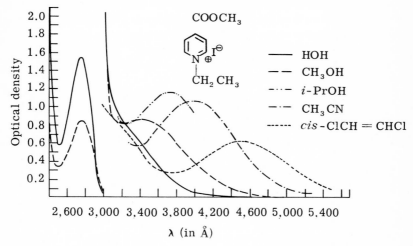

Fig. 9-7 *Long wavelength charge-transfer band of 1-ethyl-4-carbomethoxypyridinium iodide in water, methanol, isopropyl alcohol, acetonitrile, and cis-1,2-dichloroethylene. (Ref. 61.)*

Besides the interaction between iodide and pyridinium ions, other reactions are thought to involve charge-transfer complexes. In alkaline solution the reaction of dithionite with $NAD^\oplus$ and its analogs forms a yellow- or orange-colored solution which subsequently yields the 1,4-dihydropyridine derivative.[122-124] Wallenfels and Schüly [118] have isolated the crystalline sulfoxylate adduct for the 1-(2,6-dichlorobenzyl)-3,5-dicarbamidopyridinium bromide, and have proposed an α-adduct because of the ultraviolet spectra (λ_{max} = 271, ϵ = 5730; λ_{max} = 348, ϵ = 1320 in methanol). This adduct can rapidly eliminate SO_2 to yield the dihydro-

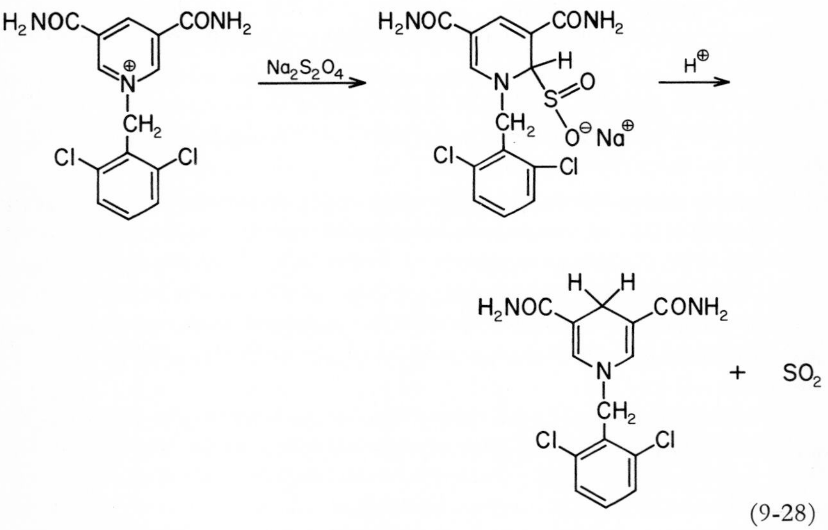

(9-28)

pyridine.[118, 122-124] Kosower [61] contends that, although a solid is isolated from solution, the possibility remains that the species in solution is not the adduct but a charge-transfer complex. Evidence in support of this view stems from a comparison of the band positions for the intermediate derived from the reaction of dithionite with 1-ethyl-3- and -4-carbamidopyridinium ions, with the band positions for the corresponding charge-transfer complex formed with iodide ion. Furthermore, one can derive from the empirical linear relationship between the position of charge-transfer light absorption (expressed in terms of transition energies $E_T = h_\nu$) and the ionization potential of a donor the following relationship:

$$\Delta E_T(D_n) = b_i - b_j \qquad (9\text{-}29)$$

[122] H. von Euler, E. Adler, and H. Hellström, *Z. Physiol. Chem.* **241**, 239 (1936).
[123] E. Adler, H. Hellström, and H. von Euler, *Z. Physiol. Chem.* **242**, 225 (1936).
[124] M. B. Yarmolinsky and S. P. Colowick, *Biochim. Biophys. Acta* **20**, 177 (1956).

Table 9-3 *   *Spectra of intermediates in dithionite reduction of pyridinium ions*

Pyridinium ion	λ_{max}	E_T (kcal/mole)	ΔE_T (kcal/mole)
1-Methyl-3-carbamido-	3730	76.65	
1-Methyl-4-carbamido-	4030	70.94	5.7 ± 0.3
1-Ethyl-3-carbamido-	3720	76.85	
1-Ethyl-4-carbamido-	4025	70.98	5.9 ± 0.3
Value expected from iodides			6.7 ± 0.3 [a]

* Ref. 61.

[a] The difference was determined for the 1-ethyl-3- and -4-carbamidopyridinium iodides in pure pyridine. A study of the variation of the band positions with solvent change indicated that the difference (ΔE_T) would be smaller in aqueous solution.

Thus, for a given donor, the difference in the transition energies of complexes with a pair of pyridinium ions should be a constant. The data for the dithionite reduction are given in Table 9-3. Nevertheless, the question remains whether this complex or the adduct serves as the product-determining intermediate, in spite of the assertion that the specificity of the reduction is a natural consequence of the geometry predicted for the complex.

Reduction of $NAD^{\oplus}$ and its analogs by electrolysis, X- or γ-rays, and sodium borohydride yields none or only a fraction of the starting material as a 1,4-dihydropyridine. Sodium borohydride reduction under mildly alkaline conditions apparently can lead to all three isomers with a preponderance of the 1,6-dihydropyridine besides 1,4- and 1,2-dihydro-pyridine products.[44, 124a] Use of n.m.r. spectra has recently led to the unequivocal structural assignments of the γ- and α-isomers obtained from the sodium borohydride reduction of the β-unsubstituted 1-phenylpyridin-ium chloride.[125] The formation of a proposed 1,2-dihydro derivative in the electrolytic[126] and the X- or γ-ray[127] reduction of 1-propylnicotin-amide chloride, which are processes where single-electron-equivalent transfer steps operate, suggests that borohydride is also capable of acting partially by a single-electron transfer pathway. Consistent with the notion of free-radical intermediates is the isolation of a dimeric *para* dihydropyridine on electrolytic reduction, the structural assignment being

[124a] S. Chaykin and L. Meissner, *Biochem. Biophys. Res. Commun.* **14,** 233 (1964).

[125] M. Saunders and E. H. Gold, *J. Org. Chem.* **27,** 1439 (1962).

[126] G. Stein and A. J. Swallow, *Nature* **173,** 937 (1954).

[127] Y. Paiss and G. Stein, *J. Chem. Soc.* 2905 (1958).

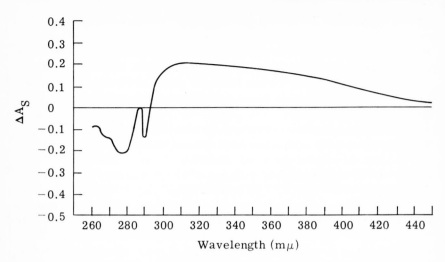

Fig. 9-8   *Difference spectrum of 1.98 · 10⁻⁴ M indolylethylnicotinamide in methanol vs. 1.98 · 10⁻⁴ M tryptamine hydrochloride and 1.98 · 10⁻⁴ M nicotinamide methochloride.   (Ref. 128.)*

based on the ultraviolet spectrum of the compound.   Although a charge-transfer complex is also possible and has been suggested in the borohydride reduction,[61] the present evidence is not convincing.   It should be obvious, however, that the distinction between nonlocalized combinations of the interacting species (complexes) and localized combinations (addition combinations) is in some cases not easily drawn.

An interesting extension of the concept of charge-transfer complexes has led to the study of a series of compounds in which indole, phenol, imidazole, benzene, thiomethyl ether, or a quaternary ammonium ion is joined to a nicotinamide ring at the ring nitrogen by two methylene groups.[128, 129]   The first five functional groups interact with the pyridinium ion to give rise to a featureless absorption band which is associated with the intramolecular complex.   For example, interaction of the indole and nicotinamide rings results in the appearance of a broad absorption band extending from 300 to 450 mμ with an apparent maximum at 325 mμ (ϵ 1000), as determined from the difference spectrum (Fig. 9-8).   The normally intense emission of indole is quenched in the intramolecular complex.   The absorption spectrum of the 1,4-reduced compound, indolylethyldihydronicotinamide, however, is simply the sum of the individual absorbancies of 1-methyl-1,4-dihydronicotinamide and tryptamine,

[128] S. Shifrin, *Biochim. Biophys. Acta* **81,** 205 (1964).
[129] S. Shifrin, *Biochemistry* **3,** 829 (1964).

but intramolecular interaction can be detected by fluorescence spectroscopy. Although more than 90% of the light intensity at 280 mμ is absorbed by the indole moiety, only emission characteristic of the dihydronicotinamide ring at 460 mμ can be detected. Thus, there is a quantitative transfer of excitation energy from the amino acid side chain to the emitting species. A similar transfer of excitation energy also is found for the phenolic substituent.

With N-(β-trimethylaminoethyl)-3-carbamidopyridinium dichloride there is no detectable interaction from spectral measurements. However, the reduced dihydronicotinamide derivative shows a shift of 15 mμ to shorter wavelengths compared with 1-methyl-1,4-dihydronicotinamide in the same solvent, methanol. This observation correlates with the shift, mentioned earlier in this chapter, for a system in which a quaternary nitrogen atom is located 3.1 Å from an α,β-unsaturated ketone. Molecular models give the distance of the quaternary ammonium ion from the ring nitrogen of the dihydropyridine as 2.7 Å when the substituents are cis, and 3.9 Å when they are trans. Whereas the other functional groups do not markedly alter the intensity of the fluorescence of the dihydronicotinamide moiety of the model system relative to 1-methyl-1,4-dihydronicotinamide, the intensity for the trimethylamine is $\frac{1}{50}$ of that value. The absorption and emission properties for all the model compounds are summarized in Table 9-4.

Table 9-4 *   *Absorption and emission properties of β-substituted 1-ethyl-3-carbimidopyridinium chlorides*

Side chains	Difference spectrum λ_{max} (mμ)	ϵ	Cyanide adduct λ_{max} (mμ)	ϵ	Dithionite reduction λ_{max} (mμ)	ϵ	Emission intensity [a] (at 450 mμ)
Indole	325	(1000)	340	(7000)	356	(7000)	1.00
Thiomethyl	300	(900)	337	(6100)	355	(7000)	0.95
Phenol	296.5	(1000)	341	(6800)	356.5	(7000)	1.10
Imidazole	294.5	(900)	337.5	(7900)	355		1.00
Benzene	282.5	(1000)	338	(7000)	355	(7100)	1.12
Trimethylamino			330	(6000)	340		0.02

* Ref. 129.

[a] The emission intensity of a methanolic solution of 1-methyl-1,4-dihydronicotinamide ($A_s = 0.100$ at 355 mμ) was arbitrarily chosen as 1.00. All solutions were adjusted to have an absorbancy of 0.100 at the long wavelength maximum for comparison of their fluorescence intensity.

Inspection of Table 9-4 reveals the variability of the wavelength of the new transition arising from the intramolecular interaction, and the constancy of the intensity of this transition. A plot of the absorption maximum of the corresponding nicotinamide versus the energy of the highest occupied molecular orbital for the aromatic substituents is linear. All these observations are in accord with charge-transfer behavior.

The similarity between the absorption properties of the indole-substituted derivative, or the bimolecular complex formed between $NAD^\oplus$ or 1-benzylnicotinamide and indole, and the spectrum of $NAD^\oplus$–glyceraldehyde-3-phosphate dehydrogenase has promoted the suggestion that the coenzyme is bound in the vicinity of a tryptophan residue.[128, 130, 131] However, the enhanced emission properties of NADH observed on binding to a large number of dehydrogenases remain unexplained. More importantly, the above study re-emphasizes the possible role of donor-acceptor complexes in biological systems. It remains for future research to elaborate the function of these complexes in a ground state as would be found in an enzyme-coenzyme system, rather than the presently studied excited state, and to conclusively prove the existence of such complexes in aqueous enzyme systems.

3. ADDITIONS TO 1,4-DIHYDROPYRIDINES The reaction of cationic and anionic species with 3-substituted 1,4-dihydropyridines appears to be directed generally toward the 5- and 6-positions, respectively. Stock [48] postulates that, although the anion affinity is higher at the 2-position relative to the 6-position, the cation affinity is greater at the 5-position relative to the 3-position; thus, the irreversible addition is across the 5,6 double bond. The effect of acid on the 1,4-dihydropyridines is essentially then a model for other reactions.

Stock and co-workers [48] have examined the addition of various cations in aqueous solution to NADH and several of its analogs. The structural assignments are, however, again made on the basis of spectral evidence. Disappearance of the double bond in the 5,6-position leads to a loss of absorption at 340–360 mμ and the appearance of a more intense band at ca. 280 mμ. The formation of the primary acid product is an example already discussed. Saturation of the double bond in the 2,3-position with the 5,6 bond still intact leads to a loss of absorption at 340 mμ without the concomitant increase in absorption at 260 or 280 mμ. Saturation of the double bond in the 2,3-position with the 5,6 bond already saturated results in a decrease in absorption of the 280-mμ band.

[130] S. G. A. Alivisatos, F. Ungar, A. Jibril, and G. A. Mourkides, *Biochim. Biophys. Acta* **51**, 361 (1961).

[131] G. Cilento and P. Tedeschi, *J. Biol. Chem.* **236**, 907 (1961).

[132] K. A. Hofmann and J. Sand, *Ber.* **33**, 1340, 2692 (1900).

[133] J. Sand, *Ber.* **34**, 1385 (1901).

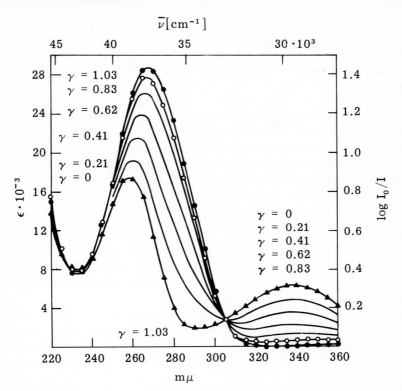

Fig. 9-9   *Titration of NADH with HgCl$_2$:* ▲—▲—▲, *0.48 × 10^{-4} M (NADH in 0.033 M phosphate buffer at pH 7);* ——, *stepwise change in the absorption spectra upon the addition of 1 × 10^{-5} M, 3 × 10^{-5} M, 4 × 10^{-5} M, and 5 × 10^{-5} M HgCl$_2$ (α = mole HgCl$_2$/mole NADH);* ○—○—○, *absorption spectra for α = 1.03;* ●—●—●, *NADH-Hg-adduct, 0.48 × 10^{-4} M NADH + 10^{-4} M HgCl$_2$.   (Ref. 48.)*

The reaction of NADH with Hg(II) salts [132–135] is typical of the cationic reactions.   The effect of incremental additions of HgCl$_2$ to NADH is shown in Fig. 9-9, illustrating the loss of the 340-mμ band and the formation of a new absorption band at 268 mμ.   So the reaction (9-30)

$$(9\text{-}30)$$

[134] J. Sand, *Ann.* **329,** 135 (1903).
[135] B. R. Hill, *Cancer Res.* **16,** 460 (1956).

is formulated as a 5,6-addition. The tight isosbestic point does not reveal
the existence of a detectable intermediate. The dissociation constant for
the adduct is small (7×10^{-7}), indicating its great stability.

Other ions, Ag(I), Au(IV), and Pd(IV), give products with NADH
that have been formulated as π-complexes with the 5,6 double bond. In
acidic strong LiCl solutions ($16M$) NADH almost instantaneously undergoes a spectral change to that of the protonated primary acid product,
suggesting either an interaction of Li(I) at the 5,6 bond or a salt effect on
the normal acid reaction. Cu(II) acts primarily as a catalyst for formation of the primary acid product. Ir(IV), on the other hand, very rapidly
oxidizes NADH quantitatively to $NAD^{\oplus}$ at pH 7. At this pH, Cd(II),

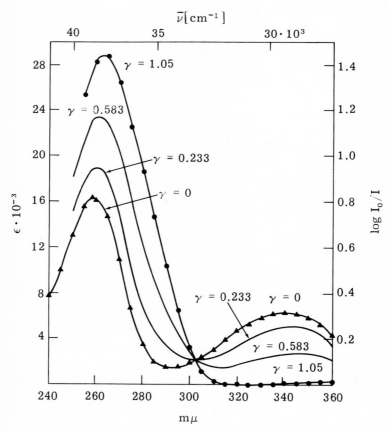

Fig. 9-10   *Titration of NADH with I₂:* ▲—▲—▲, *0.43 × 10⁻⁴ M NADH (in
0.033 M phosphate buffer at pH 7);* ———, *stepwise change in the absorption spectra upon the
addition of methanolic iodine solution:* 1 × 10⁻⁵ M, 2.5 × 10⁻⁵ M, *and* 4.5 × 10⁻⁵ M I₂
(α = mole I₂/mole NADH); ●—●—●, NADH-I adduct, 0.43 × 10⁻⁴ M NADH (in
0.033 M phosphate buffer at pH 7) + 0.45 × 10⁻⁴ M I₂.   (Ref. 48.)

Zn(II), Mg(II), Fe(II), Co(II), Ni(II), BiO(III), As(III), $(PtCl_6)^{-2}$, $(RhCl_6)^{-2}$, and SbO(III) show no measurable interaction with NADH. Thus it appears that those metal ions with a closed electron shell are incapable of interacting with the dihydropyridine ring.

Iodine reacts with NADH in two stages leading to the formation of primary and secondary products. Spectral examination of the reaction disclosed the rapid disappearance of the 340-mμ band with the simultaneous appearance of a 260-mμ band which then decays if excess iodine is present (Fig. 9-10). The reaction has been formulated as an addition to the 5,6 double bond followed by an addition to the remaining 2,3 double bond (9-31). The spectrum of the secondary product exhibits no change in alkali. The addition of bromine, formaldehyde, and the tosyl group of p-toluenesulfonyl chloride appears also to be at the 5-position.

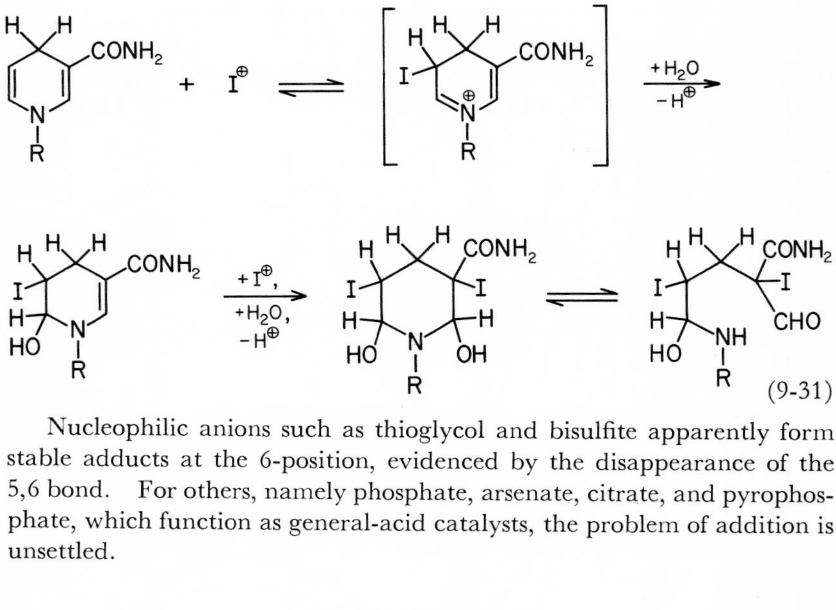

(9-31)

Nucleophilic anions such as thioglycol and bisulfite apparently form stable adducts at the 6-position, evidenced by the disappearance of the 5,6 bond. For others, namely phosphate, arsenate, citrate, and pyrophosphate, which function as general-acid catalysts, the problem of addition is unsettled.

V. MECHANISM

As previously stated, the dehydrogenases promote the direct stereospecific transfer of hydrogen between their substrates and the coenzyme $NAD^{\oplus}$ or $NADP^{\oplus}$. *A priori* this transfer may occur through two possible mechanistic routes involving (1) a two-electron and proton transfer or more probably a hydride ion transfer, and (2) a free-radical process with one-electron and hydrogen atom transfer. Model studies have obtained evidence for both routes, as will later be indicated. In Table 9-5 are listed a variety of acceptor compounds that have been reduced non-

Table 9-5

Donor	% Oxidized	Acceptor	% Reduced	Product	Solvent, T	Ref.
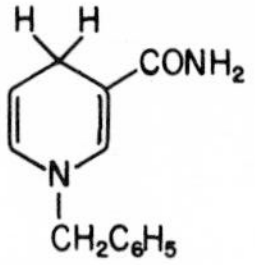 [1,4-dihydropyridine, H H, 3-CONH$_2$, N–CH$_2$C$_6$H$_5$]	25–75 (av)	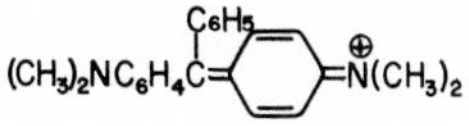 $(CH_3)_2NC_6H_4C$ [$=N(CH_3)_2^{\oplus}$, C$_6$H$_5$]	55 (av.)	$(CH_3)_2NC_6H_4CHC_6H_4N(CH_3)_2$ [C$_6$H$_5$]	95% C$_2$H$_5$OH, 25–30°	136
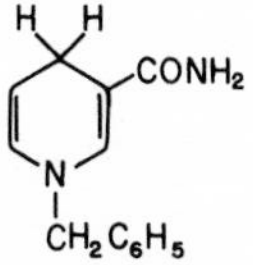 [1,4-dihydropyridine, H H, 3-CONH$_2$, N–CH$_2$C$_6$H$_5$]	$\underline{ca}$ 50	$(C_6H_5)_2C{=}S$	$\underline{ca}$ 50	$(C_6H_5)_2CHSH$	70% C$_2$H$_5$OH, 30°	137, 138
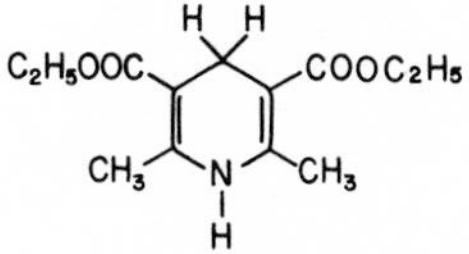 [1,4-dihydropyridine, H H, 3,5-bis-ester COOC$_2$H$_5$ / C$_2$H$_5$OOC, 2,6-CH$_3$, N–H]	97	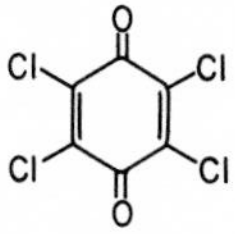 [tetrachloro-1,4-benzoquinone, Cl Cl Cl Cl]	97	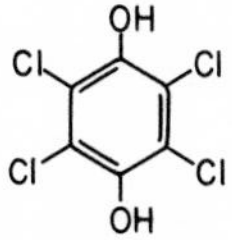 [tetrachlorohydroquinone, Cl Cl Cl Cl, 2×OH]	OCH$_2$CH$_2$CH$_2$CH$_2$, 25°	139
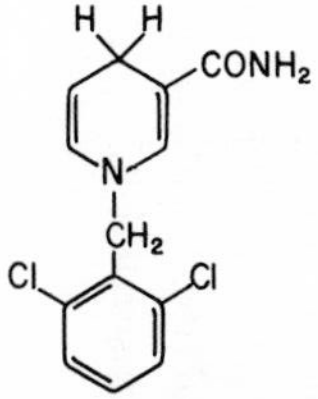 [1,4-dihydropyridine, H H, 3-CONH$_2$, N–CH$_2$(2,6-dichlorophenyl)]	70	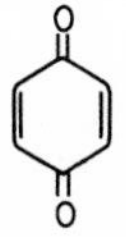 [1,4-benzoquinone]	62	 [hydroquinone, 2×OH]	50% CH$_3$OH, 25°	140

344

Starting material	Yield	Product	Yield	Product	Conditions	Ref.
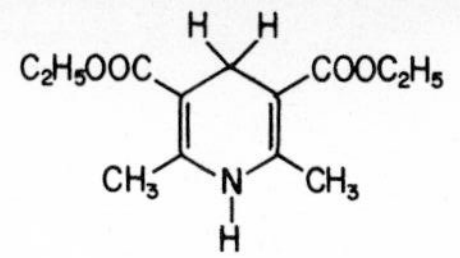 dihydropyridine ($COOC_2H_5$, CH_3, C_2H_5OOC, CH_3, N–H)	70	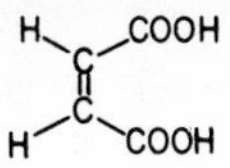 maleic/fumaric acid (HC(COOH)=CH(COOH))	29	CH_2COOH / CH_2COOH	$OCH_2CH_2OCH_2CH_2$, 101°	139
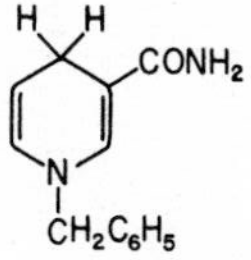 dihydropyridine ($CONH_2$, N–$CH_2C_6H_5$)	30	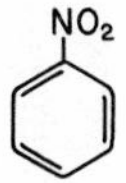 NO_2–C_6H_5 (nitrobenzene)	60–68 (as aniline)	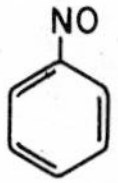 NO–C_6H_5 (nitrosobenzene)	no solvent, 139°	141
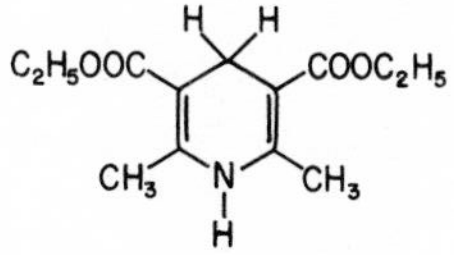 dihydropyridine ($COOC_2H_5$, CH_3, C_2H_5OOC, CH_3, N–H)	—	$C_6H_5\overset{O}{C}COOH$	5–16	$C_6H_5CHCOOH$ / OH	C_2H_5OH, 85°	142
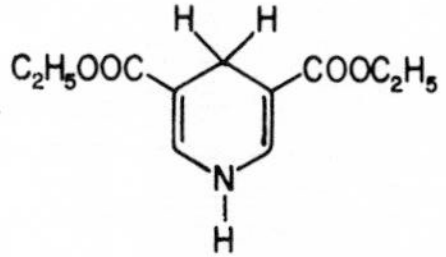 dihydropyridine ($COOC_2H_5$, C_2H_5OOC, N–$CH_2C_6H_5$)	99	$C_6H_5COCH=CHCF_3$	84	$C_6H_5COCH_2CH_2CF_3$	CH_3OH, reflux T°	143
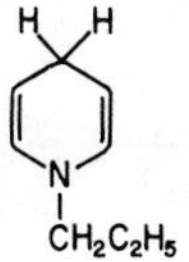 dihydropyridine (N–$CH_2C_6H_5$)	—	$CCl_3\overset{O}{C}CCl_3$	57	CCl_3CHCCl_3 / OH	$HCONH_2$, 25°	144
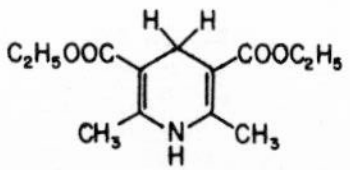 dihydropyridine ($COOC_2H_5$, CH_3, C_2H_5OOC, CH_3, N–H)	ca 100	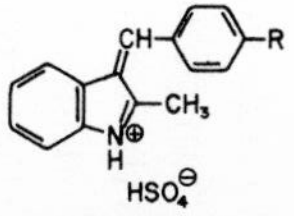 indolium (CH_3, N–H, $HSO_4^{\ominus}$, R); R = H, OH	ca 100	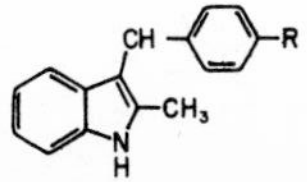 indole (CH_3, N–H, R)	CH_3CH_2OH, CH_3CN, 25°	32 d

345

enzymically by 1,4-dihydropyridine derivatives, including thioketones, keto acids, dyes, quinones, derivatives of malic and fumaric acids, nitrobenzene, halogenated ketones, olefins, and phenyl-α-methylindolidene-methanes.[32d,136—144] Table 9-5 points out that the "model studies" utilize either highly activated, abnormal substrates or dihydropyrindine derivatives and in some cases drastic conditions in order to demonstrate a net oxidation-reduction reaction. Thus these studies as yet are reduced in value by their inability to closely approximate the enzyme system.

In spite of this failure the model studies have revealed some noteworthy information. For example, Westheimer and co-workers [138] have found with a series of thioketones that (1) electron-donating substituents slow the rate, whereas electron-withdrawing substituents accelerate it, (2) the reaction proceeds more rapidly in polar solvents, (3) the monodeuterium analog of the dihydro compound exhibits a rate factor k_H/k_D of about 4–5, and (4) free-radical chain inhibitors are without effect upon the reaction rate. All these data can be explained in terms of the direct transfer of a hydride ion in the rate-controlling step from the dihydro compound to the thioketone. Mechanisms which require prior attachment of the thioketone group to the pyridine ring cannot be formulated without either adding a proton to the ring or placing a negative charge on the carbamido group. Neither of these is consistent with the experimental data, since the reaction rate is independent of pH and other derivatives not possessing a carbamido group may be utilized. A second example is the nonenzymic reduction of riboflavin by 1-n-propyl-1,4-dihydronicotinamide [145] which possesses characteristics similar to the thioketone reduction, namely, that a decrease in the electron density of the dihydronicotinamide decreases its oxidation rate, and that the monodeuterated dihydronicotinamide is oxidized 3.2 times slower than that of the diprotiated form. The reaction is actually an oxidation of 1-n-propyl-1,4-dihydronicotinamide by riboflavin, since under the experimental conditions the dihydroriboflavin is immediately reoxidized by oxygen. In

---

[136] D. Mauzerall and F. H. Westheimer, *J. Am. Chem. Soc.* **77,** 2261 (1955).

[137] R. H. Abeles and F. H. Westheimer, *Federation Proc.* **15,** 675 (1956).

[138] R. H. Abeles, R. F. Hutton, and F. H. Westheimer, *J. Am. Chem. Soc.* **79,** 712 (1957).

[139] E. A. Braude, J. Hannah, and R. Linstead, *J. Chem. Soc.* 3249, 3257 (1960).

[140] K. Wallenfels and M. Gellrich, *Ann.* **621,** 149 (1959).

[141] D. C. Dittmer and J. M. Kolyer, *J. Org. Chem.* **27,** 56 (1962).

[142] R. Abeles and F. H. Westheimer, *J. Am. Chem. Soc.* **80,** 5459 (1958).

[143] B. E. Norcross, P. E. Klinedinst, Jr., and F. H. Westheimer, *J. Am. Chem. Soc.* **84,** 797 (1962).

[144] D. C. Dittmer and R. A. Fouty, *J. Am. Chem. Soc.* **86,** 91 (1964).

[145] C. H. Suelter and D. E. Metzler, *Biochim. Biophys. Acta* **44,** 23 (1960).

this case, however, as well as for the reduction of 2,6-dichlorophenol-indophenol by 1-(2,6-dichlorobenzyl)-1,4-dihydronicotinamide, the rate exhibits a pH dependence, increasing greatly as the pH is lowered. This behavior most likely results from a more rapid reaction of the protonated form of the substrate with the dihydropyridine derivative. On this basis Suelter and Metzler estimate that the second-order rate constant for the protonated riboflavin is 6×10^7 liter mole^{-1} min^{-1} (pH 6.65, 20°), nearly 10^4 times that for neutral riboflavin. The riboflavin anion, in contrast, is unreactive. All these results are indeed consistent with oxidation by hydride ion transfer. It should be mentioned that experiments were conducted to disprove the possibility that photochemical processes were responsible for these results, as they are in the dihydropyridine reduction of bromotrichloromethane.[146] Third, other tracer experiments in the keto acid, olefin, and malachite green reductions have shown that hydrogen is directly transferred from the 4-position of the dihydropyridine ring to the substrate, consistent with this view of mechanism.

Support for the free-radical process stems from such studies as that of Dittmer and Fouty,[144] who have found that when the reduction of hexachloroacetone by 1-benzyl-1,4-dihydronicotinamide is carried out in nitromethane, two types of hydrogen transfer occur. In addition to hexachloroisopropyl alcohol (48–60%), pentachloroacetone also is formed. The reaction is over in ca. 2 minutes. Added t-butyl-catechol and hydroquinone completely suppress the formation of pentachloroacetone, although the yield of hexachloroisopropyl alcohol is unchanged. This inhibition strongly suggests that the formation of pentachloroacetone occurs through a free-radical mechanism. It is also possible that the formation of hexachloroisopropyl alcohol occurs within a charge-transfer complex, represented below by one of the many possible resonance structures (9-32), and thereby is not affected by these two inhibitors (a hydride-

(9-32)

transfer mechanism is not ruled out). Transfer of a hydrogen atom then would complete the reaction. An analogous complex, of course, may be involved in the above thioketone and riboflavin reductions. In the latter case, although no definite proof for such a complex was obtained, the low

[146] J. L. Kurz, R. Hutton, and F. H. Westheimer, J. Am. Chem. Soc. 83, 584 (1961).

(4–5 kcal mole^{-1}) activation energy suggests that its formation with a corresponding negative enthalpy change may be involved.

Schellenberg and Hellermann[147] have observed that NADH is oxidized almost instantaneously to NAD$^{\oplus}$ by the radical, spirocyclohexylporphyrexide, and less rapidly by porphyrindine and other reagents capable of functioning as one-electron acceptors. Under identical experimental conditions, o-iodosobenzoate, hydrogen peroxide, and other reagents considered as two-electron acceptors do not promote the oxidation. These data also then implicate the possibility of a free-radical sequence.

An intriguing model system was discovered by Wallenfels and Hofmann [148] in an effort to duplicate the conversion of bisulfite to hydrogen sulfide (9-33) obtained in the presence of certain microorganisms. Start-

$$SO_3^{\ominus} + 3NADPH + 5H^{\oplus} \rightarrow H_2S + 3NADP^{\oplus} + 3H_2O \quad (9\text{-}33)$$

ing with the bisulfite adduct of 1-(2,6-dichlorobenzyl)-1,4-dihydronicotinamide in the presence of excess 1-(2,6-dichlorobenzyl)pyridinium ion, they effected its transformation to hydrogen sulfide and the 6-hydroxy-1,4,5,6-tetrahydropyridine derivative through the proposed reaction sequence (9-34). Compounds II and III have been isolated. The overall conversion of the adduct to the final products is ca. 48%, based on the amount of hydrogen sulfide and 6-hydroxypyridine derivative produced. Similarly ethylenesulfite is converted to hydrogen sulfide in the presence of the above NAD$^{\oplus}$ model.

Model studies have revealed transhydrogenation which takes place between pyridine nucleotide pairs like NADH–3-acetyl-NAD$^{\oplus}$ and NADH–1-benzyl-3-carbamidopyridinium chloride.[149, 150, 150a] Similar interactions have been demonstrated with the components of tritiated NADP$^{\oplus}$–NADPH, NADH–NAD$^{\oplus}$, and 1-n-propylnicotinamide chloride–1-n-propyl-1,4-dihydronicotinamide systems.[151] With the latter three systems there is no net oxidation-reduction, but the reversible formation of a complex was noted spectrophotometrically. However, there is as yet no evidence to suggest that the exchange process and the appearance of what may be a charge-transfer complex are dependent upon each other.

In conclusion, it must be asked whether the nonenzymic and enzymic reactions proceed by similar mechanisms. In essence the model studies have mainly dealt with but a rudimentary part of the overall enzyme

[147] K. A. Schellenberg and L. Hellerman, *J. Biol. Chem.* **231**, 547 (1958).
[148] K. Wallenfels and D. Hofmann, *Tetrahedron Letters* **4**, 151 (1962).
[149] G. Cilento, *Arch. Biochem. Biophys.* **88**, 352 (1960).
[150] M. J. Spiegel and G. R. Drysdale, *J. Biol. Chem.* **235**, 2498 (1960).
[150a] G. Cilento and S. Schreier, *Arch. Biochem. Biophys.* **107**, 102 (1964).
[151] J. Ludowieg and A. Levy, *Biochemistry* **3**, 373 (1964).

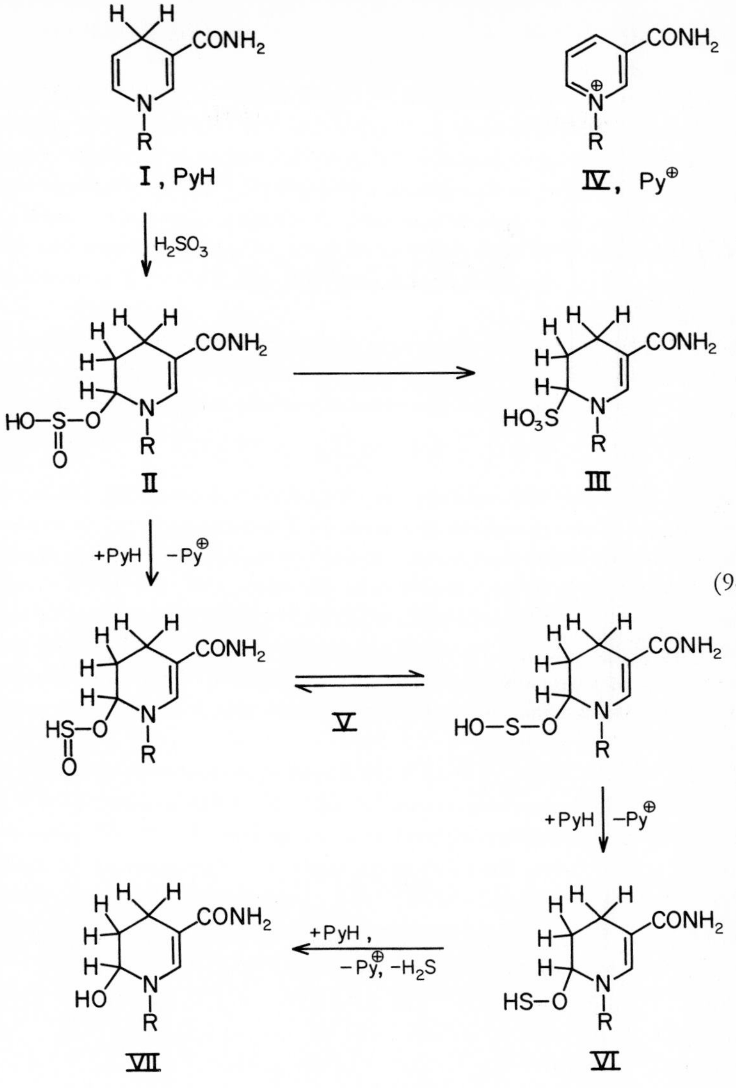

where R = 2,6-Dichlorobenzyl

process—that of the hydrogen transfer. However, these studies have led to a perception of this particular step that would be difficult, if not impossible, in their absence. Yet the remaining challenges in understanding enzyme processes are formidable and probably will be answered only by a combined approach involving both model and enzyme studies.

chapter
ten

Folic Acid

I. INTRODUCTION

Folic acid, in the tetrahydrofolate form is a requisite cofactor in the biological transfer of one-carbon units at varying levels of oxidation. The structure of folic acid (10-1) was originally established by an alkaline degradation of one of several naturally occurring folic acid "conjugates" known to be polyglutamate forms [1, 2] of the parent compound.[3] Alkaline

[1] B. L. Hutchings, E. L. R. Stokstad, N. Bohonos, N. H. Sloane, and Y. SubbaRow, *J. Am. Chem. Soc.* **70,** 1 (1948).

[2] J. J. Pfiffner, D. G. Calkins, E. S. Bloom, and B. L. O'Dell, *J. Am. Chem. Soc.* **68,** 1392 (1946).

[3] It is unknown whether folic acid compounds occur in nature primarily as the mono- or polyglutamate conjugates: L. Jaenicke, *Ann. Rev. Biochem.* **33,** 287 (1964); nor is the reason for the existence of the conjugates firmly established: F. M. Huennekens and M. J. Osborn, *Advan. Enzymol.* **21,** 369 (1959).

$$2-\text{Amino}-4-\text{hydroxy}-6-\text{methylpteridine} \qquad \text{p-Aminobenzoic acid} \qquad \text{L-Glutamate} \qquad (10\text{-}1)$$

Pteroic acid

FOLIC ACID

hydrolysis of the triglutamate conjugate [4] under *anaerobic* conditions yields (10-1) and 2 moles of glutamic acid, thus suggesting a polypeptide structure for the conjugate.[4] Resolution of the stereochemistry of the glutamic acid was achieved by autoclaving the monoglutamate conjugate at pH 4.0 in aqueous solution, which results in the sole formation of L-pyrrolidonecarboxylic acid.[5] Under *aerobic* conditions, alkaline hydrolysis of (10-1) yields a fluorescent pigment, identifiable as 2-amino-4-hydroxy-6-carboxy-pteridine, and a diazotizable aromatic amine, p-aminobenzolyglutamate.[4] The structure of the pteridine was unequivocally established by direct synthesis.[6] Thus, natural folic acid is a stereoisomer composed of the three moieties 2-amino-4-hydroxy-6-methylpteridine, p-aminobenzoic acid, and L-glutamic acid. The structural combination of the pteridine and p-aminobenzoic acid is known as pteroic acid, consequently folic acid is also commonly referred to as pteroylmonoglutamic acid. The several different approaches to the total synthesis of folic acid which directly followed its structural proof are summarized elsewhere.[7, 8]

The chemical reactivity of the various functional groups in folic acid has been studied extensively. However, since the biologically active form of the cofactor possesses the reduced tetrahydro structure, in which the pyrazine ring is completely reduced (10-8), only a few of the studies on

[4] E. L. R. Stokstad, B. L. Hutchings, J. H. Mowat, J. H. Boothe, C. W. Waller, R. B. Angier, J. Semb, and Y. SubbaRow, *J. Am. Chem. Soc.* **70,** 5 (1948).

[5] B. L. Hutchings, E. L. R. Stokstad, J. H. Mowat, J. H. Boothe, C. W. Waller, R. B. Angier, J. Semb, and Y. SubbaRow, *J. Am. Chem. Soc.* **70,** 10 (1948).

[6] J. H. Mowat, J. H. Boothe, B. L. Hutchings, E. L. R. Stokstad, C. W. Waller, R. B. Angier, J. Semb, D. B. Cosulich, and Y. SubbaRow, *J. Am. Chem. Soc.* **70,** 14 (1948).

[7] D. I. Weisblat, B. J. Magerlein, A. R. Hanze, D. R. Myer, and S. T. Rolfson, *J. Am. Chem. Soc.* **75,** 3625 (1953).

[8] E. L. R. Stokstad, in W. H. Sebrell, Jr., and R. S. Harris (eds.) "The Vitamins," Academic Press, New York, 1954, Vol. III, pp. 104–124.

folic acid will be considered. In addition to *aerobic* alkaline cleavage of the C-9–N-10 linkage, cleavage at the same bond is achieved by treatment of folic acid with sulfurous acid yielding the 2-amino-4-hydroxy-6-pteridine carboxaldehyde, or by reductive cleavage with zinc and dilute acid leading to 2-amino-4-hydroxy-6-methyl-pteridine.[5, 9] The aldehyde disproportionates in dilute alkali under *anaerobic* conditions in a Cannizzaro-type reaction to approximately equal amounts of the corresponding carboxylic acid and 6-methylpteridine.[5] The same disproportionation is observed upon the irradiation of folic acid by ultraviolet light.[10, 11] Reductive hydrogenation of folic acid, at pH 1.0 or 3.0 at atmospheric pressure using a palladium-barium sulfate catalyst, resembles the zinc-acid reduction by again splitting the C-9–N-10 bond [5] as does an oxidative degradation utilizing either neutral permanganate or a sodium chlorate–hydrochloric acid mixture.[12] The pteridine product of the oxidative procedure was identified as the 6-carboxylic acid. Treatment with the sodium chlorate-hydrochloric acid mixture also introduces chlorine into the 3'- and 5'-positions of (10-1), and under more drastic conditions can lead to the destruction of the pyrimidine ring. Oxaloguanidine and chloroanil are the products under the latter conditions.[4, 13] Preparation of the intact 3',5'-dihalo analogs of folic acid, however, can be accomplished by direct halogenation of folic acid in cold aqueous acid.[14] Nitration under similar conditions yields the corresponding 3',5'-dinitropteroyl derivative.[15]

Formylation of folic acid with concentrated formic acid leads to N_{10}-formylfolic acid,[16] in analogy with the formylation of pteroic acid [13] which gives N_{10}-formylpteroic acid (rhizopterin). The location of the formyl group in rhizopterin was confirmed by chemical synthesis.[13] Nitrous acid similarly reacts in the cold with folic acid to produce the N_{10}-nitroso derivative [17] and at higher temperature will also act to deaminate the 2-amino group.[13]

[9] W. R. Boon and T. Leigh, *J. Chem. Soc.* 1497 (1951).

[10] O. H. Lowry, O. A. Bessey, and E. J. Crawford, *J. Biol. Chem.* **180,** 389 (1949).

[11] H. M. Rauen and H. Waldmann, *Experientia* **6,** 387 (1950).

[12] E. L. Wittle, B. L. O'Dell, J. M. Vandenbelt, and J. J. Pfiffner, *J. Am. Chem. Soc.* **69,** 1786 (1947).

[13] D. E. Wolf, R. C. Anderson, E. A. Kaczka, S. A. Harris, G. E. Arth, P. L. Southwick, R. Mozingo, and K. Folkers, *J. Am. Chem. Soc.* **69,** 2753 (1947).

[14] D. B. Cosulich, D. R. Seeger, M. J. Fahrenbach, B. Roth, J. H. Mowat, J. M. Smith, Jr., and M. E. Hultquist, *J. Am. Chem. Soc.* **73,** 2554 (1951).

[15] D. B. Cosulich, D. R. Seeger, M. J. Fahrenbach, K. H. Collins, B. Roth, M. E. Hultquist, and J. M. Smith, Jr., *J. Am. Chem. Soc.* **75,** 4675 (1953).

[16] M. Gordon, J. M. Ravel, R. E. Eakin, and W. Shive, *J. Am. Chem. Soc.* **70,** 878 (1948).

[17] D. B. Cosulich and J. M. Smith, Jr., *J. Am. Chem. Soc.* **71,** 3574 (1949).

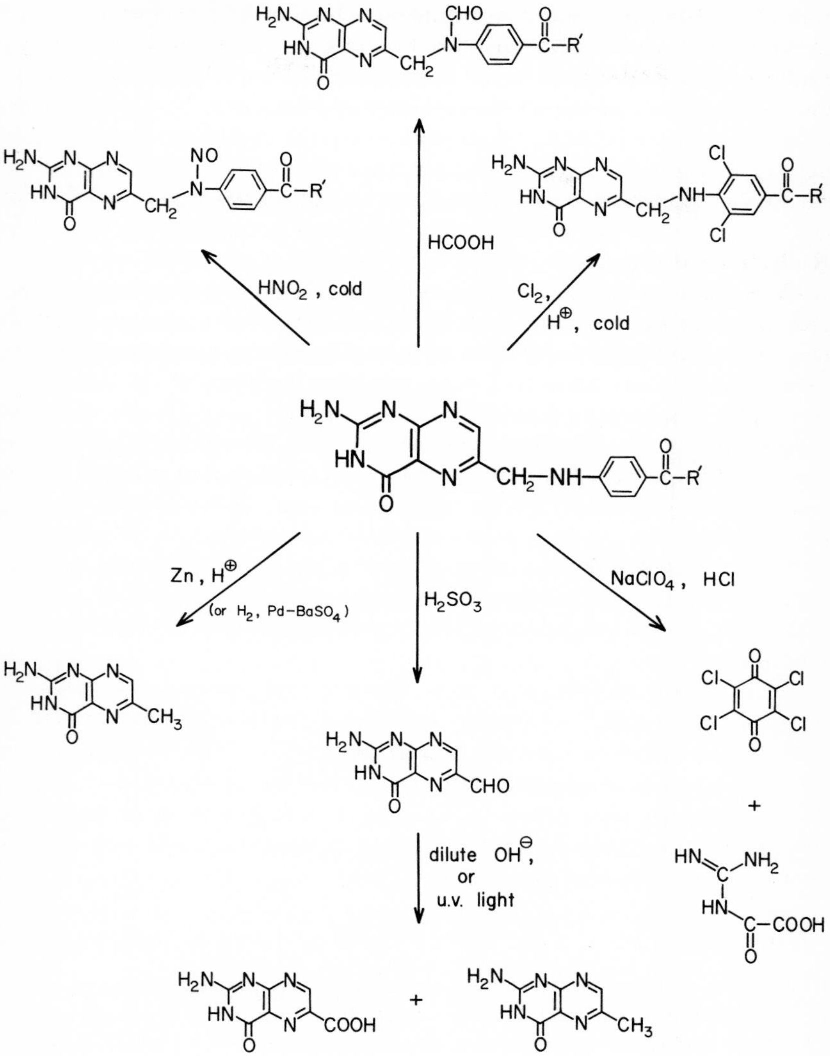

where   R' = L-Glutamic acid

(10-2)

It is called to the reader's attention that the pyrimidine ring of structure (10-1) is written in the lactam form, which is the principal species at neutral pH for the related 4-hydroxypyrimidine.[18]   The enolic properties of the 4-oxy group, however, are manifested by its low pK_a' value [4] of ca. 8.0.   A summary of the aforementioned reactions is presented in (10-2).

II. COMPOUNDS RELATED TO THE COENZYME FORM

A. *Dihydrofolic Acid*

The reduction of folic acid through the addition of 1 mole of hydrogen may result in the formation *a priori* of one isomer or a mixture of three possible isomers (10-3).   O'Dell *et al.* found that in the catalytic hydrogen-

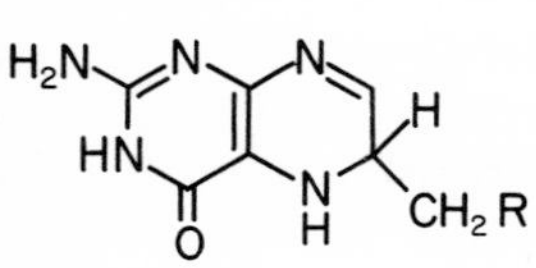

5, 6—FH$_2$ 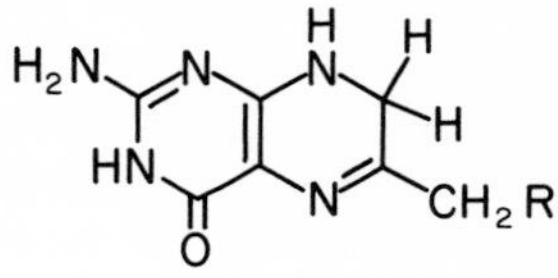   7,8—FH$_2$

(10-3)

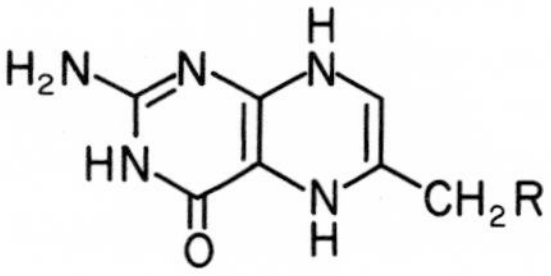

5,8—FH$_2$

where R = p—aminobenzoylglutamic acid

ation of folic acid, in dilute alkali over palladium or platinum oxide, 1 mole of hydrogen is consumed.[19]   The crystalline product was assigned the 7,8-dihydrostructure on the basis of an argument derived from observations on the catalytic hydrogenation of xanthopterin.   Isoxanthopterin (10-4 I) is resistant to catalytic hydrogenation in dilute alkali, whereas xanthopterin (10-4 II) readily adds 1 mole of hydrogen.   Thus it would

[18] D. J. Brown, E. Hoerger, and S. F. Mason, *J. Chem. Soc.* 211 (1955).
[19] B. L. O'Dell, J. M. Vandenbelt, E. S. Bloom, and J. J. Pfiffner, *J. Am. Chem. Soc.* **69,** 250 (1947).

$$(10\text{-}4)$$

I   II

appear that the 5,6 double bond and the enolic double bonds are refractory and reduction of the pteridine ring occurs at the 7,8-position.[19] This conclusion is supported by the work of Boon et al.[20] and Elion and Hitchings,[21] who synthesized 7,8-dihydroxanthopterin by an alternate method and found it to possess an absorption spectrum identical to the product obtained through catalytic hydrogenation. Reduction of the pyrazine ring rather than the pyrimidine nucleus is anticipated since the latter is more resistant to catalytic hydrogenation.[22, 23]

Dihydrofolic acid has also been prepared by the sodium dithionite reduction of folic acid in aqueous solution at pH 6.0 in the presence of an antioxidant such as ascorbic acid.[24, 25] This method is preferred over that of catalytic hydrogenation because the latter procedure yields product contaminated by traces of the tetrahydro derivative.[26] Due to the similarities between the absorption spectra for the dithionite and catalytic hydrogenation products, a 7,8-dihydro structure was again assigned. It is of experimental value to be cognizant of the fact that the dihydrofolic acid product is readily degraded on exposure to air in dilute alkali to folic acid, p-aminobenzoylglutamic acid, and other unidentified oxidation products[19, 24, 27] and is only slightly more stable in acidic solutions.[28]

The assignment of the 7,8-dihydro structure was jeopardized by the later observation of Albert and Matsuura that xanthopterin could be reduced by palladium to the 5,6-dihydro-4,7-dihydroxypteridine.[29] In brief, a considerable controversy has arisen in regard to the structure of the hydrogenated and dithionite-prepared dihydrofolic acids, which has seen the postulation of all three possible isomers at one time or another.

[20] W. R. Boon, W. G. M. Jones, and G. R. Ramage, J. Chem. Soc. 96 (1951).
[21] G. B. Elion and G. H. Hitchings, J. Am. Chem. Soc. 74, 3877 (1952).
[22] F. B. Kipping, J. Chem. Soc. 2889 (1929); 1336 (1932).
[23] E. B. Brown and T. B. Johnson, J. Am. Chem. Soc. 45, 2702 (1923).
[24] S. Futterman, J. Biol. Chem. 228, 1031 (1957).
[25] R. L. Blakley, Nature 188, 231 (1960).
[26] R. L. Blakley, Biochem. J. 72, 707 (1959).
[27] S. F. Zakrzewski and C. A. Nichol, Federation Proc. 15, 390 (1956).
[28] B. E. Wright, M. L. Anderson, and E. C. Herman, J. Biol. Chem. 230, 271 (1958).
[29] A. Albert and S. Matsuura, J. Chem. Soc. 2162 (1962).

However, Pastore et al.[30] and Fu and Chinoporos[31] have, of late, gained direct evidence that the original assignment of a 7,8 isomer is probably correct. Pastore et al. conducted the dithionite reduction of folic acid in a deuterium oxide medium and obtained a dihydrofolic acid which, after exchange with water, still contained approximately 1 atom of deuterium per molecule. Thus, the second deuterium was directly incorporated into a nonexchangeable position, thereby eliminating a possible 5,8-dihydro assignment. An n.m.r. study of the reduction product unambiguously demonstrated that the deuterium was attached to carbon, and furthermore gave a spectrum interpretable only in terms of a 7,8-dihydro structure. The two-proton singlet at +3.05 p.p.m. for the nondeuterated product was observed to be replaced by a single proton singlet at −1.82 p.p.m. in the deuterated dihydro compound (benzene, external standard). A 5,8- or 5,6-dihydro structure would have given rise to a spectrum with an H-7 singlet appearing in the unsaturated region, −0.4 to +1.5 p.p.m., or a doublet H-7 in the unsaturated region, respectively. The failure of Zakrzewski[32] to observe tritium incorporation into dihydrofolic acid prepared by dithionite reduction in tritiated water, and which therefore led to a 5,8 structural assignment, may have been caused by isotopic discrimination.[30] Further support for the 7,8-dihydro relative to the 5,8-dihydrofolic acid is derived from ultraviolet spectral studies.[31] Whereas in the 7,8 derivative the double bond in the dihydropyrazine ring resonates with the pyrimidine, in the 5,8 isomer the double bond is isolated. Comparison of the spectral shift and observed resonance energies for dihydrofolic acid and tetrahydrofolic acid relative to 1,4- and 1,2-dihydronaphthalene led to the conclusion that the 7,8-dihydro structure is the correct assignment for the dithionite and catalytic hydrogenation product of folic acid.

In contrast, the oxidation with platinum oxide and oxygen of 5-methyltetrahydrofolic acid is believed to yield the 5,6 isomer.[33] The structural proof is based on the preservation of the asymmetric C-6 in a 5,6-dihydro structure in contrast to its loss in the 7,8- and 5,8-dihydro isomers. Beginning with an optically active 5-methyltetrahydrofolic acid obtained from enzyme sources, it was reasoned that a cyclic nonenzymic oxidation-reduction procedure should yield a mixture of diastereoisomers if oxidation resulted in either the 7,8- or 5,8-dihydro isomer. Sulfhydryl reagents were found to function as efficient reducing agents. The 5-methyltetrahydrofolic acid generated in this manner retained its enzymic activity,

[30] E. J. Pastore, M. Friedkin, and O. Jardetzky, J. Am. Chem. Soc. 85, 3058 (1963).
[31] S. C. J. Fu and E. Chinoporos, 145th Natl. Meeting of Am. Chem. Soc., September (1963), 6c.
[32] S. F. Zakrzewski, Federation Proc. 22, 231 (1963).
[33] K. O. Donaldson and J. C. Keresztesy, J. Biol. Chem. 237, 3815 (1962).

thus supporting a 5,6-dihydro assignment.[33]   On the other hand, the earlier proposal of a 5,6-FH_2 isomer arising from dichlorophenolindophenol oxidation of tetrahydrofolic acid has been revised.[34]   Kaufman [35] has shown that the dye oxidation product is probably a quinonoid dihydro structure (10-5 I or II).   The 5,6-dihydro structure was inconsistent with

$$(10\text{-}5)$$

I   II

the findings that (1) in the enzymic reduction of the dye oxidation product by NADPH[3] no tritium was incorporated into a stable position on the pteridine ring, and (2) in the nonenzymic oxidation by dichlorophenol-indophenol of tritium-labeled tetrahydropteridine (H^3 at C-7) very little tritium was lost.   This unusual form [35a] of FH_2 functions in the coupled enzymic conversion of phenylalanine to tyrosine (10-6).   In the absence of the sheep liver enzyme, (10-5 I or II) tautomerizes rapidly to 7,8-dihy-

$$\text{Tetrahydrofolic acid} + \text{phenylalanine}$$

$$+ \ O_2 \xrightarrow[\substack{\text{rat liver} \\ \text{enzyme}}]{} \text{tyrosine} + \text{quinonoid-}FH_2$$

$$\text{Quinonoid-}FH_2 + \text{NADPH}$$ $$(10\text{-}6)$$

$$+ \ H^{\oplus} \xrightarrow[\substack{\text{sheep} \\ \text{liver} \\ \text{enzyme}}]{} \text{NADP}^{\oplus} + \text{tetrahydrofolic acid}$$

drofolic acid.[34, 36]   In view of these experiments a more definitive structural proof of the 5-methyltetrahydrofolic acid oxidation product is desirable.

An unknown dihydro isomer has been reported by Smith *et al.* as the product of the potassium borohydride reduction of folic acid.[37]   The absorption spectrum differs from that of an authentic sample of 7,8-FH_2, in that it possesses a principal absorption maximum at 282 mμ and a second maximum at 350 mμ (pH 7).   The 7,8 isomer by comparison at pH 7 has

[34] S. Kaufman, *J. Biol. Chem.* **236,** 804 (1961).

[35] S. Kaufman, *J. Biol. Chem.* **239,** 332 (1964).

[35a] Tetrahydrofolic acid, FH_4, as well as 2-amino-4-hydroxy-6,7-dimethyltetra-hydropteridine, can replace the naturally occurring cofactor, which is actually a dihydrobioterin: R of (10-5) is $CHOH—CHOH—CH_3$: S. Kaufman, *Proc. Natl. Acad. Sci. U.S.* **50,** 1085 (1963).

[36] C. K. Mathews and F. M. Huennekens, *J. Biol. Chem.* **238,** 4005 (1963).

[37] K. Smith, K. G. Scrimgeour, and F. M. Huennekens, *Biochem. Biophys. Res. Commun.* **11,** 388 (1963).

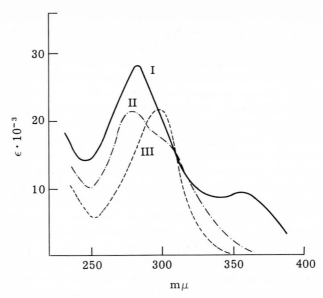

Fig. 10-1   *Spectra of folic acid derivatives (pH 8): folic acid (I); 7,8-dihydrofolic acid (II); 5,6,7,8-tetrahydrofolic acid (III).   (Ref. 38.)*

its maximum at 282 mμ with a shoulder at ca. 310 mμ.   Pertinent ultraviolet spectra at pH 8.8 for folic acid and the 7,8-dihydro- and tetrahydrofolic acid structures are presented in Fig. (10-1).   Additional absorption maxima at various pH values are tabulated in Table 10-1.[33, 38]

Table 10-1 *   *Ultraviolet absorption spectra for folic acid and reduced forms*

Compound	pH	λ_{max} (mμ)	λ_{min} (mμ)	$\epsilon_{max} \times 10^{-3}$
Folic acid	13	256; 282; 356	330	30; 26; 9.8
Folic acid [a]	7	282; 350	330	27; 7
7,8-Dihydrofolic acid	7.5	283	250	21
5-Methyl-5,6-dihydrofolic acid	6.6	249; 290	—	20; 30.8
5,6,7,8-Tetrahydrofolic acid	7.5	298	245	22

* Ref. 33, 38.
[a] Folic acid in 0.1 N HCl has one λ_{max} at 300 mμ.[39]

[38] L. Jaenicke and C. Kutzbach, *Fortschr. Chem. Org. Naturstoffe* **21,** 183 (1963).
[39] J. C. Rabinowitz, in P. D. Boyer, H. Lardy, and K. Myrbäck (eds.) "The Enzymes," Academic Press, New York, 1960, Vol. II, pp. 185–252.

Comparison of the unknown isomer's spectrum with that of folic acid at acidic, neutral, and alkaline pH values leads us to conclude that the unknown isomer of Smith *et al.* is unreacted starting material. This assignment also explains the unusual chemistry of the "isomer." Furthermore, caution is advised in basing structural assignments solely on spectral considerations because of such anomalies as: (1) the conversion of the conjugated 7,8-dihydro to the tetrahydro structure shifts the absorption maximum to *longer* wavelengths, and (2) the reduction of the conjugated 5,6-dihydro to the tetrahydro structure causes little apparent change in the position of the principal ultraviolet maximum.

It is pertinent to introduce at this point the enzymic reactions in which 7,8-FH$_2$ participates. Dihydrofolate reductase from chicken liver and other sources [40] catalyzes the following reaction (10-7):

$$7,8\text{-FH}_2 + \text{NADPH} + \text{H}^\oplus \rightleftharpoons l,\text{L-tetrahydrofolic acid} + \text{NADP}^\oplus \quad (10\text{-}7)$$

Complete utilization of the dithionite-prepared dihydrofolic acid by the enzyme is consistent with a 7,8-dihydrofolic acid rather than a 5,6-dihydro structure,[41] the latter presumably being a racemic product. The 7,8-FH$_2$ also appears to be formed in the synthesis of thymidine-5′-phosphate,[42, 43] which will be treated later in this discussion, and in the reduction of folic acid by pterin reductase from *Clostridium sticklandii*.[44] Huennekens [45] and Mathews [36] have compared the dihydrofolic acid prepared from the above two enzyme sources to the chemically prepared dithionite and indophenol products, and found them to be identical with respect to the following physical and chemical properties: (1) absorption maximum at 282 mμ (pH 7) with a shoulder at 300 mμ; (2) fluorescence maximum at 425 mμ; (3) conversion to a yellow degradation product (λ_{max} 420 mμ) when treated with trichloroacetic acid [28]; (4) facile reduction to tetrahydrofolic acid with borohydride; (5) optical rotation, $[\alpha]_D^{27}$; and (6) R_F values in three different solvent systems. Enzymic assays with dihydrofolic reductase preparations from various sources showed that the above samples of dihydrofolic acid underwent reduction at the same initial rate and to the same extent (95–100%). Therefore the 7,8 isomer generally appears as the stable FH$_2$ derivative isolated from enzymic or chemical synthesis.

[40] M. Friedkin, *Ann. Rev. Biochem.* **32**, 185 (1963) and earlier references therein.
[41] M. J. Osborn and F. M. Huennekens, *J. Biol. Chem.* **233**, 969 (1958).
[42] A. J. Wahba and M. Friedkin, *J. Biol. Chem.* **236**, PC11 (1961).
[43] R. L. Blakley and B. M. McDougall, *J. Biol. Chem.* **237**, 812 (1962).
[44] R. Nath and D. M. Greenberg, *Biochemistry* **1**, 435 (1962).
[45] F. M. Huennekens, *Biochemistry* **2**, 151 (1963).

B. Tetrahydrofolic Acid

Folic acid in glacial acetic acid over platinum or platinum oxide adds 2 moles of hydrogen to complete the reduction of the pyrazine ring and forms the 5,6,7,8-tetrahydrofolic acid, FH_4 (10-8).[19]   The reduction also

$$
\begin{array}{c}
\text{H}_2\text{N} \\
\end{array}
\quad (10\text{-}8)
$$

where   R = p-aminobenzoylglutamic acid

occurs in neutral aqueous solutions [46, 47] or in 98% formic acid.[48]   Since folic acid is soluble in aqueous or formic acid solutions in contrast to glacial acetic acid, the rate of hydrogen uptake is considerably more rapid in these solutions.   The FH_4 product is isolated under *anaerobic* conditions generally by ether precipitation [49] or lyophilization of the glacial acetic acid solution.[50, 51]   Alternately, reduction of folic acid to FH_4 can be effected by sodium borohydride [49] or the dithionite-ascorbic acid system.[52]

Tetrahydrofolic acid rapidly decomposes upon exposure to air and is also highly prone to reoxidation in solution.   Among the degradation products identified are folic acid, *p*-aminobenzoylglutamic acid, xanthopterin, and 2-amino-4-hydroxy-6-methylpteridine.[27, 46]   As a result, aqueous solutions are usually stabilized through addition of a reducing agent such as 2-mercaptoethanol,[49] ascorbic acid,[53] or 2,3-dimercaptopropanol.[54]   Tetrahydrofolic acid is also sensitive to other oxidizing agents including MnO_2, $MnO_4^{\ominus}$, and I_2,[55, 88] with the latter reagent being useful in determining the degree of unsaturation.[27, 55]   The instability of FH_4 is similar to that observed with 5,6,7,8-tetrahydro-2,4-dihydroxy- or 2,4-

[46] R. L. Blakley, *Biochem. J.* **65,** 331 (1957).

[47] B. V. Ramasastri and R. L. Blakley, *J. Biol. Chem.* **237,** 1982 (1962).

[48] M. May, T. J. Bardos, F. L. Barger, M. Lansford, J. M. Ravel, G. L. Sutherland, and W. Shive, *J. Am. Chem. Soc.* **73,** 3067 (1951).

[49] G. R. Greenberg and L. Jaenicke, in G. E. W. Wolstenholme and C. M. O'Connor (eds.) "The Chemistry and Biology of Purines," Ciba Foundation Symposium, Little, Brown, Boston, 1957, p. 204.

[50] J. C. Rabinowitz and W. E. Pricer, Jr., *J. Biol. Chem.* **229,** 321 (1957).

[51] Y. Hatefi, P. T. Talbert, J. J. Osborn, and F. M. Huennekens, in H. A. Lardy (ed.) "Biochemical Preparations," Wiley, New York, 1960, Vol. VII, p. 89.

[52] M. Silverman and J. M. Noronha, *Biochem. Biophys. Res. Commun.* **4,** 180 (1961).

[53] H. A. Bakerman, *Anal. Biochem.* **2,** 558 (1961).

[54] R. L. Blakley, *Biochem. J.* **74,** 71 (1960).

[55] R. L. Kisliuk, *J. Biol. Chem.* **227,** 805 (1957).

diaminopteridines and contrasts with the stability of 5,6,7,8-tetrahydro-pteridines bearing only an amino or hydroxy group in the 2-position.[29, 56] Hence the structural requirements for instability are idicated.

The chemical reduction of folic acid to the tetrahydro level generates an asymmetric C-6. The reaction is not stereospecific, consequently synthetic FH_4 and its various derivatives possess only 50% reactivity in enzymic systems.[57] Mathews and Huennekens, employing dihydrofolate reductase, have prepared the biologically active l,L-stereoisomer ($[\alpha]_D^{27}$ -16.9) as compared to the synthetic dl,L-diastereoisomer ($[\alpha]_D^{27}$ $+14.9$).[58] With the reduction to the tetrahydrofolic acid level the molecular arena, including the reduced pyrazine ring and the aromatic amine group of the p-aminobenzoic acid, necessary for one-carbon transfers has been attained.

C. 10-Formyl, 5-Formyl, and 5,10-Methenyl-5,6,7,8-tetrahydrofolic Acid

1. CHEMICAL SYNTHESIS The synthesis of the 10-formyl derivative was greatly aided by the establishment of the structure of N_{10}-formylpteroic

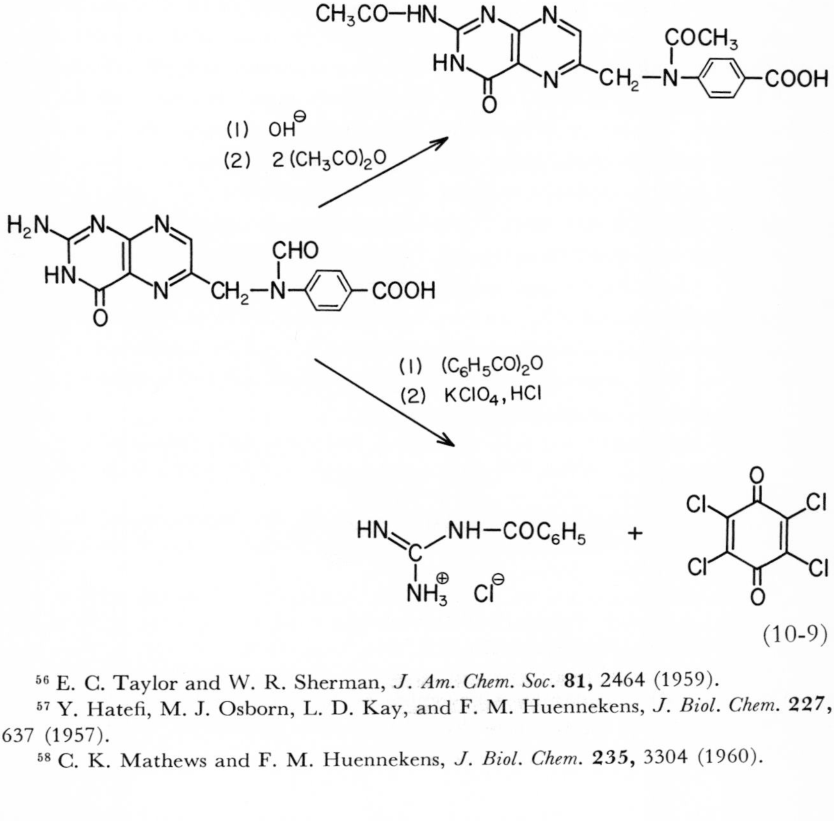

(10-9)

[56] E. C. Taylor and W. R. Sherman, *J. Am. Chem. Soc.* **81**, 2464 (1959).

[57] Y. Hatefi, M. J. Osborn, L. D. Kay, and F. M. Huennekens, *J. Biol. Chem.* **227**, 637 (1957).

[58] C. K. Mathews and F. M. Huennekens, *J. Biol. Chem.* **235**, 3304 (1960).

acid [13] (rhizopterin), in which the location of the formyl group was shown by the facts that (1) oxidative degradation of benzoic anhydride-treated rhizopterin yields a benzoylguanidine, thus indicating that the 2-amino group is not formylated, and (2) acetylation of the hydrolysis product of rhizopterin (the formyl group is cleaved in 0.1 N NaOH at room temperature) requires 2 equivalents of reagent, thereby implicating the N-10 of the p-aminobenzoic acid, since the aromatic ring nitrogens are not reactive under these conditions.   Catalytic hydrogenation of N_{10}-formylfolic acid in glacial acetic acid or neutral aqueous solution, or formylation of FH_4, yields N_{10}-formyl-FH_4 ($f^{10}FH_4$).[48, 59]   This compound is extremely labile

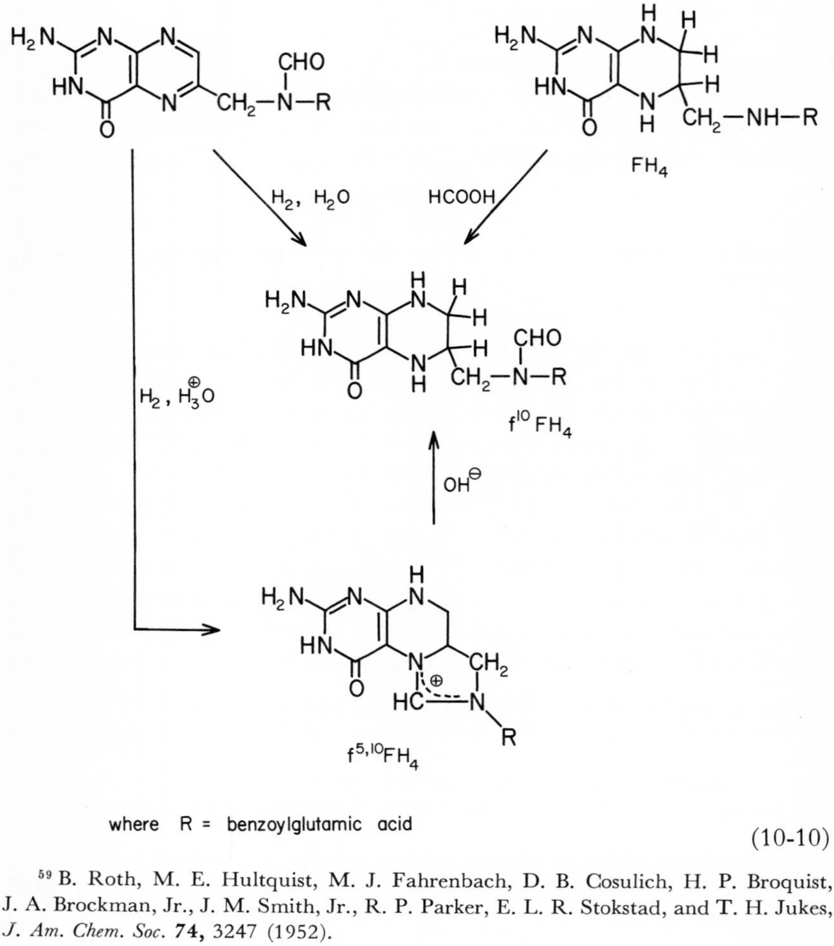

where   R = benzoylglutamic acid

(10-10)

[59] B. Roth, M. E. Hultquist, M. J. Fahrenbach, D. B. Cosulich, H. P. Broquist, J. A. Brockman, Jr., J. M. Smith, Jr., R. P. Parker, E. L. R. Stokstad, and T. H. Jukes, *J. Am. Chem. Soc.* **74**, 3247 (1952).

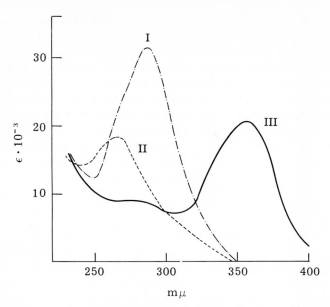

Fig. 10-2   *Spectra of folic acid derivatives (pH 8): f^5FH_4 (I), $f^{10}FH_4$ (II); (pH 2) $f^{5,10}FH_4$ (III).   (Ref. 38.)*

to air oxidation and has not been isolated.   Under acidic conditions the actual product of the catalytic hydrogenation is N_5N_{10}-methenyl-FH$_4$ ($f^{5,10}$FH$_4$), also referred to as anhydroleucovorin or isoleucovorin,[60] which under alkaline conditions opens selectively to give f^{10}FH$_4$.[61]   Exhaustive formylation leads to the diformyl N_5N_{10} derivative.[59, 62]

The isomeric 5-formyl-FH$_4$ (f^5FH$_4$), known also as leucovorin or folinic acid-SF, was synthesized by simply heating or by long standing of the above f^{10}FH$_4$ in basic solution.[48, 59, 63]   The rate of conversion may be followed spectrophotometrically through the decrease in absorption at ca. 260 mμ and concomitant increase at 282 mμ [62] (see Fig. 10-2).   The position of the formyl group at N-5 was established on the following lines of

[60] Several isomeric forms of $f^{5,10}$ FH$_4$ have been reported, including the HCl salt, a betaine formed by the glutamate carboxyl and the quaternary nitrogen, and a third unknown isomer.   See Ref. 65.

[61] F. M. Huennekens, P. P. K. Ho, and K. G. Scrimgeour, in S. P. Colowick and N. O. Kaplan (eds.) "Methods in Enzymology," Academic Press, 1963, Vol. VI, pp. 806–811.

[62] A. Pohland, E. H. Flynn, R. G. Jones, and W. Shive, *J. Am. Chem. Soc.* **73**, 3247 (1951).

[63] E. H. Flynn, T. J. Bond, T. J. Bardos, and W. Shive, *J. Am. Chem. Soc.* **73**, 1979 (1951).

evidence: (1) the comparison of the ultraviolet spectra of the model compounds, 2-amino-4-hydroxy-6,7-dimethyl-5,6,7,8-tetrahydropteridine and the corresponding 5-formyl derivative, reveals that the presence of the 5-formyl group more than doubles the molecular extinction as is observed for FH_4 and f^5FH_4,[62] (2) the absorption spectrum of the model compound closely resembles f^5FH_4,[62] and (3) the comparison of the chemical properties of the model compound, 2-amino-4-hydroxy-5-formyl-6,7-diphenyl-8-ethyl-5,6,7,8-tetrahydropteridine (10-11), with f^5FH_4 reveals their simi-

(10-11)

larity with both being resistant to basic hydrolysis, unreactive with nitrous acid unless previously treated with mineral acid, and inert polarographically.[64, 65]   The latter property contrasts with the facile oxidation of FH_4.   The stability of the 5-formyl group in basic solution does not appear to be related to the 4-oxo group, because the latter's replacement by a methyl group does not alter the alkaline stability of the model 5-formylpteridine.[65]   Under acidic conditions, in which the model pteridine is labile, the f^5FH_4 derivative is converted to the imidazolinium $f^{5,10}FH_4$,[48, 59, 61] which is consistent with an N_5-formyl group assignment. Concurrent with the synthesis of f^5FH_4 was the isolation from liver by Keresztesy and Silverman [66] and Sauberlich [67] of the naturally occurring stereoisomer, the *citrovorum* factor, which has the same chemical and physical properties as the synthetic material but is twice as active biologically because of a nonracemized configuration at C-6.   Synthetic f^5FH_4 has been separated into two diastereoisomers differing in configuration about C-6 by fractional crystallization of the calcium salts.[68]   The $l,$L-form ($[\alpha]_D^{26}$ -15.1) is as active as the natural material.

Inferred in the above discussion is the existence of an acid-base mediated equilibrium between these three derivatives of FH_4 (10-12).   The dehydration of f^5FH_4 and $f^{10}FH_4$ to $f^{5,10}FH_4$ is, as implied above, acid

[64] W. Allen, R. L. Pasternak, and W. Seaman, *J. Am. Chem. Soc.* **74,** 3264 (1952).

[65] D. B. Cosulich, B. Roth, J. M. Smith, Jr., M. E. Hultquist, and R. P. Parker, *J. Am. Chem. Soc.* **74,** 3252 (1952).

[66] J. C. Keresztesy and M. Silverman, *J. Am. Chem. Soc.* **73,** 5510 (1951).

[67] H. E. Sauberlich, *J. Biol. Chem.* **195,** 337 (1952).

[68] D. B. Cosulich, J. M. Smith, Jr., and H. P. Broquist, *J. Am. Chem. Soc.* **74,** 4215 (1952).

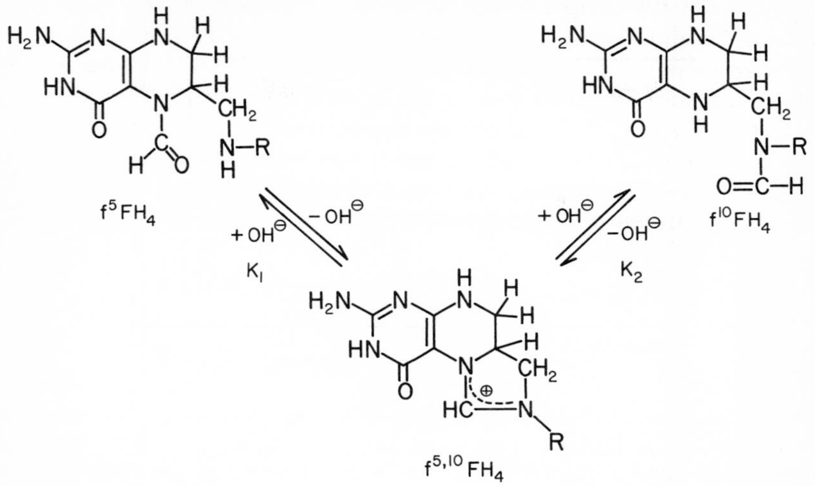

where R = benzoylglutamic acid

$$(10\text{-}12)$$

catalyzed.[48, 59, 61, 65] The equilibrium $(f^{5,10}FH_4 \rightleftarrows f^{10}FH_4)$ may be approached in both directions with $f^{5,10}FH_4$ selectively cleaving to $f^{10}FH_4$ at room temperature. Consequently the equilibrium $(f^5FH_4 \rightleftarrows f^{5,10}FH_4)$ is only readily approached experimentally (pH > 2) from f^5FH_4. Partitioning of $f^{5,10}FH_4$ to f^5FH_4 appears to be competitive at elevated temperatures. The early synthetic work is in accord with this postulation. Kay and co-workers [69] have determined the average values of the equilibrium constants K_1 and K_2 to be 6.5×10^2 M^{-1} and 0.9×10^6 M^{-1} at room temperature where

$$K_1 = \frac{(f^{5,10}FH_4)}{(f^5FH_4)a_H}$$

$$K_2 = \frac{(f^{5,10}FH_4)}{(f^{10}FH_4)a_H}$$

$$(10\text{-}13)$$

The system is analyzed conveniently through ultraviolet absorption spectra, as depicted in Fig. (10-2). From the above values the equilibrium constant for the hypothetical isomerization reaction:

$$f^5FH_4 \rightleftarrows f^{10}FH_4 \qquad (10\text{-}14)$$

[69] L. D. Kay, M. J. Osborn, Y. Hatefi, and F. M. Huennekens, *J. Biol. Chem.* **235,** 195 (1960).

Table 10-2 *   *Stability of $f^{5,10}FH_4$ in neutral aqueous solution*

Buffer	Half-life (min)
Maleate	40
Versene	14.7
Triethanolamine	12.6
Hydroxymethylaminomethane	9.4
Phosphate	6.0
Arsenate	4.9
Pyrophosphate	4.8

* Ref. 39.

can be calculated to be 7.2×10^{-4}, favoring the N-5 form.   In terms of the free energy of hydrolysis the order of increasing stability is $f^{5,10}FH_4 >$ $f^{10}FH_4 > f^5FH_4$ at pH 7.

The rate of hydration of $f^{5,10}FH_4$ to $f^{10}FH_4$ is markedly affected by the buffer species present.[39]   The compound is rapidly hydrolyzed by phosphate and arsenate buffers at pH 7.0 (Table 10-2), indicating the probable occurrence of general-base catalysis.   It remains of interest to definitely establish the nature of the catalytic role of these buffer species, and especially their relative influence on the rate of attainment of both equilibria.

2. ENZYMIC ACTIVATION OF FORMATE   The enzymic synthesis of the above formate-carrying FH_4 derivatives proceeds through the initial formation of $f^{10}FH_4$ from formic acid, FH_4, and adenosine triphosphate (10-15):

$$HCOOH + ATP + FH_4 \rightleftarrows f^{10}FH_4 + ADP + P_i \qquad (10\text{-}15)$$

The mechanism of the formate-activating enzyme from three different biological sources has been studied extensively and, although certain unifying features exist, different detailed schemes have been postulated for the reaction.   For our purposes it will suffice merely to summarize the salient features of these schemes in order to provide a contrast to the chemical pathway.   The experimental findings behind these postulations can be found in several reviews.[40, 70]

For the crystalline preparation from *Clostridium cylindrosporum*, Himes and Rabinowitz [71] have suggested that the reaction proceeds by a "con-

[70] S. H. Mudd and G. L. Cantoni, in M. Florkin and E. H. Stotz (eds.) "Comprehensive Biochemistry," Elsevier, New York, 1964, Vol. XV, pp. 1–42.

[71] R. H. Himes and J. C. Rabinowitz, *J. Biol. Chem.* **237,** 2915 (1962).

$$(10\text{-}16)$$

certed" mechanism in which the three substrates and the enzyme interact to produce the three products without participation of free activated intermediates or of enzyme-phosphate complexes (10-16). The absence of such intermediates is implied by the results of exchange experiments; moreover, the unique transfer of an oxygen atom from formate to the inorganic phosphate formed is consistent with tracer studies.

The schemes proposed by Whiteley and Huennekens [72] for *Micrococcus* and by Jaenicke and Brode [73] for the pigeon liver enzymes are similar and can be represented by (10-17)

$$ATP + E \rightleftharpoons E \cdots ATP$$

$$FH_4 + E \cdots ATP \rightleftharpoons E \cdots phosphoryl\text{-}FH_4 + ADP$$

$$HCOOH + E \cdots phosphoryl\text{-}FH_4 \rightleftharpoons E \cdots f^{10}FH_4 + P_i$$

$$E \cdots f^{10}FH_4 \rightleftharpoons E + f^{10}FH_4 \qquad (10\text{-}17)$$

which is the sequence postulated for the *Micrococcus aerogenes* enzyme. The scheme envisioned for the pigeon liver enzyme features instead a simultaneously formylated and phosphorylated form of FH_4 as an intermediate arising in the third step of (10-17). The data presented do not definitively establish the existence of these intermediates and further evidence is awaited. Therefore it is possible that a single scheme may represent the mechanism of all these enzymes.[40, 70]

The $f^{10}FH_4$ derivative is converted in a reversible reaction to $f^{5,10}FH_4$ by the enzyme cyclohydrolase.[74, 75] In addition an ATP-mediated isomerization of f^5FH_4 to the $f^{10}FH_4$ isomer has been described as occurring in several different enzyme preparations.[69, 76, 77] At present there is some question as to the existence of possible FH_4 intermediates in this reaction, such as $f^{5,10}FH_4$, although with a purified enzyme preparation from chicken liver [69] no intermediate has been detected.

In biological systems a 5-formimino-FH_4 is also found, which may be converted in an essentially irreversible reaction to the $f^{5,10}FH_4$ by formiminotetrahydrofolic cyclodeaminase [74, 78–80] (10-18). The related f^5FH_4 is not cyclized by the bacterial enzyme.[74] Similar to the 5-formyl

[72] H. R. Whiteley and F. M. Huennekens, *J. Biol. Chem.* **237**, 1290 (1962).
[73] L. Jaenicke and E. Brode, *Biochem. Z.*, **334**, 108 (1961).
[74] J. C. Rabinowitz and W. E. Pricer, Jr., *J. Am. Chem. Soc.* **78**, 5702 (1956).
[75] J. C. Rabinowitz and W. E. Pricer, Jr., *J. Am. Chem. Soc.* **78**, 4176 (1956).
[76] J. M. Peters and D. M. Greenberg, *J. Biol. Chem.* **226**, 329 (1957).
[77] J. M. Peters and D. M. Greenberg, *J. Am. Chem. Soc.* **80**, 2719 (1958).
[78] H. Tabor and J. C. Rabinowitz, *J. Am. Chem. Soc.* **78**, 5705 (1956).
[79] H. Tabor and L. Wyngarden, *J. Biol. Chem.* **234**, 1830 (1959).
[80] A. Miller and H. Waelsch, *J. Biol. Chem.* **228**, 397 (1957).

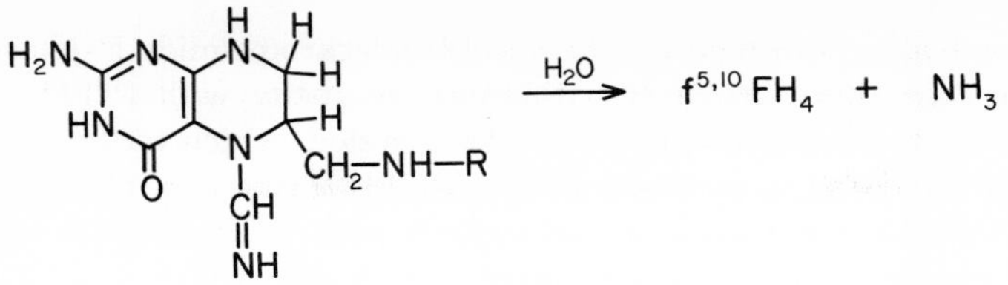

$$\xrightarrow{H_2O} \quad f^{5,10} FH_4 \quad + \quad NH_3$$

(10-18)

where R = benzoylglutamic acid

derivative, 5-formimino-FH_4 (λ_{max} 285 mμ, $\epsilon = 35,400$ at pH 7)[81] is rapidly cyclized nonenzymically over the pH range 5–9.

This completes the number of FH_4 derivatives which function in formyl-transfer reactions. With the exception of the cyclization reactions, the enzymic transformations, particularly the biological synthesis of the formylated derivatives, bear little superficial resemblance to the chemical preparation of these compounds. The enzymic activation of formate by ATP (or bicarbonate in the case of biotin; see p. 382) thus remains an intriguing and significant problem for future research.

3. FORMYL-TRANSFER REACTIONS Four examples will be given that serve to illustrate the involvement of the above FH_4 derivatives in biological formyl-transfer reactions. The investigations leading to the characterization of these reactions have been reviewed by Buchanan[82] and Greenberg.[40]

The first enzyme exhibits an absolute requirement for $f^{5,10}FH_4$ since it has been demonstrated that the N_5- and N_{10}-formyl derivatives are inactive.[83, 84] The enzyme, 2-amino-N-ribosylacetamido-5'-phosphate transformylase, catalyzes the essentially irreversible reaction (10-19).

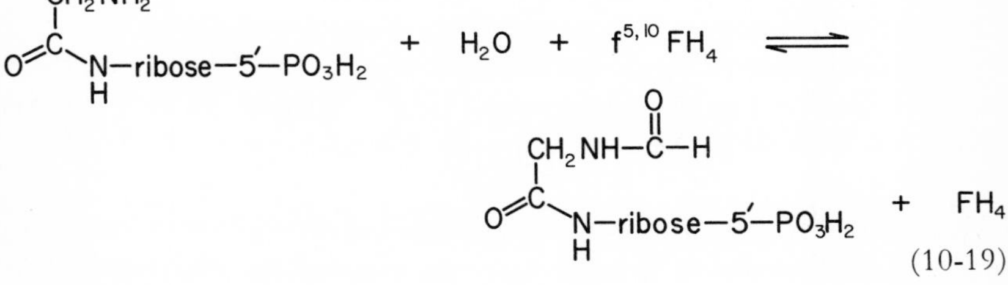

(10-19)

[81] K. Uyeda, Ph.D. Thesis, University of California, Berkeley (1962).

[82] J. M. Buchanan, in J. W. Rebuck, F. H. Bethell, and R. W. Monto (eds.) "The Leukemias: Etiology, Pathology, Physiology and Treatment," Academic Press, New York, 1957, p. 523.

[83] L. Warren and J. M. Buchanan, *J. Biol. Chem.* **229**, 613 (1957).

[84] S. C. Hartman and J. M. Buchanan, *J. Biol. Chem.* **234**, 1812 (1959).

The second, 5-amino-l-ribosyl-4-imidazolecarboxamide-5′-phosphate transformylase, has a markedly different specificity with $f^{10}FH_4$ being required as the formyl donor.[84, 85]   The reaction, which requires $K^{\oplus}$, is reversible and involves synthesis of C-2 in the purine ring (10-20).[86]

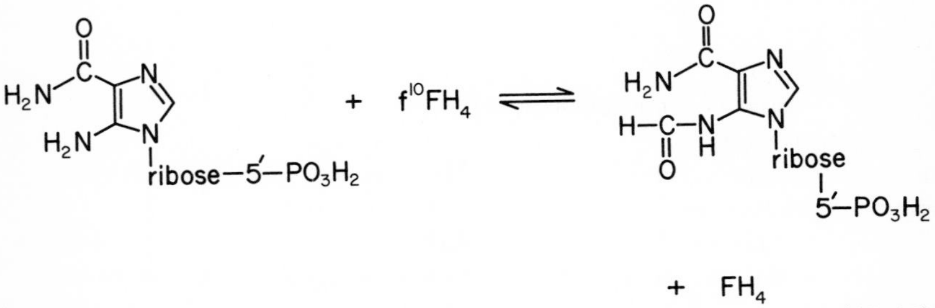

$$+ \quad FH_4$$

$$(10\text{-}20)$$

A third pathway which appears to be specific for f^5FH_4 is active in the reversible conversion of glutamic and N-formylglutamic acids [87] (10-21):

$$\text{Glutamic acid} + f^5FH_4 \rightleftarrows N\text{-formylglutamic acid} + FH_4 \quad (10\text{-}21)$$

The reaction catalyzed by the enzyme, glutamic acid transformylase, is reversible and may serve as a source for f^5FH_4.[88]   Lastly, the related reaction catalyzed by formiminoglutamate formiminotransferase serves to depict a utilization of the remaining FH_4 derivative [78, 79, 80] (10-22):

$$\text{Glutamic acid} + N_5\text{-formimino-}FH_4 \rightleftarrows N\text{-formiminoglutamic acid} + FH_4$$

$$(10\text{-}22)$$

Model studies have not been very successful in duplicating the above transformylation reactions.   Jaenicke and Brode [89] have synthesized a series of N-formyl-N,N'-diarylethylenediamines (10-23) (where R = H,

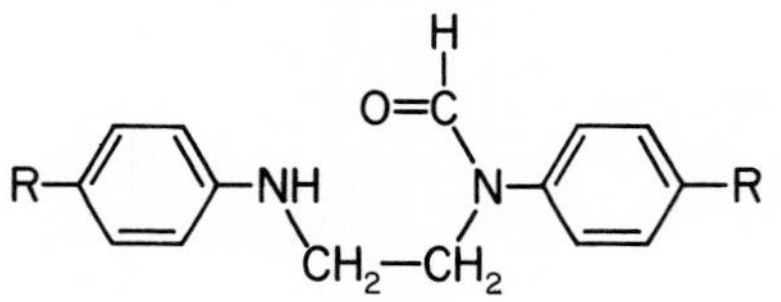

$$(10\text{-}23)$$

CH_3, and Br), which have been treated with excess hydroxylamine at 34°, pH 7.5.   The course of the reaction was followed by assaying for hy-

[85] J. G. Flaks, M. J. Erwin, and J. M. Buchanan, *J. Biol. Chem.* **229**, 603 (1957).

[86] L. Warren, J. B. Flaks, and J. M. Buchanan, *J. Biol. Chem.* **229**, 627 (1957).

[87] M. Silverman, J. C. Keresztesy, G. J. Koval, and R. C. Gardiner, *J. Biol. Chem.* **226**, 83 (1957).

[88] F. M. Huennekens and M. J. Osborn, *Advan. Enzymol.* **21**, 369 (1959).

[89] L. Jaenicke and E. Brode, *Ann.* **624**, 120 (1959).

droxamic acid. Appreciable amounts (35% of theory) occurred only with R = CH_3 and then after a 16-hour incubation period. By heating a mixture of 2,5,6-triamino-4-hydroxypyrimidine and N-formyl-N,N'-diarylethylenediamine (R = CH_3) at 180° for 10 minutes a 61% yield of guanine could be obtained (10-24). These studies should be extended to

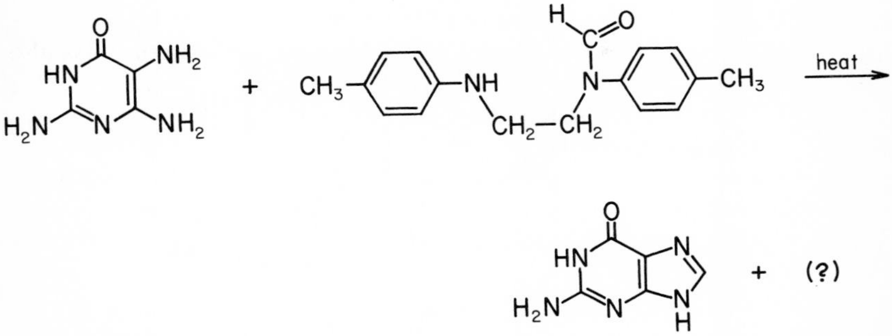

$$(10\text{-}24)$$

cover a broader pH range, but admittedly experimental complications due to cyclization will arise. However, formamidinium salts (10-25) which

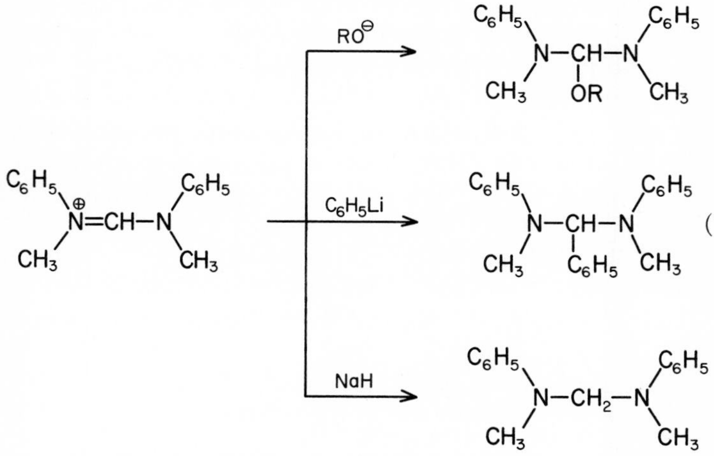

$$(10\text{-}25)$$

structurally resemble $f^{5,10}FH_4$ are readily attacked by a variety of reagents, including phenyllithium, methoxide, t-butoxide, and sodium hydride, at the central carbon atom, yielding the correspondingly substituted diaminomethanes.[90] In equation (10-19) an analogous nucleophilic attack by the amino group would lead to the formation of an orthoamide which is anticipated to undergo rapid hydrolysis to give the desired product.

[90] D. H. Clemens and W. D. Emmons, J. Am. Chem. Soc. 83, 2588 (1961).

D. 5,10-Methylene-5,6,7,8-tetrahydrofolic Acid

1. CHEMICAL SYNTHESIS   The chemical synthesis of the "hydroxy-methyl donor" form of FH_4 by the simple admixing of formaldehyde and tetrahydrofolic acid was first reported by Kisliuk [91] and Jaenicke [92] and has been studied in detail by Blakley,[26, 54, 93, 94] Kisliuk,[55] and Osborn et al.[95]   It has been proposed that this FH_4 derivative has the bridge structure (10-26),[49, 55, 94—98] although the N_5-hydroxymethyl structure has also

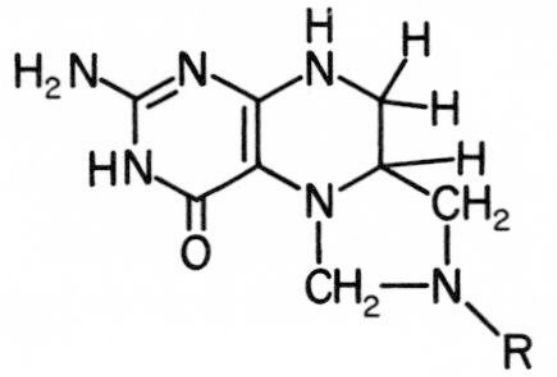

$$hf^{5,10}FH_4$$

where   R = benzoylglutamic acid

been considered.[93, 94]   Our discussion will concern the structure proof for the assignment of (10-26) to the adduct and to its chemical properties.

When a dilute solution of FH_4 ($7 \times 10^{-5}\ M$) is treated with a 20–50-fold excess of formaldehyde at pH 7.5 (room temperature), the spectrum of FH_4 is gradually replaced by that of a new species having a λ_{max} 294 mμ, $\epsilon = 32,000$.[38]   In contrast to FH_4, the above species is resistant to chemical oxidation,[38, 49, 55, 96, 99] which, in analogy with the aforementioned stability of N_5-substituted FH_4 derivatives, suggests that at least the N-5 position is involved in the binding.   The bridge compound, N_5N_{10}-methylene-FH_4 ($hf^{5,10}FH_4$), would be expected a priori to be relatively stable toward dissociation to the parent components by analogy with other cyclic 5-membered formaldehyde adducts, such as thiazolidinecarboxylic acid [100] and N,N-diphenylimidazolidine.[46]   Osborn et al. found the

[91] R. L. Kisliuk, Federation Proc. 15, 289 (1956).

[92] L. Jaenicke, Federation Proc. 15, 281 (1956).

[93] R. L. Blakley, Biochim. Biophys. Acta 23, 654 (1957).

[94] R. L. Blakley, Nature 182, 1719 (1958).

[95] M. J. Osborn, P. T. Talbert, and F. M. Huennekens, J. Am. Chem. Soc. 82, 4921 (1960).

[96] R. L. Blakley, Biochem. J. 58, 448 (1954).

[97] F. M. Huennekens, M. J. Osborn, and H. R. Whiteley, Science 128, 120 (1958).

[98] M. J. Osborn, E. N. Vercamer, P. T. Talbert, and F. M. Huennekens, J. Am. Chem. Soc. 79, 6565 (1957).

[99] R. L. Blakley, Biochem. J. 61, 315 (1955).

[100] S. Ratner and H. T. Clarke, J. Am. Chem. Soc. 59, 200 (1937).

dissociation of the formaldehyde-FH_4 adduct to be greatly dependent on pH with the material completely decomposing at room temperature within 15 minutes at pH values of 7.0 and below.[95]   At pH 9.5 the material appears to be completely stable.   This contrasts with the stability of N,N-diphenylimidazolidine from which free formaldehyde could not be recovered by steam distillation from a neutral, strongly acid, or alkaline solution.[89]   On the other hand, N,N-diphenylethylenediamine has been employed as a useful reagent for preparing crystalline derivatives of aldehydes [101] from which the aldehyde is conveniently recovered by hydrolytic bond cleavage in acidic solution.   The reasons for this anomaly are not clear.   An average value of the equilibrium constant for adduct formation is $1.3 \times 10^4 \ M^{-1}$ at pH 4.3, 22°.   The large value for the association constant is in accord with both nitrogen atoms being involved as later discussion will reveal.

The structure proof was consolidated by sodium borohydride reduction of $f^{5,10}FH_4$ to yield a compound possessing spectral characteristics identical to the formaldehyde-FH_4 adduct.   The reduction under identical conditions does not appear to proceed with either f^5- or $f^{10}FH_4$, providing evidence that the bridge structure is retained during the reduction.   The borohydride reduction product exhibited the anticipated 50% activity in the hydroxymethyltetrahydrofolic dehydrogenase system, thereby being conclusively identified as the active "hydroxymethyl donor."

The pH dependence of $hf^{5,10}FH_4$ synthesis furnishes additional direct evidence for the participation of both the N-5 and N-10 nitrogens.   The rate of synthesis follows a smooth bell-shaped curve with a pH optimum in the range 4.0–4.5 (see Fig. 10-3).   The pK_a' values for FH_4 may be inferred from model compounds such as those investigated by Shive and co-workers,[62] who performed electrometric titrations of 2-amino-4-hydroxy-6,7-dimethyl-5,6,7,8-tetrahydropteridine and the corresponding 5-formyl derivative.   The former compound possesses two titratable groups with pK_a' values of 5.6 and 10.4 whereas the latter has only a pK_a' of 10.0.   Titration data on the 2,5,6-triamino-4-hydroxypyrimidine and its formylated derivative, 2,6-diamino-5-formylamino-4-hydroxypyrimidine, give pK_a' values of 2.0, 5.1, and 10.1 for the nonformylated pyrimidine, and 2.5 and 9.9 for the formyl derivative.   Thus the pK_a' value for N-5, the microscopic pK_a' value for the pyrimidine nitrogens and the 2-amino group, and the pK_a' value of the enolic keto group may be approximated.   The pK_a' value of N-8 is expected to be quite small and may possibly be included in the lowest pK_a' value of the above model compound

[101] H. W. Wanzlick and W. Löchel, Ber. **86,** 1463 (1953).

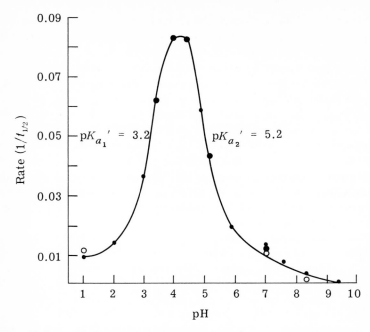

Fig. 10-3 *pH dependence of the chemical synthesis of "active formaldehyde." The experimental cuvette initially contained 0.075 μmole of tetrahydrofolate and 10 μmoles of mercaptoethanol in 1.5 ml buffer of the desired pH. 2.5 μmoles of formaldehyde was added to start the reaction and the rate of formation of "active formaldehyde" was measured by the increase in light absorption at 290 mμ over a 10-min period. Optical density readings were corrected for separate blank cuvettes omitting tetrahydrofolate and formaldehyde. Since the difference in extinction coefficient between tetrahydrofolate and "active formaldehyde" (and hence the total increase in optical density) varies with pH, the rate of "active formaldehyde" formation at any pH value is expressed as the reciprocal of the time required for the reaction to reach 50% completion. This rate is linear over this period at all pH values. The buffers used were: pH 1.1–2.0, 0.1 M KCl–HCl; pH 3.0–6.0, 0.05 M citrate; pH 7.0–9.5, 0.05 M phosphate. (Ref. 95.)*

(o-aminoaniline has a pK'_a value of 1.3).[102]   The pK'_a value of the amino nitrogen of p-aminobenzoylglutamic acid is reported [103] to be 2.61, which compares favorably with a pK'_a of 2.9 obtained by spectrophotometric titration of the N-methyl derivative.   With the inclusion of the known pK'_a values for the glutamate carboxyl groups [103] the approximate pK'_a

[102] H. C. Brown, in E. A. Braude and F. C. Nachod (eds.) "Determination of Organic Structures by Physical Methods," Academic Press, New York, 1955, pp. 567–662.

[103] S. F. Mason, in G. E. W. Wolstenholme and M. P. Cameron (eds.) "Chemistry and Biology of Pteridines," Little, Brown, Boston, 1954, p. 81.

values for the functional groups of FH_4 are completed and are summarized in (10-27). The observed pH dependence for the rate of formation of

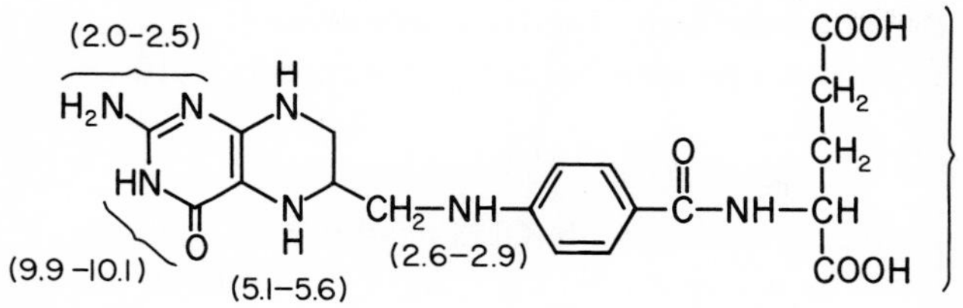

$$(3.8)\ (10\text{-}27)$$

$hf^{5,10}FH_4$ is in accord, then, with a mechanism involving unprotonated N-10 and protonated N-5 (10-28), assuming that the assignment of pK'_a

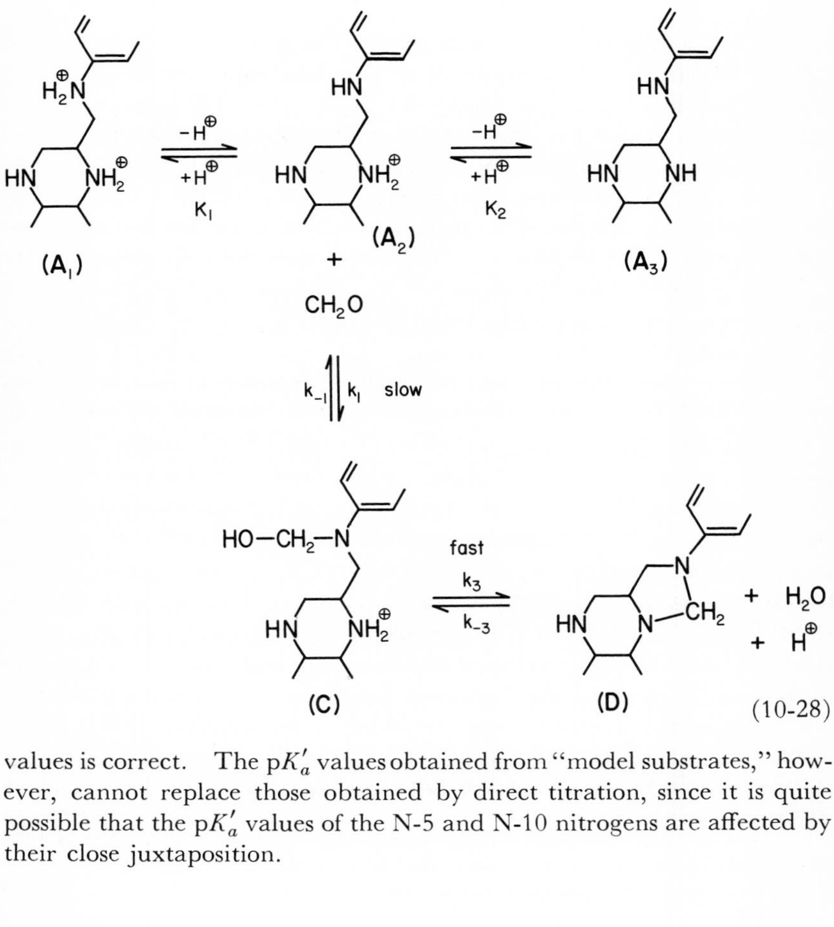

$$(10\text{-}28)$$

values is correct. The pK'_a values obtained from "model substrates," however, cannot replace those obtained by direct titration, since it is quite possible that the pK'_a values of the N-5 and N-10 nitrogens are affected by their close juxtaposition.

The rate of formation of hf[5,10]FH$_4$ is given by

$$dP/dt = k'_2[A_T][CH_2O] \qquad (10\text{-}29)$$

where k'_2 is the apparent second-order rate constant. In terms of the experimentally observed pseudo-first-order rate constant, (10-29) becomes simply

$$k_{obs} = k'_2[CH_2O] \qquad (10\text{-}30)$$

Equating the above expressions with [C] in steady state and introducing the various ionic species, where $A_T = A_1 + A_2 + A_3$, obtains the observed pseudo-first-order rate constant as a function of pH at fixed formaldehyde concentration (10-31). The expression is then an example of the general

$$k_{obs}/[CH_2O] = \frac{k_3 k_1}{k_{-1} + k_3}\left[\frac{K_1 a_H}{K_1 K_2 + K_1 a_H + a_H^2}\right] \qquad (10\text{-}31)$$

case for a bell shaped pH-rate profile derived in Chapter 1. Inspection of (10-31) reveals that the assumption of a carbinolamine intermediate [C] is not required to explain the observed kinetics, which has been postulated only in analogy with the imine chemistry described previously.[103a] The inability of species A_3 to form product underlines the requirement of either an intramolecular acid-catalyzed formylation (k_1) or dehydration (k_3). The dependency of k'_2 on the formaldehyde concentration has not been systematically investigated mainly because of the difficulty introduced by the high reaction velocities encountered. However, appreciable adduct formation occurs at concentrations of 0.5 mM FH$_4$ and 0.05 mM formaldehyde, respectively.[54]

Blakley [54] has extended the formaldehyde reaction to include various other related bases. For compounds such as tetrahydroquinoxaline, 4-hydroxy-6-methylpteridine, or 2-chloro-4-methyl-N-8-benzyltetrahydropteridine, which lack the N-10 amino group, the derivatives formed in the presence of formaldehyde are the corresponding N-5 hydroxymethyl compounds. For tetrahydroquinoxaline and 4-hydroxy-6-methyltetrahydropteridine the respective bis N-8 and N-3 hydroxymethyl derivatives are formed at higher formaldehyde concentrations. The dissociation constants for the N-5, N-8, and N-3 hydroxymethyl derivatives, however, are relatively high (0.1–0.5 M) so that ca. a 1000-fold molar excess of formaldehyde is required for derivative formation in significant amounts. The low dissociation constant observed with the formaldehyde-FH$_4$ adduct

[103a] It has been reported recently that the pK'_a values of the N-5 and N-10 groups are 4.82 and -1.25, respectively; the bell-shaped curve of Fig. 10-3 may then be interpreted as involving rate-determining condensation of FH$_4$ and CH$_2$O on the acid side and rate-determining dehydration of the hydroxymethyl adduct on the alkaline side of the profile, analogous to the imine chemistry discussed in Chapter 8: R. G. Kallen and W. P. Jencks, *Federation Proc.* **24**, 541 (1965).

lends further support for the involvement of both the N-5 and N-10 nitrogens.

In addition to formaldehyde, glyoxylic acid reacts with FH_4 at pH 4 to form the N_5N_{10}-methylene-FH_4 glyoxylate analog.[104]   At room temperature with glyoxylic acid in ca. 100-fold excess, the reaction is completed within 1 minute.   The conversion is identical with the synthesis of $hf^{5,10}FH_4$ with respect to changes in absorption spectrum, pH optimum at 4, and excess aldehyde to force the equilibrium in favor of the adduct. The addition of 2-mercaptoethanol as an antioxidant likewise inhibits the reaction, presumably through hemiacetal and acetal formation with the aldehyde.   In contrast to $hf^{5,10}FH_4$ the glyoxylate analog is reported to be spontaneously oxidized to $f^{5,10}FH_4$, most likely due to the labilizing effect of the carboxyl group.

The enzymic interconversion of $hf^{5,10}FH_4$ and $f^{5,10}FH_4$ is accomplished by hydroxymethyltetrahydrofolate dehydrogenase with the participation of NADPH (10-32).[47, 57, 92]   Thus the onium structure of $NADP^{\oplus}$ is

$$NADP^{\oplus} + hf^{5,10}FH_4 \rightleftarrows NADPH + f^{5,10}FH_4 \qquad (10\text{-}32)$$

conserved through the generation of $f^{5,10}FH_4$.[97]   Consequently the above mentioned formation of the glyoxylate analog of $f^{5,10}FH_4$, or the peracetic acid or lead tetraacetate oxidation of a series of 1,3-diarylimidazolidines to the 1,3-diarylimidazolinium salts, may be viewed as crude organic models for the enzymic conversion.[89]

2. HYDROXYMETHYL-TRANSFER REACTIONS   The enzymic interconversion of serine and glycine utilizes FH_4 as a cofactor and proceeds in the presence of serine hydroxymethylase as follows:

$$\underset{\underset{NH_2}{|}}{HOH_2CCHCOOH} + FH_4 \rightleftarrows \underset{\underset{NH_2}{|}}{CH_2COOH} + hf^{5,10}FH_4 \quad (10\text{-}33)$$

A requirement for pyridoxal phosphate has been found for preparations derived from mammalian,[99, 105, 106] avian,[107, 108] bacterial,[109] and plant[110] sources, and the cofactor presumably functions in a manner similar to that proposed in Chapter 8.   The equilibrium constant ($K = 4.6$) in the avian enzyme favors the synthesis of $hf^{5,10}FH_4$.   A related α-methyl-

[104] P. P. K. Ho, K. G. Scrimgeour, and F. M. Huennekens, *J. Am. Chem. Soc.* **82,** 5957 (1960).

[105] F. M. Huennekens, Y. Hatefi, and L. D. Kay, *J. Biol. Chem.* **224,** 435 (1957).

[106] N. Alexander and D. M. Greenberg, *J. Biol. Chem.* **220,** 775 (1956).

[107] W. Sakami, in W. D. McElroy and H. B. Glass (eds.) "Amino Acid Metabolism," Johns Hopkins, Baltimore, 1955, p. 658.

[108] S. Deodhar and W. Sakami, *Federation Proc.* **12,** 195 (1953).

[109] B. E. Wright, *Biochim. Biophys. Acta* **16,** 165 (1955).

[110] A. P. Wilkinson and D. D. Davies, *Nature* **181,** 1070 (1958).

serine hydroxymethylase from *Pseudomonas* catalyzes the interconversion of
α-hydroxymethylserine and $(+)$-α-methylserine to D-serine and D-alanine,
respectively.[111] These examples represent the classical cases of hydroxymethyl-transfer reactions and may be completed by the inclusion of
studies on deoxycytidylate hydroxymethylase. (A discussion of this system may be found in Refs. 112, 113.)

A model study of the serine hydroxymethylase reaction by Brode and
Jaenicke [114] employed N,N'-diarylethylenediamines as substitutes for
FH$_4$. Although no kinetic studies were done the authors found that the
splitting of the α,β-carbon-carbon bond of serine could be accomplished
(pH 5.5, 100°) in the presence of pyridoxal, N,N'-diarylethylenediamine
and Al(III). Snell reports but a 5% conversion of serine to glycine in
the presence of Al(III) and pyridoxal under these conditions. In the
absence of any of these species no C-C cleavage occurred. Product
analysis revealed the diamine to have been converted to the corresponding
1,3-diphenylimidazolidine. Other than to establish that the observed
C-C cleavage requires the simultaneous addition of both "cofactors,"
little may be deduced from this study about the mechanism of the
conversion. It is possible that the actual "hydroxymethyl donor" may
not be hf^{5,10}FH$_4$ but rather a Mannich base form (10-33a), a more
reactive species analogous to f^{5,10}FH$_4$.

(10-33a)

E. Methyl-Transfer Reactions

The remaining example of FH$_4$-mediated one-carbon unit transfers
may be treated by considering the biosynthesis of the methyl group of
methionine. In the enzyme system, hf^{5,10}FH$_4$ is reduced to 5-methyl-
FH$_4$ through participation of a flavin-reducing system [115, 116] (10-34):

$$hf^{5,10}FH_4 + FADH_2 \rightleftharpoons 5\text{-methyl-}FH_4 + FAD \qquad (10\text{-}34)$$

The chemically synthesized 5-methyl-FH$_4$ obtained by treatment of
hf^{5,10}FH$_4$ with potassium borohydride [117] is only partially active in the

[111] E. M. Wilson and E. E. Snell, *Biochem. J.* **83,** 1P (1962).
[112] J. G. Flaks and S. S. Cohen, *Biochim. Biophys. Acta* **25,** 667 (1957).
[113] J. G. Flaks, J. Lechtenstein, and S. S. Cohen, *J. Biol. Chem.* **234,** 1507 (1959).
[114] E. Brode and L. Jaenicke, *Biochem. Z.* **332,** 259 (1960).
[115] W. Wilmanns, B. Rucker, and L. Jaenicke, *Z. Physiol. Chem.* **322,** 283 (1960).
[116] A. R. Larrabee and J. M. Buchanan, *Federation Proc.* **20,** 9 (1961).
[117] W. Sakami and I. Ukstins, *J. Biol. Chem.* **236,** 50PC (1961).

enzyme system, since this method probably yields a mixture of both 5- and 10-isomers.[118, 119] Synthetic 10-methyl-FH_4 prepared by reduction of the 10-formylfolic acid is, however, completely inactive.[117] It has been shown that 5-methyl-FH_4 is identical with prefolic A, a folate derivative isolated from natural sources.[120]

Further direct support for (10-34), which predicts that a hydrogen atom in the 5-methyl group should be derived from $FADH_2$, has been obtained by Kisliuk,[121] who found that conducting the enzymic synthesis in D_2O leads to incorporation of one deuterium atom in the methyl group. This finding is in accord with the reductant being $FADH_2$, since the hydrogens of $FADH_2$ readily exchange with those of water. The final step involving the transfer of the methyl group to the sulfhydryl group of homocysteine has not been fully elucidated, although the presence of ATP, Mg(II), NADH, FAD, and vitamin B_{12} is necessary.

A second example of methyl group transfer mediated by $hf^{5,10}FH_4$ involves the conversion of deoxyuridylate to thymidylic acid (10-35).

$$(10\text{-}35)$$

Inspection of (10-35) reveals that the major difference from the methionine-methyl synthesis is the fact that $f^{5,10}FH_4$ functions as both the carbon donor and reductant. This conclusion is supported by the following evidence: (1) $hf^{5,10}FH_4$ tritiated in the pyrazine ring leads to incorporation of tritium in the methyl group of thymidylic acid,[122, 123] (2) dihydrofolic acid is a product of the reaction,[42, 123] and (3) formation of thymidylic acid is always directly proportional to the concentration of the added FH_4 derivative. Furthermore, 5-methyl-FH_4 is inactive in thymidylate synthesis.[122] Therefore, there is at present no unifying mechanistic feature for methyl-transfer reactions although the problem is actively under investigation.

[118] A. R. Larrabee, S. Rosenthal, R. E. Cathou, and J. M. Buchanan, *J. Am. Chem. Soc.* **83**, 4094 (1961).

[119] L. Jaenicke, *Z. Physiol. Chem.* **326**, 168 (1961).

[120] K. O. Donaldson and J. C. Keresztesy, *J. Biol. Chem.* **237**, 1298 (1962).

[121] R. L. Kisliuk, *J. Biol. Chem.* **238**, 397 (1963).

[122] E. J. Pastore and M. Friedkin, *J. Biol. Chem.* **237**, 3802 (1962).

[123] B. M. McDougall and R. L. Blakley, *Nature* **188**, 944 (1960).

chapter
eleven

Biotin

I. ENZYMIC STUDIES

It has long been realized that biotin is a key component in the metabolism of carbon dioxide, fatty acids, and various dicarboxylic acids. More specifically, biotin is known to be required in some manner for a variety of carboxylation reactions including the enzymic synthesis of oxaloacetic acid from pyruvate plus CO_2,[1-5] and also in the enzymic conversion of acetyl-CoA[6-8] and β-methylcrotonyl-CoA[9] to malonyl-CoA and β-methylglutaconyl-CoA, respectively. The structure and stereochemistry of the coenzyme, which preceded the elucidation of biotin's biochemical

[1] R. J. Winzler, D. Burk, and V. DuVigneaud, *Arch. Biochem. Biophys.* **5**, 25 (1944).
[2] J. L. Stokes, A. Larsen, and M. Gunness, *J. Bacteriol.* **54**, 219 (1947).
[3] H. A. Lardy, R. L. Potter, and C. A. Elvehjem, *J. Biol. Chem.* **169**, 451 (1947).
[4] W. Shive and L. L. Rogers, *J. Biol. Chem.* **169**, 453 (1947).
[5] H. C. Lichtstein and W. W. Umbreit, *J. Biol. Chem.* **170**, 329 (1947).
[6] S. J. Wakil, E. B. Titchener, and D. M. Gibson, *Biochim. Biophys. Acta* **29**, 225 (1958).
[7] S. J. Wakil and D. M. Gibson, *Biochim. Biophys. Acta* **41**, 122 (1960).
[8] M. Waite and S. J. Wakil, *J. Biol. Chem.* **237**, 2750 (1962).
[9] F. Lynen, *Proc. Intern. Symp. Enzyme Chem. Tokyo Kyoto 1958*, p. 57.

role, were established by two groups of investigators [10-13] and are shown as revealed by X-ray data in (11-1).[14] The rings are fused cis, and the hydrogens on all three asymmetric carbons are in a cis relationship.

$$(11\text{-}1)$$

The first clues to the chemical mechanism whereby biotin functions in the above carbon dioxide fixation reactions were uncovered by Lynen and co-workers [15] in their study of β-methylcrotonyl-CoA carboxylase. They showed that the specific activity of various enzyme preparations was directly proportional to the biotin content and, furthermore, that the carboxylase activity could be completely inhibited by the addition of avidin, which binds to the enzyme-bound biotin [6,7] forming a practically undissociable complex.[16] Having thus established the enzyme's requirement for biotin, a series of exchange experiments yielded results in accord with a two-step mechanism (11-2a and b):

$$\text{ATP} + \text{HCO}_3^{\ominus} + \text{biotin-enzyme} \underset{}{\overset{\text{Mg(II)}}{\rightleftarrows}} \text{CO}_2\text{-biotin-enzyme}$$
$$+ \text{ADP} + \text{H}_3\text{PO}_4 \quad (11\text{-}2a)$$

$$\begin{array}{ccc} \beta\text{-Methylcrotonyl-CoA} & & \beta\text{-Methylglutaconyl-CoA} \\ + & \rightleftarrows & + \\ \text{CO}_2\text{-biotin-enzyme} & & \text{biotin-enzyme} \end{array} \quad (11\text{-}2b)$$

[10] V. DuVigneaud, *Science* **96,** 455 (1942).

[11] K. Hofmann, *Advan. Enzymol.* **3,** 289 (1943).

[12] D. B. Melville, "Vitamins and Hormones," Academic Press, New York, 1944, Vol. II, p. 29.

[13] S. A. Harris, D. E. Wolf, R. Mozingo, R. C. Anderson, G. E. Arth, N. R. Easton, D. Heyl, A. N. Wilson, and K. Folkers, *J. Am. Chem. Soc.* **66,** 1756 (1944); S. A. Harris, N. R. Easton, D. Heyl, A. N. Wilson, and K. Folkers, *J. Am. Chem. Soc.* **66,** 1757 (1944); S. A. Harris, R. Mozingo, D. E. Wolf, A. N. Wilson, G. E. Arth, and K. Folkers, *J. Am. Chem. Soc.* **66,** 1800 (1944); S. A. Harris, D. E. Wolf, R. Mozingo, G. E. Arth, R. C. Anderson, N. R. Easton, and K. Folkers, *J. Am. Chem. Soc.* **67,** 2096 (1945); D. E. Wolf, R. Mozingo, S. A. Harris, R. C. Anderson, and K. Folkers, *J. Am. Chem. Soc.* **67,** 2100 (1945); S. A. Harris, R. Mozingo, D. E. Wolf, A. N. Wilson, and K. Folkers, *J. Am. Chem. Soc.* **67,** 2102 (1945).

[14] W. Traub, *Science* **129,** 210 (1959).

[15] F. Lynen, J. Knappe, E. Lorch, G. Jütting, and E. Ringelmann, *Angew. Chem.* **71,** 481 (1959).

[16] H. F. Launer and H. Fraenkel-Conrat, *J. Biol. Chem.* **193,** 125 (1951).

The demonstration of the intermediate carboxylated enzyme is based on experiments with $(1,3,5\text{-}C^{14})\text{-}\beta$-methylglutaconyl-CoA which, when incubated with β-methylcrotonyl-CoA and biotin-enzyme, gives rise to labeled β-methylcrotonyl-CoA (11-3). In the absence of carboxylase or β-methyl-

$$HOO\overset{14}{C}-CH_2-\overset{14}{C}=CH-\overset{14}{C}O-SCoA \rightleftharpoons CH_3-\overset{14}{C}=CH-\overset{14}{C}O-SCoA$$
$$\quad\quad\quad\quad\;\;|\quad\quad\quad\quad\quad\quad\quad\quad\quad\quad\quad\;\;|$$
$$\quad\quad\quad\quad\;CH_3\quad\quad\quad\quad\quad\quad\quad\quad\quad\quad\;CH_3$$

$$+\quad\quad\quad\quad\quad\quad\quad\quad\quad\quad\quad\quad +$$

Biotin—enzyme $\overset{14}{C}O_2$—biotin—enzyme

$$CH_3-\underset{|}{C}=CH-CO-SCoA \rightleftharpoons HOO\overset{14}{C}-CH_2-\underset{|}{C}=CH-CO-SCoA$$
$$\quad\quad CH_3\quad\quad\quad\quad\quad\quad\quad\quad\quad\quad\quad CH_3$$

$$+\quad\quad\quad\quad\quad\quad\quad\quad\quad\quad\quad\quad +$$

$\overset{14}{C}O_2$—biotin—enzyme   Biotin—enzyme

$$(11\text{-}3)$$

crotonyl-CoA no exchange is observed, indicating that the reaction is not a simple decarboxylation but requires a decarboxylated biotin-enzyme. The requirement for Mg(II) is limited to the first step since it fails to stimulate the incorporation.

Exchange experiments with radioactive inorganic phosphate and labeled ADP indicate that the formation of ATP requires simultaneous addition of the four substrates ATP, ADP, inorganic phosphate, and bicarbonate in the presence of biotin-enzyme. The fact that labeled inorganic phosphate is not incorporated into ATP in the absence of ADP precludes the formation of an ADP-biotin-enzyme complex in (11-2a), and suggests the concerted participation of three reactants (ATP, biotin-enzyme, $HCO_3^{\ominus}$) at the active site.[17] Details of this aspect of the mechanism are lacking. However, the overall scheme (11-2) may be applied to other biotin-requiring reactions including acetyl,[18] propionyl,[19–21] and pyruvate carboxylases.[22, 23] In addition there exists a second group of

[17] J. M. Buchanan, S. C. Hartman, R. L. Herrmann, and R. A. Day, *J. Cellular Comp. Physiol.* **54**, Suppl. 1, 139 (1959).

[18] S. J. Wakil and D. M. Gibson, *Biochim. Biophys. Acta* **41**, 122 (1960).

[19] Y. Kaziro, E. Leone, and S. Ochoa, *Proc. Natl. Acad. Sci. U.S.* **46**, 1319 (1960).

[20] M. D. Lane and D. R. Halenz, *Biochem. Biophys. Res. Commun.* **2**, 436 (1960).

[21] M. D. Lane, D. R. Halenz, D. P. Kosow, and C. S. Hegre, *J. Biol. Chem.* **235**, 3082 (1960).

[22] M. F. Utter and D. B. Keech, *J. Biol. Chem.* **235**, 17PC (1960).

[23] W. Seubert and U. Remberger, *Biochem. Z.* **334**, 401 (1961).

carboxylase reactions, the transcarboxylations in which a carboxyl donor replaces bicarbonate and ATP in (11-2a). For example, extracts of *Propionibacterium shermanii* catalyze the reversible transcarboxylation between methylmalonyl-CoA and pyruvic acid, leading to propionyl-CoA and oxaloacetic acid.[24]

An insight into the possible chemical structure of the CO_2-biotin-enzyme complex was gained by Lynen and co-workers with the discovery that β-methylcrotonyl carboxylase catalyzes the carboxylation of free (+)-biotin when the latter is substituted for the natural substrate. The carboxylated biotin was esterified with diazomethane and the stable methyl ester extracted with ether and purified by paper chromatography. The structure was proven to be that of the dimethyl ester of 1'-N-carboxybiotin (11-4) by independent synthesis.[25] In both enzymic and chemical syntheses the proximity of the side chain to the 3'-N directs the carboxylation to the 1'-N site. No 3'-carboxybiotin is formed in the enzyme process and only 10% of theory via the chemical route.

(11-4)

Other compounds closely related to (+)-biotin, including biotin sulfoxide, biotin sulfone, desthiobiotin, and (−)-biotin are not carboxylated. The marked specificity of the reaction led the authors to propose that the generated 1'-N-carboxybiotin served as a model for the CO_2-biotin-enzyme.[26, 27] This hypothesis has subsequently been confirmed by Knappe et al., who degraded the actual $C^{14}O_2$-biotin-enzyme of β-methylcrotonyl carboxylase in a sequence of reactions given in (11-5).[28, 29] Essentially all of the C^{14} activity originally present in the $C^{14}O_2$-enzyme was recovered as 1'-N-carbomethoxy-(+)-biotin. The isolation of 1'-N-carbomethoxybiocytin (11-5 I) identifies the site of the coenzyme attachment as a lysine residue. Similar results have been obtained for the CO_2-biotin-enzyme associated with propionyl carboxylases[30] and

[24] R. W. Swick and H. G. Wood, *Proc. Natl. Acad. Sci. U.S.* **46**, 28 (1960).
[25] J. Knappe, E. Ringelmann, and F. Lynen, *Biochem. Z.* **335**, 168 (1961).
[26] J. Knappe, H. G. Schlegel, and F. Lynen, *Biochem. Z.* **335**, 101 (1961).
[27] F. Lynen, J. Knappe, E. Lorch, G. Jütting, E. Ringelmann, and J. P. Lachance, *Biochem. Z.* **335**, 123 (1961).
[28] J. Knappe, K. Biederbick, and W. Bruemmer, *Angew. Chem.* **74**, 432 (1962).
[29] J. Knappe, B. Wenger, and U. Wiegand, *Biochem. Z.* **337**, 232 (1963).
[30] M. D. Lane and F. Lynen, *Proc. Natl. Acad. Sci. U.S.* **49**, 379 (1963).

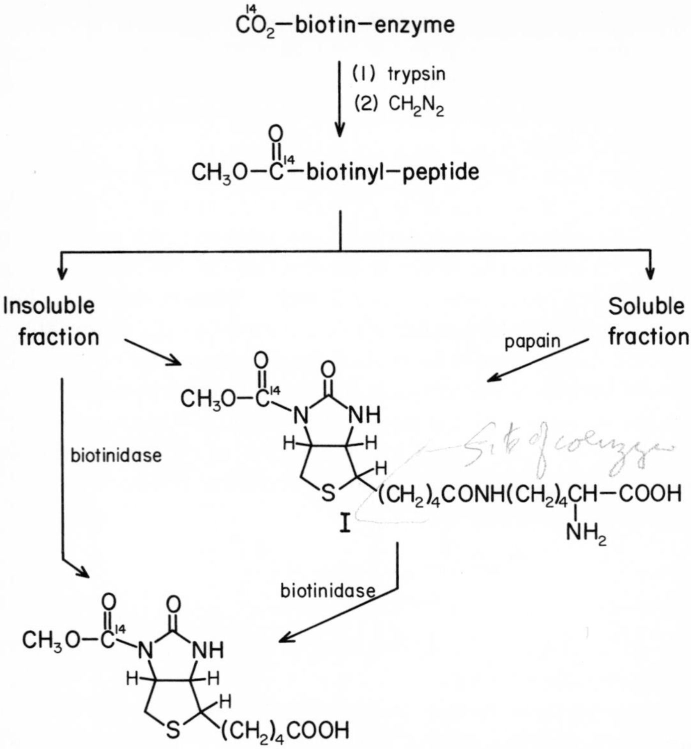

$$\overset{14}{C}O_2-biotin-enzyme$$

$$\downarrow \begin{array}{l} (1)\ trypsin \\ (2)\ CH_2N_2 \end{array}$$

$$CH_3O-\overset{O}{\overset{\|}{C}}{}^{14}-biotinyl-peptide$$

Insoluble fraction   papain   Soluble fraction

(11-5)

biotinidase

Site of coenzyme attachment

I

biotinidase

oxaloacetic transcarboxylase,[31] thus further substantiating the proposed mechanism (11-2).

It should be mentioned that the identity of the CO_2-biotin-enzyme has been a subject of some controversy. Waite and Wakil [32, 33] had proposed that the ureido carbon of the enzyme-bound biotin is the active carbon of biotin. A mechanism was envisaged in which the carbonyl group of the biotin-enzyme was transferred to the acceptor substrate, giving rise to a "diaminobiotin" which could then be reconverted to biotin in the presence of $HCO_3^{\ominus}$, ATP, and Mn(II) (11-6). Their conclusions were based, for the most part, on an experimental result which indicates that the hydrolysis of $C^{14}O_2$-biotin-acetyl-CoA carboxylase with $4\ N\ H_2SO_4$ or $4\ N\ Ba(OH)_2$ yields free biotin containing over 85% of the radioactivity.

[31] H. G. Wood, H. Lochmüller, C. Riepertinger, and F. Lynen, *Biochem. Z.* **337**, 247 (1963).

[32] M. Waite and S. J. Wakil, *J. Biol. Chem.* **238**, 77 (1963).

[33] M. Waite and S. J. Wakil, *J. Biol. Chem.* **238**, 81 (1963).

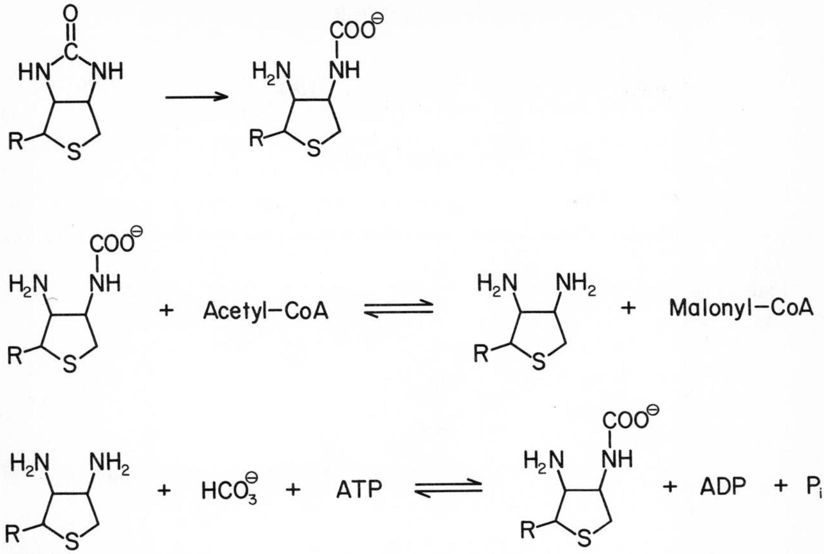

$$(11\text{-}6)$$

Since 1'-N-carboxybiotin should be highly unstable in acidic solution (the parent compound, allophanic acid, is unstable and immediately decomposes into urea and carbon dioxide [34]), their finding was inconsistent with Lynen's original proposal. This experimental discrepancy awaits clarification, especially in view of the experiments of Wood et al.,[35] who did not observe a transfer of C^{14} from biotin-2'-C^{14} to oxaloacetic acid in the presence of oxaloacetic transcarboxylase. Moreover, Lane and Lynen [30] found the CO_2-biotin-propionyl carboxylase to be acid-labile under conditions similar to those employed by Waite and Wakil. Since it is extremely doubtful that acetyl-CoA carboxylase operates through an entirely different sequence than the aforementioned carboxylases, the mechanism proposed by Waite and Wakil is most likely incorrect. (The reader is referred to the reviews by Lynen et al. for other aspects of the enzymic studies.[36, 37])

[34] J. Liebig and F. Wöhler, Ann. **59,** 293 (1846).

[35] S. H. G. Allen, R. Stjernholm, and H. G. Wood, J. Biol. Chem. **238,** 2889PC (1963).

[36] F. Lynen, J. Knappe, and E. Lorch, in A. V. S. de Reuck and M. O'Connor (eds.) "The Mechanism of Action of Water-Soluble Vitamins," Little, Brown, Boston, 1961, pp. 80–101.

[37] F. Lynen, J. Knappe, and E. Lorch, Proc. 5th Intern. Congr. Biochem. Moscow 1961, pp. 225–254.

II. MODEL STUDIES

The properties of the biotin structure which foster its function as a CO_2 donor-acceptor have as yet been scarcely defined. Knappe [38] has observed that substitution of the parent urea moiety serves to enhance the alkaline hydrolysis of the carbomethoxy ester. These data are tabulated in Table 11-1. Preliminary experiments indicate that this substitution also can affect the course of hydrolysis which may proceed via two pathways (11-7):

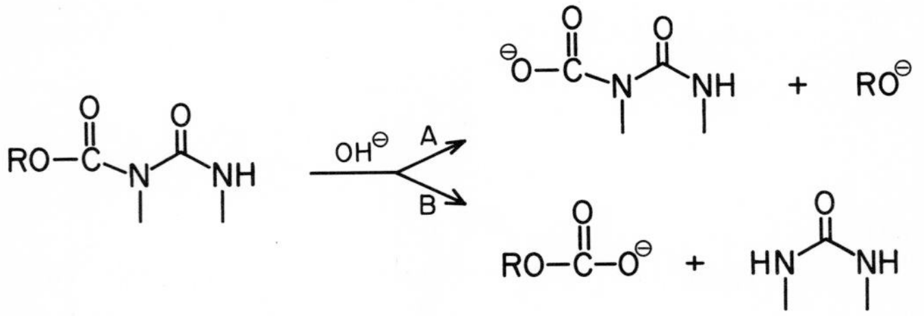

(11-7)

Whereas carbomethoxyurea and 1-carbomethoxy-2-imidazolidone hydrolyze 95% via pathway A, with carbomethoxybiotin both pathways are equally favored. Surprisingly, the elimination of the amide is greatly

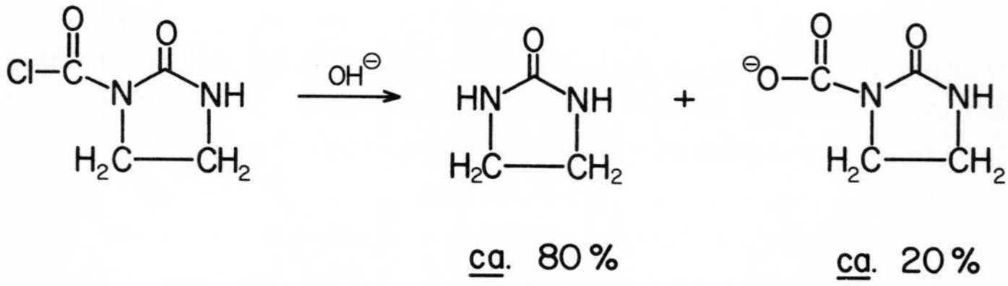

ca. 80%   ca. 20%

Table 11-1 *   *Alkaline hydrolysis of $R_2NCOOCH_3$ compounds*

N'-Carbomethoxy	k_2 (liter mole^{-1}min^{-1}) [a]
-urea	0.063
-N,N'-dimethylurea	0.79
-2-imidazolidone	1.32
-biotin methyl ester (1'-N-)	1.08

* Ref. 38.
[a] 20% H_2O-propanol (0.1 N KOH) at 25°C.

[38] J. Knappe, private communication.

favored when the acid chloride is hydrolyzed (11-8), perhaps through a mechanism such as (11-9).

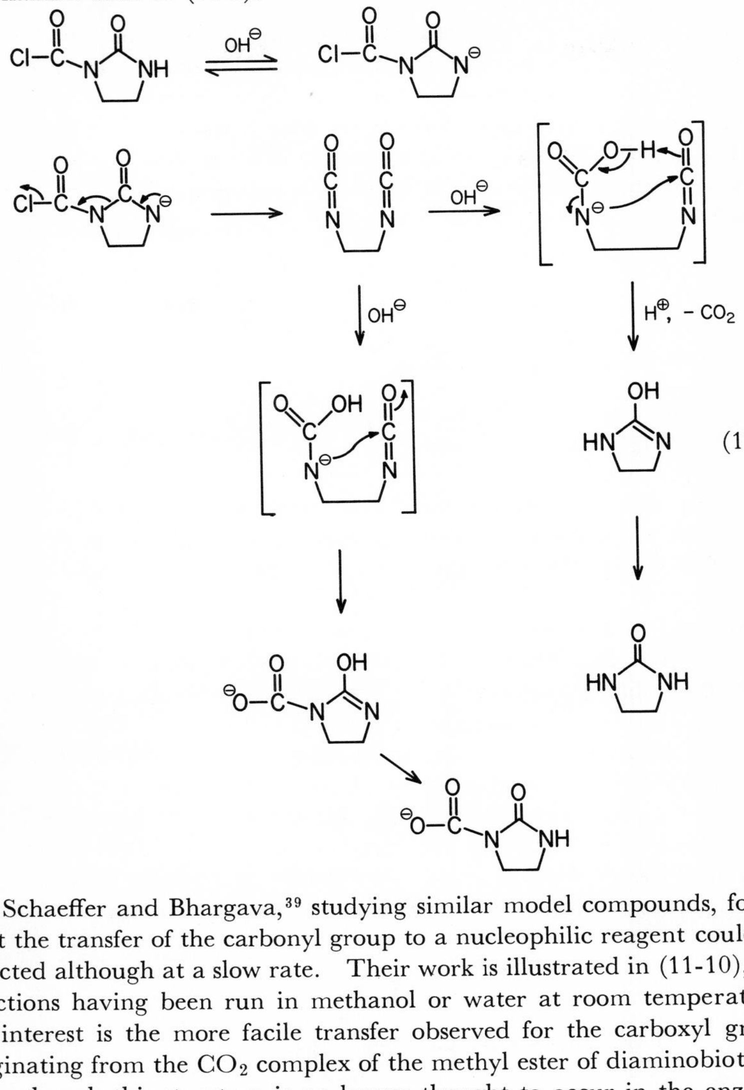

(11-9)

Schaeffer and Bhargava,[39] studying similar model compounds, found that the transfer of the carbonyl group to a nucleophilic reagent could be effected although at a slow rate. Their work is illustrated in (11-10), the reactions having been run in methanol or water at room temperature. Of interest is the more facile transfer observed for the carboxyl group originating from the CO_2 complex of the methyl ester of diaminobiotin,[40] even though this structure is no longer thought to occur in the enzyme mechanism.[41]

[39] H. J. Schaeffer and P. S. Bhargava, *J. Pharm. Sci.* **51**, 1116 (1962).

[40] H. J. Schaeffer and P. S. Bhargava, *Biochem. Biophys. Res. Commun.* **14**, 468 (1964).

[41] Just recently some interesting work has been reported by M. Caplow [*J. Am. Chem. Soc.* **87**, 5774 (1965)] on the transfer of the carboxyl group.

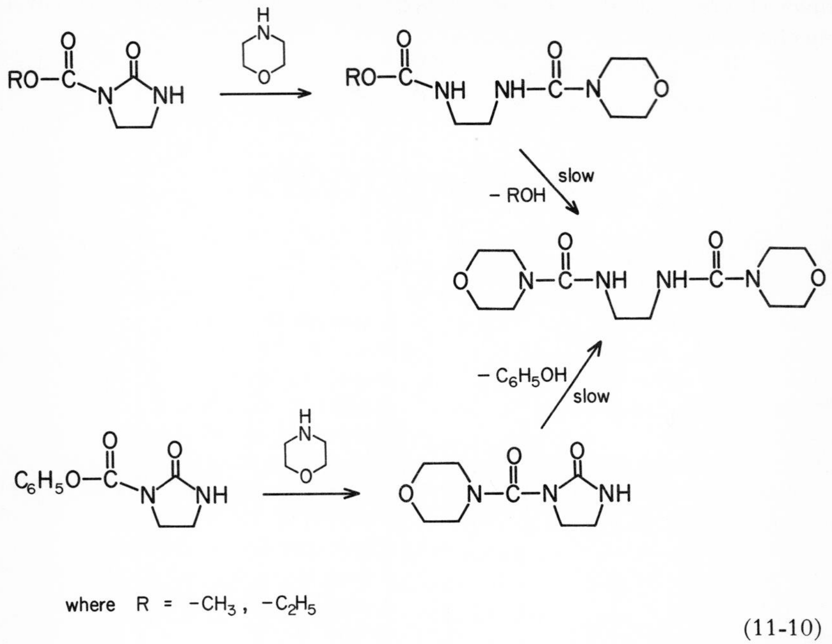

where   R = $-CH_3$, $-C_2H_5$

(11-10)

Attempts to demonstrate a CO_2 transfer to compounds via a nucleophilic carbon atom have in the past been unsuccessful. Knappe [38] has found that phloroglucinol may be transformed into the corresponding carboxylic acid by alkali salts of the "model compounds" listed in Table 11-1, but the true carboxylating agent appears to be bicarbonate. It is noteworthy that the decarboxylation of these anionic species is characterized by a large activation enthalpy, E_a being 19–20 kcal mole^{-1} for carboxyurea and 1-carboxy-2-imidazolidone. The neutral species as mentioned decarboxylates much more readily, suggesting the operation of a cyclic mechanism (11-11). It is hoped that this discussion serves to

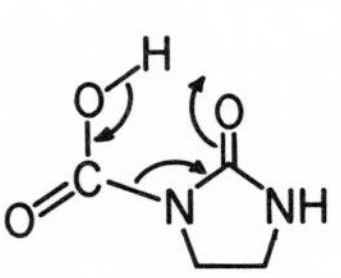

(11-11)

illustrate that the mode of carboxylation and decarboxylation of biotin is only partially understood.

Author Index

Siliprandi, N., 262–263
Silver, B., 163
Silver, B. L., 15, 26, 30–31, 35
Silver, M. S., 52–53
Silverman, M., 360, 364, 370
Silverstein, O., 102
Simmonds, S., 88
Simms, E. S., 155
Simpson, W. T., 314
Siu, P. M. L., 109
Sizer, I. W., 267
Skeggs, H. R., 222–223
Skrabal, A., 106–107
Slater, E. C., 89
Slater, R. H., 161
Slaughter, C., 297
Slein, M. W., 303
Sloane, N. H., 350
Smith, E. E. B., 156
Smith, J. D., 17, 48
Smith, J. M., Jr., 352, 362–365
Smith, K., 357, 359
Smith, M., 46
Smith, R. A., 98, 155–156
Smith, S. G., 233
Snaprud, S. I., 115
Snell, E. E., 26, 185, 199, 239, 255–258,
  263–264, 266, 285–286, 289–291,
  294–297, 299–300, 378
Snoswell, A. M., 89–90
Snyder, E. R., 239
Snyder, H. R., 307
Sobel, A. E., 72
Sobotka, H., 48
Solmssen, U., 320
Souchleris, I., 81
Southwick, P. L., 352, 362
Spalding, R. E., 99–102
Spanjaard, C., 219
Spector, L., 84–86
Spencer, E. Y., 55, 108
Spiegel, M. J., 347
Sprague, J. M., 222–223
Sprinson, D. B., 104
Srinivasan, P. R., 104
Staab, H. A., 81
Stacey, G. J., 131

Stadtman, T., 99
Stafford, F. E., 23, 125
Stanford, S. C., 114
Stansfield, M., 138–139, 147
Stein, G., 320–321, 337
Stein, R., 330
Steinberg, G. M., 134–136
Stephani, R. A., 145
Stern, K. G., 188, 211
Stevens, J. R., 257
Stiller, E. T., 257
Stjernholm, R. L., 109, 385
Stock, A., 310–313, 320, 323, 325, 340–
  342
Stokes, J. L., 380
Stokstad, E. L. R., 350–352, 354, 362–
  365, 380
Stolberg, M. A., 134, 137, 141
Stolzenbach, F. E., 303, 314
Stoppani, A. O. M., 104
Stoppelenburg, J. C., 40
Streitwieser, A., 287
Stutz, R. L., 331
SubbaRow, Y., 350–352, 354
Subrahmanyan, V., 182–183
Suelter, C. H., 321–325, 346, 347
Summerson, W. H., 111, 131
Sund, H., 314
Sung, S. C., 302
Sutherland, G. L., 360, 362–365
Suzuki, I., 223–226
Swain, C. G., 121, 132, 137, 191
Swain, M. L., 313
Swallow, A. J., 337
Swan, J. M., 7
Swick, R. W., 383
Swidler, R., 134–136
Swoboda, P. A. T., 5
Szabo, L., 48
Szabo, P., 48
Szulmajster, J., 84

Tabor, H., 368, 370
Tagaki, W., 219
Takeuchi, Y., 209
Talalay, P., 305–306
Talbert, P. T., 40, 360, 372, 374

Subject Index